Symbol	Meaning	Page
Δ	sometimes used to denote an operation	76
$\blacktriangledown$	sometimes used to denote an operation	83
$\in$	is an element of	39
$\notin$	is not an element of	109
$\{\ \}$	braces (commonly used in denoting sets)	99
$\subset$	is contained in	100
$\supset$	contains	100
$\varnothing$	the empty set	100
Ω	the universal set	102
$\cup$	union	104
$\cap$	intersection	104
$\sim$	relation symbol (often read "tilde")	210
$\nsim$	does not have the relation tilde	211
$\frown$	relation symbol	242
$\parallel$	relation symbol	280
$*$	relation symbol	282
$\overline{AB}$	segment with endpoints A and B	121
$\overleftrightarrow{AB}$	line containing points A and B	132
$\overrightarrow{AB}$	ray from A through B	134
$\angle ABC$	angle ABC	134
$\angle A$	angle A	134
$\triangle ABC$	triangle with vertices A, B, and C	135
$\parallel$	is parallel to	188
$\perp$	is perpendicular to	206
$\cong$	is congruent to	148
$\underset{a}{\cong}$	is congruent to by congruence a	147
$A \underset{a}{\leftrightarrow} B$	A is matched with B under congruence a	147
$m(\overline{AB})$	measure of segment $\overline{AB}$	286
$m(\angle ABC)$	measure of angle ABC	340
$\lvert x \rvert$	absolute value of number x	295
$[a, b]$	the set of numbers x such that $a \leqq x \leqq b$	304
$\approx$	is approximately equal to	319
(a, b)	point whose coordinates are a and b	415
$\sqrt{}$	the positive square root of	310
$S \sim S'$	set S is *similar to* set S'	426
$\sin \theta$	the sine function	444
$\tan \theta$	the tangent function	444
$\widehat{PAQ}$	circular arc from P to Q through A	478

Mathematics for Elementary School Teachers

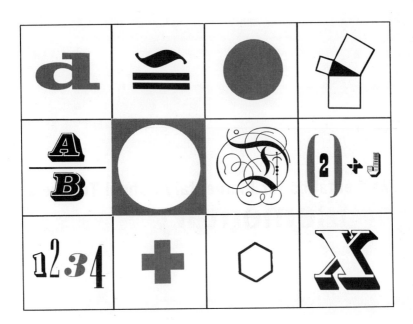

A Mathematics Text Under the Editorship of

Carl B. Allendoerfer

Helen L. Garstens & Stanley B. Jackson

THE UNIVERSITY OF MARYLAND

Mathematics for Elementary School Teachers

THE MACMILLAN COMPANY, NEW YORK

COLLIER-MACMILLAN LIMITED, LONDON

First Printing

Library of Congress catalog card number: 67-16709

THE MACMILLAN COMPANY, NEW YORK
COLLIER-MACMILLAN CANADA, LTD., TORONTO, ONTARIO

Printed in the United States of America

Preface

This book has been written specifically to be of assistance in the mathematical training of present and prospective elementary school teachers. If you are in this category, it is hoped that the book will provide you with a sufficient depth of understanding to treat, with confidence, the mathematical ideas that normally occur at the elementary school level. No topics have been included that do not appear relevant to such an understanding. This does not mean that the content of the text is merely the material taught to elementary school pupils. The adequate handling of the basic mathematical ideas developed in the elementary school requires on the part of the teacher a much greater comprehension than you would attempt to convey to the pupils. Hence you will discover here, at least in places, a fair amount of sophistication. While every effort has been made to keep the text readable and the explanations clear, the book is primarily intended to be used in a class with a competent instructor. Most students will probably find this class use more profitable than use of the text as a self-teaching device.

Since mathematics is, by its nature, a strongly deductive science, the first chapter is a brief exploration of the essential ideas of logic which must form the groundwork of any deduction. This is followed by two chapters examining the structural properties of the familiar system of whole numbers and of other mathematical structures suggested by the observed properties. Chapter 4, after an introduction to the language of sets, starts the exploration of the ideas of geometry and takes you behind the scenes to participate in formulating axioms on which a deductive system is then built. Chapter 5 continues the geometry development, exploiting the intuitively important concept of congruence and the logical consequences of axioms adopted to characterize it. Chapters 6 and 7 return to the methodical extension of the number ideas, first to the system of integers and then to the system of rational numbers. Much is made of the dependence of the arithmetic of a system upon the structure of that system.

In Chapter 8 the separate streams of thinking about number systems and about geometry come together in the discussion of linear measure and coordinates on a line. The techniques and ideas of number systems are brought to bear on the geometric problems of measurement, to the great enrichment of both subjects. The struggle with measurement leads to still another extension of the number concept, this time to the system of real numbers. The problems related to the approximate character of measurement as an applied process are examined.

Chapter 9 continues the measurement discussions, passing from the measurement of segments to that of angles and plane and solid regions. In order to do so, an examination of properties of parallel lines and of the famous Theorem of Pythagoras is necessary. Chapter 10 uses the idea of coordinates in a plane in an unconventional development of the properties of similar figures. There is a strong emphasis on the idea of using scale drawings to solve problems in indirect measurement, and a glimpse is given of how the ideas of coordinates and similarity lead to trigonometry and analytic geometry.

There are four appendixes. Appendix A gives an added insight on the volume formula for pyramids discussed in Chapter 9. In Appendixes B and C will be found intuitive discussions of the main facts of spherical geometry and of mapping. Because of its inherent importance—owing to the approximately spherical character of the earth's surface—we believe this material should be available to you even though it is not included as an integral part of the text. The most important of the appendixes is Appendix D, "A Geometric Fantasy," which you should plan to read toward the end of the course for the light it sheds on the geometric part of the text material. If you have a rudimentary acquaintance with great circles on a sphere, you need nothing else to understand Appendix D. In any case the first few pages of Appendix B will be sufficient background.

After studying a chapter in the text, your understanding of the material should be evidenced by the ability to carry out certain tasks. In order to help you evaluate your mastery, the last numbered section in each chapter, entitled "Terminal Tasks," details the behavior expected of you. This in turn is followed by a set of Review Exercises to provide an opportunity for you to see how well you can perform these tasks. It is hoped you will find this feature of the book helpful in evaluating your progress.

This text does not pretend to discuss actual classroom procedures for an elementary classroom, as this seems to belong more appropriately in a methods course. However, as noted earlier, every chapter in the text is relevant to what goes on in the classroom. In addition, the last item in the Review Exercises at the end of each chapter indicates possible classroom situations and asks you to identify what you found in the chapter relevant to the situation described.

Most of the sections are followed by Problem Sets. Some of the problems in the Problem Sets are simply applications of the subject matter of the chapter in a variety of circumstances. Some give you an opportunity to experiment and anticipate what is to come, and some will stimulate you to try your hand at extending the content or strategies in the text to new mathematical situations.

In each chapter the section before the Terminal Tasks contains a complete listing of axioms and theorems for that chapter. This should assist you in identifying axioms and theorems mentioned by number in the book.

In the discussion of integers and rational numbers you will find in this text a notation of ordered pairs differing from that which is customarily used. The rationale for this is given in the individual chapters. Further, in denoting the negative of the number 2, you are probably familiar with the notation -2. The same negative sign is used to indicate the *operation* of subtraction, as in $8 - 5$. These are clearly two different meanings of the symbol "$-$." Since we try in this text to explore carefully the structure of the number systems, it has seemed better to avoid such an ambiguous notation. Hence you will find the negative of the number 2 consistently denoted by $^-2$ and in general the negative (that is, the additive inverse) of a number a by ^-a. This is not an attempt to wean you permanently from the conventional notation but to help you understand it more thoroughly.

Any text owes much to many people. Among those to whom the authors wish to express special appreciation are Professors Wade Ellis and Allene Archer and Mrs. Julia Hirsch, all of whom have read the entire text critically and made many helpful suggestions. Professor Carl B. Allendoerfer also read parts of the manuscript and aided by discussing many phases of the proposed content and presentation. Stimulating discussions were held with individual members of the staff of the University of Maryland Mathematics Project. In a different sphere, thanks are due to Miss Anne Morgan and Mrs. Marie Symes, who bore the major burden of typing, often from barely legible handwriting. Finally, we appreciate the assistance and encouragement of Mr. Arthur Evans and the support of The Macmillan Company in general.

For any virtues this book may have the authors are jointly willing to accept the credit (deserved or otherwise), while for its defects they cheerfully blame each other.

H. L. G.

S. B. J.

Contents

Contents

1 Mathematical Reasoning

1.1 Beyond the "How" and "Why" in Mathematics

A large part of your mathematical experience is spent in learning *how* to perform certain operations, *how* to solve particular problems, *how* to prove specific theorems. In a good mathematics program, the students also learn *why* the procedure gives the desired result. The classroom teacher ought to be able to go one step further. He should be able to decide whether the argument for the rationale being presented is logically valid. Consider the following problem:

> In place of $\square$ write a numeral for a whole number, to make $12 = 3 + \square$ a true statement.
>
> *How:* Think, "What must be added to 3 to give 12?" $9 = \square$.
>
> *Why:* If $3 + 9 = 12$, then $3 + 9 = 3 + \square$ and $9 = \square$.
>
> *Reasoning:* Two logical rules are being applied to reach a valid conclusion.
>
> *Transitivity of equality:* If $3 + 9 = 12$ and $12 = 3 + \square$, then $3 + 9 = 3 + \square$.
>
> *Cancellation Law for Addition:* If $3 + 9 = 3 + \square$, then $9 = \square$.

This example may seem trivial because it is concerned with simple arithmetic suitable for a first or second grade class. However, the logical principles involved are the same as those applied in finding candidates for the solution set of the equation $x^2 + y + 8 = 15 + x^2$.

Suppose a student reasons as follows: "If $n = 7$, then $n^2 = 7 \cdot 7 = 49$. Hence I know that if $n^2 = 49$, it follows that n must be 7." You should recognize at once that this *reasoning* is not valid. The conclusion *"n must be 7"* is not necessarily true, for if $n^2 = 49$, then n might be $^-7$.

Let us assume that the pupils in a sixth grade class have agreed that if x and y each has a factor of 3, then $(x + y)$ has a factor of 3. This is a true statement.

Suppose a subsequent problem involves r and s, neither of which has a factor of 3. A pupil concludes on the basis of the above agreement that $(r + s)$ cannot have a factor of 3. Again, it is the pupil's reasoning that is in error, and you should be aware of this. It is a simple matter to convince the child that his conclusion is incorrect by presenting him with a counterexample: 4 does not have a factor of 3; 8 does not have a factor of 3; but $(4 + 8)$ or 12 does have a factor of 3.

Another common error in reasoning that children make is illustrated in the following example. To negate the sentence: "She is short and fat" children often think they *must* say: "She is tall and thin." Yet they would also have negated the original sentence if they had said: "She is tall and fat" or "She is short and thin." The same type of error arises in mathematics when we think the negation of "6 is an even number less than 10" must be "6 is an odd number greater than 10." As a matter of fact we could also negate "6 is an even number less than 10" by saying "6 is an odd number less than 10" or "6 is an even number greater than 10." It is not necessary for 6 to be both odd and greater than 10 to negate our original sentence.

So often we make logically invalid conclusions because they "sound right" to us. By the time you have studied the material in this chapter we hope you will become alert to such errors. You will also learn something of the nature of a valid proof and its place in a deductive system. You should be aware of some of the ideas and concepts of logic basic to mathematical reasoning. We will not aspire to the rigor of the professional logician.

1.2 Sentences and Statements

A declarative sentence in English simply asserts something. It does not ask a question. It does not issue a command. A **mathematical sentence** makes an assertion about numbers or other mathematical ideas. A mathematical sentence may be written in English: "The sum of three and one is four," or it may be written in mathematical symbols: $3 + 1 = 4$.

Observe the symbols in the following mathematical sentences:

Seven is greater than three.	$7 > 3.$
The product of two and eight is sixteen.	$2 \cdot 8 = 16.$
Five is less than one.	$5 < 1.$
Three fourths and seven twelfths name the same number.	$\dfrac{3}{4} = \dfrac{7}{12}.$
The third power of two is eight.	$2^3 = 8.$

Although your attention was drawn to a review of commonly used mathematical symbols, you must have noticed that the third and fourth sentences are false. There is nothing in our above agreement about a mathematical sentence that says it must be true. It may be true; it may be false; it may be so worded that it doesn't mean anything to say it is true or false.

$2 + 7 = 5$ is clearly false.

$\dfrac{0}{4} = 0$ is clearly true.

□ is an odd number is neither true nor false as it stands. If we replace □ by **7**, the sentence becomes true. If we replace □ by **8**, the sentence becomes false.

A sentence that is either true or false is called a **statement.** In order for the sentence to be a statement we do not have to determine its truth or falsity. However, we must be certain that the sentence is *either* true or false. For instance, the sentence "There are exactly 50,000,000,000 grains of sand in this sandbox" is a statement. We know the sentence is true or false, even though we may not be able to determine which it is. On the other hand, we cannot sensibly assert anything about the truth or falsity of the sentence: "It is full." Hence this sentence is not a statement. The following sentences are statements:

> The binary number system is used in programming for computers.
> The telephone lines were down somewhere, because I could not reach my doctor by phone.
> $5 + 5 = 55$.
> $11 \cdot 13 = 13 \cdot 11$.
> For every whole number n: $n \cdot 0 = 0$.

However, the sentence $27 \neq 10 + x$ is not a statement. It is neither true nor false as it stands. It will become false only if we use 17 in place of x; it will become true if we use any number other than 17 in place of x. Because replacements for x may be different numbers, x is a **variable.** Frequently mathematical sentences containing variables are not statements because, as written, they are neither true nor false. The following mathematical sentences are not statements:

$$2 \cdot p = 6.$$
$$k = 2 \cdot n + 1.$$
$$a^2 = b^2 + c^2.$$
$$3 + x > 3.$$
$$\frac{m}{10} < 1.$$

Each of the above sentences may be made true or false by suitable replacements for the variables. Such mathematical sentences are often called **open sentences.**
The open sentence $2 \cdot p = 6$ becomes true if $p = 3$, false if $p = 7$. Similarly,
(a) $k = 2 \cdot n + 1$ becomes true if $k = 5$, $n = 2$ and false if $k = 5$, $n = 3$,

(b) $a^2 = b^2 + c^2$ becomes true if $a = 5$, $b = 4$, $c = 3$ and false if $a = 3$, $b = 2$, $c = 1$,

(c) $3 + x > 3$ becomes true if $x = 4$ and false if $x = 0$,

(d) $\frac{m}{10} < 1$ becomes true if $m = 9$ and false if $m = 20$.

Consider the mathematical sentence:

For *some* whole number p: $2 \cdot p = 6$.

This sentence is a true statement since there exists *some* whole number p (i.e., $p = 3$) which makes $2 \cdot p = 6$ true. If we were to write,

For *all* whole numbers p: $2 \cdot p = 6$

or

For *no* whole number p: $2 \cdot p = 6$

we would also be making statements. These two statements happen to be false.

The words "some," "all," and "no" are called **quantifiers.** When we limit an open sentence by applying a quantifier, then we change the open sentence (which it makes no sense to label true or false) to a statement (which definitely is true or false). Thus:

For all a, all b, and all c: $a^2 = b^2 + c^2$ is a false statement.
For some a, some b, and some c: $a^2 = b^2 + c^2$ is a true statement.
For no a, no b, and no c: $a^2 = b^2 + c^2$ is a false statement.

Also:

For all x: $x + 4 = 4 + x$ is a true statement.
For some x: $x + 4 = 4 + x$ is a true statement.
For no x: $x + 4 = 4 + x$ is a false statement.

Problem Set 1.2

A. Decide which of the following sentences are statements.
  1. Green is a color.
  2. It is green.
  3. The key of C has no sharps and no flats.
  4. Michelangelo was a celebrated Italian artist of the sixteenth century.
  5. He painted the frescoes on the ceiling of the Sistine Chapel.
  6. There are 100 senators in the Congress of the United States.
  7. Reading is taught in the first grade.

8. If you complete it, then you will receive your degree in June.

9. Christmas Day is a school holiday.

10. Mercury is 13.5 times as dense as water.

B. Rewrite each sentence using mathematical symbols, and indicate which sentences are true and which are false. Are there any sentences which are not statements?

1. The difference between 16 and 9 is 7.

2. If zero is divided by five, then the quotient is not five.

3. Three is a factor of six.

4. Every even number has a factor of two.

5. For every whole number x, the square of x is even.

6. Six hundredths is greater than six thousandths.

7. Four tenths is less than nine twenty-fifths.

8. Every number is greater than zero.

9. The product of any whole number and one is the whole number.

10. The sum of any two whole numbers remains the same, if the addends are interchanged.

C. Decide which of the following sentences are statements. Indicate the statements which are true and those which are false. Identify the open sentences.

1. $\frac{1}{2} + \frac{3}{8} < \frac{1}{2} + \frac{2}{5}$.

2. $3 \cdot (4 + 7) = 3 \cdot 4 + 3 \cdot 7$.

3. For all whole numbers n: $n + 0 = n$.

4. $\frac{16}{0} = 0$.

5. $2 \cdot p + 1 > 2 \cdot t$.

6. $3 \cdot x \neq 21$.

7. $\left(\frac{3}{4}\right)^3 = \frac{3^3}{4^3}$.

8. $y^2 = 2 \cdot k$.

9. For all whole numbers a and b: $a \cdot b = b \cdot a$.

10. For all whole numbers r and s: $r - s = s - r$.

1.3 Conjunctions and Disjunctions

Two connectives which occur frequently in mathematics are "and" and "or." If two sentences are connected by the word "and," a new sentence called a **conjunction** is formed. For example, let S and T be the following two sentences.

S: Family-rate plane fares are in effect Monday through Thursday.

T: Family-rate plane fares are in effect January, February, and March.

The conjunction of S and T is:

> Family-rate plane fares are in effect Monday through Thursday and family-rate plane fares are in effect January, February, and March.

Because the English of this particular conjunction sounds clumsy, it would probably be written as:

> Family-rate plane fares are in effect Monday through Thursday, during the months of January, February, and March.

Symbolically, the conjunction of S and T is written $S \wedge T$. Because of our understanding of the nature of the word "and," we would expect $S \wedge T$ to be true only if both S and T are true. If you expect family-rate plane fares you must travel in January, February, or March *and* your flight must originate on Monday, Tuesday, Wednesday, or Thursday. If either S or T is false, we would expect $S \wedge T$ to be false. If you leave on your trip on a Monday in June, you will not be eligible for family-rate fares. If you leave on a Saturday in February, you will not be eligible for family-rate fares. Neither will you be eligible for the family-rate, if you leave on a Friday in August.

As a matter of fact mathematicians have agreed to define the truth value of $S \wedge T$ in conformity with our intuitive impressions. Hence, we make the following definitions:

> $S \wedge T$ is true if and only if S and T are both true.
> $S \wedge T$ is false if either S is false, or T is false, or if both S and T are false.

Consider the examples:

$$\left(\frac{5}{8} = \frac{35}{56} \right) \wedge \left(\frac{35}{56} = \frac{70}{112} \right) \text{ is true because } S \text{ is true and } T \text{ is true.}$$

$$\left(\frac{5}{8} = \frac{35}{56} \right) \wedge \left(\frac{35}{56} = \frac{70}{110} \right) \text{ is false because } S \text{ is true but } T \text{ is false.}$$

$$\left(\frac{5}{8} = \frac{30}{56} \right) \wedge \left(\frac{30}{56} = \frac{70}{100} \right) \text{ is false because } S \text{ and } T \text{ are both false.}$$

If two sentences are connected with the word "or," a new sentence called a **disjunction** is formed. Suppose:

> S: I plan to teach in kindergarten.
> T: I plan to teach in the primary grades.

The disjunction of S and T is:

I plan to teach in kindergarten or I plan to teach in the primary grades.

Such a sentence is usually stated in English as:

I plan to teach in kindergarten or in the primary grades.

The intent of this English sentence is that I wish to follow a course of study such that I shall be eligible to teach at the kindergarten level or I wish to follow a different course of study such that I shall be eligible to teach in the primary grades 1, 2, and 3. The presence of the word "or" is meant to indicate that I do not intend to take all the courses necessary to teach at both levels. I shall prepare to teach either in kindergarten or in the primary grades, but not at both levels.

This usage of the word "or" to mean "either . . . or . . ." but not "both" is common in our everyday language, i.e., "dead or alive," "rain or shine," "pass or fail." However, there are times when we use "or" to mean one or the other or both. If your hostess asks, "Cream or sugar?" she anticipates the possibility that some of her guests will answer, "Both, please." When a young man says "Job satisfaction is more important to me than salary or status," it is clear he considers the nature of the work of primary importance, whereas the "or" means that both salary and status are of secondary importance.

Symbolically, the disjunction of S and T is written $S \vee T$. From the above discussion, we interpret $S \vee T$ to mean either S or T or both. This leads us to define $S \vee T$ as true if S is true, or T is true, or both S and T are true. In accordance with this definition:

$(5 \cdot 0 = 0) \vee \left(\dfrac{5}{0} = 0\right)$ is true because S is true, though T is false.

$(7 + 3 = 3 + 7) \vee (7 \cdot 3 = 3 \cdot 7)$ is true because S is true and T is true.

$(^-5 > {^+}5) \vee (^-5 = {^+}5)$ is false because S and T are both false.

The last of these illustrations is usually written: $^-5 \geqq {^+}5$ and is read: negative five is greater than *or* equal to positive five.

Problem Set 1.3

A. Write two sentences, S and T, for each of the following conjunctions or disjunctions.

1. I'm tired and hungry.
2. In a plane, two lines are parallel or they intersect.
3. The number 2 is even and prime.
4. An isosceles triangle has two congruent sides and two congruent angles.
5. Three noncollinear points or two intersecting lines determine a plane.

6. All sentences are statements and all statements are sentences.

7. Zero is neither positive nor negative.

8. $(2 + 3)$ in base ten is 5, but $(2 + 3)$ in base five is 10.

9. Ten may name a whole number or an integer.

10. A conjunction and a disjunction are compound sentences.

B. Decide on the truth value of each statement.

   1. Two is a prime number that is even and all the rest of the prime numbers are odd.

   2. The fraction $\dfrac{5}{12}$ may be named by the numeral $\dfrac{15}{36}$ or by the numeral $\dfrac{15}{35}$.

   3. $7 \cdot 0 \geqq 7$.

   4. For all numbers a and b: $a = b$ or $a \neq b$.

   5. $6 \cdot (8 + 3) = 6 \cdot 8 + 6 \cdot 3$ and $6 + (8 \cdot 3) = (6 + 8) \cdot (6 + 3)$.

   6. Every whole number has a successor or there is no last whole number.

   7. Every whole number has a successor and there is no least whole number.

   8. $(1 > 0) \lor (1 < 0)$.

   9. Six may be thought of as a multiple of 2 or as a multiple of 3.

   10. For all triangles, a triangle has three sides and three angles.

C. We may symbolize the negation of a sentence S in mathematics by placing the word "not" in front of it. Not–S is the negation of S. If and only if S is true, not–S is false; if and only if S is false, not–S is true. You are aware that in English we may negate a sentence S, as follows:

S: Exercise is healthy.

not–S: Exercise is not healthy.

or not–S: It is false that exercise is healthy.

Write the negation of each of the following statements and determine the truth value of the negation.

   1. Meat is rich in protein.

   2. Child psychology is an essential part of a teacher's training.

   3. Democracy is consistent with dictatorship.

   4. The three B's in music are Bach, Beethoven, and Brahms.

   5. $\dfrac{1}{2} + \dfrac{1}{3} = \dfrac{2}{5}$.

   6. $\dfrac{1}{2} \cdot \dfrac{1}{3} = \dfrac{1}{6}$.

   7. $\dfrac{1}{2} \div \dfrac{1}{3} < \dfrac{1}{2}$.   (Watch out!)

   8. $^-1 > 0$.

   9. $\dfrac{0}{0} = 1$.

   10. The positive square root of 16 is 4.

D. Recall that $S \land T$ is true if and only if both S and T are true.

Not–$(S \wedge T)$ is true if and only if $S \wedge T$ is false. This suggests that not–$(S \wedge T)$ is true

>   if S is false (not–S is true)
>   or if T is false (not–T is true)
>   or if S and T are both false (not–S and not–T are both true)

But these are the conditions under which not–$S \vee$ not–T is true. Hence we will say that:

The truth value of not–$(S \wedge T)$ is the same as the truth value of not–$S \vee$ not–T.

Example. The negation of "The test was long and difficult" is "The test was not long or not difficult."

Write the negation of each of the following conjunctions:
1. She is short and fat.
2. 7 is an odd number greater than 5.
3. The diagonals of the square $ABCD$ are perpendicular to each other and bisect each other.
4. Oregon is north of California and south of Washington.
5. The table was more than 45 but less than 46 inches long.

E. In **D** we gave some rationale for defining the truth value of the negation of $S \wedge T$ as the same as that of not–$S \vee$ not–T.
1. Present some reasonable basis for defining the truth value of the negation of $S \vee T$ as the same as that of not–$S \wedge$ not–T.
2. Write the negation of each of the following disjunctions:
    a. $2 \gtrless 3$.
    b. The statement is true or false.
    c. 43 is prime or composite.
    d. The weather forecast for tomorrow is cloudy or rain.
    e. The least common multiple of 9 and 6 is divisible by 9 or 6.

1.4 Implications

Frequently in mathematics, sentences are written in the form: If . . . , then . . . . Such sentences are called **implications.** Every implication is a compound sentence made up of two sentences. One of the sentences, the **antecedent,** follows the word "if" and the other sentence, the **consequent,** follows the word "then." Consider the implication:

If 711 is divisible by 9, then 711 is divisible by 3.

The antecedent is: 711 is divisible by 9.
The consequent is: 711 is divisible by 3.

If we let P represent the antecedent and Q represent the consequent, then we may write: If P, then Q. In symbols, the implication is often written: $P \rightarrow Q$. This may be read: "If P, then Q" or "P implies Q."

The antecedent and the consequent of an implication may be open sentences or they may be statements. In the example above, P and Q are statements, both true. In this instance, the implication $P \rightarrow Q$ appears to be true also. Now look at the implication:

If 573 is divisible by 3, then 573 is divisible by 9.

P is a true statement and Q is a false statement. Our intuition tells us that in this case, the implication $P \rightarrow Q$ appears to be false.

Now consider the implication:

If $x + 1$ is an integer divisible by 2, then x is a whole number.

P is the open sentence: $x + 1$ is an integer divisible by 2.
Q is the open sentence: x is a whole number.

The truth values of P and Q depend upon the replacements we use for x:

If $x = 7$, then P is true and Q is true.
If $x = 6$, then P is false and Q is true.
If $x = {}^-7$, then P is true and Q is false.
If $x = {}^-6$, then P is false and Q is false.

Our first reaction to this implication, $P \rightarrow Q$, might be that sometimes it appears to be true and sometimes it appears to be false. Beyond this wishy-washy conclusion we cannot go. As the implication is stated, we have nothing upon which to base a decision about *when* it might be true or *when* it might be false.

However, what the mathematician has in mind when he says: If $x + 1$ is an integer divisible by 2, then x is a whole number, is:

For all integers x: If $x + 1$ is an integer divisible by 2, then x is a whole number.

It is the intention that for this implication to be true, it must hold for *all* integers whose numerals are written in place of the variable x. This gives us a basis for reaching an agreement about the truth value of an implication whose antecedent and consequent involve variables. If P and Q involve variables, we shall define $P \rightarrow Q$

    (a) as true, if for every replacement of the variable which makes P true, Q will also be true;

    (b) as false, if we can produce at least one replacement of the variable which makes P true and Q false.

In accordance with this definition, the implication considered above is false, because P is true and Q is false when $x = {}^-7$.

The implications which we shall be called upon to prove in the course of our work will be general statements involving variables. We shall indicate this by the symbols P_x, Q_x, and $\forall_x$ where P_x will be the antecedent, Q_x will be the consequent and $\forall_x$ will mean "for all x." Of course, we are not required to use x to indicate a variable; we may use any letter. Thus, if we write:

$$\forall_n \, (P_n \rightarrow Q_n),$$

we mean "For all n, P_n implies Q_n," where n is the variable.

Now let us apply our definition for truth value to some implications which we know to be true or false from our previous mathematical experiences, to see if the definition is in accord with prior agreements.

Example 1. For all whole numbers a, b: If $a \cdot b = 6$, then $b \cdot a = 6$.
   All possible replacements for a which make $P_{a,b}$ true are 1, 2, 3, 6.
   All possible replacements for b which make $P_{a,b}$ true are 1, 2, 3, 6.
   All possible replacements for a and b which make $P_{a,b}$ true are

$$a = 1, b = 6,$$
$$a = 6, b = 1,$$
$$a = 2, b = 3,$$
$$a = 3, b = 2.$$

All these replacements also make $Q_{a,b}$ true. Hence by our definition: $\forall_{a,b} \, (P_{a,b} \rightarrow Q_{a,b})$ is true. This agrees with what we already knew.

Example 2. For all integers x: If $x^2 = 25$, then $x = 5$.
   We can produce a replacement for the variable x which will make P_x true but Q_x false. If $x = {}^-5$, then $x^2 = 25$ but ${}^-5 \neq 5$. Hence this implication is false.

Example 3. For all whole numbers n: If n is a whole number, $\dfrac{n}{n} = 1$.
   This implication is false for if $n = 0$, P_n is true but Q_n is false.

Example 4. For all whole numbers x: If x is odd, then $2 \cdot x$ is even.
   All possible replacements x which make P_x true are the odd numbers: 1, 3, 5, 7, 9, $\ldots$, $2 \cdot p + 1, \ldots$.
   Every one of them makes Q_x true: $2 \cdot (2 \cdot p + 1)$ is even since it has a factor of 2.
   $\forall_x(P_x \rightarrow Q_x)$ is true by our definition of truth value for an implication involving variables.

Example 5. For all quadrilaterals q: If q is a rectangle, then q has four right angles.

This implication is true, for any quadrilateral which is a rectangle (making P_x true) can be shown to have four right angles (making Q_x true).

Example 6. For all n: If $\dfrac{0}{n} = 5$, then $0 = 5 \cdot n$.

There is no possible replacement for n which will make P_n true. This means that there are no replacements for n which make P_n true and for which we must demonstrate that Q_n is true. The number of replacements for n which make P_n and Q_n both true is zero. This special situation does fulfill the requirement of our definition which makes $\forall_n (P_n \rightarrow Q_n)$ a true implication.

Obviously, we are not going to be able to produce *one* replacement of n which makes P_n true and Q_n false, since there are *no* replacements to make P_n true. Hence, applying our definition, we have no case for considering the implication $\forall_n (P_n \rightarrow Q_n)$ false.

We will have little occasion in our work to consider an implication such as that of Example 6 in which the antecedent, P_n, is false for all replacements of the variable.

Problem Set 1.4

A. Let us define the truth value of an implication whose antecedent and consequent are statements with P always true, as follows:

(a) If Q is true, then $P \rightarrow Q$ is true.

(b) If Q is false, then $P \rightarrow Q$ is false.

Apply this definition to each of the following implications and see if the resulting truth values agree with your intuitive conclusions. Assume P is true.

1. If this sentence is an implication, then it is composed of two clauses.

2. If your seats are reserved, then they will be occupied when you arrive at the theater.

3. If $x = 2 \cdot y$ is an open sentence, then it has no truth value.

4. If the newspaper article is an editorial, then it is an expression of opinion.

5. If you make a long distance call from Seattle to Portland in the evening, then the fee is one dollar for every three minutes.

6. There is a change in the weather, if a cold front passes through.

7. If Steven is under eight years of age, then no activities in his daily life require any mathematics.

8. Flight time between San Francisco and New York is $4\frac{1}{2}$ hours, if you fly nonstop by jet.

9. If you are twenty-one years of age and are registered, then you may vote.

   10. You will need a master's degree to fulfill certification requirements, if
   you plan to teach in the elementary grades.

B. For each implication below, involving variables, determine the truth value
in accordance with the definition in Section 1.4.
   1. For all whole numbers n: If n is a whole number, then $n \cdot 0 = 0$.
   2. For all whole numbers p: If $p < 10$, then $10 < p$.
   3. For all x: If $3 \cdot x = 21$, then $x = 7$.
   4. For all triangles: If a triangle is equilateral, then it is equiangular.
   5. For all whole numbers a and b: If $a + b = 8$, then $b + a = 8$.
   6. For all whole numbers a and b: If a and b are whole numbers, then
   $a - b = b - a$.
   7. For all lines: If two lines do not meet no matter how far extended, then
   they are parallel.
   8. For all y: If $y \cdot 1 = y + 1$, then $y \cdot 2 = 2 \cdot y + 2$.
   9. For all m and n: If $3 + m = 3 + n$, then $m = n$.
   10. For all x, y, z: If $x = y$ and $y = z$, then $x = z$.

1.5 Related Implications

   In Problem Set 1.3 you learned that we use the words "not" or "it is false
that" to form the negation of a statement. For example, the negation of the statement: A counting number has a successor, is: A counting number does not have a
successor, or: It is false that a counting number has a successor. If the original
statement is true, its negation must be false. If the original statement is false, its
negation must be true. A statement and its negation cannot be simultaneously
true or simultaneously false. The negation of statement P is written not–P. If
P is true, not–P is false. If P is false, not–P is true. Since $P \rightarrow Q$ is just a special
kind of statement, the rule for the truth values of a statement and its negation
hold for an implication. If $P \rightarrow Q$ is true, then not–$(P \rightarrow Q)$ is false. If $P \rightarrow Q$ is
false, then not–$(P \rightarrow Q)$ is true.
   Other implications which are related to $P \rightarrow Q$ are defined and illustrated
below:

Implication:	$P \rightarrow Q$
Converse of implication:	$Q \rightarrow P$
Inverse of implication:	not–$P \rightarrow$ not–Q
Contrapositive of implication:	not–$Q \rightarrow$ not–P

Consider the example:
   Implication: If you brush your teeth with toothpaste x, then your
   cavities decrease in number.
   Converse: If your cavities decrease in number, then you brush your
   teeth with toothpaste x.

> *Inverse:* If you do not brush your teeth with toothpaste x, then your cavities do not decrease in number.
>
> *Contrapositive:* If your cavities do not decrease in number, then you do not brush with toothpaste x.

Let us assume that the original implication is true. Is the converse necessarily true? Not at all! Your cavities might well be decreasing in number though you brush with toothpaste y. Is the inverse necessarily true? This is the implication the advertiser hopes you will assume is true when he asserts the original implication. Actually the inverse is not necessarily true. You might be brushing with toothpaste y and enjoying a decrease in the number of cavities. Only the contrapositive is surely true, if the original implication is true. All the contrapositive says is that if your cavities are not decreasing in number, then one thing is certain, you are not using toothpaste x.

In mathematics we deal frequently with open sentences. The statements we make are often obtained by asserting that certain open sentences are true for all values of the variable. Thus the statement $\forall_x(P_x \rightarrow Q_x)$ is quite a typical situation and it seems sensible to consider the truth values assigned to its negation and to its related implications.

> *Implication:* $\forall_x(P_x \rightarrow Q_x)$ is true, if for all replacements of x which make P_x true, Q_x is also true; $\forall_x(P_x \rightarrow Q_x)$ is false, if there is at least one replacement of x which makes P_x true and Q_x false.
>
> *Negation:* The negative of $\forall_x(P_x \rightarrow Q_x)$ will be true if and only if $\forall_x(P_x \rightarrow Q_x)$ is false. Hence the negation of $\forall_x(P_x \rightarrow Q_x)$ will be true if and only if there exists some replacement of x which makes P_x true and Q_x false (not-Q_x true). We use the symbol $\exists_x$ to represent "for some x" and it makes sense to define the negation of $\forall_x(P_x \rightarrow Q_x)$ as having the same truth value as $\exists_x(P_x \wedge \text{not-}Q_x)$. Observe that the negation of an implication is a conjunction which is true only if both of its statements are true.

Example 1. $\forall_x(P_x \rightarrow Q_x)$: For all x: If $3 \cdot x = 6$, then $x = 2$.   True.

$\exists_x(P_x \wedge \text{not-}Q)$: For some x: $3 \cdot x = 6$ and $x \neq 2$.   False.

Example 2. $\forall_r(P_r \rightarrow Q_r)$: For all whole numbers r: If r is odd, then r^2 is even.   False.

$\exists_r(P_r \wedge \text{not-}Q_r)$: For some whole numbers: r is odd and r^2 is not even.   True.

> *Converse:* $\forall_x(Q_x \rightarrow P_x)$. Since this is an implication the definition of its truth value is already familiar. What we would like to investigate is whether the fact that an implication is true automatically assures us that its converse is true. The example discussed above, concerning

dental habits, suggests that the answer to our problem is "not always."

The implication $\forall_x(P_x \to Q_x)$ will be true if all replacements of x that make P_x true also make Q_x true. This does not preclude the possibility that there may well be replacements for x that make Q_x true and P_x false. In this case $\forall_x(P_x \to Q_x)$ will be true, but $\forall_x(Q_x \to P_x)$ will be false.

Example 3. $\forall_x(P_x \to Q_x)$: For all lines: If 2 lines are parallel, then they do not intersect.   True.

$\forall_x(Q_x \to P_x)$: For all lines: If 2 lines do not intersect, then they are parallel. (Look up definition of skew lines.)   False.

Example 4. $\forall_a(P_a \to Q_a)$: For all whole numbers a: If a is even, then a has a factor of 2.   True.

$\forall_a(Q_a \to P_a)$: For all whole numbers a: If a has a factor of 2, then a is even.   True.

Example 5. $\forall_y(P_y \to Q_y)$: For all y: If $y + 1 > y$, then $y < 5$.   False.

$\forall_y(Q_y \to P_y)$: For all y: If $y < 5$, then $y + 1 > y$.   True.

Example 6. $\forall_k(P_k \to Q_k)$: For all k: If $18 + 17 = k$, then $k = 39$.   False.

$\forall_k(Q_k \to P_k)$: For all k: If $k = 39$, then $18 + 17 = k$.   False.

The most useful idea to be dredged from this paragraph is that if you want to know the truth value of the converse of a given implication you must investigate the converse. The truth value of an implication does not determine the truth value of its converse.

Inverse: $\forall_x(\text{not-}P \to \text{not-}Q)$. Recall that even if every replacement of x which makes P_x true also makes Q_x true, there may well be some replacements of x which make P_x false (not-P_x true) and still make Q_x true (not-Q_x false). Thus $\forall_x(P_x \to Q_x)$ may be true while $\forall_x(\text{not-}P_x \to \text{not-}Q_x)$ may be false. Observe the following examples. They illustrate that the truth values of an implication and its inverse are not necessarily the same.

Example 7. $\forall_t(P_t \to Q_t)$: For all triangles t: If t is equilateral, then t is isosceles.   True.

$\forall_t(\text{not-}P_t \to \text{not-}Q_t)$: For all triangles t: If t is not equilateral, then t is not isosceles.   False.

Example 8. $\forall_n(P_n \to Q_n)$: For all n: If $n = 8$, then $7 \cdot n = 56$.   True.

$\forall_n(\text{not-}P_n \to \text{not-}Q_n)$: For all n: If $n \neq 8$, then $7 \cdot n \neq 56$.   True.

Example 9. $\forall_a(P_a \rightarrow Q_a)$: For all a: If $\dfrac{0}{a} = 0$, then $\dfrac{a}{0} = 0$.   False.

$\forall_a(\text{not-}P_a \rightarrow \text{not-}Q_a)$: For all a: If $\dfrac{0}{a} \neq 0$, then $\dfrac{a}{0} \neq 0$.   True.

Example 10. $\forall_c(P_c \rightarrow Q_c)$: For all c: If $c^2 > 100$, then $c < 10$.   False.
$\forall_c(\text{not-}P_c \rightarrow \text{not-}Q_c)$: For all c: If $c^2 \not> 100$, then $c \not< 10$.   False.

This business of the truth of an inverse when the implication is true is a ticklish one because in our everyday life the inverse of a true implication "sounds" so reasonable that we have a tendency to assume it is true. Thus, Mr. Jones wrote to his daughter Mary: "If you do finish college, then I shall surely give my consent to your marriage." Mary got married at the end of her junior year *with* her father's blessing. All the relatives thought that Mr. Jones was exhibiting the manliness of a mouse. But Mary knew better. Her father had not written: "If you do not finish college, then I shall surely not give my consent to your marriage."

> *Contrapositive:* $\forall_x(\text{not-}Q_x \rightarrow \text{not-}P_x)$. We have already indicated that the contrapositive has the same truth value as the original implication. $\forall_x(P_x \rightarrow Q_x)$ is true, if every replacement of x which makes P_x true also makes Q_x true. Under this condition every replacement which makes Q_x false (not-Q_x true) will also make P_x false (not-P_x true), for if the replacement made P_x true it would have to make Q_x true also. Thus when $\forall_x(P_x \rightarrow Q_x)$ is true, $\forall_x(\text{not-}Q_x \rightarrow \text{not-}P_x)$ is also true. Now if there were a single replacement of x which made P_x true and Q_x false, the implication would be false. This very same replacement will make not-P_x false and not-Q_x true. Hence when $\forall_x(P_x \rightarrow Q_x)$ is false, $\forall_x(\text{not-}Q_x \rightarrow \text{not-}P_x)$ will also be false. The following examples support these conclusions.

Example 11. $\forall_n(P_n \rightarrow Q_n)$: For all n: If $3 \cdot n + 2 = 11$, then $n = 3$.   True.
$\forall_n(\text{not-}Q_n \rightarrow \text{not-}P_n)$: For all n: If $n \neq 3$, then $3 \cdot n + 2 \neq 11$.   True.

Example 12. $\forall_x(P_x \rightarrow Q_x)$: For all lines: If two lines lie on the same plane, then they intersect.   False.
$\forall_x(\text{not-}Q_x \rightarrow \text{not-}P_x)$: For all lines: If two lines do not intersect, then they do not lie on the same plane.   False.

Occasionally we use our knowledge about the truth values of an implication and its contrapositive by proving the contrapositive of a theorem instead of the theorem, when that procedure is simpler. For instance, instead of proving

> If two sides of a triangle have unequal measures, then the angles opposite them have unequal measures,

we could prove

> If two angles of a triangle have equal measures, then the sides opposite them have equal measures.

This contrapositive is a familiar theorem from the early weeks of a plane geometry course.

Problem Set 1.5

A. **1.** The negation of not–P is not–(not–P). Present an argument to show that not–(not–P) and P are simultaneously true or simultaneously false.
   2. Write the negations of each of the following sentences:
      a. In the study of botany, the peanut is not classified as a nut.
      b. The food shops in this area are not open on Sunday.
      c. $8 \neq 3$.
      d. It is false that $0 < {}^-1$.
      e. A square is not a rectangle.

B. Provide the converse, inverse, and contrapositive of each of the following implications:
   1. If a rocket rises seven miles above the earth's surface, then the rocket is in the stratosphere.
   2. If cheddar cheese is aged, then its flavor becomes more subtle.
   3. If the tree is a giant sequoia, then it is one of the biggest trees on earth.
   4. If a meteorologist reports "ceiling zero," then the fog is too thick to land a plane safely.
   5. If there is a heavy snow, then the schools are closed.
   6. If people refer to the Green Mountain state, then they mean Vermont.
   7. You may go, if you have finished your homework.
   8. If a scientist is an ichthyologist, then he spends his time studying fish.
   9. Food stains can be easily removed from your kitchen sink, if you use cleanser A.
   10. If you complete this course successfully, then you will be prepared to teach mathematics in grades K–6.

C. Provide the converse, inverse, and contrapositive of each of the following implications:
   1. For all whole numbers x, y, and z: If $x + y = z + x$, then $y = z$.
   2. For all whole numbers r and s: If r and s are whole numbers, then $r + s = s + r$.
   3. For all whole numbers a and b: If $a = 0$, then $a \cdot b = 0$.
   4. For all whole numbers p, q: If $\dfrac{p}{q} = 6$, then $q \neq 0$.
   5. For all triangles: If two triangles are congruent, then regions bounded by these triangles have equal areas.

6. For all a and k: If $a = 3 \cdot k$, then k is one-third of a.

7. For all n: If $5 \cdot n = 5$, then $n = 1$.

8. For all quadrilaterals: If the four sides of a quadrilateral have the same measure, then the quadrilateral is a square.

9. For all whole numbers c and d: If $c < d$, then $c - d$ is not a whole number.

10. For all numbers a, b, and c: $a - b = c$, if $a = c + b$.

D. The following diagram may be helpful to you in rationalizing the definitions

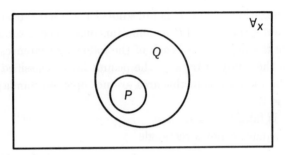

of the truth values of the related implications. Let the interior of the rectangle represent all replacements of x; the interior of the circle P represent all replacements of x which make P_x true; the interior of the circle Q represent all replacements of x which make Q_x true. This diagram represents a situation in which $\forall_x(P_x \to Q_x)$ is true; i.e., every replacement for x which makes P_x true (inside circle P) also makes Q_x true (inside circle Q).

1. a. Define the circumstance under which the converse, $\forall_x(Q_x \to P_x)$, will be true.

b. What must be the position of circle Q relative to that of circle P?

c. Is this condition fulfilled in our diagram?

d. What conclusion can you reach about the truth value of the converse?

2. In the diagram below we repeat the diagram above, showing replace-

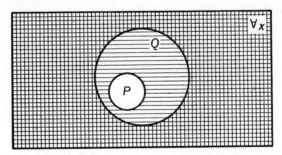

ments for not–P_x and not–Q_x. The horizontal striped region represents all replacements of x which make not–P_x true. The vertical striped region represents all replacements of x which make not–Q_x true. Observe that the horizontal striped region contains the vertical striped region.

a. Is the inverse, $\forall_x(\text{not–}P_x \to \text{not–}Q_x)$, true?

b. Is the contrapositive, $\forall_x(\text{not–}Q_x \to \text{not–}P_x)$, true?

E. Decide on the truth value of each implication and of its negation, of its converse, of its inverse, and of its contrapositive.

1. For all whole numbers k: If k is odd, then $2 \cdot k$ is even.

2. For all whole numbers n: If the ones' digit of a whole number n is odd, then n is odd.

3. $\forall_x: \dfrac{x}{1} \cdot \dfrac{1}{x} = 1 \to \dfrac{x}{2} \cdot \dfrac{2}{x} = 2$.

4. For all lines: If two lines are skew, then they do not intersect.

1.6 Equivalent Sentences

Sometimes two sentences P_x and Q_x are so related that Q_x can be deduced if P_x is assumed as a true premise, and P_x can be deduced if Q_x is assumed as a true premise. Symbolically $\forall_x: P_x \to Q_x$ is true and its converse $\forall_x: Q_x \to P_x$ is also true. We then say that the sentences P_x and Q_x are equivalent.

Example. $P_x:\ x + 2 = 7$.

$Q_x:\qquad x = 5$.

$\forall_x(P_x \to Q_x)$: For all x: If $x + 2 = 7$, then $x = 5$.

$\forall_x(Q_x \to P_x)$: For all x: If $x = 5$, then $x + 2 = 7$.

If we start with the premise $x + 2 = 7$, we can deduce that $x = 5$. The only replacement for x which makes $x + 2 = 7$ true is 5. This same replacement for x makes $x = 5$ true. Hence, $\forall_x: (P_x \to Q_x)$ is true. If we start with $x = 5$, we can deduce that $x + 2 = 7$. The only replacement for x which makes $x = 5$ true is 5. This same replacement for x makes $x + 2 = 7$ true. Thus, $\forall_x: (Q_x \to P_x)$ is true. Then P_x and Q_x are equivalent sentences and we write $\forall_x(P_x \leftrightarrow Q_x)$, which is read "For all x: P_x is true if and only if Q_x is true."

If we know that two sentences P_x and Q_x are equivalent, then we may know that $\forall_x(P_x \to Q_x)$ is true and also $\forall_x(Q_x \to P_x)$ is true. If we wish to prove that two sentences P_x and Q_x are equivalent, then we must establish that for all replacements of x which make P_x true, Q_x is also true and for all replacements of x which make Q_x true, P_x is also true. Suppose we had the following two sentences:

$$a + c = b + c$$

and

$$a = b,$$

and we wished to show that they are equivalent. We would need to be able to establish by reasoning the truth of the following two implications:

For all numbers a, b, and c: If $a + c = b + c$, then $a = b$.
For all numbers a, b, and c: If $a = b$, then $a + c = b + c$.

Since the statements we will want to establish in our work are primarily general statements of the form $\forall_x(P_x \rightarrow Q_x)$ let us agree not to reiterate the symbol $\forall_x$ constantly. From now on we will understand when we write $P_x \rightarrow Q_x$ that we mean $\forall_x(P_x \rightarrow Q_x)$.

Problem Set 1.6

A. In each problem present a reasonable argument to show that the two sentences are equivalent.
  1. P_y: $3 \cdot y = 15$. Q_y: $y = 5$.
  2. P_a: $\dfrac{a}{8} = 7$. Q_a: $a = 56$.
  3. P_n: $7 \cdot n = 7$. Q_n: $n = 1$.
  4. P_n: $n + 13 = 13$. Q_n: $n = 0$.
  5. P_x: $5 \cdot x + 2 = 17$. Q_x: $x = 3$.

B. Decide in each problem whether or not the sentences are equivalent.
  1. P_x: $x^2 = 25$. Q_x: $x = {}^-5$.
  2. P_n: n is an even number. Q_n: $7 \cdot n$ is an even number.
  3. P_k: k is a multiple of 5. $Q_{k,n}$: $k \cdot n$ is a multiple of 5.
  4. P_q: A quadrilateral is a square. Q_q: A quadrilateral has four right angles.

1.7 The Direct Method of Proof

In discussing the truth value of an implication it was decided that if P_x is true and Q_x could be deduced as true in an argument that is based on the premise P_x, then $P_x \rightarrow Q_x$ would be considered true. If, on the other hand, we could produce sound evidence to show that there is at least one x for which Q_x is false but the premise P_x is true, then $P_x \rightarrow Q_x$ will be considered false. Your experience in and out of the mathematics classroom has made you familiar with three techniques used to establish the truth value of $P_x \rightarrow Q_x$.

The most frequently used procedure to prove $P_x \rightarrow Q_x$ is true is called the "direct method." We start our proof with the true premise P_x and proceed by a set of logically sequential steps to show that Q_x is true. These steps are assertions each of which is supported by some agreement or law or previously proved statement. The following specific illustrations may help you recall or clarify the idea of a direct proof.

Example 1. If $12 + 7 = 3 \cdot x + 7$, then $12 = 3 \cdot x$. The only replacement for

x which makes $12 + 7 = 3 \cdot x + 7$ true is 4. The same replacement is the only one which makes $12 = 3 \cdot x$ true. Hence $\forall_x \colon P_x \to Q_x$ is true.

Proofs may be written in paragraph form or in two columns headed Assertions and Supporting Statements as in the next two examples.

Example 2. If 15 has a factor of 3, then any multiple of 15 has a factor of 3.

ASSERTIONS	SUPPORTING STATEMENTS
(1) $15 = 3 \cdot k$.	(1) We are assuming P_k is true; 15 has a factor of 3.
(2) Any multiple of 15 can be written as $a \cdot 15$ where a is a counting number.	(2) Definition of multiple.
(3) $a \cdot 15 = a \cdot 3 \cdot k$.	(3) Definition of multiple; here " $=$ " means two names for the same number. Referring to the first step we may substitute $3 \cdot k$ for 15.
(4) $a \cdot 3 \cdot k$ has a factor of 3.	(4) Definition of factor.
(5) $a \cdot 15$ has a factor of 3.	(5) Fourth step and substitution.

Example 3. If $P \wedge Q$ is true, then not–$[(\text{not–}P) \vee (\text{not–}Q)]$ is true.

ASSERTIONS	SUPPORTING STATEMENTS
(1) $P \wedge Q$ is true.	(1) We assume the given premise is true.
(2) P is true; Q is true.	(2) Definition of truth value of conjunction.
(3) not–P is false; not–Q is false.	(3) Definition of truth value of negation.
(4) $(\text{not–}P) \vee (\text{not–}Q)$ is false.	(4) Definition of truth value of disjunction.
(5) not–$[(\text{not–}P) \vee (\text{not–}Q)]$ is true.	(5) Definition of truth value of negation.

Problem Set 1.7

Prove by the direct method. Use the two-column form or paragraph form, whichever seems clearer to you. Keep in mind that we have agreed that when we write an implication involving variables as $P_x \to Q_x$ we mean $\forall_x (P_x \to Q_x)$.

1. If $r + 5 = 8 + 5$, then $r = 8$ where r is a whole number.

2. If $m = n$, then $m + k = n + k$ for all numbers m, n, and k.

3. If $10^2 = 10 \cdot 10$ and $10^3 = 10 \cdot 10 \cdot 10$, then $10^2 \cdot 10^3 = 10^5$.

4. If $P \wedge Q$ is true, then $P \vee Q$ is true.

5. If $2 \cdot n$ and $2 \cdot p$ are even numbers, with n and p whole numbers, then their sum is even.

6. If $2 \cdot a + 1$ and $2 \cdot b + 1$ are odd numbers, with a and b whole numbers, then their sum $(2 \cdot a + 2 \cdot b + 2)$ is even.

7. The product of any two even numbers is even. (If $2 \cdot n$ and $2 \cdot p$ are even numbers, then $(2 \cdot n) \cdot (2 \cdot p)$ is even.)

8. If $\frac{1}{5} \cdot x = 13$, then $x = 65$.

9. If a diagonal of a rectangle is drawn, then the two resulting triangles are congruent. (In this problem we mean "for all rectangles.")

10. The contrapositive of an implication is the converse of the inverse of the implication. (In this problem we mean "for all implications.")

1.8 The Indirect Method of Proof

Sometimes it is very difficult to prove a statement by proceeding logically from a given premise, which we assume true, directly to the conclusion we wish to establish. Another technique we might employ is called the **indirect method.** This technique for proving $P_x \rightarrow Q_x$ is true involves the following reasoning:

(1) Assume $P_x \rightarrow Q_x$, for all x, is false. This is the same as saying that for some x, not-$(P_x \rightarrow Q_x)$ is true. Recall that the negation of $P_x \rightarrow Q_x$ is $P_x \wedge$ not-Q_x. So we are assuming there is an x for which P_x and not-Q_x are true.

(2) On the basis of this assumption, by a logical sequence of steps we finally arrive at a contradiction of some agreement or law or previously proved statement.

(3) This means something is wrong. If we have made no errors in the course of our argument, then we can conclude only one thing: our original assumption was wrong, and $P_x \rightarrow Q_x$ cannot be false for any x.

(4) Hence $P_x \rightarrow Q_x$ is true for all x.

Study the following examples.

Example 1. Prove: If a is a whole number other than zero, then $\frac{a}{0}$ does not name any number.

Assume the truth of $P_a \wedge$ not-Q_a for some a: a is a whole number other than zero and $\frac{a}{0}$ does name some number. Let $\frac{a}{0} = k$ where k names some number. Then $a = k \cdot 0$. Since $k \cdot 0 = 0$, $a = k \cdot 0 = 0$. This contradicts our given true premise that a is a whole number other than 0. Thus our assumption is incorrect. Not-$(P_a \rightarrow Q_a)$ is false, and $P_a \rightarrow Q_a$ is true.

Example 2. Prove: If $P \wedge Q$ is true, then $P \vee Q$ is true.

Assume: There are sentences P and Q for which $P \wedge Q$ is true and $P \vee Q$ is false. If $P \vee Q$ is false, then P and Q are both false. For this case $P \wedge Q$ would be false. This contradicts our given true premise.

Thus our assumption is incorrect. The negation of our given implication is false and the given implication must be true.

Problem Set 1.8

Use the indirect method and present a reasonable argument to show the following implications are true:

1. If $b \neq c$, then $a + b \neq a + c$ for a, b, c whole numbers.

2. If $r \neq s$, then $t \cdot r \neq t \cdot s$ with r, s, t whole numbers and $t \neq 0$.

3. If $P \rightarrow Q$ is false, then $P \wedge Q$ is false.

4. If the diagonal of a square is drawn, then the two resulting triangles are isosceles.

5. If p is a prime number greater than 2, then $p + 1$ is even.

1.9 Producing a Counterexample

We often use the technique of producing a counterexample in order to show that a statement is false. The statement "All triangles are right triangles" can be shown to be false by exhibiting a triangle which is not a right triangle. If the statement is an implication, $P_x \rightarrow Q_x$, we already know that if we can produce one replacement of x which makes P_x true and Q_x false, then $P_x \rightarrow Q_x$ will be false.

Example 1. Every prime number is odd.

Counterexample: 2 is prime and 2 is even.

Example 2. If a geometric figure is made up of three line segments, then it is a triangle.

Counterexample: The geometric figure below is made up of three line segments but is not a triangle.

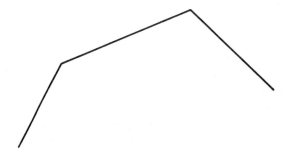

Problem Set 1.9

Produce a counterexample, if you think the statement is false.

1. For whole numbers a and b: If a is even and not divisible by b, then b is odd.
2. If two lines do not intersect, then they are parallel.
3. For all whole numbers p and q: If $(p - q)$ is a whole number, then $(q - p)$ is a whole number.
4. If a number is divisible by 4, then it is divisible by 8.
5. If two numbers are not even, then their sum is not even.
6. If two numbers are prime to each other, then the numbers are prime numbers.
7. If an implication is true, then its inverse is true.
8. For all whole numbers x and y: $\dfrac{x}{y}$ is a whole number.
9. For all whole numbers a, b, c and d: If $\dfrac{a}{b} = \dfrac{c}{d}$ with $b \neq 0$, $d \neq 0$, then $a = c$ and $b = d$.
10. If a closed curve has an inside and an outside, then the curve is a circle.
11. An implication, its converse, its inverse, and its contrapositive can never all be simultaneously true.
12. If we double the height of a rectangle, then the perimeter of the rectangle is doubled.
13. Every English sentence is a statement.
14. For all integers x, the sentences $x^2 = 36$ and $x = 6$ are equivalent.
15. Two lines perpendicular to the same line are parallel.
16. For all m, n, p: If $m \cdot n = m \cdot p$, then $n = p$.
17. For whole numbers r, s, t: If $r < s$, then $t - r < t - s$.
18. For whole numbers x, y, z, w: $\dfrac{x}{y} + \dfrac{z}{w} = \dfrac{x + z}{y + w}$ with $z \neq 0$, $x \neq 0$.
19. If a quadrilateral has four congruent sides, then the quadrilateral is a square.
20. For whole numbers p, q, and r: If $p > q$ and $q > r$, then $(p - q) > (q - r)$.

1.10 Induction

Mathematicians get the suggestions for pursuing their studies from a variety of sources. The most glamorous source is a flash of insight or intuition, an experience we may enjoy on rare occasions. More often the suggestion originates by varying the conditions surrounding a problem already under consideration. Frequently a suggestion for further study arises out of a calculated guess or hypothesis reached as a result of experimentation in the physical world.

The process of examining the results of experiments and taking a good intelligent guess at a generalization is called **induction.** Most of the better teaching of traditional arithmetic in the elementary grades employs this technique. There are two pitfalls one must avoid in using inductive procedures. The first is that you must not assume your generalization or conjecture is a mathematical fact. It's just a guess, a supposition, and nothing more. We do not prove anything by the induction that we are discussing here. We merely suggest a conjecture for possible proof.

The second pitfall is that we sometimes base our conjecture on too few experiments. A class of very young children when thinking about prime numbers might have presented to them:

3 is prime, since 3 has only the factors 1 and 3,
5 is prime, since 5 has only the factors 1 and 5,
7 is prime, since 7 has only the factors 1 and 7,

and generalizing on the basis of these three illustrations the children are likely to guess that 9 is the next prime number. A more sophisticated student might have suggested to him that $(n^2 - n + 41)$ represents a prime number for any whole number n. He might experiment as follows:

$$n = 0 \quad 0 - 0 + 41 = 41 \quad \text{41 is prime}$$
$$n = 1 \quad 1 - 1 + 41 = 41 \quad \text{41 is prime}$$
$$n = 2 \quad 4 - 2 + 41 = 43 \quad \text{43 is prime}$$
$$n = 3 \quad 9 - 3 + 41 = 47 \quad \text{47 is prime}$$
$$n = 4 \quad 16 - 4 + 41 = 53 \quad \text{53 is prime}$$

Indeed he might continue until $n = 40$. If he stopped there, he would likely conclude that $(n^2 - n + 41)$ does in fact always represent a prime number. However, if

$$n = 41 \quad 41^2 - 41 + 41 = 41^2 \quad 41^2 = 41 \cdot 41 \text{ and is } not \text{ prime}$$

It is important to realize that no matter how many experiments are performed supporting the conjecture, this corroboration does not constitute a proof.

Problem Set 1.10

  A. Decide on the missing numbers, so that the pattern is maintained.
    1. 1, 4, 7, 10, 13, 16, ?, ...
    2. 1, 2, 4, 7, ?, 16, 22, 29, 37, ...
    3. 5000, 1000, 200, ?, 8.
    Did you experiment and then generalize?

  B. Make conjectures for a rule for divisibility from the information in each example:
    1. The following numbers are divisible by 5:
            10, 35, 20, 345, 65, 30, 50, 400.

2. The following numbers are divisible by 4:

$$36, \quad 136, \quad 736, \quad 18{,}694{,}736$$
$$16, \quad 516, \quad 916, \quad 243{,}716$$
$$52, \quad 652, \quad 1152, \quad 999{,}952$$
$$8, \quad 708, \quad 4308, \quad 11{,}108$$

3. The following numbers are divisible by 3:

3, 6, 9, 12, 21, 30, 24, 42, 33, 60, 15, 51, 18, 81, 27, 72, 36, 63, 45, 54, 90.

1.11 Deduction

In both methods for proving an implication true, as considered in Sections 1.7 and 1.8, the proof consisted of a series of logically sequential steps in which each assertion is accompanied by a supporting statement. Such a procedure for proof is called **deduction.** The question that is most frequently asked by students examining a deductive proof is: "Of all the assertions that one could possibly make, how does the mathematician know which to choose?" One thing is certain, the assertions are not chosen at random. Each step is selected to bring us from the original true premise closer to the conclusion we wish to establish. In the course of the text some guidelines will be set up to assist you in determining the steps to be taken in a proof, and it is hoped that you will get some intimation about how a mathematician thinks when he attempts to solve a problem.

A second issue which arises in considering the nature of a proof is: "What are acceptable supporting statements?" Generally, it seems sensible to accept any pertinent statements previously proved true and any relevant agreements we have made among ourselves. In mathematics a statement which has been proved true is called a **theorem.** Axioms, definitions, and undefined terms are agreed upon without proof. In any proof or argument, there must be some basic, fundamental ideas or concepts or beliefs to which all parties must agree before any fruitful discussion can take place. The signers of the Declaration of Independence decided to build this country on the basis that "All men are created equal." In your algebra class you most probably decided to accept and apply the principle: "If equals are added to equals, the sums are equal." If you studied geometry you quite possibly accepted the concept: "A straight line is the path of shortest distance between two points." These basic agreements are called **axioms** in mathematics. We accept these arbitrary agreements as true and do not place any limitations on the choice of statements which may serve as axioms. However, in mathematics our axioms frequently do conform with our experience in the physical world. If we choose two points A and B and draw a set of curves with A and B as endpoints, as on page 27, then we would find that the measure of the line segment $\overline{AB}$ was actually less than the measure of any other curve we drew. Did we prove anything? No, indeed, and we are not obliged to prove that "a straight line is the path of shortest distance between two points" if it has been accepted as an axiom, an arbitrary agreement. Whenever we begin the study of

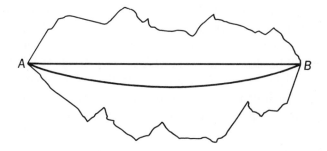

any body of knowledge of mathematics we will agree on the axioms we will need to start our investigations. It is altogether possible that as our studies continue we may wish to include additional axioms.

We are free to make any number of axioms. Mathematicians consider it a matter of elegance to keep the number of axioms as small as possible and not to include among the axioms any statements which can be established on the basis of any other axioms.

Other arbitrary agreements we must make are the **definitions** of terms we will use in our discussion. A good definition should provide us with some information about the term whose meaning we are seeking. If "love" is defined as "affection" and the definition of "affection" is given as "love," we don't have much information about "love." A definition should also be so worded that it includes the items intended and excludes all others. If a chair is defined as "something on which to sit," the definition does include the items we wish to describe, but it also includes a park bench, a bed, a hassock, and a staircase. Such a definition is inclusive but not exclusive. It does not exclude those items we do not have in mind when we say the word "chair." In mathematics we fulfill the requirement that a definition be inclusive and exclusive by making it an "if and only if" sentence. Thus we say "A sentence is a statement if and only if it is meaningful for it to be true or false." "$\forall_x(P_x \rightarrow Q_x)$ is false if and only if there is an x for which P_x is true and Q_x is false." "A sentence is a disjunction if and only if it is made up of two sentences joined by the connective 'or.' " "A number is even if and only if it has a factor of two." From now on, whenever we provide a definition, let us agree to understand that we mean "if and only if" even if we fail to say it. For instance, in English we define the implication A as the converse of an implication B if and only if the antecedent and consequent of A are respectively the consequent and antecedent of B. How much neater to write in mathematical symbols: $Q_x \rightarrow P_x$ is defined as the converse of $P_x \rightarrow Q_x$! Keep in mind that a definition is an arbitrary agreement of the meaning to be assigned to some word or symbol. In making a definition for use in a mathematical discussion, there is no restriction requiring the meaning to conform to colloquial usage. Thus the mathematical definition of a "field" is different from "a grass-covered expanse of land."

When we define words we define them in terms of other words. This means that ultimately there must be some rudimentary words which we must be willing to allow to remain **undefined.** We may have all sorts of intuitive notions about the meaning of the word or the physical representation of the word, but for the purposes of our deductive development we will leave it undefined. In the course of this text it will be clearly indicated whenever we decide to leave a term undefined. Mathematicians prefer for simplicity to have a minimum number of undefined terms. When you study the geometry sections of this text you will find that "point," "line," "plane," and "congruence of line segments" are undefined.

1.12 A Deductive System

A body of knowledge in mathematics is frequently organized as a deductive system. We agree upon the undefined terms, defined terms, and the axioms. Then we prove the theorems. As supporting statements for the first theorem we may use any of the definitions or axioms we have accepted. For the second theorem we may use as supporting statements the definitions, the axioms, and the first theorem. For the third theorem we may use as supporting statements the definitions, axioms, the first and second theorems. Clearly, then, the order in which the theorems are established in a deductive system is important. You may not quote the third theorem as a supporting statement for the first or second theorems.

You should become accustomed to this orderly systemizing of mathematical knowledge. Therefore, whenever the level of the subject matter lends itself readily, the mathematics in this text is presented as a deductive system and many examples of this logical structure appear throughout the book.

When you have come to appreciate the nature of a deductive system, you will begin to realize that the "facts" of mathematics (the theorems) are dependent upon the axioms on which we have agreed. Since the axioms are arbitrary agreements, may we change them? Certainly! If we do, will we get the same "facts" in mathematics? Not necessarily! Then which "facts" are the right ones? We cannot discuss "facts" as right per se; the "facts" are logical deductions from the agreed axioms and that's all! Of course, if the axioms conform to our experiences in the physical world, then the theorems ("facts") which depend upon them will also be borne out by our experiences in the physical world. Such "facts" are more appealing to most people. However, it is sometimes interesting to explore a deductive system even without knowing whether it can be applied to anything in our physical experience. Aside from the matter of intellectual curiosity, it is possible that a newly deductive system may better describe some aspect of our physical world.

1.13 Terminal Tasks for Chapter 1

1. To be sufficiently familiar with the following mathematical symbols and
   vocabulary to be able to use them in mathematical situations: $>$, $<$,

=, ≠, ·, whole numbers, even, odd, prime, factor, multiple, digit, numeral, exponent, variable, negative, positive, implication, antecedent, consequent, premise, negation, converse, inverse, contrapositive, truth value, equivalent sentences, conjunction, disjunction, induction, deduction, counterexample, undefined term, defined term, axiom, theorem, conjecture.

2. To recognize, having heard the following terms in the course of the chapter: perimeter, area, congruent, triangle, rectangle, square, rhombus, perpendicular, right angle, equilateral, isosceles, scalene, parallel, skew, plane, diagonal.

3. To identify the negation, converse, inverse, and contrapositive of a given implication.

4. To be able to write the negation, converse, inverse, and contrapositive of a given implication.

5. To detect fallacies in arguments which assume that the converse and inverse of an implication have the same truth value as the implication.

6. To prove, by the direct method, a theorem within the scope of the mathematical experience of the student.

7. To realize that we may prove a theorem by establishing the truth of its contrapositive.

8. To affirm the falsity of a statement, if only one counterexample is presented.

9. To differentiate between a conjecture resulting from inductive thinking and a theorem proved by deductive methods.

10. To be able to explain in a verbal interchange the function of the arbitrary agreements in a deductive system.

11. To indicate verbally some recognition of the concept that the facts of mathematics may change if the axioms are changed.

REVIEW EXERCISES

A. Match, using each element of the right-hand column only once.

(1) even number	(a) meaningless symbol
(2) 1, 2, 3, 4, 5, . . .	(b) prime numbers
(3) If A, then B	(c) inclusive and exclusive
(4) 3, 17, 19, 41	(d) contrapositive of $A \to B$
(5) greater than	(e) odd numbers
(6) negation of A	(f) a number with a factor of 2
(7) 3, 9, 15, 17	(g) $B \to A$
(8) definition	(h) X, $(1 + 9)$, $2 \cdot 5$ each names 10
(9) not–$B \to$ not–A	(i) counting numbers
(10) converse of $A \to B$	(j) inverse of $A \to B$
(11) axiom	(k) >

(*continued on next page*)

(12) not–$A \rightarrow$ not–B (l) implication
(13) numeral   (m) not–A
(14) $\dfrac{0}{0}$ (n) arbitrary agreement
                          (o) true
(15) $2 \cdot p + 1$ (p) odd number

B. Prove by proceeding from the given premise to the conclusion you wish to establish. List assertions and supporting statements.

   1. If $P \wedge Q$ is true, then (not–P) $\vee$ (not–Q) is false.

   2. If $17 \cdot a + 34 \cdot b = 85$, then $a + 2 \cdot b = 5$.

       Are the antecedent and consequent equivalent sentences? Prove your answer is correct.

C. Prove by establishing the contrapositive.

   1. If $x + y \neq x + z$, then $y \neq z$.

   2. If a number is odd, it cannot have a factor of 2.

D. A student has the following data before him:

$$2 + 12 = 14$$
$$3 + 11 = 14$$
$$4 + 10 = 14$$
$$5 + 9 = 14$$
$$6 + 8 = 14$$

On the basis of the data, which of the listed hypotheses must be discarded? Why?

   1. If a numeral for 14 is written as a sum of two addends, then one addend must be greater than 7.

   2. If one of two addends of 14 is a perfect square, then the other addend must be even.

   3. If 14 is written as the sum of two addends and one addend is odd, the other must be odd too.

   4. If 14 is written as the sum of two addends and one addend is prime, the other addend must also be prime.

   5. Since 14 is divisible by 2, addends whose sum is 14 must each be divisible by 2.

E. Indicate which statements are true and which are false. Explain your decision.

   1. An axiom must fit in with our experience in the physical world.

   2. A defined term in mathematics need not conform to everyday English usage.

   3. An axiom is a self-evident truth.

   4. Two procedures for proving a theorem are induction and deduction.

   5. If all cases are tested and found to support your hypothesis, then it can be regarded as proved true.

6. It takes only one counterexample to prove a conjecture false.

7. If the number of axioms is large, then the deductive system is logically unsound.

8. The reason we leave some terms undefined in a deductive system is that it is difficult to think up a definition.

9. Supporting statements in a deductive proof may be agreements or previously proved theorems.

10. The facts we prove in mathematics are true in all circumstances.

F. Indicate what you learned in this chapter to help you make the decisions required in the following situations.

1. During the campaign the voters were told: "If you elect Mr. Crump, then teachers' salaries will be raised." Six months after the election, the teachers did get a salary increase. Did Mr. Crump win the election?

2. The insurance company advertised: "If you take out student life insurance with our company while you are an undergraduate then we will convert it to regular term insurance when you are through with school. Our low rates and deferred payment plan bring this protection within the means of every student on this campus. For a small additional fee our company offers accident insurance covering your trips home no matter what type of transportation is used. Sign with us. If you don't, your family may live to regret it." If you don't take a policy with *this* company, will your family suffer a financial crisis in the event of your demise? Is it worthwhile investigating the offerings of other companies?

3. If you overheard the following conversation among your kindergarten children, how would you take advantage of it?

> JOE: "A ball is something you can roll."
> JIM: "But I can roll a can and that's not a ball!"
> JOHN: "And I can roll a wheel and that's not a ball!"

4. "If you smoke cigarettes you may get lung cancer. One thousand persons with lung cancer treated at our clinic had a history of cigarette smoking." Does this statement prove anything?

5. "If a number is odd, every multiple of the number is odd. However, n could be 3, and its multiple, 6, is even. So the original implication is false." Convincing argument?

6. A dancing school advertised: "If you want to become popular, then learn to dance." A young man enrolled in the school and learned to dance. He did not become popular. He sued the school for misrepresentation in their advertising. Why did he lose the case?

7. The teacher tells the class: "If you are absent from the final, then you will get a failing grade in this course." Do the students have a right to assume that if they take the final exam they will pass the course?

8. A teacher demonstrates to her primary pupils that the following arrays yield the same number of dots:

(a) . . . .   (b) . . . .

. . . .

. . . . $2 \cdot 5 = 10$ . .

$3 \cdot 4 = 12$ . . .   . .

$4 \cdot 3 = 12$ . .

$5 \cdot 2 = 10$

The class decides, without making any further arrays, that $4 \cdot 2 = 2 \cdot 4$; $3 \cdot 5 = 5 \cdot 3$; $1 \cdot 6 = 6 \cdot 1$. What method of logical reasoning was used here? Did the teacher prove: For all whole numbers a, b: $a \cdot b = b \cdot a$?

9. The school board announced that schools would be closed if the weather was inclement. It snowed and the schools were kept open. When the members of the PTA protested, the school board said: "We do not consider a one-inch snowfall inclement weather." How could this misunderstanding have been avoided?

10. A student says: "I know that: If $x^2 = 16$, then $x = 4$ is false because I can produce a replacement for x, $x = {}^-4$, which makes $x^2 = 16$ true but $^-4 = 4$ false. Hence, its negation should be true. Thus: $x^2 = 16$, then $x \neq 4$ ought to be true. But I can show that it is false for I can produce a replacement for x, $x = 4$, which makes $x^2 = 16$ true and $4 \neq 4$ false." What's wrong?

11. A student says: "I've got it! $n^2 - n + 11$ is always prime. I tried it for $n = 0$ to $n = 10$ and it works." Is he right?

2 The System of Whole Numbers

2.1 Old Stuff

Almost all of the facts and the ideas considered in this chapter are familiar to you. They will simply be presented in a new environment. They will be marshaled, examined, and organized into a deductive system. Thus you will have your first experience with a deductive system in a situation in which you are free to concentrate your attention on the structure of the system. You will not be smothered under a new body of knowledge while trying to gain some insight into the nature of a deductive system.

The system of whole numbers is an example of a mathematical system. Such a system contains some elements (in this case, the numbers 0, 1, 2, 3, 4, . . .), some procedures for associating elements to obtain other elements (in this case the four operations, $+$, $-$, $\cdot$, $\div$) and some distinctive properties of the system. The depth with which we wish to pursue the study of a particular system will be determined by how much we assume is already known. A rigorous development does not necessarily mean that we prove all that could be proved, but does require us to realize what we are taking for granted. In accord with the general philosophy upon which the text is based, much of the approach will be intuitive, and we will lean heavily upon the facts and experiences you bring to the topics we study. The important thing is that you will be aware when the treatment is intuitive, and not be left with the impression that you have a firmly established proof when all we really have is an axiom made on the basis of a conjecture.

We will assume that you already know how to add, subtract, multiply, and divide whole numbers. You also know many properties of these operations on whole numbers. For instance, you know that if you switch the addends of the sum $7 + 9$, the sum remains the same: $7 + 9 = 9 + 7$. If you switch the factors, the product remains the same: $8 \cdot 5 = 5 \cdot 8$. You know that $6 + 0 = 6$; $9 \cdot 1 = 9$; $(5 + 2) + 3 = 5 + (2 + 3)$. You know a lot more, but this is enough to illustrate the idea that you are familiar with many properties. What we are going to do is to name the properties and apply our generalizations to all whole numbers, not just to the specific examples supplied above.

2.2 Closure

The most fundamental property of a mathematical system is closure under a given operation. If addition of two whole numbers always yields a unique sum which is a whole number, then the set of whole numbers is said to be **closed with respect to** (or under) **addition.** Try some examples and see if you think the set of whole numbers has the property of closure under addition. Can you prove your conjecture by producing a million examples to support it? If you cannot prove a statement, does that mean it cannot be proved? Not really! However, it may well be that the time it would take to develop the necessary background to prove closure for the whole numbers under addition is not warranted for this text. So we will decide to accept as an axiom:

> *The set of whole numbers is closed under addition.*

All this tells us is that if we take any two whole numbers we may associate them with a *unique* whole number by applying the operation of addition. The axiom does not tell us that the sum of more than two whole numbers (i.e., $8 + 2 + 9 + 7 + 6$) is a whole number. That is a statement we may wish to prove and use subsequently as a theorem.

Now let us investigate the property of closure under subtraction. Can you produce two illustrations to show that if you subtract one whole number from another the difference is a whole number? How about $10 - 26$? Is 10 a whole number? Is 26 a whole number? Is $(10 - 26)$ a whole number? Observe that we have proved by producing a single counterexample that the statement "The set of whole numbers is closed under subtraction" is false! Its negation must be true:

> *It is false that the set of whole numbers has the property of closure under subtraction.*

Is this an axiom or a theorem? Does this theorem tell us that we may never subtract in the system of whole numbers and get a difference which is a whole number? Obviously not. We may subtract lots and lots of times in the set of whole numbers and the differences will be whole numbers. The disadvantage is that we cannot *always* be sure that the difference will be a whole number. This is a nuisance. It means that we must check every subtraction example, $a - b$, in the set of whole numbers, to be sure $a \geqq b$ if we want the difference to be a whole number.

The discussion concerning closure of the set of whole numbers under multiplication and division is parallel to that of addition and subtraction. Give some examples to show that the axiom:

The set of whole numbers is closed under multiplication,

fits in with our experience in arithmetic.

Prove that the set of whole numbers is not closed with respect to division. Does this mean that the quotient of two whole numbers is never a whole number? Why is the absence of the property of closure under division a troublesome thing? Note that if $\frac{a}{b}$ is a whole number then b must be a factor of a and we must be able to write $a = b \cdot k$ where k is some whole number.

Problem Set 2.2

A. Tell which are axioms and which are theorems.
  1. $x + y$ is always a whole number.
  2. $x - y$ is not always a whole number.
  3. $x \cdot y$ is always a whole number.
  4. $\frac{x}{y}$ is not always a whole number.

B. If p, q, and r are any whole numbers, prove:
  1. $(p + q) + r$ is a whole number.
    [How many addends which are whole numbers do you think we may add and still get a sum which is a whole number?]
  2. $p \cdot (q \cdot r)$ is a whole number.
    [How many factors which are whole numbers do you think we may multiply and still get a product which is a whole number?]
  3. $p \cdot (q + r)$ is a whole number.
  4. $p \cdot q + p \cdot r$ is a whole number.
  5. $p = q \cdot r \to \frac{p}{q}$ is a whole number for p, q, $r \neq 0$.

C. What restrictions, if any, must be placed on the whole numbers a, b, c in order that each of the following shall name a whole number?
  1. $a + (b - c)$ **6.** $(b - a) - c$

  2. $\frac{a}{b}$ **7.** $\frac{\frac{a}{b}}{c}$

  3. $\frac{0}{c}$ **8.** $a \cdot b + c$

  4. $(a + c) - c$ **9.** $a - a$

  5. $\frac{a \cdot c}{c}$ **10.** $b - 4$

D. The property of closure involves two requisites: existence and uniqueness. Show how these may be applied to prove each of the following:

1. If a, b, c are whole numbers, $a = b \rightarrow a + c = b + c$.

2. If a, b, c are whole numbers, $a = b \rightarrow a \cdot c = b \cdot c$.

3. If a, b, c, d are whole numbers, $[(a = b) \wedge (c = d)] \rightarrow a + c = b + d$.

2.3 Commutative Property

The commutative property is not entirely unfamiliar to you if you have studied the first chapter. This property of an operation tells us that if we interchange the two elements being combined by the operation, the result will remain the same. Thus, if we are concerned with the set of whole numbers and the operation addition, then we could test the commutative property by examining the sums $7 + 6$ and $6 + 7$, $10 + 143$ and $143 + 10$, $0 + 19$ and $19 + 0$. In each case the sums remain the same when the addends are interchanged. How many examples would it take to satisfy you that we have proved that addition of whole numbers is commutative? If you answered this correctly, then you should be willing to accept as an axiom:

Addition is commutative in the system of whole numbers.

The axiom may be written very neatly in mathematical symbols. Let W represent the set of whole numbers and $\in$ represent "is a member of" or "belongs to." Then the statement of the commutative property of addition in the system of whole numbers may be written:

For all a, $b \in W$, $a + b = b + a$.

We will also make an axiom stating the commutative property for multiplication in the system of whole numbers:

If a, $b \in W$, then $a \cdot b = b \cdot a$.

Think of some illustrations to show that this fits in with your experiences in arithmetic.

Prove that the following two statements are false:

(1) If a, $b \in W$, then $a - b = b - a$. (Suppose $a = b$?)

(2) If a, $b \in W$, then $\dfrac{a}{b} = \dfrac{b}{a}$. (Suppose $a = b$?)

We may now use as supporting statements, the theorems:

(1) *It is false that $a - b = b - a$ for all a, $b \in W$.*

(2) *It is false that $\dfrac{a}{b} = \dfrac{b}{a}$ for all a, $b \in W$.*

We may omit the restrictions $a \neq 0$ and $b \neq 0$ in the second theorem because it doesn't make sense to discuss whether or not two meaningless symbols name the same number.

Problem Set 2.3

A. Quote the supporting statements you would need to prove: If r, s, $t \in W$, then:

1. $r \cdot (s + t) = (s + t) \cdot r$.   **4.** $r \cdot (s \cdot t) = (s \cdot t) \cdot r$.

2. $r \cdot (s + t) = r \cdot (t + s)$.   **5.** $(r \cdot s) \cdot t = t \cdot (s \cdot r)$.

3. $(r + s) + t = t + (r + s)$.

B. 1. Add: 279,683
           18,256

2. Check the addition by reversing the addends. (If you added "up" before, add "down" now.)

3. Upon what property does this procedure for checking depend?

C. Name the property stated in symbols.

1. If a, $b \in W$, then $(a + b)$ is a unique element of W.

2. If a, $b \in W$, then $(a \cdot b)$ is a unique element of W.

D. Fill in appropriate supporting statements.

If a, b, $c \in W$, then $a \cdot b + c \cdot b = b \cdot c + b \cdot a$.

ASSERTIONS	SUPPORTING STATEMENTS
(1) a, b, $c \in W$.	(1)
(2) $a \cdot b$, $c \cdot b \in W$.	(2)
(3) $(a \cdot b + c \cdot b) \in W$.	(3)
(4) $a \cdot b + c \cdot b = c \cdot b + a \cdot b$.	(4)
(5) $a \cdot b + c \cdot b = b \cdot c + b \cdot a$.	(5)

E. Complete the proof.

If m, n, p, $r \in W$, then $(m + n) \cdot (p + r) = (r + p) \cdot (n + m)$.

ASSERTIONS	SUPPORTING STATEMENTS
(1) m, n, p, $r \in W$.	(1)
$\vdots$	
$(m + n) \cdot (p + r) = (p + r) \cdot (m + n)$.	
$(m + n) \cdot (p + r) = (r + p) \cdot (n + m)$.	

F. Tell whether each statement is sometimes, always, or never true. Justify your decision.

1. If a, $b \in W$, then $(a - b) \in W$.

2. If m, $n \in W$, then $\dfrac{m}{n} = \dfrac{n}{m}$.

3. If $x, y \in W$, then $x \cdot y = y \cdot x$.

4. If $c, d \in W$, then $\dfrac{c}{d} \in W$.

5. If $p, q \in W$ with $p > q$, then $p - q = q - p$ in W.
6. If $k, l \in W$, then $k + l = k + l$.

7. If $h \in W$, then $\dfrac{h}{0} \in W$.

8. If $r, s \in W$, then $(r \cdot s) \in W$.
9. If $u, v \in W$, then $(u + v) \in W$.

10. If $t \in W$, then $\dfrac{0}{t} \in W$.

2.4 Associative Property

We have been using the four operations $(+, -, \cdot, \div)$ to describe how to combine two whole numbers to get a whole number. Thus, $3 + 2$ corresponds with 5; $7 - 1$ corresponds with 6; $5 \cdot 8$ corresponds with 40 and $\dfrac{12}{4}$ corresponds with 3. If, however, there are more than two numbers to be combined by an operation, as $9 - 6 - 1$, then we must devise some means to indicate whether we wish to subtract 6 from 9 and subtract 1 from the difference or whether we wish to subtract 1 from 6 and take the difference from 9. Mathematicians use parentheses to punctuate the strings of symbols and clarify the intent. The two possibilities illustrated above become $(9 - 6) - 1$ or 2, and $9 - (6 - 1)$ or 4.

Under certain operations the two groupings we are discussing give the same result. Then we say the operation has the associative property. For instance, $(7 + 11) + 6$ and $7 + (11 + 6)$ both name the number 24. Also $(8 \cdot 2) \cdot 3$ and $8 \cdot (2 \cdot 3)$ both name the number 48. We will add two more axioms to those for our system of whole numbers:

Addition is associative in the set of whole numbers.

Multiplication is associative in the set of whole numbers.

We write these axioms symbolically as follows:

If $a, b, c \in W$, then $(a + b) + c = a + (b + c)$, and if $a, b, c \in W$, then $(a \cdot b) \cdot c = a \cdot (b \cdot c)$.

From the illustration in the first paragraph in this section it is clear that subtraction is not associative in our number system. Does $(24 \div 2) \div 3 = 24 \div$

$(2 \div 3)$? State a theorem concerning the associative property under division in the set of whole numbers. Have you taken account of the case $(8 \div 8) \div 8 = 8 \div (8 \div 8)$? Of the case $(8 \div 1) \div 1 = 8 \div (1 \div 1)$? Of the case $(0 \div 4) \div 2 = 0 \div (4 \div 2)$?

Problem Set 2.4

A. Identify each sentence as an axiom, a theorem we have established, or a conjecture. For all $a, b, c \in W$:

1. $(a - b) - c \neq a - (b - c)$.   **6.** $(a \div b) \div c \neq a \div (b \div c)$.
2. $(b + a) + c = b + (a + c)$.   **7.** $(a + b) + c = c + (a + b)$.
3. $(a + b) + c = a + (c + b)$.   **8.** $(a + b) - c = a + (b - c)$.
4. $(a \cdot b) \cdot c = c \cdot (b \cdot a)$.   **9.** $(a - b) + c = a - (b + c)$.
5. $(a \cdot b) \cdot c = a \cdot (b \cdot c)$.   **10.** $(c + b) \cdot a = a \cdot (c + b)$.

B. 1. Show that if $a, b, c \in W$, then the associative property of addition gives meaning to $a + b + c$.
2. Show that if $x, y, z \in W$, then the associative property of multiplication gives meaning to $x \cdot y \cdot z$.

C. 1. Indicate how you could use the properties we have considered, to simplify the calculations, so that they may be performed mentally.
　　a. $2 \cdot (5 \cdot 13)$ **d.** $[13 + (17 + 7)] + 13$
　　b. $6 + (19 + 4)$ **e.** $(21 \cdot 15) \cdot 2$
　　c. $25 \cdot (18 \cdot 4)$
2. What properties make each of the following simplifications possible?
　　a. $7 + 5 = (7 + 3) + 2 = 12$.
　　b. $99 + 101 = (99 + 1) + 100 = 200$.

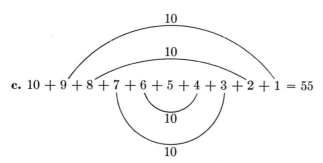

　　c. $10 + 9 + 8 + 7 + 6 + 5 + 4 + 3 + 2 + 1 = 55$

　　d. $(5 \cdot 6) \cdot 4 = 20 \cdot 6 = 120$.
　　e. In the addition algorithm we list the addends so that the ones' digits are in the first column, the tens' digits are in the next column, and so forth.

D. Fill in appropriate supporting statements.

If $p, q, r \in W$, then $(p + q) + r = q + (r + p)$.

ASSERTIONS	SUPPORTING STATEMENTS
(1) $p, q, r \in W$.	(1)
(2) $(p + q) + r = (q + p) + r$.	(2)
(3) $\qquad = q + (p + r)$.	(3)
(4) $\qquad = q + (r + p)$.	(4)
(5) $(p + q) + r = q + (r + p)$.	(5)

E. Prove:

1. If $a, b, c, d \in W$, then $[(a + b) + c] + d = (a + b) + (c + d)$.

2. If $a, b, c \in W$, then $(a \cdot c) \cdot b = (c \cdot b) \cdot a$.

2.5 Distributive Property

Each of the three properties studied so far: closure, commutativity, and associativity, was concerned with a single operation. We said: "W is closed under addition" and "Multiplication is commutative in W" and "Addition is associative in W." Now we will consider a property which concerns itself with two operations, multiplication and addition. It is the property you applied in your algebra course when you multiplied a monomial by a binomial: $4 \cdot (x + y) = 4 \cdot x + 4 \cdot y$. You also applied it when you found a common monomial factor: $6 \cdot t + 2 \cdot r = 2 \cdot (3 \cdot t + r)$. You apply this property frequently in performing arithmetic calculations. Suppose there are 18 men and 15 women in an organization which has dues of $5 a year. How much should be collected in dues? Did you think $(18 + 15) = 33$; $33 \cdot 5 = 165$? Perhaps you thought $5 \cdot 18 = 90$; $5 \cdot 15 = 75$; $90 + 75 = 165$. Both lines of thought resulted in the same number. Hence we may write:

$$5 \cdot (18 + 15) = 5 \cdot 18 + 5 \cdot 15.$$

We say multiplication is distributive over addition for 5, 18, and 15. We would like this to be a property for all whole numbers so we make the axiom:

If $a, b, c \in W$, then $a \cdot (b + c) = a \cdot b + a \cdot c$.

Is division distributive over addition? Is the statement:

$$24 \div (4 + 2) = (24 \div 4) + (24 \div 2)$$

a true one? Is multiplication distributive over subtraction in the system of whole numbers? Try the following examples: $7 \cdot (10 - 1) = 7 \cdot 10 - 7 \cdot 1$; $5 \cdot (8 - 6) = 5 \cdot 8 - 5 \cdot 6$. Are you willing to make a conjecture? Now think about $6 \cdot (2 - 8) = 6 \cdot 2 - 6 \cdot 8$. Would you like to modify your conjecture?

We have agreed that multiplication is to be distributive over addition. Should we expect addition to be distributive over multiplication? If this were true, then $25 + (4 \cdot 5) = (25 + 4) \cdot (25 + 5)$ should be a true statement. Is it?

Problem Set 2.5

A. Apply the distributive property in each case.
   1. Show that $(2 \cdot p + 2 \cdot q)$ is an even number.
   2. Show that $(3 \cdot k + 9)$ has a factor of 3.
   3. Show that $(42 + t \cdot 14)$ is divisible by 14.

B. Study the following example. Then time yourself and see how rapidly you can complete the other computations as mental exercises.

Example. $27 \cdot 101 = 27 \cdot (100 + 1) = 2700 + 27 = 2727.$

   1. $25 \cdot 102$ **4.** $31 \cdot 18$
   2. $51 \cdot 16$ **5.** $12 \cdot 26$
   3. $97 \cdot 11$

C. Fill in appropriate supporting statements.
   If $a, b, c, d \in W$, then $a \cdot (b + c + d) = a \cdot b + a \cdot c + a \cdot d$.

ASSERTIONS	SUPPORTING STATEMENTS
(1) $a, b, c, d \in W$.	(1)
(2) $b + c + d = b + (c + d)$.	(2)
(3) $a \cdot [b + (c + d)] =$ $a \cdot b + a \cdot (c + d)$.	(3)
(4) $= a \cdot b + (a \cdot c + a \cdot d)$.	(4)
(5) $a \cdot (b + c + d) =$ $a \cdot b + a \cdot c + a \cdot d$.	(5)

D. Prove:
   1. The sum of 2 odd numbers is an even number.
   2. The sum of an odd number and an even number is odd.

E. If $a, b, c \in W$, state the necessary conditions:
   1. For $(9 \cdot a + b)$ to be divisible by 9, _____.
   2. For $[9 \cdot a + (b + c)]$ to be divisible by 9, _____.
   3. For $[(9 \cdot a + 9 \cdot b) + c]$ to be divisible by 9, _____.
   4. For $[(9 \cdot a + 9 \cdot b + 9 \cdot c) + (a + b + c)]$ to be divisible by 9, _____.
   5. For $[(9 \cdot a + a) + (9 \cdot b + b) + (9 \cdot c + c)]$ to be divisible by 9, _____.

F. 1. $a \cdot (b + c) = a \cdot b + a \cdot c$ is called a **left distributive property**.

$(b + c) \cdot a = b \cdot a + c \cdot a$ is called a **right distributive property.** Does this right distributive property hold true in W?

2. We know that the left distributive property $a \div (b + c) = (a \div b) + (a \div c)$ in W is not always true. (Try letting $a = 0$.)

   a. Do you think the right distributive property $(b + c) \div a = (b \div a) + (c \div a)$ holds true in W?

   b. Give an example to support your conjecture.

2.6 Properties of 0 and 1

You are already familiar with the two axioms we shall now adopt.

   (a) If $n \in W$, then there exists a unique whole number 0 such that $n + 0 = n$.

   (b) If $n \in W$, then there exists a unique whole number 1 such that $n \cdot 1 = n$.

Axiom (a) tells us that 0 is the **additive identity** in W. Axiom (b) tells us that 1 is the **multiplicative identity** in W.

2.7 Review of Properties for the System of Whole Numbers

Axiom 2.1 *W is closed with respect to addition. $(a + b)$ is a unique sum in W.*

Axiom 2.2 *Addition is commutative in W. $a + b = b + a$.*

Axiom 2.3 *Addition is associative in W. $(a + b) + c = a + (b + c)$.*

Axiom 2.4 *Zero is the additive identity in W. $a + 0 = a$.*

Axiom 2.5 *W is closed with respect to multiplication. $a \cdot b$ is a unique product in W.*

Axiom 2.6 *Multiplication is commutative in W. $a \cdot b = b \cdot a$.*

Axiom 2.7 *Multiplication is associative in W. $(a \cdot b) \cdot c = a \cdot (b \cdot c)$.*

Axiom 2.8 *One is the multiplicative identity in W. $a \cdot 1 = a$.*

Axiom 2.9 *Multiplication is distributive over addition in W. $a \cdot (b + c) = a \cdot b + a \cdot c$.*

Theorem 2.1 *It is false that W is closed with respect to subtraction.*

Theorem 2.2 *It is false that subtraction is commutative in W.*

Theorem 2.3 *It is false that subtraction is associative in W.*

Theorem 2.4 *It is false that W is closed with respect to division.*

Theorem 2.5 *It is false that division is commutative in W.*

Theorem 2.6 *It is false that division is associative in W.*

Problem Set 2.7

A. Decide whether each statement is true or false. Support your decision.
1. We may always add a given number of whole numbers in whatever order we choose.
2. We may always multiply in W.
3. We may never subtract in W.
4. We may divide in W except by 0.
5. We may multiply a given number of factors in whatever order we choose in W.
6. Subtraction is commutative in W.
7. $\dfrac{n}{n} = 1$ with $n \neq 0$.
8. $(7000 + 500 + 30 + 6)$ is divisible by 2.
9. $b \cdot a + c \cdot a = (b + c) \cdot a$.
10. $p \cdot (s + r) + q \cdot (s + r) = (p + q) \cdot (s + r)$.

B. 1. Identify the properties being used in the following calculation:

$$46 \cdot 27 = (40 + 6) \cdot (20 + 7) = 40 \cdot (20 + 7) + 6 \cdot (20 + 7)$$
$$= (800 + 280) + (120 + 42)$$
$$= 1080 + 162 = 1242$$

2. Now review the algorithm you learned in elementary school for performing this calculation:

$$
\begin{array}{r}
27 \\
\times\ 46 \\
\hline
162 \\
108 \\
\hline
1242
\end{array}
$$

3. Compare the steps taken in each procedure. How does it affect the product if we switch the factors 46 and 27?

4. Observe that the algorithm is simply a short cut for the first calculation. What properties of the system of whole numbers are being applied when the familiar algorithm is used?

2.8 Subtraction in *W*

Now that we have set up 9 axioms and 6 theorems for W, let us use what we learned about the structure of a deductive system to place some of our conjectures on firmer footing, and even devise some new, useful and interesting facts.

Theorems 2.1, 2.2, and 2.3 tell us that W is not closed under subtraction and that subtraction does not enjoy commutativity or associativity. Still we know that we do subtract in W, and in our arithmetic we have used freely many facts about subtraction which seemed to make sense to us. For instance, the first grader has a set of 4 bottle tops adjacent to a set of 3 bottle tops. He pushes the set of 3 bottle tops to the other side of his desk and observes that he has 4 bottle tops in the remainder set. This is an application of the idea: $(4 + 3) - 3 = 4 + (3 - 3) = 4 + 0 = 4$. It would be of interest to us to know whether, in general, the following is a true statement in W:

$$(a + b) - c = a + (b - c).$$

Nothing in the axioms or theorems already accepted says explicitly that when the first operation is addition and the second is subtraction, associativity holds. We ought to look into it. We ought also investigate whether $(a - b) + c = a - (b + c)$. Why won't we spend any more time considering whether or not: $(a - b) - c = a - (b - c)$?

At an early point in his arithmetic career the child is faced with the problem: $4 + 3 = \square + 3$ and is asked to replace $\square$ by some numeral so that the statement will be true. Many experiences with concrete objects guide the child to the answer: 4. Actually, this is an application of the Cancellation Law for Addition: If $a + b = c + b$, then $a = c$. We have considered this and referred to it in our work; now let us try to establish it in terms of our axioms and theorems. This also suggests the question: Does a Cancellation Law for Subtraction hold true in W? We will give this some attention too. Perhaps our work on these theorems will suggest other avenues for investigation.

Let us consider the Cancellation Law for Addition first, because we've already given this some thought. What we wish to establish is that:

If $a, b, c \in W$ and $a + b = c + b$, then $a = c$.

If we set this up in two columns, we see that we start with

ASSERTIONS	SUPPORTING STATEMENTS
(1) $a + b = c + b$.	(1)
(2)	(2)
(3)	(3)
$\vdots$	

and would like to end up with

$$a = c.$$

Let us toy around with this for a while. Suppose we subtract b from $(a + b)$ and
from $(c + b)$. Then we would have in the second step $(a + b) - b = (c + b) - b$.
Now, may we apply the associative property to get $a + (b - b) = c + (b - b)$?
Unfortunately, not at this time. We have not yet proved this. Then you may say,
well, let us prove it now and then we can use it. Why don't you try it? You will
find that in order to prove $(a + b) - b = a + (b - b)$ you will need to know the
Cancellation Law for Addition. You would be arguing in a circle and getting no-
where fast.

Since we see problems arising from an attempt at a direct proof for the Cancellation Law, let us resort to another possible approach. We know that the truth
value of $P \rightarrow Q$ is the same as that of its contrapositive, not–$Q \rightarrow$ not–P. Instead
of going from $a + b = c + b$ to $a = c$, let us show that if $a \neq c$, then $a + b \neq$
$c + b$. The fact that we know something about a and c and would like to establish something about $(a + b)$ and $(c + b)$ suggests to us that we add b to a
and b to c and examine the sums. Since $a, b, c \in W$, the existence requirement of
closure under addition assures us that $(a + b)$ and $(c + b)$ are both in W. Because $a \neq c$, we would like to say that if we add the same numbers to a as we do
to c, the sums will also be unequal. However, if we search through our axioms and
theorems, we find nothing we can use as a supporting statement for the assertion:
$a + b \neq c + b$. So we're stuck again in our effort to prove a Cancellation Law
for Addition in W. Nonetheless, we feel in the marrow of our bones, as a result of
our arithmetic experience, that $a + b = c + b \rightarrow a = c$ would be most useful in
our work. Hence we will make the Cancellation Law for Addition in W an axiom.

If $a, b, c \in W$ and $a + b = c + b$, then $a = c$.

Now we are ready to tackle the conjecture:

If $a, b, c \in W$, then $(a + b) - c = a + (b - c)$.

Obviously we will have to place some restrictions on b and c in order that the
elements $(a + b) - c$ and $(b - c)$ will be in W.

We decided earlier in our work that $(a - b) \in W$ if and only if $a \geq b$. Now,
when we are working in the set of whole numbers, we know very well which of
two given numbers is the greater. We can even tell exactly by how much one
number is greater than the other. "Seven is greater than four because I have to
add three to four to get seven." In symbols, we write $a > b$ if and only if there
exists a number $k \neq 0$ such that $a = b + k$. We will now adopt the following
definition of **subtraction**:

> DEFINITION: $(a - b) \in W$ if and only if there exists a whole num-
> ber k such that $a = b + k$.

Why do we omit the restriction $k \neq 0$ in this definition? Now we have agreed that if $(a - b) = k \in W$, then $a = b + k$ and also if $a = b + k$, then $(a - b) = k \in W$. Clearly, then, $(b - c) = k \in W$ if $b = c + k$, and $(a + b) - c = m \in W$ if $(a + b) = c + m$.

Remember, whenever we are searching for clues for suitable steps to be taken in a proof we keep our eyes on what we have and what we wish to show. In this case the setup looks like this

(1) $b - c = k$.
    $(a + b) - c = m$.
(2) $b = c + k$.
    $a + b = c + m$.
    $\vdots$
    $a + k = m$
    $a + (b - c) = (a + b) - c$.

Now, if we substitute $c + k$ for b in $a + b = c + m$, we get

$$a + (c + k) = c + m.$$

We can manipulate and maneuver, using the commutative and associative properties of addition to arrive at $c + (a + k) = c + m$. Applying the Cancellation Law of Addition we have $a + k = m$. This brings us to $a + (b - c) = (a + b) - c$. Is this what we wanted?

Our conjecture turns out to be a true theorem which we may state:

If $a, b, c \in W$ such that $b \geq c$, then $a + (b - c) = (a + b) - c$.

Let us examine the possibility that $a - c = b - c \rightarrow a = b$ in the system of whole numbers. For this statement to have any meaning in W, $(a - c)$ must equal $k \in W$, and $(b - c)$ must equal $m \in W$. Thus: $a = c + k$ and $b = c + m$.

ASSERTIONS	SUPPORTING STATEMENTS
(1) $a - c = b - c$.	(1) Given premise.
(2) $k = m$.	(2) Assumed premise.
(3) $c + k = c + m$.	(3) W is closed under addition.
(4) $a = b$.	(4) Step 3 and substitution.

All this means that we have a Cancellation Law for Subtraction in W, under certain restrictions:

$$a - c = b - c \rightarrow a = b \text{ if } a \geq c \text{ and } b \geq c.$$

In Section 2.5 there arose the question of whether multiplication is distributive over subtraction. Let us see what is involved in trying to establish this, if it is true. We would want to know whether $a \cdot (b - c) = a \cdot b - a \cdot c$ for $a, b, c \in W$.

Our experiences with the proofs we have already done indicate that we will need some restrictions on b and c to insure that $(b - c) \in W$. Let $(b - c) = p \in W$, whence $b = c + p$. Remember our eyes are on what we are to prove: $a \cdot (b - c) = a \cdot b - a \cdot c$. If $b - c = p$ and $b = c + p$, then $a \cdot b = a \cdot (c + p) = a \cdot c + a \cdot p$. Since $a \cdot p \in W$, then $a \cdot b \geq a \cdot c$, and $a \cdot b - a \cdot c = a \cdot p \in W$. Finally, $a \cdot b - a \cdot c = a \cdot (b - c)$ or $a \cdot (b - c) = a \cdot b - a \cdot c$. Can you formulate a statement for the theorem whose proof is indicated in the preceding steps?

We have added the following axiom and theorems to our body of knowledge about the system of whole numbers:

Axiom 2.10 *If $a + b = c + b$, then $a = c$.*

Theorem 2.7 *If $b \geq c$, then $a + (b - c) = (a + b) - c$.*

Theorem 2.8 *If $a \geq c$ and $b \geq c$, then $a - c = b - c$ implies $a = b$.*

Theorem 2.9 *If $b \geq c$, then $a \cdot (b - c) = a \cdot b - a \cdot c$.*

In proving these theorems concerning subtraction there was a consistent pattern of which, it is hoped, you took note. We made sure that the subtraction was permissible in W and then wrote an equivalent equation involving addition. Thus, $a - b = k \in W$ and $a = b + k$. Once we had the problem restated so that the operation was addition, we had loads of axioms to depend upon for procedures to achieve the required conclusion.

Problem Set 2.8

A. Indicate the axioms or theorems being applied in the following calculations.
1. $26 \cdot 89 = 26 \cdot (90 - 1) = 2340 - 26 = 2314$.
2. $23 - 7 = (10 + 13) - 7 = 10 + (13 - 7) = 10 + 6 = 16$.
3. $x - 8 = 64; x - 8 = 72 - 8; x = 72$.
4. $y + 5 = 44; y + 5 = 39 + 5; y = 39$.
5. $51 \cdot 23 = (50 + 1) \cdot (25 - 2) = 50 \cdot (25 - 2) + 1 \cdot (25 - 2)$
$\quad = (1250 - 100) + (25 - 2) = 1150 + 23 = 1173$.

B. Prove, in the system of whole numbers:
1. $(r + s) - s = r$.
2. $(p - q) + q = p$ for $p \geq q$.
3. It is false that $(t - s) + r = t - (s + r)$ for $r \neq 0$.
4. $(a - b) = (c - d) \to (a + d) = (b + c)$ for $a \geq b$ and $c \geq d$.
5. $(a + d) = (b + c) \to (a - b) = (c - d)$ for $a \geq b$ and $c \geq d$.

C. Provide the missing supporting statements.
If $a, b, c, d \in W$ such that $(a - b) = k \in W$ and $(c - d) = m \in W$, then $(a - b) + (c - d) = (a + c) - (b + d)$.

ASSERTIONS	SUPPORTING STATEMENTS
(1) $(a - b) + (c - d) = k + m$.	(1) W is closed under addition.
(2) $a = b + k; c = d + m$.	(2) Definition of subtraction in W.
(3) $a + c = (b + k) + (d + m)$.	(3)
(4) $a + c = b + (k + d) + m$.	(4)
(5) $(a + c) = b + (d + k) + m$.	(5)
(6) $(a + c) = (b + d) + (k + m)$.	(6)
(7) $(a + c) - (b + d) = (k + m)$.	(7) Definition of subtraction in W.
(8) $(a - b) + (c - d) =$ $(a + c) - (b + d)$.	(8) Steps 1 and 7.

D. Complete the proof. (Not to be considered a minor achievement.)

If a, b, c, $d \in W$ such that $(a - b) = k \in W$ and $(c - d) = m \in W$, then $(a - b) \cdot (c - d) = (a \cdot c + b \cdot d) - (b \cdot c + a \cdot d)$.

ASSERTIONS	SUPPORTING STATEMENTS
(1) $(a - b) \cdot (c - d) = k \cdot m$.	(1)
(2) $a = b + k; c = d + m$.	(2)
(3) $a \cdot c = (b + k) \cdot (d + m)$.	(3)

$$\vdots$$

$$(a \cdot c + b \cdot d) = (b \cdot c + a \cdot d) + k \cdot m.$$
$$(a \cdot c + b \cdot d) - (b \cdot c + a \cdot d) = k \cdot m.$$
$$(a - b) \cdot (c - d) =$$
$$(a \cdot c + b \cdot d) - (b \cdot c + a \cdot d).$$

2.9   Division in W

Division is a second operation which can be used in W only under special circumstances. You already know this from your experience in arithmetic. If we consider the numbers

$$\frac{12}{2}, \frac{12}{3}, \frac{12}{4}, \frac{12}{5}, \frac{12}{6}, \frac{12}{7}, \frac{12}{8}, \frac{12}{9}, \frac{12}{10}$$

we recognize at once that $\frac{12}{2}, \frac{12}{3}, \frac{12}{4}, \frac{12}{6}$ name elements in W, while $\frac{12}{5}, \frac{12}{7}, \frac{12}{8}, \frac{12}{9}, \frac{12}{10}$ do not name elements in W. We observe that $\frac{12}{a} \in W$ if a is a factor of 12. This conjecture gives us a good clue for making an agreement about the special circumstances under which $\frac{a}{b} \in W$ if a, $b \in W$. We will say $\frac{a}{b} \in W$ if and only if b is a factor of a and, of course, $b \neq 0$. It is now time for us to record somewhat more precisely what we mean by "factor." We will say b is a **factor** of a if and only if there exists some number k in W such that $a = b \cdot k$. If $a = b \cdot k$ then $\frac{a}{b}$

is defined to be k. Symbolically we now write

If $a, b, k \in W$ with $b \neq 0$, $\dfrac{a}{b} = k$ if and only if $a = b \cdot k$.

We will want to examine some theorems about division in W just as we did about subtraction in W in the previous section. You will soon realize that the ideas we will examine follow the pattern of ideas considered for subtraction. The theorems we will prove about division will depend upon the axioms about multiplication, just as the theorems we proved about subtraction depended upon the axioms about addition.

Let us turn our attention first to a Cancellation Law for Multiplication because it is fundamental to a study of division, and also because it is applied so frequently in arithmetic. Every time a child is faced with the problem $3 \cdot \Delta = 12$ he uses the Cancellation Law for Multiplication, if he thinks $3 \cdot \Delta = 3 \cdot 4$ and hence $\Delta = 4$. We should like to establish that if $a, b, c \in W$ and $b \neq 0$, then $a \cdot b = c \cdot d \rightarrow a = c$. If we look back at the discussion for the Cancellation Law for Addition we recall that, based on our axioms and theorems, we could not present a reasonable proof for the Cancellation Law. A parallel situation exists for the Cancellation Law for Multiplication. If, based on our axioms and theorems, you try to prove this Law, you will find yourself backed up against a brick wall. However, as in the case of the Cancellation Law for Addition, we recognize the usefulness of such a Law. We will therefore state the Cancellation Law for Multiplication as an axiom:

If $a, b, c \in W$ with $b \neq 0$, then $a \cdot b = c \cdot b \rightarrow a = c$.

We need this restriction on b, for if $b = 0$, then $a \cdot 0 = c \cdot 0$ is true, and a does not have to be equal to c.

We will want to be sure that if $\dfrac{p}{q} = m \in W$, then m is unique. In other words, if $\dfrac{p}{q} = m \in W$ and $\dfrac{p}{q} = n \in W$, then m must equal n. This is not difficult to show and puts to use at once the Cancellation Law for Multiplication that we have just decided to accept as an axiom. Since $\dfrac{p}{q} = m$, $p = q \cdot m$. Since $\dfrac{p}{q} = n$, $p = q \cdot n$. Hence $q \cdot m = q \cdot n$, and $m = n$. Provide all the necessary supporting statements for this proof.

Now we would like to know whether $\dfrac{a}{b} = \dfrac{c}{b} \rightarrow a = c$ in W. Since we are working in W, $\dfrac{a}{b}$ and $\dfrac{c}{b}$ must be in W. This means first that $b \neq 0$ because we recall from Chapter 1 that division by 0 is not meaningful in W. Also, we may write $a = b \cdot r$ and $c = b \cdot t$. Since $\dfrac{a}{b} = \dfrac{c}{b}$, $r = t$. Then $b \cdot r = b \cdot t$ and $a = c$, which is what we wished to show.

If a, b, $c \in W$ with $b \neq 0$, then $\dfrac{a}{b} = \dfrac{c}{b} \rightarrow a = c$.

In your algebra course you may have solved the equation $\dfrac{x}{2} = \dfrac{21}{3}$ by a process you called crossmultiplication: $x \cdot 3 = 21 \cdot 2$; $3 \cdot x = 42$; $x = 14$. Let us try to prove once and for all that if $\dfrac{a}{b}$ and $\dfrac{c}{d}$ are in W, then $\dfrac{a}{b} = \dfrac{c}{d} \rightarrow a \cdot d = c \cdot b$. You will find it very useful eventually if you also prove the converse: $a \cdot d = c \cdot d \rightarrow \dfrac{a}{b} = \dfrac{c}{d}$ for $b \neq 0$, $d \neq 0$. Study and complete the following proof:

If $\dfrac{a}{b}, \dfrac{c}{d} \in W$, then $\dfrac{a}{b} = \dfrac{c}{d} \rightarrow a \cdot d = c \cdot b$.

ASSERTIONS	SUPPORTING STATEMENTS
(1) $\dfrac{a}{b} = k \in W, \dfrac{c}{d} = m \in W.$	(1)
(2) $\dfrac{a}{b} = \dfrac{c}{d}.$	(2)
(3) $k = m.$	(3)
(4) $a = b \cdot m$; $c = d \cdot m.$	(4)

(Now is the time for you to eye the conclusion. We want $a \cdot d$ and also $c \cdot b$.)

(5) $a \cdot d = (b \cdot m) \cdot d.$	(5) W is closed under multiplication.
(6) $a \cdot d = c \cdot b.$	(6) Multiplication is commutative and associative in W; step 4.

This shows why "crossmultiplication" works.

Consider the converse: If $\dfrac{a}{b}, \dfrac{c}{d} \in W$ with $b \neq 0$, $d \neq 0$, then $a \cdot d = c \cdot b \rightarrow \dfrac{a}{b} = \dfrac{c}{d}$ in W.

ASSERTIONS	SUPPORTING STATEMENTS
(1) $a \cdot d = c \cdot b.$	(1)
(2) $a = b \cdot r$; $c = d \cdot t.$	(2)

(Now make use of what you are given; go over the preceding proof for clues.)

(3) $r = t.$	(3)
(4) $\dfrac{a}{b} = \dfrac{c}{d}.$	(4)

Finish up!

We may now add the following axiom and theorems to the deductive system we are developing in W:

Axiom 2.11 *If* $a \cdot b = c \cdot b$ *with* $b \neq 0$, *then* $a = c$.

Theorem 2.10 *If* $\dfrac{a}{b}, \dfrac{c}{b} \in W$ *and* $\dfrac{a}{b} = \dfrac{c}{b}$, *then* $a = c$.

Theorem 2.11 *If* $\dfrac{a}{b}, \dfrac{c}{d} \in W$ *and* $\dfrac{a}{b} = \dfrac{c}{d}$, *then* $a \cdot d = c \cdot b$.

Theorem 2.12 *If* $b \neq 0$, $d \neq 0$, $a = b \cdot k$ *and* $c = d \cdot l$, *then* $a \cdot d = c \cdot b \rightarrow$ $\dfrac{a}{b} = \dfrac{c}{d}$.

Problem Set 2.9

A. Tell whether the following statements are sometimes, always, or never true. If your answer is sometimes, describe the limiting circumstances.

1. $\dfrac{a}{b} \in W$.

2. $\dfrac{n}{0} \in W$.

3. $\dfrac{0}{n} \in W$.

4. $\dfrac{a}{7} = \dfrac{b}{7} \rightarrow a = b$ in W.

5. $\dfrac{7}{a} = \dfrac{7}{b} \rightarrow a = b$ in W.

6. $\dfrac{a}{b} \in W \rightarrow \dfrac{b}{a} \in W$.

7. $\dfrac{24}{n} = \dfrac{6}{3} \rightarrow n = 12$.

8. $\dfrac{n}{n} = 1$.

9. $\dfrac{a}{b} = \dfrac{n}{9} \rightarrow a \cdot 9 = b \cdot n$ in W.

10. $a \cdot 0 = b \cdot 0 \rightarrow \dfrac{a}{0} = \dfrac{b}{0}$ in W.

B. Read the discussion and then write the proof of the theorem in the two-column form. We would like to show that:

If $\dfrac{a}{b}, \dfrac{c}{b} \in W$, then $\dfrac{a}{b} + \dfrac{c}{b} = \dfrac{a+c}{b}$ in W.

Let's assume $\dfrac{a}{b} = k$ and $a = b \cdot k$; $\dfrac{c}{b} = l$ and $c = b \cdot l$. There are really two

things we must establish. First, that $\dfrac{a+c}{b}$ is actually an element in W.

Second, that $\dfrac{a+c}{b}$ is another name for the sum $\dfrac{a}{b} + \dfrac{c}{b}$. If $a = b \cdot k$ and

$c = b \cdot l$, then $(a + c) = b \cdot k + b \cdot l = b \cdot (k + l)$. Now we know that

$\dfrac{a+c}{b} = k + l$, which is an element in W. Hence we have shown that

$\dfrac{a+c}{b} \in W$. Since $\dfrac{a}{b} = k$ and $\dfrac{c}{b} = l$, $\dfrac{a+c}{b} = k + l = \dfrac{a}{b} + \dfrac{c}{b}$. Therefore

$\dfrac{a+c}{b}$ is another name for $\dfrac{a}{b} + \dfrac{c}{b}$.

C. Complete the proof: If $\dfrac{a}{b}, \dfrac{c}{d} \in W$, then $\dfrac{a}{b} \cdot \dfrac{c}{d} = \dfrac{a \cdot c}{b \cdot d}$.

Remember you must demonstrate two things:

(a) $\dfrac{a \cdot c}{b \cdot d} \in W$.

(b) $\dfrac{a \cdot c}{b \cdot d}$ is another name for $\dfrac{a}{b} \cdot \dfrac{c}{d}$.

ASSERTIONS	SUPPORTING STATEMENTS
(1) $a, b, c, d \in W$, $b \neq 0$, $d \neq 0$.	(1)
(2) $\dfrac{a}{b} = k \in W$, $\dfrac{c}{d} = l \in W$.	(2)
$\vdots$	
$a \cdot c = (b \cdot d) \cdot (k \cdot l)$.	
$\dfrac{a \cdot c}{b \cdot d} = k \cdot l$.	
$\dfrac{a \cdot c}{b \cdot d} = \dfrac{a}{b} \cdot \dfrac{c}{d}$.	

D. Keeping in mind the clues and hints suggested for finding the significant steps needed for a proof, try the following:

If $\dfrac{a}{b}, \dfrac{c}{d} \in W$ with $b \neq 0$, $d \neq 0$, then $\dfrac{a}{b} + \dfrac{c}{d} = \dfrac{a \cdot d + b \cdot c}{b \cdot d}$.

2.10. Primes, Composites, and Factorizations

Let us review the algorithm for adding two fractions.

$$\frac{4}{15} + \frac{11}{42} = \frac{4}{3 \cdot 5} + \frac{11}{2 \cdot 3 \cdot 7} = \frac{4 \cdot 2 \cdot 7}{3 \cdot 5 \cdot 2 \cdot 7} + \frac{11 \cdot 5}{2 \cdot 3 \cdot 7 \cdot 5}$$
$$= \frac{56}{210} + \frac{55}{210} = \frac{111}{210} \quad \text{or} \quad \frac{37}{70}.$$

For an elementary school child to perform this computation efficiently and effectively, he must be able to provide the prime factorization of a given whole number, and he must be able to select the least common multiple of two whole numbers. This section will concern itself with some fundamental ideas that you should know in order to help your students achieve these tasks. In addition we may uncover some other interesting and useful facts about those whole numbers which are primes or composites.

We have already defined a factor. We have agreed that p is a factor of q if and only if there exists a whole number n such that $q = p \cdot n$. If $q = p \cdot n$, then q is a multiple of p; q is also a multiple of n. We may define a multiple as follows:

> DEFINITION: a is a **multiple** of b if and only if there exists a whole number x such that $a = b \cdot x$.

It is clear that if r is a multiple of s, then s is a factor of r. Thus 100 is a multiple of 25 and 25 is a factor of 100 because there exists a whole number 4 such that $100 = 25 \cdot 4$.

The number 4 is also a factor of 100. In fact we have named 100 as the product of two factors, 25 and 4. Thus, one factorization of 100 is $25 \cdot 4$. Another factorization of 100 is $10 \cdot 10$. Still others are $2 \cdot 50, 5 \cdot 2 \cdot 10, 20 \cdot 5, 2 \cdot 2 \cdot 5 \cdot 5$, $4 \cdot 5 \cdot 5, 1 \cdot 100$. How about $1 \cdot 2 \cdot 50$? $1 \cdot 1 \cdot 2 \cdot 2 \cdot 5 \cdot 5$? $1 \cdot 1 \cdot 1 \cdot 1 \cdot 1 \cdot 4 \cdot 25$? Would a listing of all the factors of 100 supply you with all the information necessary to write factorizations of 100? Think about it. The factors of 100 are 1, 2, 4, 5, 10, 20, 25, 50, 100. Unless you know the multiplication facts you do not know how to select factors which will give a product of 100. There is a difference between listing the factors of a number and providing a factorization of the number. If you are told that some of the factors of 1365 are 13, 15, 21, 35, 91, 65, and 39, can you write a factorization of 1365 simply by looking at the factors? Unlikely! What has to be done is that we must find the whole numbers n such that $1365 = 13 \cdot n$ or $15 \cdot n$ or $21 \cdot n$ or $35 \cdot n$ or $91 \cdot n$, and so forth. We agreed that $1365 = 13 \cdot n \rightarrow \dfrac{1365}{13} = n$. So we must divide 1365 by 13 to find the other factor which will provide a factorization: $\dfrac{1365}{13} = 105$ and $1365 = 13 \cdot 105$.

Every whole number has itself and 1 as two of its factors. When a whole number has *only* two different factors, itself and 1, the number is said to be **prime.** For example, the numbers 2, 3, 5, 29, 37 are prime. A whole number which has factors in addition to itself and 1 is called a **composite** number. The numbers 6, 14, 100, 1365 are examples of composite numbers. The number 1 is neither prime nor composite; it does not have two *different* factors, itself and 1, and it has no factors other than itself and 1. Zero is also excluded from our discussion of primes and composites because every whole number is a factor of 0 and this property makes 0 an exception to the generalizations we can otherwise make about composite numbers. Aside from 0 and 1, every whole number is either prime or composite.

The first ten primes are 2, 3, 5, 7, 11, 13, 17, 19, 23, 29. Even a brief look at this list gives rise to the conjecture that aside from 2, all the primes are odd. If a prime other than 2 were even, it would have not only itself and 1 as factors, but also the number 2. Since this is contradictory to our definition of a prime number, there is no even prime other than 2.

We have seen that a number may have many factorizations: $60 = 30 \cdot 2$, $60 = 4 \cdot 15$, $60 = 10 \cdot 6$. If we write $60 = 3 \cdot 20 = 3 \cdot 2 \cdot 10 = 3 \cdot 2 \cdot 2 \cdot 5$, we find that we have finally written 60 as a product of primes. If we start with $60 = 4 \cdot 15 = 2 \cdot 2 \cdot 3 \cdot 5$, we find that we arrive at a product of the same primes in different order. We will call two factorizations the same if they contain the same factors, regardless of order. If we start with $60 = 10 \cdot 6$, we get $60 = 2 \cdot 5 \cdot 2 \cdot 3$. This leads us to suspect that no matter how many different factorizations of 60 there are, there is only one prime factorization of 60. As a matter of fact there is a **Fundamental Theorem of Arithmetic:**

Theorem 2.13 *Every composite number has a unique prime factorization.*

We will not prove this theorem in this text but we will discuss a specific example so that the theorem seems reasonable. The number 6 has the prime factorization: $2 \cdot 3$. Suppose it had another prime factorization: $a \cdot b$. Then $2 \cdot 3 = a \cdot b$. If a and b were both odd, then $a \cdot b$ would be odd. Since $a \cdot b$ is even, then at least one of the factors must be even. If a is 2, then b has to be 3 and the prime factorization $a \cdot b$ must be the same as $2 \cdot 3$. If a or b is a multiple of 2, then $a \cdot b$ is not a prime factorization. Hence the only prime factorization of 6 is $2 \cdot 3$. If 1 were a prime number, would 6 have a unique prime factorization?

It is comforting to know that a whole number has only one prime factorization. An algorithm for finding this prime factorization consists simply of successive division by primes. The following example illustrates the procedure.

$$
\begin{array}{r|l}
2 & 1092 \\
\hline
2 & 546 \\
\hline
3 & 273 \\
\hline
7 & 91 \\
\hline
 & 13
\end{array}
$$

Why don't we show division by 5? Why do we stop here? The prime factorization of 1092 is $2 \cdot 2 \cdot 3 \cdot 7 \cdot 13$.

Now suppose we are required to find the prime factorization of 209. We discover that 209 is not divisible by 2 or 3 or 5 or 7. By now we might begin to wonder whether 209 itself is prime. If not, how would we know when to stop dividing by prime numbers? Do we continue dividing by all prime numbers up to 209? Let us think about this. Since $14 \cdot 14 = 196$ and $15 \cdot 15 = 225$ then, if $x \cdot x = 209$, x is not a whole number, but is somewhere between 14 and 15. If 209 is composite, at least one of its prime factors must be 13 or less. For if 17 (the next higher prime beyond 13) were the *smallest* prime factor of 209, then any other prime factor would have to be greater than or equal to 17. But $17 \cdot 17 > 209$, hence 17 times any prime factor greater than 17 is also greater than 209. This discussion yields the result that we need try no prime factors beyond 13 in seeking the prime factorization of 209. Does this mean that 209 may not have a prime factor greater than 13? What is the prime factorization of 209?

Once we have the prime factorization of two numbers, it is a simple matter to write a least common multiple of the two numbers. If a number is to be a multiple of 6, it must have 6 as a factor. This means it must have the prime factors 2 and 3. If this same number is to be a multiple of 15, it must have the prime factors 3 and 5. A number which is a common multiple of 6 and 15 is easily composed because we know what prime factors it must have. We might choose the multiple

$$\underbrace{2 \cdot 3}_{6} \cdot \underbrace{3 \cdot 5}_{15} \quad \text{or} \quad 90.$$

However, we observe that if we omitted one of the factors, 3, we would have

$$\underbrace{2 \cdot \overbrace{3 \cdot 5}^{15}}_{6}$$

or 30, which is also a multiple of 6 and a multiple of 15. In fact, 30 is the least common multiple of 6 and 15, for none of the factors 2, 3, or 5 could be eliminated and still have a multiple of 6 and 15, and if any other factor were included, the multiple would be greater than 30.

Returning to the illustration at the beginning of this section, we sought the least common multiple of 15 and 42. The prime factorizations of 15 and 42 are: $15 = 3 \cdot 5$ and $42 = 2 \cdot 3 \cdot 7$. The least common multiple must have the prime factors 3 and 5 (so that it is a multiple of 15); the least common multiple also must have the factors 2, 3, 7 (so that it is a multiple of 42). Hence we select as the prime factorization of the least common multiple $3 \cdot 5 \cdot 2 \cdot 7$. Why do we omit the other factor 3? Consider

$$\underbrace{5 \cdot \overbrace{3 \cdot 2 \cdot 7}^{42}}_{15}.$$

Suppose we needed the least common multiple of 9 and 6. How many times would the factor 3 appear in the prime factorization of the least common multiple of 9 and 6?

In the first illustration we also wrote $\dfrac{111}{210} = \dfrac{37}{70}$. To rewrite a fraction so that the numerator and denominator have no common factor, it is useful to be able to choose the greatest common factor of two numbers. An examination of the prime factorization of the two numbers is a suggestion for an efficient way to choose the greatest common factor. The prime factorizations of 111 and 210 are $111 = 3 \cdot 37$ and $210 = 2 \cdot 3 \cdot 5 \cdot 7$. Clearly the greatest common factor is 3. The greatest common factor of $1092 = \underline{2} \cdot \underline{2} \cdot 3 \cdot \underline{7} \cdot 13$ and $196 = \underline{2} \cdot \underline{2} \cdot \underline{7} \cdot 7$ is $2 \cdot 2 \cdot 7$ or 28.

Problem Set 2.10

A. Eratosthenes, a Greek who lived in the third century B.C., described the following technique for "sieving" out the composite numbers between 1 and 100. Fulfill the instructions and then list all primes between 1 and 100.

1	2	3	4	5	6	7	8	9	10
11	12	13	14	15	16	17	18	19	20
21	22	23	24	25	26	27	28	29	30
31	32	33	34	35	36	37	38	39	40
41	42	43	44	45	46	47	48	49	50
51	52	53	54	55	56	57	58	59	60
61	62	63	64	65	66	67	68	69	70
71	72	73	74	75	76	77	78	79	80
81	82	83	84	85	86	87	88	89	90
91	92	93	94	95	96	97	98	99	100

   1. Cross out 1.
   2. Beginning to count with 3 (the first number after the prime 2), cross out every second number. This will eliminate all multiples of 2.
   3. Beginning to count with 4 (the first number after the prime 3), cross out every third number. What composite numbers will you be eliminating? Why is it that some of the numbers you wish to cross out will already have been eliminated?
   4. Why is it that we will skip crossing out every multiple of 4?
   5. Beginning to count with 6 (the first number after the prime 5), cross out every fifth number. What composite numbers will you be eliminating?
   6. Do we need to cross out multiples of 6? Why?
   7. Are you beginning to observe a pattern? For which of the following numbers will you proceed to cross out multiples: 7, 8, 9, 10, 11?
   8. When will we have eliminated all composites between 1 and 100?

B. Find the prime factorization of each of the following numbers.

   1. 170   **6.** 437
   2. 264   **7.** 2940
   3. 91   **8.** 1295
   4. 1053   **9.** 2604
   5. 1044   **10.** 22,790

C. Find the least common multiple and greatest common factor of each pair of numbers.

   1. 63 and 24   **4.** 94 and 4
   2. 36 and 27   **5.** 252 and 315
   3. 15 and 77

D. Write each sum as a single fraction whose numerator and denominator have no common factor.

1. $\dfrac{5}{18} + \dfrac{7}{27}$

2. $\dfrac{6}{13} + \dfrac{8}{39}$

3. $\dfrac{9}{50} + \dfrac{7}{30}$

4. $\dfrac{1}{3} + \dfrac{3}{4} + \dfrac{5}{12}$

5. $\dfrac{6}{31} + \dfrac{5}{32}$

E. Find the prime factorizations and apply the Cancellation Law for Multiplication to find a numeral for x which will make each statement true.

1. $35 \cdot x = 455$.
2. $77 \cdot x = 4620$.
3. $38 \cdot x = 1596$.
4. $27 \cdot x = 432$.
5. $53 \cdot x = 371$.

F. 1. Prime couples are two consecutive odd primes like 3, 5 and 5, 7 and 11, 13. How many prime couples are there less than 100?

2. Three consecutive odd primes like 3, 5, 7 might be called a **prime triple.** Although mathematicians still do not know how many prime couples there are, they do know that 3, 5, 7 is the only prime triple. Suppose we represent three consecutive odd numbers by $2 \cdot n + 1$, $2 \cdot n + 3$, $2 \cdot n + 5$ where $n = 1, 2, 3, 4, 5, \ldots$. Show that no matter what we write for n, one of the numbers $2 \cdot n + 1$, $2 \cdot n + 3$, or $2 \cdot n + 5$ must be a multiple of 3.

2.11 How Many?

We may not be able to name any counting number which tells how many whole numbers there are, but we can certainly show that there is no largest whole number. This would be the same as saying that there are more whole numbers than we can count. No matter what whole number k you name, we can name the whole number $k + 1$, which is larger than k. There are also more even numbers than you can count, for if you name the even number n, then we can name a larger even number, $n + 2$. A similar argument is used to show that there are more odd numbers than we can count—we simply show that there is no largest odd number.

We will use this approach to show that there are more prime numbers than we can count. We will establish

Theorem 2.14 *There is no largest prime number.*

Euclid, a Greek mathematician who lived in Alexandria in the fourth century B.C., knew this and proved that if you named what you thought was the largest prime, he could produce one that was larger. He reasoned as follows. Suppose you insist that p is the largest prime. Consider the number k which is formed as the product of all known primes from the smallest to the largest: $k = 2 \cdot 3 \cdot 5 \cdot 7 \cdot 11 \cdot 13 \cdots p$. The number k is a composite number divisible by every known prime, since every known prime is a factor of k. Let us compose another number n which shall be equal to $k + 1$. Hence

$$n = \underbrace{2 \cdot 3 \cdot 5 \cdot 7 \cdot 11 \cdot 13 \cdots p}_{k} + 1$$

and we may write $n - k = 1$.

Observe that 2 is a factor of k: $2 \cdot r = k$. If 2 is also a factor of n, then $2 \cdot q = n$ and $2 \cdot q - 2 \cdot r = 1$. Hence $2 \cdot (q - r) = 1$ and 2 would have to be a factor of 1. Clearly 2 is not a factor of 1 and, therefore, 2 could not have been a factor of n. Similarly, 3 is a factor of k, but 3 is not a factor of 1; therefore, 3 could not be a factor of n. In this way we could show that not a single known prime, from the smallest, 2, to the largest, p, is also a factor of n. Thus if n is composite, it must have some prime factor greater than p. If n is prime, it is, of course, greater than p since $k > p$. We have produced a prime number greater than the prime p which you thought was the greatest. This means there is no greatest prime and hence there are more primes than we can count.

Now we know that there are more whole numbers than we can count, more even numbers than we can count, more odd numbers than we can count, and more prime numbers than we can count. Does this mean that there are the same number of even numbers as whole numbers, the same number of odd numbers as whole numbers, the same number of prime numbers as whole numbers? Is it possible that even though we cannot count them, there are fewer even numbers than there are whole numbers?

Since we cannot answer this question by counting the whole numbers and the even numbers and examining the total, we will need to look at another procedure for comparing the set of whole numbers with the set of even numbers. Suppose we have a bag of marbles and a bag of pennies. We do not know how many marbles we have; we do not know how many pennies we have. However, if we match the marbles with the pennies we see that we have the same number of each, even though we do not know what that number is. Every marble is matched with one specific penny. Every penny is matched with one specific marble. There are no marbles that are unmatched and no pennies that are unmatched. We say

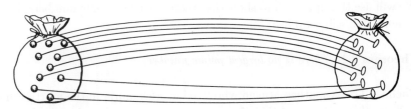

there is a **one-to-one correspondence** between the set of pennies and the set of marbles, and the set of pennies is **equivalent** to the set of marbles. Whenever it is possible to set up a one-to-one correspondence between two collections of elements that can be counted, then we know the two equivalent collections have the same number of elements. The theatre manager hopes there is a one-to-one correspondence between the seats occupied for the performance and the tickets sold. There should be a one-to-one correspondence between the students in the class and the grade cards the instructor submits to the registrar.

If we can set up a one-to-one correspondence between the whole numbers and the even numbers, then it seems plausible to say that there are as many even numbers as there are whole numbers. Observe

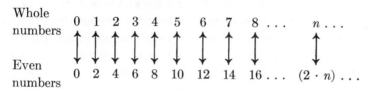

Every time you name a whole number n all we need to do is match it with an even number $2 \cdot n$. If you name an even number $2 \cdot k$, then we will match it with the whole number k. Thus we have demonstrated that we can set up a one-to-one correspondence between the whole numbers and the even numbers. This means that the set of even numbers is equivalent to the set of whole numbers. There are as many even numbers as there are whole numbers. Surprised?

There are also as many odd numbers as whole numbers.

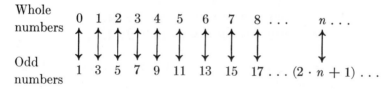

If you name the whole number 157, we will match it with the odd number $2 \cdot 157 + 1$ or 315. If you name the odd number 157 we will match it with the whole number 78, since $2 \cdot n + 1 = 157$; $2 \cdot n + 1 = 156 + 1$; $2 \cdot n = 156$; $n = 78$. Have we set up a one-to-one correspondence?

Problem Set 2.11

   A. 1. If a nursery school child did not know how to count, how would he know that there were more children in the group than crayons in the box?

      2. List at least three situations outside the mathematics classroom in which the principle of one-to-one correspondence is applied.

   B. Demonstrate that there are as many even numbers as there are odd numbers.

C. Is it possible to set up a one-to-one correspondence between the set of whole numbers and the set of counting numbers? Justify your answer.

2.12 Rules for Divisibility

You already know that if you wish to find the prime factors of a whole number n, all you need do is divide n by those primes whose squares are less than n. If $n = 140$, then you divide n by 2, 3, 5, 7, 11. In this particular case you divide by 2 twice; the quotient is not divisible by 3 in W (so we know 3 is not a factor of 140); then divide by 5. The prime factorization of 140 is $2 \cdot 2 \cdot 5 \cdot 7$.

That was an easy one. Suppose you are asked to provide the prime factorization of 93,961. Some simple rules for divisibility tell you, in less than 10 seconds, that this number is not divisible by 2, 3, or 5. Hence you would begin your search for prime factors by dividing by 7. Familiarity with simple rules for divisibility is a convenience, facilitating certain computations. Development of the rules for divisibility is also an elegant opportunity to apply the properties of the system of whole numbers.

The place-value property of the Hindu-Arabic System of Numeration which we use makes it possible for us to write a very special numeral for a given whole number. This numeral is written in **expanded notation.** Examine the following illustrations of numerals written in expanded notation.

$$123 = 1 \cdot 100 + 2 \cdot 10 + 3 \cdot 1.$$
$$231 = 2 \cdot 100 + 3 \cdot 10 + 1 \cdot 1.$$
$$312 = 3 \cdot 100 + 1 \cdot 10 + 2 \cdot 1.$$

Each of the numbers 123, 231, and 312 has 3 digits: 1, 2, and 3. The position of the digit in the numeral determines whether the digit is to be multiplied by 100, by 10, or by 1, in the expanded notation. Recall from your arithmetic experiences such terms as the ones' place, the tens' place, the hundreds' place, the thousands' place, the ten thousands' place, and so forth.

Let us experiment with the number 312 and see if we can get some clues about how to proceed if we wish to develop general rules for divisibility. Just about all of you would say "312 is even because the ones' digit is 2. Hence it is divisible by 2." How do you know that if the ones' digit of a numeral is even, the number which is named by the numeral is divisible by 2? There is no law of nature which says this. We have no axiom to this effect. Perhaps we had better get on to it and see if we can demonstrate that this is so in our system of numeration. Working with a specific number like 312 may give us a hunch about how to develop a general statement. If 312 is divisible by 2 we ought to be able to write a factorization of 312 in which 2 is a specific factor. If we observe the expanded notation.

$$3 \cdot 100 + 1 \cdot 10 + 2 \cdot 1$$

it occurs to us that we might apply the distributive property to isolate the factor 2, if it actually is a factor of 312. If we are going to use the distributive property, then 3 · 100 must have a factor 2. We know that 100 has a factor 2 and hence any multiple of 100 has a factor 2. Thus 3 · 100 has a factor 2. Similarly 10 has a factor 2 and hence any multiple of 10 has a factor 2. Thus 1 · 10 has a factor 2. Also 2 · 1 has a factor 2. Since 3 · 100, 1 · 10, and 2 · 1 each has a factor 2, the distributive property tells us that 3 · 100 + 1 · 10 + 2 · 1 has a factor 2.

Notice that 2 is a factor of 3 · 100 because 2 is a factor of 100. The 3 is ignored in making this decision. Similarly 2 is a factor of 1 · 10 because 2 is a factor of 10. The 1 is ignored in making this decision. On the other hand, 2 · 1 has a factor 2 because the number 2 has a factor 2. The 1, which tells us that the digit 2 is in the ones' place, obviously does not have a factor 2. What can we conclude from all this? In determining whether 312 is divisible by 2

(a) we may ignore the hundreds' digit since its place value will take care of divisibility by 2.
(b) we may ignore the tens' digit since its place value will take care of divisibility by 2.
(c) the ones' digit must be divisible by 2.

For the sake of brevity and when no confusion can result we will use the single word "digit" instead of "the number named by the digit" in our study of rules for divisibility.

Can you tell whether $(a \cdot 100 + b \cdot 10 + 6 \cdot 1)$ is divisible by 2?

Keep in mind that if 10 is divisible by 2, every multiple of 10 is divisible by 2. Since all the numbers other than 1 which indicate place value (10, 100, 1000, 10,000, 100,000, etc.) are multiples of 10, they are divisible by 2. Thus, if we consider the number, written in expanded notation,

$$n = (a \cdot 10{,}000 + b \cdot 1000 + c \cdot 100 + d \cdot 10) + e \cdot 1,$$

the parentheses separate that part of the number which is surely divisible by 2, regardless of the digits, from that part of the number whose divisibility by 2 depends upon the digit. This discussion suggests

Rule 1. The whole number is divisible by 2 if the ones' digit is divisible by 2.

Since 10 is also divisible by 5 and by 10 you should also be able to develop:

Rule 2. A whole number is divisible by 5 if the ones' digit is divisible by 5. (What two digits may be in the ones' place if a number is divisible by 5?)

Rule 3. A whole number is divisible by 10 if the ones' digit is divisible by 10. (What is the only digit that may be in the ones' place if a number is divisible by 10?)

Let us further examine a number, written in expanded notation with the digits indicated by variables.

$$n = a \cdot 10{,}000 + b \cdot 1000 + c \cdot 100 + d \cdot 10 + e \cdot 1.$$

We wish to investigate the possibility of deriving a rule for divisibility by 4. It is clear at once that neither 1 nor 10 is divisible by 4. However, 100 is divisible by 4 and hence every multiple of 100 (including 1000, 10,000, 100,000, . . .) is divisible by 4. The parentheses separate that part of the number which is surely divisible by 4 from that part which will depend upon the digits for divisibility by 4: $n = (a \cdot 10{,}000 + b \cdot 1000 + c \cdot 100) + d \cdot 10 + e \cdot 1$. This suggests

> *Rule* 4. A whole number is divisible by 4 if that part of the number composed of the tens' and ones' digits is divisible by 4.

For example, 59,617,236 is divisible by 4 because 36 is divisible by 4. Also 48,203,671 is not divisible by 4 because 71 is not divisible by 4.

Once again, examine

$$n = a \cdot 10{,}000 + b \cdot 1000 + c \cdot 100 + d \cdot 10 + e \cdot 1$$

to find a rule for divisibility by 8. Neither 1, 10, nor 100 is divisible by 8. The number 1000 is divisible by 8 and so will every multiple of 1000 by divisible by 8. Thus we write:

$$n = (a \cdot 10{,}000 + b \cdot 1000) + c \cdot 100 + d \cdot 10 + e \cdot 1$$

to show which part of the number is surely divisible by 8. We can easily foresee:

> *Rule* 5. A number is divisible by 8 if that part of the number composed of the hundreds', tens', and ones' digits is divisible by 8.

The number 9,617,832 is divisible by 8 because 832 is divisible by 8. The number 40,856,126 is not divisible by 8 because 126 is not divisible by 8. Suppose you have a three-digit number, how would you decide if it is divisible by 8? Suppose you have a two-digit number, how would you decide if it is divisible by 8?

The procedure we have been using will obviously not hold for developing a rule for divisibility by 9 because no multiple of 10 has a factor 9. However, one idea can be carried over. We ought to try to separate the expanded notation of the number into two parts, one surely divisible by 9, and the other with the divisibility depending upon the digits. Let

$$n = a \cdot 1000 + b \cdot 100 + c \cdot 10 + d \cdot 1.$$
$$n = a \cdot (999 + 1) + b \cdot (99 + 1) + c \cdot (9 + 1) + d \cdot 1.$$

Using the distributive property:

$$n = (a \cdot 999 + a \cdot 1) + (b \cdot 99 + b \cdot 1) + (c \cdot 9 + c \cdot 1) + d \cdot 1.$$

Applying the associative and commutative properties:

$$n = (a \cdot 999 + b \cdot 99 + c \cdot 9) + (a \cdot 1 + b \cdot 1 + c \cdot 1 + d \cdot 1).$$

Applying the property of multiplicative identity:

$$n = (a \cdot 999 + b \cdot 99 + c \cdot 9) + (a + b + c + d).$$

Now it ought to be clear that $(a \cdot 999 + b \cdot 99 + c \cdot 9)$ is divisible by 9. The number n will be divisible by 9 if $(a + b + c + d)$ is divisible by 9. Recall that a, b, c, d were the four digits of our number n. Hence we may state:

> *Rule* 6. A whole number is divisible by 9 if the sum of its digits is divisible by 9.

Consider the number 315. It is divisible by 9 because $3 + 1 + 5 = 9$. The number 738,162 is also divisible by 9 because $7 + 3 + 8 + 1 + 6 + 2 = 27$, which is divisible by 9. However, 99,919 is not divisible by 9. Test it.

Observe that $(a \cdot 999 + b \cdot 99 + c \cdot 9)$ is also divisible by 3. Hence $n = (a \cdot 999 + b \cdot 99 + c \cdot 9) + (a + b + c + d)$ will be divisible by 3 if $(a + b + c + d)$ is divisible by 3. Thus we have:

> *Rule* 7. A whole number is divisible by 3 if the sum of its digits is divisible by 3.

As an example, consider 627. Is it divisible by 3? What is the sum of the digits? Is 283 divisible by 3?

Problem Set 2.12

A. Of the following numbers select all those divisible by 2, by 3, by 4, by 5, by 8, by 9, by 10.

546,   465,   6138,   19,   2730,   1179,   6128,   51,   13,116,   840.

B. Use the rules for divisibility to facilitate writing prime factorizations for each number.

1. 420   **4.** 9768

2. 1260   **5.** 137

3. 522

C. 1. Write out in detail the steps leading to the rule for divisibility by 3.

2. Using the rules for divisibility already established, describe how you would test a number for divisibility by 6.

D. Mark true or false. Justify your decision.

1. If n is divisible by 4, it is divisible by 2.

2. If n is divisible by 3, it is divisible by 9.

3. If n is divisible by 8, it is divisible by 4.
4. If n is divisible by 2, it is divisible by 6.
5. If n is divisible by 5, it is divisible by 10.
6. If n is divisible by 4 and 6, it is divisible by 8.
7. If n is divisible by 4 and 6, it is divisible by 12.
8. If n is divisible by 8 and 10, it is divisible by 40.
9. If n is divisible by 8 and 10, it is divisible by 16.
10. If n is divisible by 8, it is divisible by 2 and 4.

2.13 Axioms and Theorems in Chapter 2

Axiom **2.1** W is closed with respect to addition.
Axiom **2.2** Addition is commutative in W.
Axiom **2.3** Addition is associative in W.
Axiom **2.4** Zero is the additive identity in W.
Axiom **2.5** W is closed with respect to multiplication.
Axiom **2.6** Multiplication is commutative in W.
Axiom **2.7** Multiplication is associative in W.
Axiom **2.8** One is the multiplicative identity in W.
Axiom **2.9** Multiplication is distributive over addition in W.
Axiom **2.10** In W, if $a + b = c + b$, then $a = c$.
Axiom **2.11** In W, if $a \cdot b = c \cdot b$ with $b \neq 0$, then $a = c$.

Theorem **2.1** It is false that W is closed with respect to subtraction.
Theorem **2.2** It is false that subtraction is commutative in W.
Theorem **2.3** It is false that subtraction is associative in W.
Theorem **2.4** It is false that W is closed with respect to division.
Theorem **2.5** It is false that division is commutative in W.
Theorem **2.6** It is false that division is associative in W.
Theorem **2.7** In W, if $b \geq c$, then $a + (b - c) = (a + b) - c$.
Theorem **2.8** In W, if $a \geq c$, $b \geq c$, then $a - c = b - c$ implies $a = b$.
Theorem **2.9** In W, if $b \geq c$, then $a \cdot (b - c) = a \cdot b - a \cdot c$.

Theorem **2.10** If $\frac{a}{b}, \frac{c}{b} \in W$ and $\frac{a}{b} = \frac{c}{b}$, then $a = c$.

Theorem **2.11** If $\frac{a}{b}, \frac{c}{d} \in W$ and $\frac{a}{b} = \frac{c}{d}$, then $a \cdot d = c \cdot b$.

Theorem **2.12** In W, if $b \neq 0$, $d \neq 0$, $a = b \cdot k$ and $c = d \cdot l$, then $a \cdot d = c \cdot b \rightarrow \frac{a}{b} = \frac{c}{d}$.

Theorem **2.13** Every composite number has a unique prime factorization.
Theorem **2.14** There is no largest prime number.

2.14 Terminal Tasks for Chapter 2

1. To identify in an example and make appropriate use of the following vocabulary: closure, commutativity, associativity, distributivity, whole number, additive identity, multiplicative identity, factor, factorization, multiple, prime number, composite number, least common multiple, greatest common factor, cancellation law, one-to-one correspondence, equivalent sets.

2. To illustrate with examples in W the properties: closure of W under $+$ and $\cdot$, commutativity for $+$ and $\cdot$, associativity for $+$ and $\cdot$, distributivity of $\cdot$ over $+$, and identity elements for $+$ and $\cdot$.

3. To identify the properties: closure, commutativity, associativity, distributivity, and identity element for $+$ and $\cdot$ when these are written in mathematical symbols.

4. To produce counterexamples to show that $-$ and $\div$ do not have the properties of commutativity and associativity in W, and W is not closed under $-$ and $\div$.

5. To state the axioms we designated for the system of whole numbers.

6. To identify the theorems established in W from a list of miscellaneous statements.

7. To write a simple deductive proof of three or four steps in demonstrating the use of the definitions, axioms, and previously proved theorems as supporting statements.

8. To specify particular steps to be taken in a given problem in searching for clues to indicate the direction the proof should take.

9. To apply the rules for divisibility by 2, 3, 4, 5, 6, 8, 9, 10.

10. To find the prime factorization of a number whose prime factors are less than 100.

R E V I E W   E X E R C I S E S

A. Identify each sentence as a definition, axiom, or theorem in the system of whole numbers.

  1. If $n \in W$, then $n \cdot 1 = n$.

  2. If $a, b \in W$, then $a - b \in W$, if there exists $k \in W$ such that $a = b + k$.

  3. If $x, y \in W$, then $x + y = y + x$.

  4. If $a, b, c \in W$, then $a + b = c + b \rightarrow a = c$.

  5. If $\frac{p}{q}, \frac{r}{s} \in W$ and $\frac{p}{q} = \frac{r}{s}$, then $p \cdot s = q \cdot r$.

  6. If $m, n \in W$, then $m \cdot n = n \cdot m$.

7. If $(a - b), (c - d) \in W$, then $(a - b) + (c - d) = (a + c) - (b + d)$.
8. If $x, y \in W$, then x is a factor of y, if there exists $z \in W$ such that $y = x \cdot z$.
9. If $a, b \in W$, then $(a + b) \in W$.
10. If $x, y \in W$, then $x - y \neq y - x$ for $x \neq 0, y \neq 0$.
11. If p is prime, then there exists a prime number q such that $q > p$.
12. If $m, n \in W$, then $m > n$ if there exists $c \in W$ such that $c \neq 0$ and $m = n + c$.
13. If $g, h, k \in W$, then $g \cdot (h + k) = g \cdot h + g \cdot k$.
14. If $\dfrac{a}{b}, \dfrac{c}{d} \in W$, then $\dfrac{a}{b} \cdot \dfrac{c}{d} = \dfrac{a \cdot c}{b \cdot d}$.
15. If $a, b, c \in W$, then $a + (b - c) = (a + b) - c$ for $b \geqq c$.
16. If $r, s, t \in W$, then $(r \cdot s) \cdot t = r \cdot (s \cdot t)$.
17. If $u, v, w \in W$ and $u \cdot v = w \cdot v$, then $u = w$ for $v \neq 0$.
18. If $a, b \in W$ with $b \neq 0$, then $\dfrac{a}{b} \in W$ if there exists $k \in W$ such that $a = b \cdot k$.
19. If $x \in W$, then $x + 0 = x$.
20. If $a, b, c \in W$, then $a \cdot (b - c) = a \cdot b - a \cdot c$ for $b \geqq c$.

B. 1. Write the prime factorizations of each number.

$$52, \ 282, \ 485, \ 72, \ 73, \ 580, \ 32, \ 60, \ 144, \ 81.$$

In each case name the largest prime you need test to determine whether it is a factor.

2. Write the prime factorizations of each number and choose the least common multiple of each pair of numbers.

$$12 \text{ and } 15, \ 36 \text{ and } 48, \ 2 \text{ and } 64, \ 9 \text{ and } 42, \ 75 \text{ and } 100.$$

3. Find the greatest common factor of the numerator and denominator and rewrite each fraction so that the numerator and denominator are prime to each other.

$$\frac{70}{105}, \ \frac{51}{119}, \ \frac{24}{78}, \ \frac{116}{56}, \ \frac{61}{91}, \ \frac{19}{38}.$$

4. Apply the rules for divisibility to determine whether each of the numerals names a number in W.

$$\frac{6273}{9}, \ \frac{1792}{4}, \ \frac{1792}{8}, \ \frac{12,122}{6}, \ \frac{78}{3}.$$

C. Prove each of the following.

1. If $a, b, c \in W$ and $\dfrac{a}{b} \in W$, then $\dfrac{a \cdot c}{b}$ is also an element in W.

2. If $a, b, c \in W$ and $a - c \in W$, then $(a + b) - c$ is also an element in W.

3. If $a, b, c \in W$, then $a > c \rightarrow a + b > c$.

D. Find the error or errors in the following arguments. Provide a valid argument in each case.

1. In W, show $a + (b - c) = (a - c) + b$ for $b \geqq c$ and $a \geqq c$.

 Proof: $a + (b - c) = a + (-c + b) = (a - c) + b$.

2. In W, show $a \cdot \dfrac{b}{c} = \dfrac{a \cdot b}{c}$ if $a, \dfrac{b}{c} \in W$.

ASSERTIONS	SUPPORTING STATEMENTS
(1) $a \cdot \dfrac{b}{c} = k \in W$.	(1) Given premise.
(2) $a \cdot b = c \cdot k$.	(2) Definition of division in W.
(3) $\dfrac{a \cdot b}{c} = k$.	(3) Definition of division in W.
(4) $a \cdot \dfrac{b}{c} = \dfrac{a \cdot b}{c}$.	(4) Steps 1 and 3; substitution.

3. In W, show $3 \cdot n + (n + 1)$ is odd.

ASSERTIONS	SUPPORTING STATEMENTS
(1) $3 \cdot n + (n + 1) =$ $(3 \cdot n + n) + 1$.	(1) Addition is associative in W.
(2) $(3 \cdot n + n) + 1$ is odd.	(2) Any whole number that ends in 1 is odd.

E. We wish to prove: In W, $p \cdot (a + b) - c = (b \cdot p - c) + p \cdot a$ for $b \cdot p \geqq c$. Which of the following suggestions offers reasonable clues to indicate the direction to take for a proof?

(1) "Since I need $p \cdot a$, I'll probably need the distributive property."

(2) "Because the position of the c is switched to the left, I'd need the commutative property for subtraction. There is none. The problem is impossible."

(3) "There are three elements, so maybe associativity is used. The only theorem I have for associativity involving a subtraction is $x + (y - z) = (x + y) - z$. I could switch, to get $(y - z) + x = (x + y) - z$."

(4) "Why bother? $(b \cdot p - c)$ may not even be an element of W. After all, W is not closed under subtraction."

F. Indicate how the mathematics in this chapter might help you in the following hypothetical elementary school situations.

1. A second grader asks: "Why is it that in every subtraction example you give us, the bigger number is always on top? In addition, you sometimes put the smaller number on top!"

2. "Why isn't the number one a prime number?"

3. "When my father subtracts he 'borrows.' Why do we 'regroup'?"

4. A sixth grader asks: "Why does 'casting out nines' work as a check in computation?"

5. "My brother told me that to multiply by 25 all you need to do is add two zeros and divide by 4. He does it like this:

$$
\begin{array}{r}
312 \\
\times\ \underline{25}
\end{array}
\qquad
4\,\overline{\big)\,31200}\ \ 7800
$$

Why does it work?"

6. You use the distributive property of multiplication over addition to teach the multiplication of a two digit number by a one digit number.

7. You teach first graders subtraction by approaching the operation as "finding the missing addend."

8. Some introductions to division consider the operation as "finding the missing factor." You decide to use this approach in your third grade class.

9. "There are half as many even numbers as whole numbers."

10. A nursery school child who does not know how to count is trying to decide if there are enough cookies so each child at his table will have one with his juice.

11. "What's wrong with saying $\dfrac{a}{b} + \dfrac{c}{d} = \dfrac{a+c}{b+d}$?"

12. "What would happen if I *did* divide 15 by 0?"

13. A fifth grader seeks your help. "We learned that if you don't know a division fact you can simplify the problem like this:

$$48 \div 8 = (40 + 8) \div 8 = (40 \div 8) + (8 \div 8) = 5 + 1 = 6.$$

Why doesn't it work if we rewrite the divisor as a sum, i.e.,

$$48 \div 8 = 48 \div (6 + 2) = (48 \div 6) + (48 \div 2) = 8 + 24 = 32?"$$

14. "Can't an odd number have *any* even factor?"

15. "How is it that Miss Jones' class has a different rule for divisibility by 4? We learned that $1000 \cdot d + 100 \cdot c + 10 \cdot b + a$ is divisible by 4 if $(10 \cdot b + a)$ is divisible by 4. In Miss Jones' class they learned that the number is divisible by 4 if $(2 \cdot b + a)$ is divisible by 4. Can there be two rules, both right?"

3 Structures
in Mathematics

3.1 What's New?

As soon as a preschool child has had to share a candy bar he has had a significant mathematical experience outside the system of whole numbers. A second critical mathematical episode is experienced when the child not only loses every marble he brought to a game, but ends the game owing his opponent seven marbles that he does not have. The first piece of behavior involves an application of an element in the system of rational numbers; the second occurrence demonstrates a use for a negative integer.

The system of integers and the system of rationals constitute a substantial part of the mathematics studied by children in K–6. Therefore it is important that the elementary school teacher be informed of the deductive development (structure) of these two systems. Two subsequent chapters will concern themselves with these number systems. In order to appreciate the mathematics of these systems we will need to consider properties that did not characterize the system of whole numbers and were therefore not discussed in the chapter which dealt with that system. The properties we have in mind are vividly illustrated in a special mathematical system called a modular arithmetic. We will want to spend some time examining such an arithmetic.

You already know from your study of Chapter 2 that a mathematical system must have a definition of the elements in the system, a definition of the operation(s) which associate elements of the system, and a study of the properties of the system under the defined operations. We could conceive of a mathematical system whose structure would comprise elements, an operation, and none of the properties (closure, associativity, commutativity, identity element, distributivity) with which we are familiar. Now that we realize how important the properties are in the development of the arithmetic in a system, we suspect that a system whose structure does not include any such properties will have a barren arithmetic. Mathematicians have studied several structures with specific proper-

69

ties and developed interesting algebraic theorems within such structures. We will consider only two structures: the group, as an example of a structure with one operation, and the field, as an example of a structure with two operations. The group and field are of particular interest to us because they are the structures of the number systems we shall study.

3.2 A Modular Arithmetic under Addition

Suppose we have a mathematical system which has three elements, the numbers 0, 1, 2. The system has one operation which we call addition and symbolize by $+$. Since there are only three elements in this system we can define the operation, addition, by simply listing the nine possible additions which can occur and indicating what we wish the sum to be. Because we will want the system to be closed under the operation, all the sums must be 0, 1, or 2. No other element exists in this system. We may therefore define the operation as follows:

$$(1)\ 0 + 0 = 0.$$
$$(2)\ 0 + 1 = 1.$$
$$(3)\ 0 + 2 = 2.$$
$$(4)\ 1 + 0 = 1.$$
$$(5)\ 1 + 1 = 2.$$
$$(6)\ 1 + 2 = 0.$$
$$(7)\ 2 + 0 = 2.$$
$$(8)\ 2 + 1 = 0.$$
$$(9)\ 2 + 2 = 1.$$

Everything seems to go smoothly and sensibly until we get to (6), $1 + 2 = 0$. You must keep in mind that we are defining the operation and that a definition is arbitrary. You have, of course, the right to ask if there is anything in your experience which might warrant this particular definition. The answer is yes.

The arithmetic you perform every day with the 12 numbers whose numerals appear on your clock face resembles that which we shall do in the system we are developing above. If you leave for class at 9 o'clock and return to your dorm six hours later, what time will you be back in the dorm? If you answered 15 o'clock, you may be associated with the armed forces. If you answered 3 o'clock, you're with the rest of us. Without too much ado, you said $9 + 6 = 3$, and it didn't upset you a bit. In performing "clock-arithmetic" $3 + 11 = 2$, $1 + 5 = 6$, $7 + 9 = 4$. Check these on your watch. Observe that every time you pass the 12, you begin over again at 1. Thus, if $3 + 11 = 14$ in ordinary arithmetic, then this will be 2 beyond the 12. Hence in clock arithmetic $3 + 11 = 2$.

We might picture the elements 0, 1, 2 on the face of a clock: Every time we pass the 2 we start over again at 0. Hence $1 + 2$ brings us to two places beyond the 1, at 0. Also $2 + 1$ brings us to one place beyond the 2, at 0; and $2 + 2$ brings us two places beyond the 2, to 1.

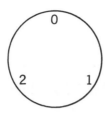

The system described above is an example of a modular arithmetic under addition. Because there are three elements, the system is called a mod 3 arithmetic.

Problem Set 3.2

A. List all possible sums for mod 2 arithmetic under addition, if the elements are 0 and 1.

B. The symbols for elements of mod 5 arithmetic are placed on a clock face.

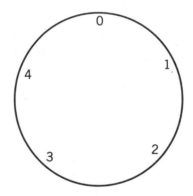

Write the sums for the indicated additions.

1. $2 + 2 =$ ____.   6. $2 + 4 =$ ____.
2. $1 + 4 =$ ____.   7. $1 + 3 =$ ____.
3. $3 + 2 =$ ____.   8. $4 + 4 =$ ____.
4. $3 + 3 =$ ____.   9. $3 + 0 =$ ____.
5. $0 + 4 =$ ____.   10. $4 + 3 =$ ____.

C. The elements of mod 7 arithmetic are 0, 1, 2, 3, 4, 5, 6. Write the indicated sums in mod 7 arithmetic.

1. $2 + 4 =$ ____.   6. $0 + 2 =$ ____.
2. $5 + 3 =$ ____.   7. $4 + 1 =$ ____.
3. $1 + 6 =$ ____.   8. $6 + 6 =$ ____.
4. $4 + 4 =$ ____.   9. $4 + 5 =$ ____.
5. $6 + 5 =$ ____.   10. $3 + 6 =$ ____.

D. Write the sums in the indicated mod arithmetic.

1. $2 + 4 =$ ____ mod 5.   3. $2 + 4 =$ ____ mod 7.
2. $2 + 4 =$ ____ mod 6.   4. $8 + 9 =$ ____ mod 10.

5. $3 + 7 =$ ____ mod 8.   **8.** $7 + 7 =$ ____ mod 9.
6. $3 + 3 =$ ____ mod 4.   **9.** $10 + 6 =$ ____ mod 12.
7. $4 + 3 =$ ____ mod 11.   **10.** $19 + 3 =$ ____ mod 20.

3.3 Properties of Mod 3 Arithmetic under Addition

With the elements listed and the definition of the operation all set we are ready to consider the properties of mod 3 arithmetic under addition. We took care of closure when we defined the operation. In considering commutativity we observe at once that we need not worry about the sums (1) $0 + 0$, (5) $1 + 1$, or (9) $2 + 2$ because the addends are the same; (2) and (4) show that $0 + 1 = 1 + 0$; (3) and (7) show that $0 + 2 = 2 + 0$; (6) and (8) show that $1 + 2 = 2 + 1$. Hence addition is commutative for every possible sum in this system.

The technique for asserting the associative property for addition is once again that of listing all possible cases and testing each one. We would need to assure ourselves that each of the following sentences is true.

$$(0 + 0) + 0 = 0 + (0 + 0).$$
$$(0 + 0) + 1 = 0 + (0 + 1).$$
$$(0 + 0) + 2 = 0 + (0 + 2).$$
$$(0 + 1) + 0 = 0 + (1 + 0).$$
$$(0 + 1) + 1 = 0 + (1 + 1).$$
$$(0 + 1) + 2 = 0 + (1 + 2).$$
$$(0 + 2) + 0 = 0 + (2 + 0).$$
$$(0 + 2) + 1 = 0 + (2 + 1).$$
$$(0 + 2) + 2 = 0 + (2 + 2).$$
$$(1 + 0) + 0 = 1 + (0 + 0).$$
$$(1 + 0) + 1 = 1 + (0 + 1).$$
$$(1 + 0) + 2 = 1 + (0 + 2).$$
$$(1 + 1) + 0 = 1 + (1 + 0).$$
$$(1 + 1) + 1 = 1 + (1 + 1).$$
$$(1 + 1) + 2 = 1 + (1 + 2).$$
$$(1 + 2) + 0 = 1 + (2 + 0).$$
$$(1 + 2) + 1 = 1 + (2 + 1).$$
$$(1 + 2) + 2 = 1 + (2 + 2).$$
$$(2 + 0) + 0 = 2 + (0 + 0).$$
$$(2 + 0) + 1 = 2 + (0 + 1).$$
$$(2 + 0) + 2 = 2 + (0 + 2).$$
$$(2 + 1) + 0 = 2 + (1 + 0).$$
$$(2 + 1) + 1 = 2 + (1 + 1).$$
$$(2 + 1) + 2 = 2 + (1 + 2).$$
$$(2 + 2) + 0 = 2 + (2 + 0).$$
$$(2 + 2) + 1 = 2 + (2 + 1).$$
$$(2 + 2) + 2 = 2 + (2 + 2).$$

This is a laborious task and is therefore left to the student, who will be proficient in addition in our mathematical system by the time he has checked all 27 cases. We will check one together to serve as a sample: Show that $(1 + 2) + 0 = 1 + (2 + 0)$:

$$(1 + 2) + 0 = 0 + 0 = 0.$$
$$1 + (2 + 0) = 1 + 2 = 0.$$

What we have done is to show that addition of the three elements 1, 2, and 0, in that order, is associative. By the time all 27 cases have been checked we will know that for any three of the elements, taken in any order whatsoever, addition is associative.

To facilitate further study of the system it is convenient to organize the addition facts in a table:

+	0	1	2
0	0	1	2
1	1	2	0
2	2	0	1

The numerals in the first column to the left of the box name the first addends; the numerals in the row above the box name the second addends; the numerals in the boxes name the sums. Thus if we were seeking the sum $2 + 1$ we would proceed as follows:

+	0	1	2
0	0	1	2
1	1	2	0
2	2	0	1

If you examine this table you will observe that the first column of sums *in the* box is the same as the first column of addends to the left of the box. This means that when the second addend is 0 (at the top of the first column outside the box) the sum is the same as the first addend.

First Addend		Second Addend		First Column of Sums
0	+	0	=	0
1	+	0	=	1
2	+	0	=	2

Observe also that

$$0 + 0 = 0.$$
$$0 + 1 = 1.$$
$$0 + 2 = 2.$$

We have shown that $0 + a = a + 0 = a$ for our system. The element 0 is called the **additive identity** for this system.

Three other sums that interest us particularly are

$$0 + 0 = 0.$$
$$1 + 2 = 0.$$
$$2 + 1 = 0.$$

In each case the sum of the two addends is the additive identity. When this happens, the second addend is called the **additive inverse** of the first addend. In this case the additive inverse of 0 is 0; the additive inverse of 1 is 2; and the additive inverse of 2 is 1. We write this symbolically as $^-0 = 0 \bmod 3$; $^-1 = 2 \bmod 3$; $^-2 = 1 \bmod 3$. The importance of this property will be demonstrated subsequently.

Problem Set 3.3

A. Complete the table for addition in mod 6 arithmetic.

+	0	1	2	3	4	5
0						
1						
2						
3						
4						
5						

B. 1. Prove mod 6 arithmetic under addition is closed.

   2. Is there an additive identity in mod 6 arithmetic? If so, what is it? Indicate a procedure for searching the addition table to identify an additive identity if it exists.

   3. If any elements of mod 6 arithmetic have additive inverses, indicate what they are. Show how to use the addition table to identify readily additive inverses when they exist.

C. Explain why the following procedure works as a short cut to determine whether addition is commutative for a mod arithmetic. In the table below draw a diagonal from the upper left-hand corner of the addition table to the lower right-hand corner. If the two parts into which the table is separated are the mirror images of each other, then the commutative property holds.

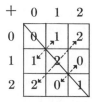

D. Prove addition is associative in mod 2 arithmetic.

E. 1. $(3 + \underline{\quad})$ mod $7 = 0$.   Therefore $\underline{\quad}$ is the additive inverse of 3 in mod 7 arithmetic.

  2. $(5 + \underline{\quad})$ mod $7 = 0$.   Therefore $^-5$ mod $7 = \underline{\quad}$.

  3. $(1 + \underline{\quad})$ mod $8 = 0$. $^-1$ mod $8 = \underline{\quad}$.

  4. $^-3$ mod $8 = \underline{\quad}$.

  5. $^-4$ mod $5 = \underline{\quad}$.

  6. $^-9$ mod $12 = \underline{\quad}$.

  7. $^-2$ mod $3 = \underline{\quad}$.

  8. $^-(^-3)$ mod $5 = {}^-2 = \underline{\quad}$.

  9. $^-(^-1)$ mod $4 = {}^-3 = \underline{\quad}$.

10. $^-(^-5)$ mod $6 = \underline{\quad}$.

3.4 Groups

A **group** is a mathematical system with elements, one operation and the following properties:

  (1) The set of elements is closed under the operation.

  (2) The operation is associative.

  (3) The system has an identity element, and the operation is commutative for any element and the identity element.

  (4) Every element in the system has an inverse in the system and the operation is commutative for the element and its inverse.

If, in addition to these four properties, the operation is commutative for all elements, not only for the identity and inverse elements, then we have a commutative group. If you review the properties of mod 3 arithmetic under addition you will recognize that its structure is that of a commutative group.

Just as we were interested in studying the arithmetic that can be performed in the system of whole numbers, we will want to be informed about the arithmetic that can be performed in the system of integers. Since we shall find the system of integers under addition is a commutative group, a study of the arithmetic for a group is pertinent. Not only will we be able to apply the results of our study to a number system in which we have basic interest, but we will also have an example of the advantage that arises from examining the structure of the number system.

We will use "G" to stand for a mathematical system which is a group. This means that G has a set of elements, one operation and the four properties listed in the beginning of this section. Not every operation needs to be indicated by $+$, $-$, $\cdot$, or $\div$. For a particular system, the operation might be defined as "Follow motion A by motion B." However, since our study of a group will not depend upon the definition of the operation, we will here arbitrarily indicate our operation by the symbol Δ (read "delta"). We may write the four properties of G in symbols:

(1) If $a, b \in G$, then $(a \Delta b) \in G$.

(2) If $a, b, c \in G$, then $(a \Delta b) \Delta c = a \Delta (b \Delta c)$.

(3) There exists $i_1 \in G$ such that for $a \in G$, $a \Delta i_1 = i_1 \Delta a = a$.

(4) For every $a \in G$ there exists $^-a \in G$ such that $a \Delta {}^-a = {}^-a \Delta a = i_1$.

Three new symbols are Δ for the operation, i_1 for the identity and ^-a for the inverse of a.

Problem Set 3.4

A. Consider the mathematical system whose elements are "odd" and "even" and whose operation is defined by the table.

$+$	odd	even
odd	even	odd
even	odd	even

Does this system have the structure of a group? Prove your answer is true.

B. Suppose we have a coin and agree that A shall be "Flip the coin over" and B shall be "Keep the same side up." Let's also agree that we begin all operations with the coin "heads up." The operation T shall be "Do _____ and follow by _____." Thus, ATB will be

(1) Start with the coin "heads up."

(2) Do A (Flip it over: tails up).

(3) Follow by B (Keep the same side up: tails up).

Thus, after performing ATB the coin is in the same position (tails up) as if we had simply flipped it over (A). Hence we say $ATB = A$. Let's try another one: ATA means

(1) Start with coin "heads up."

(2) Do A (Flip it over: tails up).

(3) Follow by A (Flip it over again: heads up).

Thus, after performing ATA the coin is in the same position (heads up) as if we had simply kept the same side up (B). Hence $ATA = B$. In this way we establish the following system with elements A and B and operation T:

T	A	B
A	B	A
B	A	B

Decide whether this system has the structure of a group.

C. Problems **A** and **B** illustrate commutative groups. The following system clearly does not have the commutative property but the operation is associative. Show that this system is an example of a noncommutative group.

$*$	a	b	c	d	e	f
a	a	b	c	d	e	f
b	b	c	a	f	d	e
c	c	a	b	e	f	d
d	d	e	f	a	b	c
e	e	f	d	c	a	b
f	f	d	e	b	c	a

3.5 $^-(^-x)$, $^-i_1$, and the Cancellation Law in a Group

One of the first things that occurs to us is, if the inverse of every element in G is also in G, and if $^-a \in G$, then $^-(^-a)$ must be in G. Further $^-[^-(^-a)] \in G$ and $^-\{^-[^-(^-a)]\} \in G$. This gets to look very complicated and we might well wonder if there were not some simpler way of writing the inverse of the inverse of the inverse of an element in G. To get some clue we can look at mod 3 arithmetic under addition since this system has the structure of a group. Here the elements are 0, 1, 2. Hence if $^-(^-2) \in$ mod 3 arithmetic under addition it must be possible to write $^-(^-2)$ as 0, 1, or 2. Since $^-2 = 1$ mod 3, $^-(^-2) = ^-1 = 2$ mod 3. Thus we find $^-(^-2) = 2$ mod 3. Also, we find $^-(^-1) = 1$ mod 3. These two examples suggest to us the possibility that in general, in a group, the inverse of the inverse of x is x, or: $^-(^-x) = x$. This conjecture we ought to investigate and we shall. Furthermore, in mod 3 arithmetic, the identity element is its own inverse, since $0 + 0 = 0$. We should ask ourselves whether or not, in a group, the inverse of the identity element is the identity element itself, i.e., $^-i_1 = i_1$? This, too, we should investigate.

Let us think how we might go about searching for clues to establish that for $y \in G$, $^-(^-y) = y$. We need some statement which will involve an element and its inverse. The one we have is $x \Delta {}^-x = {}^-x \Delta x = i_1$. Since x is any element in G we could let $x = {}^-y$ and $^-y \Delta {}^-(^-y) = i_1$. It is also true that $^-y \Delta y = i_1$. This would bring us to the statement $^-y \Delta {}^-(^-y) = {}^-y \Delta y$ or $^-(^-y) \Delta {}^-y = y \Delta {}^-y$ because Δ is commutative for the element and its inverse. Now if we had a Cancellation Law for Δ in a group we'd be all set. For then $^-(^-y) = y$. It looks as though we could easily establish that the inverse of the inverse of an element in a group is the element itself, after we have shown that we have a Cancellation Law for the operation in the group.

Recall that we also wish to investigate the possibility that $^-i_1 = i_1$ in G. Again we know that $i_1 \Delta i_1 = i_1$ because of the definition of the identity element. Also $i_1 \Delta {}^-i_1 = i_1$ because of the definition of the inverse element. Hence $i_1 \Delta i_1 = i_1 \Delta {}^-i_1$ and $i_1 \Delta i_1 = {}^-i_1 \Delta i_1$. Here we observe once more that if we had a Cancellation Law we could say $i_1 = {}^-i_1$, which is what we wanted to know. We had better turn our attention with no further delay to a possible proof of a Cancellation Law for the operation in a group.

The need of a Cancellation Law for Δ has been demonstrated, so we would like to establish:

Theorem 3.1 *If $x, y, z \in G$ and $x \Delta z = y \Delta z$, then $x = y$.*

ASSERTIONS	SUPPORTING STATEMENTS
(1) $x, y, z \in G$.	(1)
(2) $x \Delta z = y \Delta z$.	(2)
$\vdots$	
$x = y$.	

We must go from step 2 to $x = y$. What might we possibly do to proceed from $x \Delta z$ to x? Well, $z \Delta {}^-z = i_1$ and $x \Delta i_1 = x$. Does this give you a clue about what to do to $(x \Delta z)$ to get $x \Delta i_1$? Even if we were to write $(x \Delta z) \Delta {}^-z$ we would still have to regroup in order to get $x \Delta (z \Delta {}^-z)$ or $x \Delta i_1$. Have we the right to do this regrouping? What is happening to $(y \Delta z)$ while you are busy trying to go from $(x \Delta z)$ to x? How can you be sure that $(x \Delta z) \Delta {}^-z$ and $(y \Delta z) \Delta {}^-z$ are elements of G? Of course, if they are elements of G, then the uniqueness part of the closure property assures us that the two resulting elements are equal. Complete the proof. Observe that you needed all four properties of a group as supporting statements.

Now that we have a Cancellation Law you can complete the proof of two theorems.

Theorem 3.2 *If $x \in G$, then* $^-(^-x) = x$.

ASSERTIONS	SUPPORTING STATEMENTS
(1) $x \in G$.	(1)
(2) $^-x \in G$, $^-(^-x) \in G$.	(2)
(3) $x \mathbin{\Delta} {}^-x = i_1$.	(3)
(4) $^-x \mathbin{\Delta} {}^-(^-x) = i_1$.	(4)
(5) $x \mathbin{\Delta} {}^-x = {}^-x \mathbin{\Delta} {}^-(^-x)$.	(5)
(6) $x \mathbin{\Delta} {}^-x = {}^-(^-x) \mathbin{\Delta} {}^-x$.	(6)
(7) $x = {}^-(^-x)$.	(7)

Did you use all four properties of a group as supporting statements for Theorem 3.2? Recall that we needed associativity to prove the Cancellation Law.

Theorem 3.3 *In G,* $^-i_1 = i_1$.

ASSERTIONS	SUPPORTING STATEMENTS
(1) $i_1 \in G$.	(1)
(2) $^-i_1 \in G$.	(2)
(3) $i_1 \mathbin{\Delta} i_1 = i_1$.	(3)
(4) $i_1 \mathbin{\Delta} {}^-i_1 = i_1$.	(4)
(5) $i_1 \mathbin{\Delta} i_1 = i_1 \mathbin{\Delta} {}^-i_1$.	(5)
(6) $i_1 \mathbin{\Delta} i_1 = {}^-i_1 \mathbin{\Delta} i_1$.	(6)
(7) $i_1 = {}^-i_1$.	(7)

Problem Set 3.5

A. Prove: If a, $b \in G$ and $a \mathbin{\Delta} b = a \mathbin{\Delta} c$, then $b = c$. How does this exercise differ from Theorem 3.1? Do we have to go through a whole new proof or could we apply Theorem 3.1 and argue:

$$a \mathbin{\Delta} b = a \mathbin{\Delta} c,$$
$$b \mathbin{\Delta} a = c \mathbin{\Delta} a,$$
$$b = c.$$

B. 1. If $1 + 2 = 2 + x$ in mod 3 arithmetic under addition, can we conclude that $1 = x$? Why?

2. In **C**, Problem Set 3.4, if $b * d = d * x$, can we conclude that $b = x$? Why?

3. Prove: If G is a commutative group with a, b, $c \in G$ and $a \mathbin{\Delta} b = b \mathbin{\Delta} c$, then $a = c$.

C. Prove: If a, b, $c \in G$ and $(a \mathbin{\Delta} b) \mathbin{\Delta} c = y \mathbin{\Delta} (b \mathbin{\Delta} c)$, then $a = y$.

D. Prove: If x, $y \in G$ and $^-(^-x) = y$, then $x = y$.
Will this statement be true if $x = i_1$?

E. Let us assume without proof that any mod arithmetic under addition is a group. Then complete:

   1. $^-(^-5)$ mod 6 = ____.

   2. $^-0$ mod 4 = ____.

   3. $^-(^-7)$ mod 8 = ____.

   4. $^-(^-7)$ mod 11 = ____.

   5. $^-0$ mod 9 = ____.

   6. $[4 + {}^-(^-5)]$ mod 6 = ____.

   7. $[^-(^-3) + 7]$ mod 10 = ____.

   8. $[^-(^-6) + {}^-(^-7)]$ mod 9 = ____.

   9. $^-[^-(1 + 1)]$ mod 3 = ____.

   10. $\{^-[^-(2 + 3)] + 4\}$ mod 6 = ____.

F. Suppose that for all elements, a, in a group, $a \, \Delta \, i_1 = a$ and $a \, \Delta \, i_1' = a$. Prove: $i_1 = i_1'$. You will have shown that the identity element in a group is unique.

G. Prove: If $a, b \in G$ and $^-a = {}^-b$, then $b = a$.

3.6 We Can Solve the Equation $x \, \Delta \, a = b$ in G

Recall from your study of the system of whole numbers that if $a, b \in W$ we cannot always find a whole number which will make the sentence $\square + a = b$ true. The sentence $\square + 2 = 26$ does have a solution in W; the sentence $\square + 9 = 7$ does not have a solution in W. There is no whole number which when added to 9 will give a sum of 7. Let us consider a parallel situation in a group. If $a, b \in G$, is there any element $x \in G$ which would make the sentence $x \, \Delta \, a = b$ a true statement? In searching for a possible candidate for x we might think along the following lines:

$$x \, \Delta \, a = b,$$
$$\vdots$$
$$x =$$

How can we possibly modify $x \, \Delta \, a$ to get x? By now we have had some experience and we realize that if we write $(x \, \Delta \, a) \, \Delta \, {}^-a$ we can maneuver to get $x \, \Delta \, i_1$, which will yield the x above, to the left of the $=$ sign. Closure will maintain the equality if we write $b \, \Delta \, {}^-a$. Filling in the outline above, we have:

$$x \, \Delta \, a = b,$$
$$(x \, \Delta \, a) \, \Delta \, {}^-a = b \, \Delta \, {}^-a,$$
$$x \, \Delta \, (a \, \Delta \, {}^-a) = b \, \Delta \, {}^-a,$$
$$x \, \Delta \, i_1 = b \, \Delta \, {}^-a,$$
$$x = b \, \Delta \, {}^-a.$$

This suggests that we use $(b \, \Delta \, {}^-a)$ as the element in G which will make $x \, \Delta \, a = b$ a true statement. We shall try to prove:

Theorem 3.4 *If $a, b \in G$, then $x \, \Delta \, a = b$ has the unique solution $(b \, \Delta \, {}^-a)$ in G.*

What we must show here is:

   (a) $(b \, \Delta \, {}^-a)$ is a solution.

   (b) There is no other solution in G.

(a) If we write $(b \Delta {}^-a)$ for x, shall we arrive at an equivalent statement which we know to be true?

ASSERTIONS	SUPPORTING STATEMENTS
(1) $x \Delta a = (b \Delta {}^-a) \Delta a$.	(1)
(2) $x \Delta a = b \Delta ({}^-a \Delta a)$.	(2)
(3) $x \Delta a = b \Delta i_1$.	(3)
(4) $x \Delta a = b$.	(4)

Complete the supporting statements to show that $(b \Delta {}^-a)$ is a solution.

(b) If $x_1 = b \Delta {}^-a$, then any other solution x_2 is equal to x_1.

ASSERTIONS	SUPPORTING STATEMENTS
(1) $x_1 \Delta a = b$.	(1) Given premise.
(2) $x_2 \Delta a = b$.	(2) Given premise.
(3) $x_1 \Delta a = x_2 \Delta a$.	(3)
(4) $x_1 = x_2$.	(4)

Complete the supporting statements to show that $(b \Delta {}^-a)$ is a unique solution of $x \Delta a = b$ in G. We may apply Theorem 3.3 to mod 3 arithmetic under addition. Solve: $x + 2 = 0$.

$$x + 2 = 0,$$
$$x = 0 + {}^-2,$$
$$x = 0 + 1,$$
$$x = 1.$$

Problem Set 3.6

A. 1. In Theorem 3.4 we found a unique solution in G for the equation $x \Delta a = b$. Find a unique solution in G for $a \Delta x = b$.

2. If G is a commutative group, find a unique solution for $a \Delta x = b$.

B. Write the solutions if the elements are in a group.

1. $r \Delta s = t$. $r =$ ____.
2. $r \Delta s = t$. $s =$ ____.
3. $r \Delta {}^-s = p$. $r =$ ____.
4. ${}^-r \Delta s = p$. $s =$ ____.
5. $r \Delta i_1 = p$. $r =$ ____.

C. Solve in mod 3 arithmetic under addition.

1. $m + 2 = 0$. $m =$ ____.
2. $1 + k = 0$. $k =$ ____.
3. $2 + s = 1$. $s =$ ____.
4. $x + 2 = 2$. $x =$ ____.
5. $y + 0 = 1$. $y =$ ____.
Did you use the addition facts you know in this system?

Did you use Theorem 3.4 and problem **A** (above)?

Did you go through the procedure for producing a candidate? What properties of a group did you use to produce the candidate?

3.7 Another Name for $^-(a \Delta b)$

There remains another question which is somewhat tantalizing. If $a, b \in G$ we know that $(a \Delta b) \in G$. Then $^-(a \Delta b)$ must also be an element of G. Is there another symbol for $^-(a \Delta b)$ which might facilitate calculation in a system which has the properties of a group? In the light of our experience up to now, we might start our thinking about this problem by writing $(a \Delta b) \Delta {}^-(a \Delta b) = i_1$. Then we would consider what procedure would produce an equivalent statement: $^-(a \Delta b) = $ _____. Clearly we must do something that will modify the left member of the equation to eliminate the $(a \Delta b)$. This we know can be done using Δ on $(a \Delta b)$ first with ^-b and then with ^-a. Let us see how this would look if we wrote the necessary steps.

ASSERTIONS	SUPPORTING STATEMENTS
(1) $(a \Delta b) \Delta {}^-(a \Delta b) = i_1.$	(1)
(2) $^-(a \Delta b) \Delta {}^-[^-(a \Delta b)] = i_1.$	(2)
(3) $^-(a \Delta b) \Delta (a \Delta b) = i_1.$	(3)
(4) $[^-(a \Delta b) \Delta (a \Delta b)] \Delta {}^-b = i_1 \Delta {}^-b.$	(4)
(5) $[^-(a \Delta b) \Delta a] \Delta (b \Delta {}^-b) = {}^-b.$	(5)
(6) $[^-(a \Delta b) \Delta a] \Delta i_1 = {}^-b.$	(6)
(7) $^-(a \Delta b) \Delta a = {}^-b.$	(7)
(8) $[^-(a \Delta b) \Delta a] \Delta {}^-a = {}^-b \Delta {}^-a.$	(8)
(9) $^-(a \Delta b) = {}^-b \Delta {}^-a.$	(9)

Complete the proof. You will have established:

Theorem 3.5 *If $a, b \in G$, then $^-(a \Delta b) = {}^-b \Delta {}^-a$.*

The following system is a noncommutative group:

+	1	2	3	4	5	6
1	1	2	3	4	5	6
2	2	3	1	5	6	4
3	3	1	2	6	4	5
4	4	6	5	1	3	2
5	5	4	6	2	1	3
6	6	5	4	3	2	1

Let us apply Theorem 3.5. Then $^-(4 + 5)$ should be the same as $^-5 + ^-4$. Observe

$$^-(4 + 5) = ^-3 = 2.$$
$$^-5 + ^-4 = 5 + 4 = 2.$$

Might we also say $^-(4 + 5) = ^-4 + ^-5$? We already know that $^-(4 + 5)$ in our new system is equal to 2. We find $^-4 + ^-5 = 4 + 5 = 3$. Hence we may not write $^-(4 + 5) = ^-4 + ^-5$. This shouldn't surprise us too much for we knew the system was not commutative and hence we should not expect $^-5 + ^-4$ to be equal to $^-4 + ^-5$. Now try the experiment with $^-(1 + 3)$. Would you be willing to say that $^-(a + b) = ^-b + ^-a = ^-a + ^-b$ in a group?

Problem Set 3.7

A. Complete in mod 3 arithmetic.
    1. $^-(1 + 2) = ^-2 + ^-1 = $ _____.
    2. $^-(1 + x) = 1$; $^-x + ^-1 = ^-x + 2 = 1.$ $x = $ _____.
    3. $^-(y + 2) = 2$; $^-2 + ^-y = 2.$ $y = $ _____.

B. Solve in mod 3 arithmetic.
    1. $^-(t + 1) = 2.$ $t = $ _____.
    2. $1 + ^-(2 + r) = 0.$ $r = $ _____.
    3. $1 + ^-(2 + r) = 2.$ $r = $ _____.

C. Prove: In a commutative group, $(x \, \Delta \, ^-y) \, \Delta \, ^-z = x \, \Delta \, ^-(y \, \Delta \, z).$

3.8 The Inverse Operation in G

Let us define an operation ▼ for G which will be related to the given operation Δ in the following way:

> DEFINITION: For $a, b \in G$, $a \blacktriangledown b = c$ if and only if there exists $c \in G$ such that $a = c \, \Delta \, b$.

This looks familiar to us because in W we related subtraction to addition in a similar manner. Mathematicians often refer to an operation like ▼ as the **inverse operation** of Δ. In W, subtraction might be referred to as the inverse operation of addition. Recall that W was not closed with respect to subtraction. We observed that $a - b \in W$ if and only if $a \geq b$. Let us investigate whether or not $a \blacktriangledown b$ is an element of G for any $a, b \in G$. By the definition above, $a \blacktriangledown b$ will surely be in G if there exists an element $c \in G$ such that $a = c \, \Delta \, b$. Theorem 3.4 tells us that for any x and y in G there is always a unique element $z = (x \, \Delta \, ^-y) \in G$ such that $x = z \, \Delta \, y$. Accordingly there is always an element $c \in G$ such that $a = c \, \Delta \, b$ and this c is the unique element $a \, \Delta \, ^-b$. Since we have produced the required $c \in G$ for any a and b, we are ready to assert the $a \blacktriangledown b$ is always in G or G is closed under $\blacktriangledown$. Further we have shown that $a \blacktriangledown b = c = a \triangle {}^{-}b$. Use this discussion to write the assertions and supporting statements to prove:

Theorem 3.6 *If $a, b \in G$, then $a \blacktriangledown b = a \triangle {}^{-}b$.*

We now know that mod 3 arithmetic under addition is closed under the inverse operation which we will call subtraction. Furthermore, subtraction is the same as adding the additive inverse. Thus:

$$(1 - 2) \bmod 3 = 1 + {}^{-}2 = 1 + 1 = 2$$
$$(0 - 1) \bmod 3 = 0 + {}^{-}1 = 0 + 2 = 2$$
$$(2 - {}^{-}1) \bmod 3 = 2 + {}^{-}({}^{-}1) = 2 + 1 = 0$$

Problem Set 3.8

A. Recall that in **E**, Problem Set 3.5, we agreed to assume without proof that any mod arithmetic under addition is a group. Perform the indicated subtractions.

1. $(3 - 6) \bmod 7 = $ ____.   6. $(5 - {}^{-}2) \bmod 6 = $ ____.
2. $(8 - 5) \bmod 9 = $ ____.   7. $(2 - {}^{-}5) \bmod 6 = $ ____.
3. $(1 - 7) \bmod 8 = $ ____.   8. $(0 - {}^{-}1) \bmod 2 = $ ____.
4. $(2 - 4) \bmod 5 = $ ____.   9. $({}^{-}4 - {}^{-}3) \bmod 7 = $ ____.
5. $(3 - 0) \bmod 4 = $ ____.   10. $({}^{-}4 - {}^{-}3) \bmod 5 = $ ____.

B. If $a, b, c \in G$, solve the equations.

1. $x \blacktriangledown a = b$. $x = $ ____.
2. $x \blacktriangledown (a \triangle b) = c$. $x = $ ____.
3. $x \blacktriangledown (a \blacktriangledown b) = c$. $x = $ ____.

C. Solve in mod 5 arithmetic.

1. $k - 2 = 4$. $k = $ ____.
2. $t - 4 = 2$. $t = $ ____.
3. $y - 3 = 1$. $y = $ ____.

D. 1. Compare the system S:

+	a	b	c
a	a	b	c
b	b	c	a
c	c	a	b

with that of mod 3 arithmetic under addition:

+	0	1	2
0	0	1	2
1	1	2	0
2	2	0	1

Establish that S under $+$ is a group, without going through the proofs for all the properties.

2. Prove:
  a. $^-a - {}^-(a + b) = b$ in S.
  b. $^-b - (a - b) = {}^-a$ in S.

E. Prove: If $a, b, c \in G$ and $a \blacktriangledown c = b \blacktriangledown c$, then $a = b$.

3.9 A Field—The First Operation

As an example of a mathematical system with two operations, we shall study the field. There are other structures which have two operations (ring, integral domain), but we shall consider the field because it is the structure of the system of rational numbers which is so great a concern of the mathematics of K–6. This time we shall name the operations by familiar words, addition and multiplication, and use the familiar symbols, $+$ and $\cdot$ (the raised dot). No one is to make the mistake of assuming that the "addition" to which we are referring here is that which we used in the system of whole numbers. Keep in mind that we define our operations arbitrarily for each different mathematical system we study. Addition in arithmetic mod 3 was not defined to be the same as addition in W. The two operations we will use in the field will not be defined (just as we did not define Δ in our study of a group) but our application of them eventually will be to addition and multiplication in the system of rational numbers. The operations, addition and multiplication, will be clearly defined for each of the number systems we will study—integers and rationals.

We shall characterize a field as a mathematical structure with a set of elements, two operations, $+$ and $\cdot$, and eleven properties. Let F be the symbol for the set of elements in a field. With respect to the first operation, $+$, the field must have the following properties:

  (1) If $a, b \in F$, then $(a + b) \in F$.

(2) If $a, b \in F$, then $a + b = b + a$.

(3) If $a, b, c \in F$, then $(a + b) + c = a + (b + c)$.

(4) There exists an element $i_1 \in F$ such that for $a \in F$, $a + i_1 = a$.

(5) If $a \in F$, there exists an element $^-a \in F$ such that $a + {}^-a = i_1$.

Let's stop for a moment and see what we have. With respect to addition, the field must have closure, commutativity, associativity, an identity element and an inverse element in F for every element in the set. This means that for addition, F has the structure of a commutative group and hence the six theorems we proved for a group must also hold in a field. The inverse operation of addition will be called **subtraction** and will be denoted by $-$.

Theorem 3.7 *If $x, y, z \in F$ and $x + z = y + z$, then $x = y$.*

Theorem 3.8 *If $x \in F$, then $^-(^-x) = x$.*

Theorem 3.9 *In F, $^-i_1 = i_1$.*

Theorem 3.10 *If $a, b \in F$, then $x + a = b$ has the unique solution $(b + {}^-a)$ in F.*

Theorem 3.11 *If $a, b \in F$, then $^-(a + b) = {}^-b + {}^-a = {}^-a + {}^-b$.*

Theorem 3.12 *If $x, y \in F$, then $x - y = x + {}^-y$.*

Problem Set 3.9

A. 1. Write a definition for subtraction in F.

　2. If $x = y + z$, then ＿＿ $-$ ＿＿ $= y$ in F.

　3. If $r + s = t$, then ＿＿ $= t -$ ＿＿ in F.

　4. If $c - d = e$, then ＿＿ $= e +$ ＿＿ in F.

　5. If $p = q - r$, then $p +$ ＿＿ $=$ ＿＿ in F.

B. Even though we know that Theorems 3.7 through 3.12 hold in F, it is desirable to have the experience of writing out these proofs. Refer to the proofs of Theorems 3.1 through 3.6 for groups if you need any hints.

　1. Prove Theorem 3.7.   **4.** Prove Theorem 3.10.

　2. Prove Theorem 3.8.   **5.** Prove Theorem 3.11.

　3. Prove Theorem 3.9.   **6.** Prove Theorem 3.12.

C. Prove:

　1. In F, $^-(a - b) = {}^-a + b$.   **2.** In F, $^-(b - a) = a + {}^-b$.

D. Prove: If $x, y, z \in F$, then $(x + y) + z = y + (x + z) = (z + y) + x$. Does the order in which we add in F make any difference?

3.10 The Second Operation in a Field

We will need two new symbols for the properties of F with respect to the second operation, multiplication. These are i_2, the multiplicative identity: $x \cdot i_2 = x$, and x^{-1}, the multiplicative inverse of x: $x \cdot x^{-1} = i_2$. The remaining properties of F are:

(6) If $a, b \in F$, then $a \cdot b \in F$.

(7) If $a, b \in F$, then $a \cdot b = b \cdot a$.

(8) If $a, b, c \in F$, then $(a \cdot b) \cdot c = a \cdot (b \cdot c)$.

(9) There exists an element $i_2 \in F$ such that for $a \in F$, $a \cdot i_2 = a$.

(10) If $a \in F$ (and $a \neq i_1$), there exists an element a^{-1} such that $a \cdot a^{-1} = i_2$.

(11) If $a, b, c \in F$, then $a \cdot (b + c) = a \cdot b + a \cdot c$.

Properties (6) through (10) for multiplication are parallel to properties (1) through (5) for addition, with one important exception: the additive identity i_1 does not have a multiplicative identity in F. The eleventh property we recognize as distributivity of multiplication over addition.

It must surely occur to the student at this point to ask why in the statement of property (10) for a field it was stipulated that the additive identity, i_1, is not to have a multiplicative inverse in F. In order to answer this we will need to know what happens if we multiply i_1 by any element in F. Because F is closed under multiplication we know that for $x \in F$, $x \cdot i_1 \in F$. We have some idea of what the product might be, because in W the additive identity is 0 and $n \cdot 0 = 0$. Hence we might start our investigation with the thought that possibly: $x \cdot i_1 = i_1$ in F. If $x \cdot i_1$ is to be the same as i_1, then $x \cdot i_1$ should behave like an additive identity. Thus, $a + x \cdot i_1$ should equal a. This doesn't look particularly helpful. However, let us use the idea to write $x \cdot i_1 + x \cdot i_1 = x \cdot i_1$. Remember, we are not proving anything yet. We're just looking around for clues about the steps we might take when we get ready to write a proof. We might also write $x \cdot (i_1 + i_1) = x \cdot i_1$. This suggests that if we begin our proof with $i_1 + i_1 = i_1$, we would multiply by x to get $x \cdot i_1 + x \cdot i_1 = x \cdot i_1$. We also know that $x \cdot i_1 + i_1 = x \cdot i_1$. It looks as though we ought to be able to prove

Theorem 3.13 *If $x \in F$, then $x \cdot i_1 = i_1$.*

ASSERTIONS	SUPPORTING STATEMENTS
(1) $x \in F$.	(1)
(2) $i_1 + i_1 = i_1$.	(2)
(3) $x \cdot (i_1 + i_1) = x \cdot i_1$.	(3)
(4) $x \cdot i_1 + x \cdot i_1 = x \cdot i_1$.	(4)
(5) $x \cdot i_1 + i_1 = x \cdot i_1$.	(5) Definition of i_1.
(6) $x \cdot i_1 + x \cdot i_1 = x \cdot i_1 + i_1$.	(6) Steps 4 and 5, Definition of "$=$."
(7) $x \cdot i_1 = i_1$.	(7) Theorem 3.7.

Fill in appropriate supporting statements.

Now suppose we permitted a multiplicative inverse of i_1 to be in F. Then we would have to allow

$$(x \cdot i_1) \cdot i_1^{-1} = i_1 \cdot i_1^{-1}$$

and by associativity,

$$x \cdot (i_1 \cdot i_1^{-1}) = i_1 \cdot i_1^{-1}.$$

Property (10) says that $a \cdot a^{-1} = i_2$. Hence $i_1 \cdot i_1^{-1} = i_2$ and

$$x \cdot i_2 = i_2.$$

But by property (9),

$$x \cdot i_2 = x.$$

Hence $x = i_2$. This means that if we permit the multiplicative inverse of i_1 to be an element of F, we must come to the conclusion that every element $x \in F$ is equal to i_2; i.e., there is only one element in F and this element is i_2. We do not wish to consider so barren a system. Hence we must set up the restriction that the additive identity does not have a multiplicative inverse in F.

Observe that if we omit i_1 from F, then the properties (6) through (10) for F are those of a commutative group under multiplication. Once again the theorems we proved for a group under the operation Δ will hold for F under multiplication (just so long as we do not permit any element to be equal to i_1 if its multiplicative inverse is required in the proof). Thus the following theorems also hold in F:

Theorem 3.14 *If $x, y, z \in F$ with $z \neq i_1$ and $x \cdot z = y \cdot z$, then $x = y$.*

Theorem 3.15 *If $x \in F$ with $x \neq i_1$, then $(x^{-1})^{-1} = x$.*

Theorem 3.16 *In F, $i_2^{-1} = i_2$.*

Theorem 3.17 *If $a, b \in F$ with $a \neq i_1$, then $x \cdot a = b$ has the unique solution $(b \cdot a^{-1})$ in F.*

Theorem 3.18 *If $a, b \in F$ with $a \neq i_1$ and $b \neq i_1$, then $(a \cdot b)^{-1} = b^{-1} \cdot a^{-1} = a^{-1} \cdot b^{-1}$.*

The inverse operation of multiplication will be called **division** and will be denoted by the symbol $\div$.

Theorem 3.19 *If $x, y \in F$ with $y \neq i_1$, then $x \div y = x \cdot y^{-1}$.*

Problem Set 3.10

A. 1. Write a definition for division in F.

Assume no element in problems **2** through **5** is equal to i_1.

2. If $m = n \cdot p$, then ____ $\div$ ____ $= n$ in F.

3. If $t \cdot s = r$, then ____ $= r \div$ ____ in F.

4. If $k \div l = p$, then _____ $= p \cdot$ _____ in F.

5. If $a = b \div c$, then _____ $\cdot c =$ _____ in F.

B. Prove:

   1. Theorem 3.14.   **4.** Theorem 3.17.

   2. Theorem 3.15.   **5.** Theorem 3.18.

   3. Theorem 3.16.   **6.** Theorem 3.19.

C. Find the fallacy in each of the following arguments.

   1. If $x, y \in F$ such that $x \neq y$, then $x = y$.

ASSERTIONS	SUPPORTING STATEMENTS
(1) $x \neq y$.	(1) Given premise.
(2) $x \cdot i_1 = i_1$; $y \cdot i_1 = i_1$.	(2) Theorem 3.13.
(3) $x \cdot i_1 = y \cdot i_1$.	(3) Step 2, Definition of "$=$."
(4) $x = y$.	(4) Theorem 3.14.

   2. Let $a, b, c, d \in F$ and $a = b$. If $c \cdot (a - b) = d \cdot (a - b)$, then $c = d$ by application of the Cancellation Law for Multiplication.

D. Prove that in F, i_2 is unique.

E. 1. Find a possible candidate for the solution of the equation $a \cdot x + b = c$ if $a, b, c \in F$ and $a \neq i_1$.

   2. Prove that the above equation $a \cdot x + b = c$ has a unique solution in F.

F. 1. If $x, y, z \in F$, then $(x \cdot y) \cdot z = (z \cdot x) \cdot y = (y \cdot z) \cdot x$.
Does the order in which you multiply in F matter?

   2. If $a, x, y, z \in F$, prove that
$$a \cdot (x + y + z) = a \cdot x + a \cdot y + a \cdot z.$$

G. If $r, s, t \in F$, prove $(r + s) \cdot t = r \cdot t + s \cdot t$.

3.11 A Résumé

Let us review what we know about the arithmetic in a field:

   (a) We can always add.

   (b) We can always subtract.

   (c) We can always multiply.

   (d) We can divide, except by i_1.

   (e) We can solve an equation of the form $x + a = b$.

   (f) We can solve an equation of the form $x \cdot a = b$, with $a \neq i_1$.

   (g) We can solve an equation of the form $a \cdot x + b = c$, with $a \neq i_1$.

   (h) The sum of two additive inverses equals the additive inverse of the sum: $^-a + {}^-b = {}^-(a + b)$.

(i) The sum $^-a + b = ^-(a - b)$.

(j) The additive inverse of the additive inverse of an element is the element: $^-(^-x) = x$.

(k) The additive inverse of the additive identity is the additive identity: $^-i_1 = i_1$.

(l) The multiplicative inverse of the multiplicative inverse of an element other than i_1 is the element: $(x^{-1})^{-1} = x$.

(m) The multiplicative inverse of the multiplicative identity is the multiplicative identity: $i_2^{-1} = i_2$.

(n) We can use the distributive property to multiply or to exhibit a factor: $a \cdot x + a \cdot y = a \cdot (x + y)$.

(o) The product of any element and the additive identity is the additive identity: $a \cdot i_1 = i_1$.

(p) $(a \cdot b)^{-1} = b^{-1} \cdot a^{-1} = a^{-1} \cdot b^{-1}$.

Looking over this list, we may well recall that the "rules" we learned in our elementary algebra class resemble the theorems we are applying to establish the arithmetic procedures in a field.

3.12 Three Theorems about Products in *F*

Now we would like to investigate possible other names for $a \cdot {}^-b$ and for $^-a \cdot {}^-b$.

In Theorem 3.13, in which we proved that $x \cdot i_1 = i_1$, we found it sensible to begin the proof with the assertion that $i_1 + i_1 = i_1$, and then multiply by x. Now we are interested in $a \cdot {}^-b$ and $^-a \cdot {}^-b$. It would seem a reasonable first attempt to begin our investigation with $b + {}^-b = i_1$ and then multiply by a for $a \cdot {}^-b$ and by ^-a for $^-a \cdot {}^-b$. We will consider first $a \cdot {}^-b$. If we proceed as above we have $a \cdot (b + {}^-b) = a \cdot i_1$ and $a \cdot b + a \cdot {}^-b = i_1$. Property (5) on page 86 suggests that we write $a \cdot b + {}^-(a \cdot b) = i_1$. Then $a \cdot b + a \cdot {}^-b = a \cdot b + {}^-(a \cdot b)$ and the Cancellation Law for Addition leaves us with $a \cdot {}^-b = {}^-(a \cdot b)$. Write out a proof for

Theorem 3.20 *If* $a, b \in F$, *then* $a \cdot {}^-b = {}^-(a \cdot b)$.

What is another name for $^-b \cdot a$? for $^-a \cdot b$?

In thinking about a possible other name for $^-a \cdot {}^-b$ we now realize that a good beginning is $b + {}^-b = i_1$; $^-a \cdot (b + {}^-b) = {}^-a \cdot i_1$; $^-a \cdot b + {}^-a \cdot {}^-b = i_1$. If we are to use the suggestion from Theorem 3.20, we now should write a step which would show the sum of $^-a \cdot b$ and its additive inverse: $^-a \cdot b + {}^-(^-a \cdot b) = i_1$. From Theorem 3.20 we know that $^-a \cdot b = {}^-(a \cdot b)$ so that we may write $^-a \cdot b + {}^-[^-(a \cdot b)] = i_1$. We also know from Theorem 3.8 that $^-[^-(a \cdot b)] = a \cdot b$. Hence $^-a \cdot b + a \cdot b = i_1$. Since we have already shown that $^-a \cdot b + {}^-a \cdot {}^-b = i_1$, we may write $^-a \cdot b + a \cdot b = {}^-a \cdot b + {}^-a \cdot {}^-b$. This immediately suggests

Theorem 3.21 *If $a, b \in F$, then $^-a \cdot {}^-b = a \cdot b$.*

Another important theorem about a product is

Theorem 3.22 *If $a, b \in F$ and $a \cdot b = i_1$, then a or $b = i_1$.*

ASSERTIONS	SUPPORTING STATEMENTS
(1) $a, b \in F, a \cdot b = i_1$.	(1)
(2) Suppose $a \neq i_1$.	(2)
(3) $a^{-1} \cdot (a \cdot b) = a^{-1} \cdot i_1$.	(3)
(4) $(a^{-1} \cdot a) \cdot b = i_1$.	(4)
(5) $i_2 \cdot b = i_1$.	(5)
(6) $b = i_1$.	(6)

Fill in the supporting statements and complete the proof by showing

If $b \neq i_1$, then $a = i_1$.

If a and b both equal i_1, does $a \cdot b = i_1$?

Problem Set 3.12

A. Prove:
  1. If $x, y \in F$, then $^-x \cdot y = {}^-(x \cdot y)$.
  2. If $a, b \in F$, then $^-a \cdot b = {}^-b \cdot a$.

B. Apply Theorems 3.20 and 3.21 to write other names for each of the following in a field.
  1. $^-a \cdot (b + {}^-c) = $ _____.   **4.** $^-a \cdot (b - c) = $ _____.
  2. $a \cdot ({}^-b + c) = $ _____.   **5.** $a \cdot ({}^-b - {}^-c) = $ _____.
  3. $a \cdot (b - c) = $ _____.

C. Show that each is true in F.
  1. $(^-a \cdot b + {}^-a \cdot {}^-b) + (a \cdot b + a \cdot {}^-b) = i_1$.
  2. $p \cdot (r - q) + p \cdot ({}^-r + q) = i_1$.
  3. $(a + b) \cdot (a - b) = a \cdot a - b \cdot b$.

3.13 Mod 3 Arithmetic as an Example of a Field

In Section 3.2 we studied mod 3 arithmetic under addition and found it interesting as an example of a commutative group. From the heading of this section it is clear that we intend to use mod 3 arithmetic to provide an illustration of a field. To do this we must define multiplication in mod 3 arithmetic. There are only 9 multiplication facts and we may show these in a table:

	0	1	2
0	0	0	0
1	0	1	2
2	0	2	1

If the product $2 \cdot 2 = 1$ distresses you, recall the clock arrangement. In

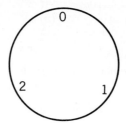

ordinary arithmetic $2 \cdot 2 = 4$. If we start at 0 on the face of our clock and move in a clockwise direction, counting out 4, it brings us to the numeral 1. This fits in with the procedure we used in addition.

It is left to the student to prove that mod 3 arithmetic has the properties of closure, commutativity, and associativity under multiplication. Observe that the second column in the multiplication table, headed by 1, is identical with that outside the box. This means that

$$0 \cdot 1 = 0$$
$$1 \cdot 1 = 1$$
$$2 \cdot 1 = 2$$

and 1 is the multiplicative identity.

Since

$$1 \cdot 1 = 1$$
$$2 \cdot 2 = 1,$$

1 is the multiplicative inverse of 1 and 2 is the multiplicative inverse of 2. The additive identity, 0, does not have a multiplicative inverse. There is no element, a, such that $0 \cdot a = 1$ in mod 3 arithmetic.

We would need to check 18 cases to establish that multiplication is distributive over addition. We will list the six cases in which the first factor is 0 and hope you will be able to list the other 12 cases and test all 18.

$$0 \cdot (0 + 0) = 0 \cdot 0 + 0 \cdot 0.$$
$$0 \cdot (0 + 1) = 0 \cdot 0 + 0 \cdot 1.$$
$$0 \cdot (0 + 2) = 0 \cdot 0 + 0 \cdot 2.$$
$$0 \cdot (1 + 1) = 0 \cdot 1 + 0 \cdot 1.$$
$$0 \cdot (1 + 2) = 0 \cdot 1 + 0 \cdot 2.$$
$$0 \cdot (2 + 2) = 0 \cdot 2 + 0 \cdot 2.$$

Mod 3 arithmetic has all the properties of a field and we are therefore able to apply all the theorems we established for a field to this mathematical system.

Problem Set 3.13

+	0	1	2
0	0	1	2
1	1	2	0
2	2	0	1

	0	1	2
0	0	0	0
1	0	1	2
2	0	2	1

A. Using the tables, complete the following in mod 3 arithmetic.

$i_1 =$ ____. $i_2 =$ ____.

$^{-}0 =$ ____. $1^{-1} =$ ____.

$^{-}1 =$ ____. $2^{-1} =$ ____.

$^{-}2 =$ ____.

B. Identify the theorems needed in each example.

1. $^{-}1 + {}^{-}2 = {}^{-}(2 + 1) = {}^{-}0 = 0.$

2. $2 \cdot x = 1,$
$$x = 1 \cdot 2^{-1} = 1 \cdot 2 = 2.$$

3. $2 \cdot {}^{-}2 = {}^{-}(2 \cdot 2) = {}^{-}(1) = 2.$

4. $^{-}1 \cdot {}^{-}2 = (1 \cdot 2) = 2.$

5. $1 \cdot x + 2 = 1,$
$$x = (1 + {}^{-}2) \cdot 1^{-1},$$
$$x = {}^{-}(2 + {}^{-}1) \cdot 1^{-1},$$
$$x = {}^{-}(2 + 2) \cdot 1,$$
$$x = {}^{-}(1) \cdot 1,$$
$$x = 2 \cdot 1 = 2.$$

6. $1 \div 2 = 1 \cdot 2^{-1} = 1 \cdot 2 = 2.$

7. $0 - 2 = 0 + {}^{-}2 = 0 + 1 = 1.$

8. $1 - {}^{-}2 = 1 + {}^{-}({}^{-}2) = 1 + 2 = 0.$

9. $2 \cdot a = 0,$
$$a = 0.$$

10. A factorization of $(1 + 2)$ is $2 \cdot (2 + 1).$

3.14 Theorems in Chapter 3

Theorem 3.1 If $x, y, z \in G$ and $x \, \Delta \, z = y \, \Delta \, z$, then $x = y$. (Cancellation Law.)

Theorem 3.2 If $x \in G$, then $^-(^-x) = x$.

Theorem 3.3 In G, $^-i_1 = i_1$.

Theorem 3.4 If $a, b \in G$, then $x \, \Delta \, a = b$ has the unique solution: $(b \, \Delta \, ^-a)$ in G.

Theorem 3.5 If $a, b \in G$, then $^-(a \, \Delta \, b) = {}^-b \, \Delta \, {}^-a$.

Theorem 3.6 If $a, b \in G$, then $a \, \blacktriangledown \, b = a \, \Delta \, {}^-b$.

Theorem 3.7 If $x, y, z \in F$ and $x + z = y + z$, then $x = y$.

Theorem 3.8 If $x \in F$, then $^-(^-x) = x$.

Theorem 3.9 In F, $^-i_1 = i_1$.

Theorem 3.10 If $a, b \in F$, then $x + a = b$ has the unique solution $(b + {}^-a)$ in F.

Theorem 3.11 If $a, b \in F$, then $^-(a + b) = {}^-b + {}^-a = {}^-a + {}^-b$.

Theorem 3.12 If $x, y \in F$, then $x - y = x + {}^-y$.

Theorem 3.13 If $x \in F$, then $x \cdot i_1 = i_1$.

Theorem 3.14 If $x, y, z \in F$ with $z \neq i_1$ and $x \cdot z = y \cdot z$, then $x = y$.

Theorem 3.15 If $x \in F$ with $x \neq i_1$, then $(x^{-1})^{-1} = x$.

Theorem 3.16 In F, $i_2^{-1} = i_2$.

Theorem 3.17 If $a, b \in F$ with $a \neq i_1$, then $x \cdot a = b$ has the unique solution $(b \cdot a^{-1})$ in F.

Theorem 3.18 If $a, b \in F$ with $a \neq i_1$ and $b \neq i_1$, then $(a \cdot b)^{-1} = b^{-1} \cdot a^{-1} = a^{-1} \cdot b^{-1}$.

Theorem 3.19 If $x, y \in F$ with $y \neq i_1$, then $x \div y = x \cdot y^{-1}$.

Theorem 3.20 If $a, b \in F$, then $a \cdot {}^-b = {}^-(a \cdot b)$.

Theorem 3.21 If $a, b \in F$, then $^-a \cdot {}^-b = a \cdot b$.

Theorem 3.22 If $a, b \in F$ and $a \cdot b = i_1$, then a or $b = i_1$.

3.15 Terminal Tasks for Chapter 3

1. To perform simple calculations in a modular arithmetic.
2. To use mathematical symbols to define the identity element for a given operation, and to identify the identity element if it exists in a system.
3. To use mathematical symbols to define an inverse element for a given operation, and to identify the inverse elements if they exist in a system.
4. To define the inverse of an operation, by an algebraic statement.
5. To identify the properties of a group.
6. To determine whether a given system has the structure of a group.
7. To identify the properties of a field.
8. To determine whether a given system has the structure of a field.
9. To indicate the ability to follow the proofs in the text by providing suitable supporting statements.

10. To indicate the ability to follow the analysis for a proof in the text, by using the analysis to write a proof.
11. To make an analysis for a simple proof.
12. To recognize the deductive nature of the development of the set of theorems for a group.
13. To perform simple algebraic procedures in a group using the abstract operation $\triangle$.
14. To apply the theorems for a group in the solution of simple exercises.
15. To apply the theorems for a group, under the abstract operation $\triangle$, to any system with the structure of a group, under operations other than $\triangle$.
16. To be familiar with the statements of the theorems proved for a group.
17. To recognize that the properties and theorems of a mathematical system are the basis for the arithmetic possible in that system.
18. To list arithmetic procedures possible in a field.

REVIEW EXERCISES

A. Determine whether or not each of the following mathematical systems is a group.
1. The system of whole numbers under addition.
2. The system of whole numbers under multiplication.
3. Mod 2 arithmetic under multiplication.
4. The system defined by the following table:

·	$\triangle$	$\bigcirc$	$\square$
$\triangle$	$\triangle$	$\bigcirc$	$\square$
$\bigcirc$	$\bigcirc$	$\triangle$	$\square$
$\square$	$\square$	$\bigcirc$	$\triangle$

B. 1. Demonstrate that arithmetic mod 5 has the structure of a field. Provide only three illustrations each, in testing associativity and distributivity.
2. Consider mod 4 arithmetic:

+	0	1	2	3
0	0	1	2	3
1	1	2	3	0
2	2	3	0	1
3	3	0	1	2

·	0	1	2	3
0	0	0	0	0
1	0	1	2	3
2	0	2	0	2
3	0	3	2	1

  a. Is this system a field?

  b. List the multiplicative inverses of the elements of mod 4 arithmetic.

  c. Does the theorem: $x \cdot i_1 = i_1$ hold for all x in mod 4 arithmetic?

  d. Does the theorem: $i_1 \div x = i_1$ for $x \neq i_1$ hold in mod 4 arithmetic?

  e. Is $0 \div 2$ unique in this system?

C. Prove:

 1. If a, b, $c \in F$, then $a - (b - c) = (a - b) + c$.

 2. If a, b, $c \in F$ with $a \neq i_1$, then $(b + c) \div a = (b \div a) + (c \div a)$.

 3. If $x \in F$ with $x \neq i_1$, then $i_1 \div x = i_1$.

 4. If $x \in F$ with $x \neq i_1$, then $x \div x = i_2$.

D. 1. Using theorems and definitions for a field, write other names for each of the following:

  a. $y + {}^-y = $ _____.

  b. $x \cdot x^{-1} = $ _____.

  c. $y + i_1 = $ _____.

  d. ${}^-(x + y) = $ _____.

  e. ${}^-({}^-x) = $ _____.

  f. $(x^{-1})^{-1} = $ _____.

  g. $y \cdot i_1 = $ _____.

  h. $x \cdot i_2 = $ _____.

  i. ${}^-x \cdot y = $ _____.

  j. $x \cdot {}^-y = $ _____.

  k. ${}^-x \cdot {}^-y = $ _____.

  l. $y + i_2 = $ _____.

  m. $x - y = $ _____.

  n. $x \div y = $ _____.

 2. Match, when possible, in a field:

   (1) ${}^-s \cdot (r + {}^-r)$.   (a) $s \cdot r$.

   (2) $(r^{-1})^{-1}$.   (b) s.

   (3) ${}^-s \cdot {}^-s$.   (c) $s^{-1} + {}^-r$.

   (4) $(r \cdot r^{-1}) \cdot s$.   (d) ${}^-({}^-r)$.

   (5) ${}^-s + r^{-1}$.   (e) i_1.

E. Mod 7 arithmetic is a field. Apply the definitions and theorems for a field to perform the following computations in mod 7 arithmetic.

 1. $5 \cdot 0 = $ _____.   **6.** $6 + 1 = $ _____.

 2. $3 \cdot 4 = $ _____.   **7.** ${}^-4 \cdot {}^-2 = $ _____.

 3. $2 - 6 = $ _____.   **8.** ${}^-3 \cdot 5 = $ _____.

 4. $1 \div 5 = $ _____.   **9.** $0 \div 1 = $ _____.

 5. $2 \div 3 = $ _____.   **10.** ${}^-(4 - 6) = $ _____.

F. Read the following discussion and use it to provide clues for writing a proof for the theorem: In a field, if 1 is the multiplicative identity, then ${}^-1 \cdot {}^-1 = 1$. "If I want to prove something about a product I shall probably use the distributive property. This means I ought to be able to produce a sum which is pertinent. Suppose I start with $1 + {}^-1 = i_1$. Since I want the product of $({}^-1)$ and $({}^-1)$, I'll try multiplying by ${}^-1$. This gives me ${}^-1 \cdot (1 + {}^-1) = {}^-1 \cdot i_1$. Then ${}^-1 \cdot 1 + {}^-1 \cdot {}^-1 = i_1$. Now I know that ${}^-1 \cdot 1 = {}^-(1 \cdot 1)$, which is also ${}^-1$. Thus ${}^-1 + {}^-1 \cdot {}^-1 = i_1$ but ${}^-1 + 1 = i_1$. That does it."

G. Indicate how the mathematics in this chapter might help you in the following hypothetical classroom situations.

   1. A student confides in you that he likes mathematics better than any other subject because he feels he's on firm ground with the facts. "Two and two are always four."

   2. A child conjectures after experimenting that if $\frac{7}{7} = 1$, $\frac{3}{3} = 1$, $\frac{8}{8} = 1$, then $\frac{0}{0}$ also equals 1.

   3. A bright sixth grader after doing some reading for a special report, asks, "How under the sun, out of all the available material, did the author of the book pick this particular statement for the second step? How did he realize it would lead to the desired result?"

   4. You wish to teach the class a procedure for naming a fraction so that the numerator and the denominator are mutually prime. You decide on the following presentation:

$$\frac{36}{42} = \frac{6}{6} \cdot \frac{6}{7} = 1 \cdot \frac{6}{7} = \frac{6}{7}.$$

   5. A child says "$\frac{4}{6} = \frac{2}{3}$ because I can cancel 2 out of the numerator and denominator." Another child says: "If $\Box + 2 = 3 + 2$, then $\Box = 3$ because I can cancel 2 from each side of the equals sign." A third child asks: "What does cancel mean? Divide? Subtract? Cross out?"

   6. A child brings to class the following procedure for dividing fractions:

$$\frac{1}{7} \div \frac{1}{3} = \frac{\frac{1}{7}}{\frac{1}{3}} = \frac{\frac{1}{7}}{\frac{1}{3}} \cdot \frac{21}{21} = \frac{3}{7}.$$

   7. "I think that to find the multiplicative inverse of a fraction, you just turn it upside down. Is that right?"

   8. "My father says that to divide two fractions all you need to do is invert and multiply."

   9. "I know from my multiplication facts that if $9 \cdot \triangle = 72$, then $\triangle = 8$. But how can I find a numeral for $\triangle$ in this example, where $9 \cdot \triangle = 24$?"

   10. "I know that milk is a nickel a carton and I know that I collected $1.15. What I don't know is how many cartons of milk to order for us."

   11. "Zero is nothing."

   12. "If division is the same as multiplying by the multiplicative inverse, why did we spend so much time learning long division?"

Sets and Geometry

4.1 What Is It All About?

One of the most primitive ideas in our experience is that of collections or sets of objects. Long before you had any conception of anything as sophisticated as counting you were concerned about your set of blocks or your set of pull toys. You became conscious of your family as a set of people. Later you may have had occasion to consider such things as the set of letters forming a word, the set of all letters of the alphabet, the set of whole numbers from 1 to 10 or the set of points on a circle. We shall use the word **set** for any such collection. This is an exceedingly fundamental idea. For example, the ideas of the whole numbers which we have been discussing in the last few chapters are motivated by our experiences with sets. The counting process is simply a way of attaching a number to a set and all the operations on whole numbers reflect procedures that we carry out with sets. Indeed this is a customary way of approaching the arithmetic operations with elementary school children. At a more sophisticated level one may speak of the set of numbers satisfying an equation, or the set of circles lying in a plane.

Because of the frequency with which the ideas of sets may occur we will develop a certain amount of language and notation concerning sets. Indeed, this language is used with such frequency with elementary school children that any teacher needs at least a minimal command of it. It should be emphasized that, while we are not developing set theory in the sense that a mathematician would understand the term, the simple ideas, as we shall see, make a very useful means of communication on many topics.

We shall quite customarily denote a set by a capital letter so we may speak of set A, set B, etc. However, how do we specify a set? Since a set is a collection it is described by telling the objects that form the set, i.e., the **elements** or **members** of the set. Thus if set A is composed of three boys named George, Jack, and Henry we write:

$$A = \{\text{George, Jack, Henry}\}.$$

To describe this set we have simply made a list of its elements. In essentially the same way the telephone directory in your town describes the set of individuals having phones. There is nothing sacrosanct about the use of braces in denoting a set but it is common usage and we shall employ it frequently.

The notation does lend itself to two confusions that it would be well to clarify. Consider, in addition to A, the sets B and C as defined below:

$$A = \{\text{George, Jack, Henry}\}.$$
$$B = \{\text{Jack, Henry, George}\}.$$
$$C = \{\text{George, Jack, Henry, George}\}.$$

The only difference between A and B is that the names have been written in a different order. But a set is simply a collection of elements and has nothing to do with order. Thus A and B are actually the same set and we write

$$A = B.$$

Indeed, the equality sign between two sets means that they consist of exactly the same elements. Now what about A and C? The only difference in the description is that in C George has been listed twice. But after all George is either in or out and it doesn't make a bit of difference how many times we repeat the statement that he is in. The elements in C are just the same as the elements in A, so $A = C$. Notice that the name George in this discussion always denotes the same boy.

A different sort of notational problem arises in the following situation. Suppose we wish to discuss the set E of even whole numbers. We quickly discover that it is impossible to list all the members of the set E as we did above since there are infinitely many members in E. One procedure is to write

$$E = \{0, 2, 4, 6, 8, \ldots\},$$

using the three dots to mean "and so on." This symbolism of three dots to indicate something omitted is common in mathematics. It is used when the writer believes the reader will understand clearly what has been left out. If the writer feels there is any possible doubt in indicating a set he will resort to some means of describing the set. For example, he might simply write in words

$$E = \text{set of even whole numbers.}$$

A more symbolic notation, and one much in use, would be the following:

$$E = \{x \mid x = 2y, y \text{ a whole number}\},$$

which we would read "E is the set of elements x such that (the vertical bar) $x = 2y$ where y is a whole number." Can you use a similar notation to express the set K of odd whole numbers?

It is convenient to introduce several symbols in connection with our discussion of sets. The first of these is a shorthand for the statement "is a member of." If we wish to say that p is a member of set A we write $p \in A$. This notation is not new to you. Earlier we found it useful if we wanted to say that n is a whole number to write $n \in W$ where W was understood to represent the set of all whole numbers. Thus we are simply extending the notation to any sets. If as above we let K stand for the set of odd numbers, then the statement $x \in K$ means that x is an odd number, i.e., x is an element of the set of odd numbers.

A concept that at first sight seems peculiar is that of an empty set, i.e., a set which has no members. For example, if you speak of the set of pennies in your piggy bank and investigation shows you are actually flat broke, you are speaking of an empty set. Notice that two empty sets are always equal since they consist of exactly the same elements—neither has any at all! For this reason we speak of *the* empty set and often designate it by $\varnothing$. Of course there are many different-sounding descriptions of $\varnothing$. We could say it is the set of women who have been president of the United States, or the set of crocodiles in Antarctica, or the set of college presidents who are illiterate.

Consider the set F of counting numbers divisible by 5 and the set T of counting numbers divisible by 10. Then we may write

$$F = \{5, 10, 15, 20, 25, 30, \ldots\}.$$
$$T = \{10, 20, 30, 40, \ldots\}.$$

It is clear at once that every element of T is also an element of F. For example, $10 \in T$ and $10 \in F$; $20 \in T$ and $20 \in F$; $50 \in T$ and $50 \in F$. We express this relationship by saying that T is a subset of F, and writing in symbols $T \subset F$ or $F \supset T$. Formally we write

DEFINITION: $A \subset B$ if and only if $x \in A$ implies $x \in B$.

Consider the set $S = \{p, q, r\}$. What subsets of S are there? Certainly we find the sets $\{p\}$, $\{q\}$, $\{r\}$, which are one-element subsets. Then there are the two-element subsets $\{p, q\}$, $\{q, r\}$, $\{p, r\}$. Is this all? What about three-element subsets? The only one would be $\{p, q, r\}$, which is S itself. Is S a subset of itself? If you refer to the definition of subset you see that the answer is "yes." Any set is a subset of itself. Finally, what about the zero-element subset, i.e., the empty set $\varnothing$? Is $\varnothing$ really a subset of S? You may want to think this one over carefully, but the answer has to be "yes." If $\varnothing$ were not a subset of S it would have to contain an element not in S. Since $\varnothing$ has no elements at all, this is impossible. Hence $\varnothing \subset S$. Thus the given set S of three elements has 8 subsets. Incidentally we have observed that $\varnothing$ is a subset of any set and that any set is a subset of itself.

Suppose you take a four-element set such as $T = \{p, q, r, s\}$. How many sub-sets would there be? The correct answer is 16. Would you care to guess the number of subsets of a set of five elements? of n elements? Can you give an argument to show this? Note problems **C1** and **C2** of Problem Set 4.1.

Pictorial diagrams are often a useful device for visualizing relationships between sets. For instance, suppose we think of the elements of a set A as being represented by the points inside some closed curve. Then we might make a drawing like diagram (a).

(a)

How would we make a drawing to represent the inclusion relation $B \subset A$? Since all the elements of B also belong to A, the region representing B should be in the region representing A and our drawing would look like diagram (b) if $B \neq A$ and like diagram (c) if $A = B$.

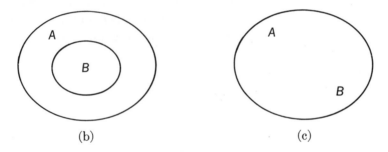

(b)   (c)

Can you make a diagram which shows at the same time the two relations $B \subset A$, $B \subset C$ if neither A nor C is a subset of the other? Does your diagram look something like (d)?

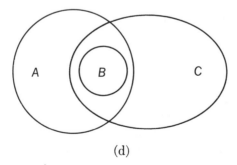

(d)

How would you make a drawing showing the two relations $A \subset B$ and $B \subset A$? If $A \subset B$ the region representing A must be inside that representing B while if

$B \subset A$ the region representing B must be inside that representing A. Thus each region must be contained in the other. What is the only way this can happen?

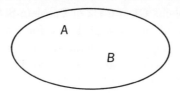

If sets A and B satisfy both of the relations $A \subset B$ and $B \subset A$ you have just observed that they must really be the same set, i.e., $A = B$. This suggests the method frequently used to show that two sets are equal: namely, to show that each is a subset of the other. Thus to show $P = Q$ we prove the following statements.

(a) If $x \in P$, then $x \in Q$ (i.e., $P \subset Q$).
(b) If $y \in Q$, then $y \in P$ (i.e., $Q \subset P$).

Quite commonly in questions involving sets all the sets we wish to discuss are subsets of some given set. In such a case the given set is called the universal set for this discussion. For example, in discussing the arithmetic of the whole numbers we were concerned only with sets of whole numbers so the set of all whole numbers was the universal set. The universal set for a discussion is often represented by the symbol Ω. As we get into the discussion of geometry in the latter part of this chapter the universal set will be the set of all points in space.

Problem Set 4.1

A. 1. Define the following sets by giving all their elements:
  a. The set A of even counting numbers less than 10.
  b. The set B of common factors of 924 and 66 in the counting numbers.
  c. The set C of prime numbers less than 25.
  d. The set D of mathematics teachers you had in high school.
  e. The set E of all divisors of 240 in the counting numbers.
  2. Define each of the following sets using the form

$$\{x \mid \qquad \}.$$

  a. The set P of counting numbers divisible by 3.
  b. The set Q of counting numbers not divisible by 5.
  c. The set R of even counting numbers less than a million.
  d. The set S of counting numbers whose ones digit is 3.

B. 1. What inclusion relations are indicated in the following diagrams?

a.   b.

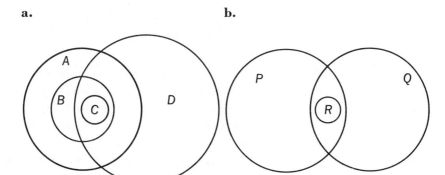

2. In each of the following cases make a drawing which shows the following inclusion relations *and no others.*

a. $A \subset B$, $B \supset C$.

b. $P \supset Q$, $R \supset Q$.

c. $S \subset T$, $T \subset U$, $U \supset S$.

C. 1. In the text it was shown that a 3-element set has 8 subsets. Show, by listing them, that a 4-element set has 16 subsets.

2. A conjecture based on problem **C1** might be that an n-element set has 2^n subsets. Try to give a proof that the conjecture is correct. (It actually is.)

D. 1. Indicate all the inclusion relations among the following sets of numbers. Are any of these sets equal?

$A = \{2, 4, 6, 8, 10\}$, $B = \{1, 2, 3, 4, 5, 6, 7, 8, 9, 10\}$, $C = \{1, 3, 6, 8\}$, $D = \{10, 8, 6, 4, 2\}$, $E = \{1, 1, 3, 6, 3, 8, 6\}$.

2. If $P = \{x \mid x = 3n, n \text{ a whole number}\}$ and $Q = \{y \mid y = 6m, m \text{ a whole number}\}$, show that $Q \subset P$.

3. If R is the set of all rectangles and S is the set of all squares, is it true that $S \subset R$? Is it true that $R \subset S$? Explain.

4. If, for some element x, $x \in A$ and $x \notin B$, is it possible that $A \subset B$? Is it possible that $B \subset A$?

E. 1. Is the set of women who have been president of the United States equal to the set of men who have been queen of England?

2. Is the set of illiterate college presidents a subset of the set of all first grade children?

3. If $A = \{a\}$, list all subsets of A. If $B = \emptyset$, list all subsets of B.

F. 1. Suppose $H \subset W$, $J \subset W$. If H and J have elements in common but neither is a subset of the other, draw a diagram showing the relationship of H, J, and W.

2. If the situation is the same as in problem **F1** except that H and J have no elements in common, draw a diagram representing the relationship.

3. If $A \subset B$, $A \supset C$, $D \subset C$, what other inclusion relations follow?

4.2 Operations on Sets

When we deal with two sets A and B there are certain other sets related to A and B which suggest themselves at once. Let us suppose a wedding is to take place. Let A be the set of people the groom's parents want invited to the wedding and B the set of people the bride's parents wish to invite. The set of people to be invited is then obtained by putting together the two lists. This set is called the *union* of A and B and is denoted by the symbol $A \cup B$. Notice that in all probability there will be many names which occur on both lists. Formally stated the definition would be:

> DEFINITION: The **union** $A \cup B$ of two sets A and B is the set of all elements which belong to A or to B (or both).

For example, if $A = \{1, 2, 3, 4, 5\}$, $B = \{2, 4, 6, 8, 10\}$, then $A \cup B = \{1, 2, 3, 4, 5, 6, 8, 10\}$.

This idea also lends itself to visual representation. If A and B are represented by the points inside the circles in diagram (a), then $A \cup B$ is the set of points in

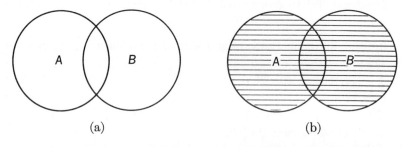

(a)   (b)

the striped region of (b). What would $A \cup B$ be if $A \subset B$? Draw a diagram to represent the situation.

A second set related to two given sets A, B may also be nicely illustrated by our example of the wedding. If A and B are, as before, the sets of people that the groom's and bride's parents, respectively, wish to invite, consider the set of people whose names are on *both* lists, i.e., those which both families wanted to invite. This set is called the intersection of A and B and is denoted by $A \cap B$. Formally we write

> DEFINITION: The **intersection** $A \cap B$ of two sets A and B is the set of all elements belonging to both A and B.

For example, if $A = \{1, 2, 3, 4, 5\}$, $B = \{2, 4, 6, 8, 10\}$, then $A \cap B = \{2, 4\}$.

Suppose $E = \{2, 4, 6, 8, \ldots\}$, $K = \{1, 3, 5, 7, \ldots\}$, i.e., suppose E is the set of even counting numbers and K is the set of odd counting numbers. What is

$E \cap K$? Clearly there are no counting numbers which are both even and odd, so there are no elements in $E \cap K$. That is, $E \cap K = \varnothing$, the empty set. When two sets have the property that their intersection is empty we say they are **disjoint**.

As in the case of union, the concept of intersection is readily illustrated pictorially. If A and B are represented in diagram (a), then $A \cap B$ is represented

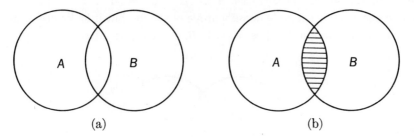

(a)   (b)

by the striped region in (b). How would the diagram look if $A \cap B = \varnothing$? Can you draw a diagram for which $A \cap B = A$? What is the relation between A and B in this case?

Let C and D be two sets and consider the two sets $C \cup D$ and $D \cup C$. What relation is there between these two sets? Without trying to agonize over a formal proof, it should be clear at once that they are the same set. After all, the definition of union is wholly symmetric. It does not distinguish between a "first" set and a "second" set. Thus we conclude that

$$C \cup D = D \cup C.$$

The following diagram also makes this plausible:

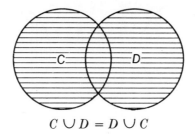

$$C \cup D = D \cup C$$

The relation $C \cup D = D \cup C$ is interesting in that it says something about the union operation. Specifically it says the operation of forming the union of sets is commutative.

What about the intersection operation? Do you think it is true that $C \cap D = D \cap C$? Give an informal argument that shows that this is true. This means that the intersection operation is also commutative.

The last two observations suggest to us the question as to whether some of the other properties we studied in number systems also hold for sets. For instance, how about the associative property? Is the following statement true?

$$A \cup (B \cup C) = (A \cup B) \cup C.$$

Perhaps we should try out a particular example. Suppose

$$A = \{1, 2, 3, 4, 5, 6\}, \ B = \{2, 4, 6, 8, 10\}, \ C = \{1, 10, 12\}.$$

Then $B \cup C = \{1, 2, 4, 6, 8, 10, 12\}$, $A \cup B = \{1, 2, 3, 4, 5, 6, 8, 10\}$, $A \cup (B \cup C) = \{1, 2, 3, 4, 5, 6, 8, 10, 12\}$, and $(A \cup B) \cup C = \{1, 2, 3, 4, 5, 6, 8, 10, 12\}$ so that in this case $A \cup (B \cup C) = (A \cup B) \cup C$.

Of course a single example doesn't prove anything, but it looks promising. Let us try using a diagram. Suppose sets A, B, C are represented as in diagram (a).

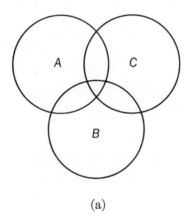

(a)

Then in (b) we show A by vertical striping and $B \cup C$ by horizontal striping.

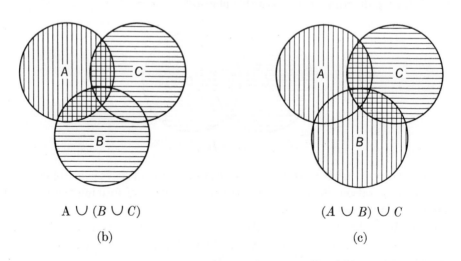

$A \cup (B \cup C)$ $(A \cup B) \cup C$

(b)   (c)

Thus $A \cup (B \cup C)$ is shown by the entire striped region. In diagram (c) $A \cup B$ is shown by vertical striping and C by horizontal striping so $(A \cup B) \cup C$ is the entire striped region. Do the two regions seem to be the same? Does it seem to be true that $A \cup (B \cup C) = (A \cup B) \cup C$? This is still not a formal proof, of course, although the ideas can quite easily be made into a proof.

However, we shall content ourselves here with this rather intuitive exploration. It is indeed true that the union operation is associative. In the problems you will be asked to make similar drawings to illustrate the fact that the intersection operation is also associative, i.e., that for all sets A, B, C:

$$A \cap (B \cap C) = (A \cap B) \cap C.$$

The last of the properties we emphasized in the number systems involved both operations. This was the distributive property of multiplication with respect to addition, i.e.,

$$a \cdot (b + c) = a \cdot b + a \cdot c,$$

where a, b, c are numbers of the system under discussion. Will there be any corresponding property for sets? For example, will the following statement be true?

$$A \cap (B \cup C) = (A \cap B) \cup (A \cap C).$$

Let us seek to discover the answer intuitively using circle diagrams as above. Both of the following diagrams show sets A, B, and C. With A striped vertically and $B \cup C$ horizontally, $A \cap (B \cup C)$ is represented on the left by the region

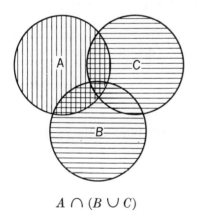

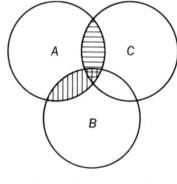

$$A \cap (B \cup C) \qquad\qquad (A \cap B) \cup (A \cap C)$$

which is striped both ways. At the right, $A \cap B$ is shown in vertical striping and $A \cap C$ in horizontal striping, so $(A \cap B) \cup (A \cap C)$ is the total striped region. Comparing the two diagrams, do the two indicated regions appear to be the same? The diagrams make it at least plausible (and it is in fact true) that this distributive property holds, i.e., that

$$A \cap (B \cup C) = (A \cap B) \cup (A \cap C).$$

Thus the intersection operation is distributive over the union operation.

An interesting question now arises. We have just indicated that there is a distributive property for sets in which the intersection operation of sets acts like multiplication of numbers and the union operation like addition. Would the distributive property still be true if we reverse the roles of the operations? That is, we wish to determine if it is true that the union operation is distributive over the intersection operation so that

$$A \cup (B \cap C) = (A \cup B) \cap (A \cup C).$$

We certainly have every reason to be skeptical. It most certainly is not true for numbers that addition is distributive over multiplication. That is, $a + (b \cdot c)$ is most emphatically *not* equal to $(a + b) \cdot (a + c)$. Surprisingly, however, in the case of sets *both* distributive properties hold. In the problems, you will be asked to draw circle diagrams illustrating this second property.

It is clear that, if we wished to take the time, we could develop a whole arithmetic for sets as we have done for numbers. We shall not do so, though some of the things we would discover are suggested in the problems. The purpose of this latter discussion has been to provide an opportunity to see some of our familiar properties operating in an unfamiliar setting.

Problem Set 4.2

A. Let $A = \{1, 2, 3, 4, 5, 6, 7, 8\}$, $B = \{1, 3, 5, 7, 9, 11\}$, $C = \{3, 6, 9, 12, 15\}$.

  1. Find $A \cup B$, $A \cup C$, $A \cap B$, $A \cap C$, $B \cap C$.

  2. Verify that $A \cap (B \cap C) = (A \cap B) \cap C$ (Associative Property of $\cap$).

  3. Verify that $A \cap (B \cup C) = (A \cap B) \cup (A \cap C)$ (Distributivity of $\cap$ over $\cup$).

  4. Verify that $A \cup (B \cap C) = (A \cup B) \cap (A \cup C)$ (Distributivity of $\cup$ over $\cap$).

B. 1. Draw a circle diagram in which $P \cup Q = P$. What is the relationship between P and Q?

  2. Draw a circle diagram in which $P \cap Q = P$. What is the relationship between P and Q?

  3. If P, Q are any sets give all the inclusion relationships among P, Q, $P \cap Q$, $P \cup Q$.

  4. Draw circle diagrams to illustrate that

$$P \cap (Q \cap R) = (P \cap Q) \cap R.$$

  5. Draw a circle diagram to show sets satisfying each of the following:

a. $R \subset S$.	**f.** $R \cap S = \varnothing$.
b. $R \subset S \subset T$.	**g** $R \cup S = R$.
c. $R = S$.	**h.** $R \cap S \subset R \cup S$.
d. $R \cap S = R$.	**i.** $R \cap S \supset R \cup S$ (tricky).
e. $R \cap S = S$.	

C. 1. a. Write the set D of all divisors of 180 in the counting numbers.

    b. Write the set E of all divisors of 105 in the counting numbers.

    c. Find $D \cap E$. This is the set of common divisors of 105 and 180.

    d. What is the greatest number in $D \cap E$? This is the greatest common divisor of 105 and 180.

    e. Earlier you found the greatest common divisor of two numbers by a method involving factoring the numbers into prime factors. Use this method to check the correctness of **d** above.

2. Repeat the steps of problem **C1** for the numbers 504 and 270.

3. a. Write the set P of multiples of 6. (Use the notation with the three dots.)

    b. Write the set Q of multiples of 15.

    c. Find $P \cap Q$. This is the set of common multiples of 6 and 15.

    d. What is the smallest number in $P \cap Q$? This is the least common multiple of 6 and 15.

    e. Check the result of **d** by using the method developed earlier in which you factor the numbers into prime factors.

4. Repeat the steps of problem **C3** for the numbers 30 and 21; for the numbers 6 and 25.

D. 1. Complete the statements below. Remember Ω denotes the universal set.

    a. $A \cup A =$ _____.   **g.** $\varnothing \cap \Omega =$ _____.

    b. $A \cap A =$ _____.   **h.** $\varnothing \cup \Omega =$ _____.

    c. $\Omega \cap B =$ _____.   **i.** $\varnothing \cup \varnothing =$ _____.

    d. $\Omega \cup B =$ _____.   **j.** $\varnothing \cap \varnothing =$ _____.

    e. $A \cap \varnothing =$ _____.   **k.** $\Omega \cap \Omega =$ _____.

    f. $A \cup \varnothing =$ _____.   **l.** $\Omega \cup \Omega =$ _____.

2. By looking at the results of problem **D1** complete the following statements.

    a. There is an identity element for the union operation and it is _____.

    b. There is an identity element for the intersection operation and it is

    _____.

See if you can make a reasonable case for the fact that there is no inverse set for a given set A under either the union or intersection operations.

E. 1. Suppose $R \cap S = T$:

    a. If $a \in T$ must $a \in R$? _____.

    b. If $b \in S$ must $b \in T$? _____.

    c. If $c \in R$ and $c \in S$ must $c \in T$? _____.

    d. Is it possible that $m \in R$ but $m \notin T$? _____ (The symbol $\notin$ means "does not belong to.")

2. Suppose $M \cup N = P$

    a. If $x \in P$ must $x \in M$? _____.

    b. If $y \in N$ must $y \in P$? _____.

    c. If $s \in M \cap N$ must $s \in P$? _____.

    d. Is it possible that $t \in M$ but $t \notin P$? _____.

F. Start with circle diagrams as below:

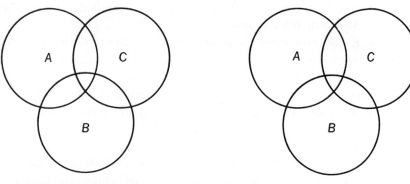

Use striping to illustrate that

$$A \cup (B \cap C) = (A \cup B) \cap (A \cup C).$$

For example, show $A \cup (B \cap C)$ on the left by striping A vertically and $(B \cap C)$ horizontally and show $(A \cup B) \cap (A \cup C)$ on the right by striping $(A \cup B)$ vertically and $(A \cup C)$ horizontally.

4.3 Equivalent Sets

Recall that in the work with whole numbers the idea of a one-to-one correspondence was used. Two sets are in one-to-one correspondence if there is a pairing of the elements of the sets so that any element of either set is paired with exactly one element of the other. Whenever two sets can be put in one-to-one correspondence they are said to be **equivalent.** It is important to recall that one-to-one correspondence and equivalence of sets are independent of counting or number.

Of course if the elements of two sets can be put in one-to-one correspondence, this can generally be done in more than one way. For example, we show here six different one-to-one correspondences of the sets $A = \{a, b, c\}$, $B = \{x, y, z\}$.

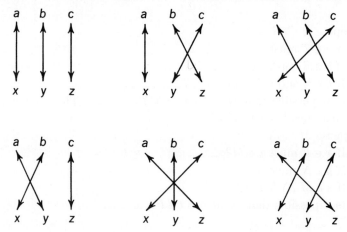

Notice, however, that the correspondences of the same sets in these next diagrams fail to be one-to-one. In (a) the elements b and y are each matched with two elements of the other set; in (b) the element a has no mate at all, while b has two.

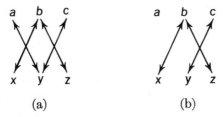

(a)   (b)

It is now possible to make a simple observation about the relation of equivalence. Suppose set A is equivalent to set B and set B is equivalent to set C. What can we conclude about A and C? It would seem plausible that they are equivalent also, and indeed this is easy to show. All we need do is produce a one-to-one correspondence of A with C. Nothing could be easier. If $a \in A$ we know that it has a mate $b \in B$; b in turn has a mate $c \in C$, so we agree to match a with c. It is easy to see that the correspondence is one-to-one. The matching is indicated pictorially below.

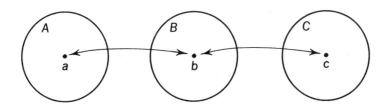

Although we have proclaimed in agonized tones that the idea of equivalence makes sense without the concept of number, you will certainly have noticed that in the simple cases of our illustrations two sets were equivalent if they had the same number of elements. Otherwise they were not equivalent. Certainly all our experience leads us to the conclusion that if two sets each have four elements, we can put them in one-to-one correspondence while if one has four elements and one has three elements we are wasting our time. This is indeed a valid observation but it deserves some consideration.

What do you really mean when you say that a set has four elements? Presumably you mean that when you count them you get up to four. What do you do when you count? To be very naïve you may imagine that you begin by putting your finger on one element of the set and saying "one." What you have done then is to associate this element with the number 1. You then put your finger on a different element and say "two," thereby associating this element with the number 2. Continuing in this way you associate each element of the set with a specific number. If, having reached the number 4, there are no more elements in the set, you say the set has four elements. What have you really done in this process? You have clearly set up a one-to-one correspondence between the elements of the given set and the set of numbers {1, 2, 3, 4}. That is, the given set is equivalent to {1, 2, 3, 4}. If two sets each have four elements, then they are each equivalent to {1, 2, 3, 4} and so by our discussion above are equivalent to each other. The reasoning applies equally well to any other natural number.

The converse is also true. If set A has four elements and set B is equivalent to set A then set B has four elements. For if A has four elements it is equivalent to {1, 2, 3, 4}, and since B is equivalent to A it also is equivalent to {1, 2, 3, 4} and thus has four elements.

You should recognize that a tacit assumption has been made in the discussion above. If two people count the same (finite) set of elements it is highly unlikely that they use the same matching of elements with numbers; i.e., they probably count the elements in a different order. When we talk about *the* number of elements in a set we are actually assuming that no matter what matching is used it always leads to the same number. This indeed is a correct assumption although we shall not attempt to give the proof.

It is often desirable to consider one-to-one correspondences between sets which contain infinitely many elements such as the set of counting numbers. For example, in the work on whole numbers you saw that the set of all counting numbers could be put into one-to-one correspondence with the set of even counting numbers. For such sets the idea of the number of elements in the set as so far developed has no meaning, illustrating again that the idea of one-to-one correspondence does not depend on that of number.

You will recall that some of the results concerning one-to-one correspondences for infinite sets proved a little startling to our intuition. It may be useful to examine a situation of a geometric nature which may also prove surprising. We shall here use only some simple geometric ideas already familiar to you.

Look at the rectangle $ABCD$. Let P be any point of side $\overline{CD}$ and draw the

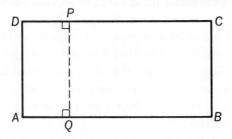

perpendicular to $\overline{CD}$ at P which will meet $\overline{AB}$ at a point Q. It is easily seen that this procedure which matches P with Q gives a one-to-one correspondence of the points of $\overline{AB}$ with those of $\overline{CD}$, so these two segments are equivalent sets of points.

Since, as you probably know, the opposite sides of a rectangle have the same length, you might make a guess that any two equivalent segments have the same length. This guess would be wrong. Actually, *any* two segments are equivalent, no matter what their lengths. To see this, look at the following drawing where, for definiteness, we will suppose $\overline{RT}$ is just half as long as $\overline{RS}$. Pick some point O

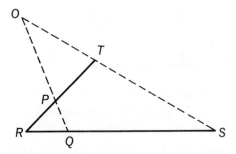

with T between O and S. If P is any point of $\overline{RT}$ let it be matched with the point Q where line OP meets $\overline{RS}$. For every point Q on $\overline{RS}$ one can easily draw line OQ and find the matching point P of $\overline{RT}$. That is, we have set up a one-to-one correspondence between the points of $\overline{RT}$ and $\overline{RS}$. Hence these segments are equivalent even though one is twice as long as the other. This emphasizes once more the need for caution in jumping to conclusions about infinite sets.

Problem Set 4.3

A. 1. Without making any use of counting the sets, show that the set of divisors of 6 is equivalent to the set of subsets of the set $S = \{a, b\}$.

2. Given a roomful of boys and girls, describe a procedure for finding whether there are more boys or girls without making any use of counting.

B. If A is a finite set, let $n(A)$ represent the number of elements in A. If A and B are *disjoint* finite sets, then it is well known that $n(A \cup B) = n(A) + n(B)$. If A and B are *not* disjoint, i.e., $A \cap B \neq \varnothing$, find an expression for $n(A \cup B)$ in terms of $n(A)$, $n(B)$, $n(A \cap B)$.

C. 1. Show at least ten one-to-one correspondences between the sets $\{a, b, c, d\}$ and $\{p, q, r, s\}$.

2. Are the sets $\{t, u, v, u, w, t\}$ and $\{a, b, c, d\}$ equivalent? If your answer is yes, show a one-to-one correspondence.

3. Is the set of states in the United States equivalent to the set of state capitals? Is it necessary to verify that the two sets contain the same number of elements in order to be sure of this answer?

D. 1. Consider the set of subsets of $\{a, b, c, d\}$ which contain at least one of the two elements a, b. Show, without counting, whether or not this set of subsets is equivalent to the set of prime numbers less than 40.

2. A man is putting stamps on a stack of wedding invitations. When he finishes there are five stamps left over. What conclusions can he draw about the set of invitations and the set of stamps? Would the conclusion still be valid if we could imagine the invitations were an infinite set?

3. Segment $\overline{AB}$ is twice as long as $\overline{PQ}$ and M is the midpoint of $\overline{AB}$. If each

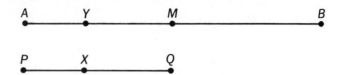

point X of $\overline{PQ}$ is matched with point Y of $\overline{AB}$ such that $\overline{AY}$ has the same length as $\overline{PX}$, this is a one-to-one correspondence of $\overline{PQ}$ with the part $\overline{AM}$ of $\overline{AB}$. Hence $\overline{PQ}$ is equivalent to $\overline{AM}$. Since part of $\overline{AB}$ is "left over" in this matching why does not this show that $\overline{PQ}$ is *not* equivalent to $\overline{AB}$?

4.4 A Finite Geometry

It has been remarked several times in earlier chapters that in a deductive system there are ultimately undefined elements. While you may have agreed intellectually that this certainly must be so, it is quite likely that this has not seemed very clear or obvious. In discussing the various number systems, for example, you may have felt that you knew perfectly well what you were talking about. As we turn next to a consideration of geometry we will be discussing such things as point, line, and plane. In devising a deductive system for use in our study of geometry we shall observe that the terms point, line and plane are undefined. Yet, certainly you have at least a rudimentary conception of what you mean by the words. Thus it seems like a lot of double talk to say they are undefined.

To try to clarify this dilemma, we shall indulge in a digression which is not important of itself but which may be useful in clearing the air. We shall invent a deductive system. There will be certain undefined objects which we will call **points**. The word **line** will also be undefined except that we understand that a line is a set of points. These points and lines are required to satisfy the following axioms.

Axiom B1 *There are at least two points.*

Axiom B2 *Two distinct points lie on exactly one line.*

Axiom B3 *Not all points lie on the same line.*

Axiom B4 *Every two lines have a point in common.*

Axiom B5 *Every line contains exactly three points.*

Note that we have agreed that a line is to be a set of points. When, as in Axiom B3, we say that a point "lies on" a line this means merely that the point belongs to the line, i.e., is an element of the set.

As an interesting intellectual exercise let us see what conclusions can be drawn from this set of axioms. Notice that by Axiom B4 two distinct lines must have a common point while by Axiom B2 two distinct lines cannot have two common points. This result can be written as follows:

Theorem I: Two distinct lines have exactly one point in common.

What other conclusions can we obtain? We notice by Axiom B1 there are at least two points. Let us label such a pair a and b. By Axiom B2 there is a line L_1 containing a and b. Moreover, by Axiom B5 there is exactly one other point, say c, on L_1 so that

$$L_1 = \{a, b, c\}.$$

By Axiom B3 there is a point d not on L_1 and hence by Axiom B2 a line L_2 so that $L_2 = \{a, d, \_\_\}$. Since $L_2 \neq L_1$ we see by Theorem I that the third point on L_2 is not on L_1 and hence is a new point e. Thus

$$L_2 = \{a, d, e\}.$$

Let L_3 be the line (by B2) containing b, d, and L_4 the line containing c, e. Then $L_3 = \{b, d, \_\_\}$ and $L_4 = \{c, e, \_\_\}$. The four lines are all distinct (why?), and each two except L_3 and L_4 already have a point in common. Thus by Theorem I the third point on L_3 must be a point f different from the five obtained so far. Moreover, f must also be the third point of L_4 since by Axiom B4 L_3 and L_4 have a point in common. Thus we have

$$L_3 = \{b, d, f\}, \qquad L_4 = \{c, e, f\}.$$

So far we have identified six points and four lines. If $L_5 = \{b, e, \_\_\}$, $L_6 = \{c, d, \_\_\}$ a similar argument shows the third point of each of these is a point g different from any of the previous ones; so we have

$$L_5 = \{b, e, g\}, \qquad L_6 = \{c, d, g\}.$$

Finally, let $L_7 = \{f, g, \_\_\}$. Observe L_7 is different from the other lines since none of those contains both f and g. L_7 already has a point in common with L_3, L_4, L_5, L_6, but by B4 (or Theorem I) it must have points in common with L_1 and L_2. The only possibility is that the third point of L_7 shall be a, the common point of L_1 and L_2. Thus

$$L_7 = \{f, g, a\}.$$

The conclusions we have so far obtained can be stated formally as theorems.

Theorem II: There are at least seven points.

Theorem III: There are at least seven lines.

What are the chances that there are still further points and lines? Suppose there were a point x different from the seven we have so far found. Then there would be a line $L_8 = \{a, x, \_\}$. So far L_8 has no point on L_3, L_4, L_5 or L_6. Thus by Axiom B4 the third point on L_8 would have to lie on all four of these lines. There is no point on all four lines. Thus there can be no line L_8 and so no point x. In other words, there are no points other than the seven we already found and no lines other than those already found. Using this fact we can write stronger versions of Theorems II and III as follows:

Theorem II': There are exactly seven points.

Theorem III': There are exactly seven lines.

Looking at the points lying on the different lines we also notice another fact.

Theorem IV: Every point lies on exactly three lines.

It is not of vital importance that you have followed every detail of this discussion though the proof is not terribly involved. The essential fact is that from the axioms it has been possible to derive this set of four theorems.

Now comes the sixty-four dollar question. What good is this system? Quite possibly you have been annoyed from the beginning by the fact that Axioms B4 and B5 are not in accord with your geometric conception about how points and lines should behave. Remember, we made no such guarantee. The words point and line were *undefined* and the observation above simply means that the system we have invented will not be useful to us in describing space as we conceive of it.

In this case is the system we have described of any value at all? Well, in a sense, the system we have created is like a woman's dress hanging in a clothing store. It was not made for any particular woman but could be useful to any woman it fits. In this case our system certainly does not seem to fit the physical space of our experience but quite possibly it might fit something else. For example, imagine the following highly fictitious situation.

In a club, the work of the organization is to be carried on by committees. It is agreed that each committee shall have three members. To promote acquaintance among the club members each two members shall serve together on exactly one committee. To coordinate the work, each two committees must have a member in common. To avoid a trivial situation we agree that the club must contain at least two members and that not all members can serve on a single committee.

It will be easy for you to verify that this is actually a situation to which our deductive system is applicable. If we interpret the undefined term "points" of the deductive system to mean "club members" and the undefined term "line" to mean "committee," then Axioms B1 through B5 are satisfied by the particular situation. For example, Axiom B2 becomes "Two different club members are on exactly one committee," which has been asserted to be true. As soon as we have verified that the axioms are satisfied for this situation we are then entitled at once to conclude the validity of the theorems. That is, we can conclude

Theorem I: Two distinct committees have exactly one member in common.

Theorem II: There are exactly seven club members.

Theorem III: There are exactly seven committees.

Theorem IV: Every club member is on exactly three committees.

Thus while point and line were undefined in the formal deductive system, if we give them an interpretation as above, in which the axioms hold, then we can at once conclude the validity of the theorems for the particular situation.

As a second and even more fictitious illustration, suppose you find a group of children who have driven some stakes into the ground and have amused themselves connecting them by different colored strings. You look at their work and notice the following facts.

Every two stakes are connected by exactly one colored string.
Every colored string is tied to exactly three stakes.
For every two different colored strings there is a stake to which both are tied.
There are at least two stakes (actually more).
Not all the stakes are connected by the same string.

Verify that, if we associate the term "point" of our deductive system with "stake" and "line" with "stakes connected by a colored string," then Axioms B1 through B5 are satisfied. Then the theorems must also be true for this system and we may conclude

Theorem I: Two different-colored strings are tied to exactly one common stake.

Theorem II: There are exactly seven stakes.

Theorem III: There are exactly seven colored strings.

Theorem IV: Every stake is tied to exactly three colored strings.

We can even draw a diagram of sorts showing how the children's network of stakes and string might look.

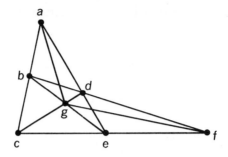

Hopefully this discussion may clarify the significance of the undefined elements. As far as the formal proofs of our theorems were concerned, we did not need to ask what points are or what lines are. When we seek to apply our system to a given situation we associate these undefined terms with specific objects and the theorems then become statements about these objects which must be true if the axioms are satisfied.

To return to the analogy suggested earlier, just as there may be many women that a dress will fit, so there may be many situations in which a given system may be applicable. We noted two such situations for our deductive system.

However, the procedure we have used above appears singularly inefficient, whatever its correctness. We invented a system at random and then looked around to see if there were anything it would fit. It was like making a dress and hoping some woman would come along who could wear it. In many cases the situation will be just the reverse. We may have quite clearly in mind a situation we wish to describe. In such a case we will try deliberately to invent a deductive system that will serve the purpose—a custom-made dress instead of a ready-made one. That is, we will examine the situation we wish to describe and try to formulate statements about it that seem to be correct to use as axioms. In the next section we will attempt such an examination for ordinary physical space.

Problem Set 4.4

A. 1. In the example of the club and the committees, verify that all Axioms B1 through B5 are satisfied.

   2. In the example of the stakes and colored strings verify that all the Axioms B1 through B5 are satisfied.

B. 1. Consider the deductive system in which the undefined terms are point and line and in which the following axioms are satisfied:

   H1. There are at least two points.
   H2. Two distinct points lie on exactly one line.
   H3. Not all points lie on the same line.

H4. Every line contains exactly two points.

H5. If point a does not lie on line L there is exactly one line containing a and not meeting L.

Prove the following:

a. There are at least four points.

b. There are at least six lines.

c. There are exactly four points.

d. There are exactly six lines.

e. Every point is on exactly three lines.

2. Let 0 and 1 be the elements of a mod 2 number system so the addition table is

+	0	1
0	0	1
1	1	0

Let the pairs of numbers from this system be called points, i.e., $(0, 1)$, $(1, 1)$, etc. Let the sets of points satisfying the following equations be called lines: $x = 0$, $y = 0$, $x = 1$, $y = 1$, $x + y = 0$, $x + y = 1$.

a. Find the points contained in each line.

b. Verify that with these interpretations of point and line Axioms H1 to H5 of problem **B1** are satisfied.

c. It follows that theorems **a** through **e** of problem **B1** must hold for this system. Verify that these results are indeed correct for this system.

4.5 What Is the Point?

All of our physical experiences involve us with the idea of space. We live at a certain location; we move from one place to another; we try to remember where we put the car key; we try to fit six people in a car designed for four. Hence we are interested in exploring more carefully our ideas of space, size, shape, and location. This study is called **geometry.**

As suggested in the last section, we will eventually wish to invent a deductive system that seems appropriate to describe our physical experiences of space. With this in mind let us begin by identifying those physical ideas which we will associate with the undefined terms point, line, and plane of our system and let us examine our physical experiences as a guide to formulating appropriate axioms.

One of our most familiar physical notions is that of location, i.e., *where* is it? This is the physical idea that we will have in mind when we use the word *point*. We wish to push this idea a step further, however, and use the word point to indicate an *exact* location. There are many objects in our physical experience that suggest an exact location—a corner of this page, the tip of a pencil, a dot on the chalkboard. Any of these objects which suggest to us an exact location is called a **representation** of a point. A little reflection makes clear that any physical object actually covers not one point but many. For example, what may appear to be a small dot on the chalkboard, if examined under a magnifying glass, will look large and clearly cover many locations. Thus there is no perfect representation of a point. In a sense the concept of point is an idealization. However, we may speak of one representation of a point as being better than another if it suggests more adequately an exact location. Thus the point of a needle is a better representation than the end of a crowbar, and a dot made by a sharp pencil is better than one made with a dull crayon. We shall often, of course, represent a point by a dot on paper but it must be kept in mind that this only suggests the exact idea of point.

The description of a point as a location involves implicitly the idea that it is fixed. After all, a location does not move. If we allow the tip of a pencil to represent a point on this page and then move the pencil to another location, we have repre-

sented two different points with the same pencil tip. That is, we have moved an object (in this case a pencil tip) from one point (location) to another. The location (i.e., the point) where the tip first was did not move. Thus we may certainly conceive of moving a representation of a point, but strictly speaking we do not move the point.

It seems necessary to make one additional comment about the matter of location. The location of a body really has no meaning except with respect to some understood frame of reference. Thus when we speak of a point as a location we are assuming that there is some agreed frame of reference with respect to which the location is to be described. For example, if you move a chair in your classroom from one place to another and then undertake to put it back where it was, you are probably locating it with respect to the walls of your classroom. On the other hand, when one makes the remark that the earth turns on its axis once every twenty-four hours he is using a frame of reference involving the sun. The problems involved may be suggested by thinking of a father driving a car down the road at sixty miles an hour and telling his children in the back seat to "sit still." It would be clear both to the father and children that he meant to sit still with respect to the car, but they certainly will not be still as viewed by an observer beside the road. In the discussion below you may think of the frame of reference as being the walls of your room.

It will be quite customary for us to label points by capital letters. Thus, in the picture of a box, three points, indicated by dots, have been given labels A, B, and C.

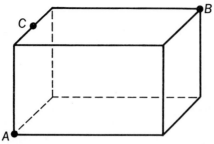

In our experience certain sets of points occur so often that they seem to deserve special names. If you hold a piece of thread by its ends and stretch it as tightly as possible you have a representation of what we call a **line segment.** The edge of a box, a crease in a sheet of paper, the edge of this page, all are representations of line segments, As in the case of points we do not say that these physical objects *are* line segments but that they suggest line segments.

The essential idea is indicated if we say that a tightly stretched string is a "good" representation of a line segment but a tightly stretched thread is a "better" one since we do not wish the ideal line segment to have any "thickness" but do want it to be "straight."

As is suggested by the representations, a line segment has two endpoints and could be described as the set consisting of these endpoints together with all points "between" them. We often name a line segment whose endpoints are A and B by the symbol $\overline{AB}$ or $\overline{BA}$.

At first sight it may not appeal to you that the part of a segment between the endpoints is a set of points. Yet if we imagine a thread held tightly to represent a segment, each molecule of the thread occupies a definite location and can be considered to represent a point. Hence a segment and indeed any geometric object is a set of points, i.e., of locations.

Let us imagine now the set of points obtained if a segment is extended without end in both directions. This must be imagined since no physical representation goes on forever. Such a figure will be called a **line.** In drawing a line we shall frequently indicate it with arrowheads, as shown, to remind the reader that he

must use his imagination to think of the whole line. It will sometimes be convenient in the following work to name lines by small letters like a, b, etc.

The third concept we wish to introduce is that of a **plane.** When you look at a wall, or a chalkboard, or a desk top, or this page, you see a representation of what we shall call a plane. It may be naïvely described as the idealized flat surface. As in the case of a line we wish to imagine a plane as extending indefinitely, i.e., having no boundaries or edges. We sometimes make a drawing to represent a plane. In a way this is unfortunate since the drawing suggests

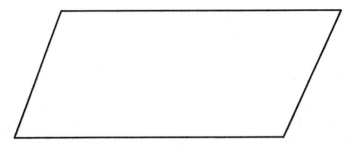

edges, but we must imagine the extension. Of course, *any* representation of a plane has the same disadvantages as such a drawing in really suggesting only part of a plane. Like the line, a plane is a set of points.

The set of all locations—i.e., of all points—we shall call **space.** Since the objects we consider in geometry are all various sets of points, space forms the universal set for our consideration.

Having identified the fundamental objects we wish to discuss, i.e., point, line, plane, we shall now want to consider relationships among them. Our ideas of these relationships are obtained from our experiences with the different models, even though we recognize that the models only approximately represent the ideal object.

Let us imagine some simple experiments and see what conjectures we can make from them. Pick out two points—say T, the corner of a table, and H, the top of a hatrack, as shown in the illustration. We ask whether there is a line through the

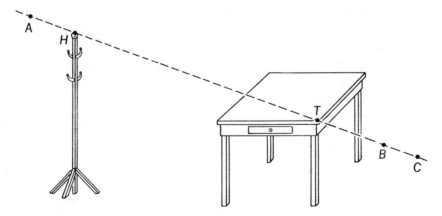

points H and T. As we have seen, a tightly stretched string is a good representation of a line, so we take a sufficiently long piece of string and, holding it stretched tightly, attempt to place it in a position so it touches both H and T. It seems intuitively clear to us that this is possible and we might thus be led to formulate the conjecture:

(1) There is a line containing two distinct points.

In the same situation we might ask another less obvious question. Could there be more than one line through H and T? We see at once there are many different line segments containing H and T. For example, in the drawing $\overline{AT}$, $\overline{AB}$, $\overline{HT}$, $\overline{HC}$ are all segments containing H and T, but are these segments all part of the same line? To put it another way, can segment $\overline{HT}$ be extended to a line in more than one way? We might try an experiment like the following. Take a very long piece of string and have two people hold it at some convenient points like A and B so that it touches H and T as before. Then have the people back carefully away from each other keeping the string on T and H. Does there seem to be any choice in how they must hold the string if it is to stay in contact with T and H? If you feel this experiment suggests there is only one way of extending $\overline{HT}$ you might be led to formulate the following conjecture:

(2) There is at most one line containing two given distinct points.

A series of equally simple experiments, some of which are suggested in the problem set, might lead us to formulate such additional conjectures as the following:

(3) There are infinitely many points on a line.

(4) There are infinitely many lines through a point.

(5) There are infinitely many lines on a plane.

(6) There are infinitely many planes in space.

(7) There are infinitely many planes on a line.

(8) If two points of a line are contained in a plane all points of the line are in the plane.

(9) The intersection set of two planes may be a line.

(10) The intersection set of two planes may be the empty set. (In this case the planes are called **parallel**.)

(11) The intersection set of two lines may be a set consisting of a single point.

(12) The intersection set of two lines may be the empty set.

(13) The intersection set of two lines contained in a plane may be the empty set. (In this case the lines are called **parallel**.)

(14) There is exactly one plane on three points which do not lie on a line.

(15) The intersection set of any two distinct planes is a line or the empty set.

(16) The intersection set of any two distinct lines is a point or the empty set.

(17) There is exactly one plane containing a line and a point not on the line.

Problem Set 4.5

Below are described some simple experiments with representations of geometric figures. In each case the experiment or the questions asked about the experiment should indicate one or more of the conjectures listed above. In each case indicate the conjecture (or conjectures) suggested by the problem.

1. You hold a piece of string stretched tight so that the two points where you are grasping it are touching the chalkboard. You notice the other points of the string also touch the chalkboard.

2. The surface of a door is a representation of a plane. The door moves freely as you push it and each new position of the door represents a different plane.

3. In the experiment of problem **2** imagine the door hung by two hinges which we imagine to represent points A and B. You notice that for each position of the door the plane seems to contain the line through A and B.

4. Imagine the door in the experiment above pushed till it comes in contact with a doorstop representing a point C (which is not on the line through the hinges). How many different positions of the door will allow it to meet C?

5. Consider a drawing of a line. Can you imagine one dot placed on this line? Two dots? Five dots? Is there any limit to the number of dots you can imagine on the line?

6. Let A be a point. Imagine you are holding a string tightly to represent a line. In how many different ways can you hold it so that it will be on the point?

7. The same question as for problem **6** except that A is on the chalkboard and the string must be placed to lie on the chalkboard.

8. Consider an ordinary rectangular box like that shown here. The faces are

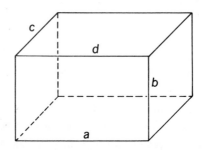

representations of planes, the edges are representations of lines, and the vertices are representations of points. What do you think is the intersection set for lines a and b?

9. What do you think is the intersection set of lines a and c?

10. What do you think is the intersection set for a and d? Note carefully that a and d are *lines*, not just segments, so you must imagine their extensions. Is the answer as "obvious" to you as for the last two problems? Are the lines a and d contained in a plane?

11. Consider the planes represented in the drawing by the top of the box and the front of the box. What seems to be their intersection set?

12. Next, consider the planes represented by the top and bottom of the box.

What seems to be their intersection set? Again notice that it is necessary to imagine the extensions of the faces since it is full planes we are considering, not just the pieces shown.

13. Take a tightly stretched string representing a line. Place this string so that it has two points in common with another representation of a line, say the edge of your desk. What do you seem to find about the two lines? If two lines are distinct, how many points can there be in their intersection set?

14. Take two cards representing planes. Place them to illustrate conjecture (9). Place them so they illustrate conjecture (10). Can you think of any way of placing them that seems to yield any other case for the intersection set?

15. You notice a poorly made chair may be unsteady in that four legs do not touch the floor at the same time. But you also notice there seems to be no such trouble with a three-legged stool no matter how crudely it is made.

4.6 Axioms and Deduction

In Section 4.5 we indulged in what might be called physical or experimental geometry. That is, on the basis of our experience with physical models we evolved what seemed to be plausible conjectures, i.e., good hunches. This process can, of course, be continued to lead us to conjectures of many other results. It is one which is used freely with elementary school children where the goal is for them to become familiar with spatial relationships and, to the extent possible, to participate in the discovery (or perhaps better the conjecture) of these relationships.

However, from a more sophisticated point of view we are not satisfied with inductive procedures only. We do not wish to go on permanently simply making unrelated conjectures. We have already seen that once some things are assumed, others can be obtained by proof rather than merely by experimental conjectures. Of the list of conjectures above quite probably some could be proved on the basis of others. We should like to make capital of the deductive procedure, i.e., create a deductive system to aid us in studying these geometric relationships.

Specifically, then, we shall select some of the conjectures of the last section as axioms and attempt to see what conclusions can be deduced from them. Many choices of axioms are possible, but we shall select the following:

Axiom A1 *There are an infinite number of points on a line, an infinite number of lines on a plane, and an infinite number of planes in space.*

Axiom A2 *On any two points there is a line.*

Axiom A3 *On any three noncollinear points there is a plane.*

Axiom A4 *The intersection set of two distinct lines is the empty set or a set containing a single point.*

Axiom A5 *The intersection set of two distinct planes is a line or the empty set.*

A comment about terminology may be helpful here. If k is a line and P a point, we know that the statement $P \in k$ means that P is one of the elements of set k, i.e., that P is one of the points which belong to line k. This relationship is expressed verbally in several ways which you should recognize when you see them. We may say that *line k contains point P* since P is indeed among the points which constitute set k. An alternative terminology is to say that *line k lies on point P*. This is the terminology used above in Axiom A2. Still another way of expressing the relationship $P \in k$ would be to say *point P lies on line k* or *point P belongs to line k*. It might be even better to say *point P lies in line k* since the word "on" often carries the connotation of "on top of," whereas we are trying to say that P is actually a part of k. Similar remarks apply to the relation $P \in M$ where M is a plane. We shall make no attempt to adopt a single preferred terminology but will use whichever of the forms above seems convenient in each situation. You should find no real difficulty in understanding the different expressions and in passing from verbal to symbolic statements.

Comparing Axioms A1 to A5 with our conjectures, we see that Axiom A1 is a composite of conjectures (3), (5), and (6). Axiom A2 is conjecture (1). Axiom A3 is a part of conjecture (14) in that Axiom A3 does not claim there is only one such plane. Axiom A4 is conjecture (16) and, finally, Axiom A5 is conjecture (15).

The undefined terms in the deductive system we are developing will be point, line, plane. This means, as we have noted earlier, that, while we have decided what geometric ideas we wish to associate with these words, it will never be necessary to use these meanings in giving the proofs. Thus the system we invent could possibly be applied to some other situation if we ever came across one whose elements satisfied the axioms. We shall be interested, however, in the geometric significance of the results to be established.

Let us see now what conclusions we can deduce from the axioms. Some of these may well be conjectures indicated in the last section.

Theorem 4.1 *Let k_1 and k_2 be lines and P_1 and P_2 distinct points. If $\{P_1, P_2\} \subset k_1 \cap k_2$, then $k_1 = k_2$.*

Be sure you understand the meaning of the symbolic statement. It says that if both P_1 and P_2 belong to the intersection of k_1 and k_2 then k_1 and k_2 are the same line. The claim of the theorem could be stated verbally in the form: There is at most one line containing two distinct points. Thus Theorem 4.1 is actually the same as conjecture (2) of Section 4.5. Let us consider how we might prove Theorem 4.1. The proof indicated below is a classic example of the contradiction proof. That is, we are asked to show that $k_1 = k_2$. Now in every case either $k_1 = k_2$ or $k_1 \neq k_2$ and we show that the second alternative is impossible. The argument might be given like this:

***Proof of Theorem* 4.1.** Suppose there is a case in which the hypotheses are true but $k_1 \neq k_2$. By Axiom A4 the intersection set $k_1 \cap k_2$ has either no points or one. This contradicts the given fact that both P_1 and P_2 belong to $k_1 \cap k_2$. Thus $k_1 \neq k_2$ is impossible and $k_1 = k_2$ must be true.

This result leads easily to the following one.

Theorem 4.2 *There is exactly one line containing two distinct points.*

Proof. Let P_1 and P_2 be the two distinct points. By Axiom A2 there is a line containing P_1 and P_2 while by Theorem 4.1 there cannot be more than one. Thus there is exactly one line containing P_1 and P_2. On the basis of Theorem 4.2 it is now legitimate to speak of *the* line containing (or on) two given points.

Notice that Axiom A3 assures us that there is a plane on any three noncollinear points. It is reasonable to ask if there could be more than one such plane. That the answer is "no" is the content of Theorem 4.3.

Theorem 4.3 *Let M_1 and M_2 be planes and P_1, P_2, P_3 noncollinear points. If $\{P_1, P_2, P_3\} \subset M_1 \cap M_2$, then $M_1 = M_2$.*

[Verbal statement of Theorem 4.3: *There is at most one plane containing (or on) three noncollinear points.*]

Proof. The same contradiction argument used in Theorem 4.1 works again here. Suppose there is a case in which the hypotheses are true but $M_1 \neq M_2$. By Axiom A5 the intersection set $M_1 \cap M_2$ is either a line or the empty set. This contradicts the given fact that P_1, P_2, P_3 belong to $M_1 \cap M_2$ but do not lie on a line. Thus $M_1 \neq M_2$ must be false and $M_1 = M_2$ is true.

This leads easily to the following result, whose proof is given as a problem.

Theorem 4.4 *There is exactly one plane which contains three noncollinear points.*

Notice that Theorem 4.4 is actually conjecture (14) of Section 4.5. On the basis of this we can now legitimately talk about *the* plane containing (or on) three noncollinear points.

Part of the price one pays for such a deductive approach as we are using here is that a statement may look "obvious" geometrically, but until we give a proof we cannot be sure whether or not it follows from our axioms. The next two theorems are examples of this.

Theorem 4.5 *If k is a line there is a point not on k.*

Proof. The steps are suggested below and you are asked to provide the supporting statements.

    (1) There is a line k' so that $k' \neq k$. (Why?)

    (2) On k' can be found two distinct points P_1 and P_2. (Why?)

    (3) Points P_1 and P_2 cannot both belong to k. (Why?)

    (4) Thus at least one of these points does not lie on k and the proof is complete.

The next conclusion is really a stronger form of Theorem 4.5 but is a fact that will presently be useful.

Theorem 4.6 *If k is a line and M a plane there is a point which does not belong to $M \cup k$.*

Proof. Somehow we must produce a point which does not belong to either M or k. As before, the sequence of statements is given and you are asked to supply the reasons.

    (1) There is a plane N so that $N \neq M$. (Why?) Note that nothing is claimed about the relation of N to k.

    (2) There exist three distinct lines k_1, k_2, k_3 on N. (Why?)

    (3) $M \cap N$ is either a line or the empty set. (Why?)

    (4) Since, of the lines k_1, k_2, k_3 at most one can equal k and at most one can equal $M \cap N$, it is possible to choose one of them, say k_1, so that $k_1 \neq k$ and $k_1 \neq M \cap N$.

    (5) Line k_1 meets k in at most one point and meets $M \cap N$ in at most one point. (Why?)

    (6) There is a point P on k_1 which is not on k or $M \cap N$. (Why?)

    (7) The point P is the required point since it does not belong either to M or to k.

Consider now conjecture (8) of Section 4.5, which claimed that a line meeting a plane twice is contained in the plane, i.e., is a subset of the plane. This can now be proved as a theorem in our system.

Theorem 4.7 *Let P_1, P_2 be distinct points, k a line, and M a plane. If $\{P_1, P_2\} \subset k \cap M$, then $k \subset M$.*

[Verbal statement of Theorem 4.7: *If the intersection set of a line and a plane contains two distinct points, the line is a subset of the plane.*]

Proof. The accompanying illustration, while not an essential part of the discussion, may help in following the indicated steps. By Theorem 4.6 there is a

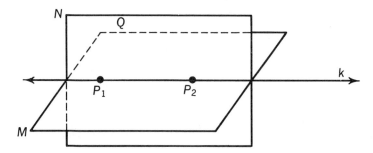

point Q which does not belong to k or to M. Let N be the plane containing P_1, P_2, Q. (How do we know P_1, P_2, Q are not collinear?)

(1) Then $M \cap N$ is a line. (Why?) And $\{P_1, P_2\} \subset M \cap N$. (Why?)

(2) But $\{P_1, P_2\} \subset k$. (Why?)

(3) Thus $k = M \cap N$. (Why?)

(4) It follows that $k \subset M$. (Why?)

Conjecture (17) concerning a plane containing a line and a point is the content of the following theorem.

Theorem 4.8 *Let P be a point and k a line such that $P \notin k$, i.e., P is not on k. Then there is a plane M such that $k \cup \{P\} \subset M$. Moreover, if M and N are planes such that $k \cup \{P\} \subset M \cap N$, then $M = N$.*

[Verbal statement of Theorem 4.8: *There is exactly one plane containing a line and a point not on it.*]

Proof. This is really a double-barreled theorem. We have two things to prove. We must show there is a plane M satisfying the given conditions and we must show it is the only one. Let us first show there is one.

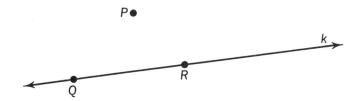

Let Q and R be two points of k. They exist by Axiom A1. Then P, Q, R are not collinear because P was given as *not* on k. There is a plane M containing P, Q, R (by Axiom A3). If M contains Q and R it contains line k (by Theorem 4.7). Thus M does satisfy the required condition: i.e., $k \cup \{P\} \subset M$.

Suppose now we know that plane N also contains k and P. Then certainly $\{P, Q, R\} \subset N$. By Theorem 4.3 (or Theorem 4.4) this means that $M = N$. This completes the proof.

Theorem 4.8 concerned itself with the question of whether a given set of points belonged to a plane. Another theorem of the same character is this.

Theorem 4.9 *Let k_1 and k_2 be distinct lines and P a point. If $k_1 \cap k_2 = \{P\}$, then there is a plane M such that $k_1 \cup k_2 \subset M$. Moreover, if M, N are planes so that $k_1 \cup k_2 \subset M \cap N$, then $M = N$.*

[Verbal statement of Theorem 4.9: *There is exactly one plane which contains two intersecting lines.*]

The proof of this is left as an exercise. Use the same approach as for Theorem 4.8, first showing there *is* such a plane, then that there cannot be but one. It may help to pick out specific points on k_1 and k_2.

The discussion here has indicated some of the principal results that can be deduced from our axioms. It has also been noted that a number of the conjectures of the last section have been proved as theorems.

In addition to the ones specifically noted, conjectures (9) and (11) have really been established incidentally and conjectures (4) and (7) are not difficult, though we shall not bother to give the proofs.

The only conjectures about which nothing has been said are (10), (12), and (13), which have to do with parallel planes (planes whose intersection set is empty) and parallel lines (coplanar lines whose intersection set is empty). This omission was not accidental. These statements, though plausible on the basis of our physical experience, are not consequences of Axioms A1 through A5.

Let us summarize what we have succeeded in doing in this section. We have created a small deductive system. We intended it to be applicable to describe the space of our physical experience since we selected axioms that were physically plausible. If the axioms are indeed correct for physical space, then we are sure that the theorems we proved will likewise be true for this space. That is, we have obtained results by deduction rather than by physical experimentation. Finally, we have seen that the axioms so far chosen are not sufficient to establish all the results which we conjecture to be true of our space. To prove more of these results we would need to add more axioms and thus create a more complex deductive system.

Problem Set 4.6

A. 1. Explain why Axiom A5 does not imply conjecture (10).
  2. Let M_1 and M_2 be distinct planes. If $M_1 \cap M_2 \neq \varnothing$, prove that $M_1 \cap M_2$ contains an infinite number of points.
  3. If k is a line, prove there is a plane containing k. [HINT: Start by applying Theorem 4.5.]

B. 1. Give the proof of Theorem 4.4.
  2. Prove Theorem 4.9.

3. Let k_1 and k_2 be lines such that $k_1 \parallel k_2$. If M and N are planes so that $k_1 \cup k_2 \subset M \cap N$, prove that $M = N$.

4. State the result of problem **B3** in words.

C. 1. If P_1, P_2, P_3 are any three distinct points prove that there is a plane M such that $M \supset \{P_1, P_2, P_3\}$. [HINT: Consider separately the two cases when the points are collinear and when they are not. Observe also the result of problem **A3**.]

2. Let k be a line and M a plane such that $k \subset M$. Prove there is a point P such that $P \in M$ but $P \notin k$. [HINT: Begin by observing there is a line k' such that $k' \subset M$ and $k' \neq k$. Why is this true?]

4.7 Some Other Sets of Points

In Section 4.6 we illustrated the use of deductive methods in the study of geometry. It is clear, however, that the axioms selected are not sufficient to allow us to discuss many topics which are immediately suggested by our physical experience. Parallelism was mentioned as one such topic, and there are many others. The obvious solution to this is to expand our list of axioms by adding new ones until we have what might be called a **complete set,** i.e., a set of axioms which we can use to discuss any of the topics in geometry. This project of choosing a complete set of axioms and formally developing from them a study of all the geometric topics of interest is praiseworthy but also rather formidable. One of the early attempts to do so was by Euclid, around 300 B.C., from whom we get the name **Euclidean geometry** for the geometry we commonly study. A version of this procedure (sometimes quite emasculated) is commonly carried out in secondary courses in geometry. At all events it is a more extensive project than seems appropriate for a book of this nature.

We shall, instead, emphasize the deductive method by developing small deductive systems like that of Section 4.6 relating to some limited areas of interest. These will be interspersed with sections which are frankly intuitive and descriptive, more in the vein of what might actually be done in discussing the topics with elementary school children. The present section in which we will explore and describe some other point sets is of this nature.

In Section 4.6 we have discussed the point, line, and plane, which were undefined as far as the formal deductive system is concerned but to which we have associated certain geometric ideas. In Section 4.5, however, there was also introduced the idea of a **line segment** or more briefly **segment.** If A and B are points of a line k, by the segment with endpoints A and B is meant the set of points of

k consisting of A and B and all points between them. Recall that this set of points is denoted by the symbol $\overline{AB}$ or the symbol $\overline{BA}$.

Notice that to make sense of this description it is necessary to suppose that the meaning of *between* is already known. Both here and later we shall suppose that this is a part of your intuitive geometric understanding. (If we should attempt a formal development along the lines of Section 4.6 it would be necessary to adopt a set of axioms describing this relation.) In particular note that if A, B, and C are any three distinct collinear points, exactly one of them is between the other two.

Notice that line k in the drawing on page 131 could be described as *the* line containing A and B (cf. Theorem 4.2). This fact is used in adopting a new symbolism for k. We shall often denote this line as $\overleftrightarrow{AB}$ or $\overleftrightarrow{BA}$. This, of course, gives rise to many symbols for the same line. For example, in the following illustration, $\overleftrightarrow{PQ} =$

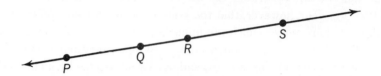

$\overleftrightarrow{PR} = \overleftrightarrow{QS}$, etc. Note, however, that $\overline{PQ}$, $\overline{PR}$, $\overline{QS}$ are *not* the same. They denote three different segments. As a review of set notations note the following relations for this drawing.

$$\overline{PQ} \cap \overline{RS} = \varnothing.$$
$$\overline{PQ} \cap \overline{QR} = \{Q\}.$$
$$\overline{PQ} \cup \overline{QR} = \overline{PR}.$$
$$\overline{PS} \cap \overline{QR} = \overline{QR}.$$
$$\overline{PQ} \cap \overleftrightarrow{RS} = \overline{PQ}.$$

With the concept of segment or betweenness understood, it is easy to describe certain other sets and relationships. Let k be a line and let P be a point of k as shown in the drawing below.

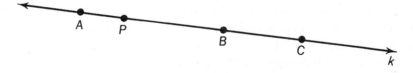

It appears that the points on k other than P now consist of two sets which we call **half lines.** We may describe one half line as consisting of points to the right of P and the other consisting of points to the left of P. Neither half line contains P. Hence k is the union of the set $\{P\}$ and of the two half lines. When, as indicated, A and B are in different half lines then P is between A and B or $P \in \overline{AB}$.

On the other hand, when B and C belong to the same half line then P is not between B and C or $P \in \overline{BC}$. That is, crudely speaking, if two points, like B, C, are
on the same half line with respect to P, then one can pass from B to C on k without meeting P, but if two points, like A, C, are on different half lines, there is no
route from A to C on k which does not contain the point P. Thus P is said to
separate k into two half lines. It would be possible to invent a special notation for
half lines but we shall not attempt to do so. We may on occasion find it convenient, however, to speak of the half line which is the A side of P or the half line
which is the B side of P.

In a quite similar way one may speak of a plane M as being *separated* into two
half planes by a line k in M, as shown in the drawing below. Note that neither half

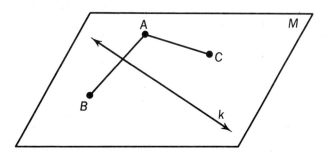

plane contains any of the points of k. Plane M is the union of k and the two half
planes. If two points such as A and C are in the same half plane, then $k \cap \overline{AC} =$
$\varnothing$; but if they are in different half planes, as A and B, then $k \cap \overline{AB} \neq \varnothing$. That
is, if A and C are in the same half plane one can pass from A to C without crossing
k, but if A and B are in opposite half planes the segment from A to B crosses k. In
fact, any continuous path from A to B in M crosses k. We may speak of the half
plane on the A side of k and the half plane on the B side of k.

Finally, a plane M separates the points of space not on M into two half spaces,
as shown below. The half spaces are on the A side and B side of M, respectively.

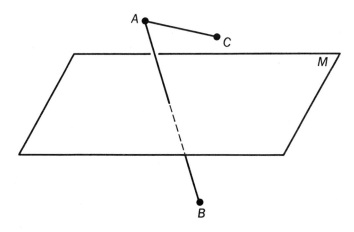

In both the last two drawings it is to be recalled that we must exercise our imagination to think of the indefinite extension of the planes. Planes have no "edges," just as lines have no ends.

A concept closely related to that of half line is that of ray. Let A be a point of a line k and B a point of one of the half lines determined by A. Then the union of $\{A\}$ and of the half line AB is called a **ray.** This particular ray is designated by

$\overrightarrow{AB}$. Symbolically we may write $\overrightarrow{AB} = \{A\} \cup$ half line AB. One may interpret the symbol as meaning the set of points one covers by starting at A and going indefinitely along the half line containing B. A ray differs from a half line only in the fact that the cutting point (in this case A) belongs to the set. This point is called the **endpoint** of the ray. Notice carefully that $\overrightarrow{AB}$ is *not* the same ray as $\overrightarrow{BA}$. What is the ray $\overrightarrow{BA}$? Notice that $\overrightarrow{AB} \cap \overrightarrow{BA} = \overline{AB}$.

One of the common figures in geometry is a union of two rays. Let $\overrightarrow{AB}$ and $\overrightarrow{AC}$ be two rays, not on the same line, having a common endpoint A, as shown. The

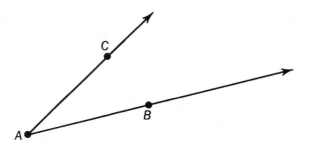

point set, $\overrightarrow{AB} \cup \overrightarrow{AC}$, is called an **angle.** The common endpoint A of the rays is the **vertex** of the angle. A notation often used to denote such an angle is $\angle BAC$ or $\angle CAB$. Note that the vertex is named in the middle position with the other two points, one on each ray. When there is no likelihood of confusion, we will simply write $\angle A$.

In the representation of $\angle PQR$ on the next page, the half plane on the P side of $\overleftrightarrow{QR}$ has been indicated by vertical striping, while the half plane on the R side of $\overleftrightarrow{PQ}$ has been shown by horizontal striping. Notice the set which is the intersection of these two half planes, i.e., the set of points striped both ways. This set is called the **interior of** $\angle PQR$. The points of the plane not belonging to $\angle PQR$ or its interior are said to form the **exterior of the angle.** The points of $\angle PQR$ belong neither to the interior nor to the exterior.

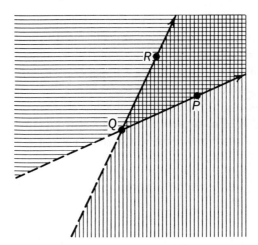

Observe that the present use of the term **angle** requires the rays to be on different lines. Otherwise the discussion of interior and exterior above is meaningless. Thus such figures as $\overrightarrow{AB} \cup \overrightarrow{AC}$ or $\overrightarrow{PQ} \cup \overrightarrow{PR}$, below, are not referred to in

this text as angles. However, it should be noted that the word *angle* occurs in mathematics at many different levels of sophistication. The present definition, simply as a **point set,** is at the lowest level. In a subject like trigonometry it is quite customary to use the word angle in some such sense as an "amount of rotation." Such figures as those above then would be associated with a "180° angle" or a "0° angle." For our purposes, however, it will be sufficient for an angle to be merely a set of points as described.

One of the most common point sets in all geometry is also readily defined in terms of unions of simple sets. Let A, B, C be three noncollinear points. Then the

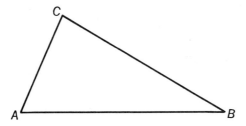

union of the three segments $\overline{AB} \cup \overline{BC} \cup \overline{CA}$ is called a **triangle.** It is completely described when the three points, called the **vertices** of the triangle, are given. The common symbol for it is $\triangle ABC$. Note carefully that a triangle consists only of the points *on* the segments, *not* those in the region bounded by the segments.

The word **curve** in mathematics is a general word meaning any kind of a continuous path. Without attempting an exact definition (which would be very difficult) we may imagine a curve as a set of points to be traced out in a particular way. Usually it will be clear without comment how it is intended the tracing be done. For a curve in the plane merely think of the drawings that can be made on a paper without lifting the pencil from the paper. Consider the accompanying drawings, each of them intended to represent a curve. Notice that in this inclusive sense a segment such as (c) is an example of a curve, as are diagrams (d), (g), (h), (l), which are composed of segments. This differs from our everyday use of the word curve which is often employed in the sense of "not straight."

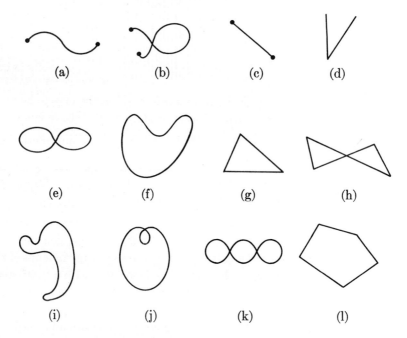

According to our discussion, a curve is a set of points together with a specified way of tracing them. Thus, strictly speaking, we should not refer to the illustration as a set of curves until we specify how they are to be traced. For example, curves (a) and (c) could be traced in the "obvious" way from one endpoint to the other, thus finishing the drawing at the end opposite to where it began. On the other hand, we could trace the set as above but then retrace the route ending the drawing at the same point where it began. These two ways of tracing the same set would be considered as two *different* curves. In the discussion below we assume the simplest tracings, i.e., those for which there is a minimum of retracing.

If, in our tracing of a curve, the first point coincides with the last—that is, if we end where we began—the curve is said to be **closed.** With the understandings noted in the last paragraph, drawings (e) through (l) show closed curves, while (a) through (d) are not closed. Thus the set of closed curves is indicated by {(e), (f), (g), (h), (i), (j), (k), (l)}. If, in tracing a curve, we never meet the same point twice (except that the first and last points may coincide), the curve is said to be **simple.** The set of the simple curves may be indicated as {(a), (c), (d), (f), (g), (i), (l)}. If a curve is both simple and closed, it is called (reasonably enough) a **simple closed curve.** The set of simple closed curves is the intersection of the set of simple curves and the set of closed curves. Thus the set of simple closed curves is {(f), (g), (i), (l)}.

An important property of simple closed curves in a plane is that such a curve, C, *separates* the points of the plane not on C into an **interior** and an **exterior.** Any two points of the interior such as I and J can be joined by a curve in the plane

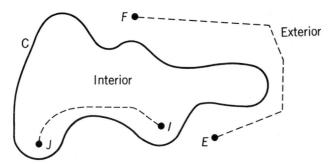

not meeting C, and similarly any two points such as E and F of the exterior can be joined by a curve in the plane not meeting C. On the other hand, every curve in the plane which contains both an interior point I and an exterior point E intersects C.

It should be emphasized again that the treatment in this section is highly intuitive. To make this material part of a deductive system in the way we developed Section 4.6 would be a major task, particularly the latter part dealing with curves. The intuitive ideas are, in fact, correct and are so geometrically appealing and reasonable that they are readily presented at the elementary school level. For this reason it has seemed desirable to discuss them in this informal way.

Among the simple closed curves shown on page 136 it may be observed that two of them, (g) and (l), are actually unions of line segments. A simple closed curve which is a union of line segments is called a **polygon.** Different types of polygons are given special names. A polygon of three sides is a **triangle** and one of four sides is a **quadrilateral.** Polygons of five and six sides are **pentagons** and **hexagons,** respectively. Many of the common sets with which you are familiar are special cases of the quadrilateral. These would include the square, rectangle, parallelogram, and rhombus.

It should be noted that many books use the word *polygon* for *any* closed curve which is a union of segments, whether simple or not. These books would describe the curves noted above as **simple polygons.**

Often it is convenient to refer to a set of points in a plane which is the union of a simple closed curve and its interior. Such a set will be called a **region.** Thus the union of a triangle and its interior is a **triangular region,** while the union of a circle and its interior is a **circular region.** Be sure to distinguish clearly between a triangle, which is a curve, and a triangular region, which is the union of the triangle and its interior. A similar remark applies to circle and circular region.

Problem Set 4.7

A. 1. Make a sketch or find an example of two lines k_1 and k_2 which are not parallel but such that $k_1 \cap k_2 = \emptyset$. (Such lines are called **skew lines**.)

2. Let M_1 and M_2 be planes as shown so that $M_1 \cap M_2 = \overleftrightarrow{PQ}$.

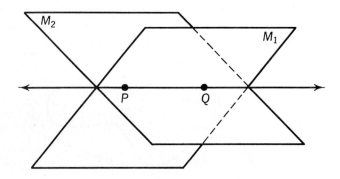

    a. Show a line k such that $k \cap (M_1 \cup M_2)$ contains exactly two points.
    b. Show a line k such that $k \cap (M_1 \cup M_2)$ contains exactly one point.
    c. Show a line k such that $k \cap (M_1 \cup M_2)$ contains more than two points.
    d. Show a line k such that $k \cap (M_1 \cup M_2) = \emptyset$.

3. Give an example of three planes that intersect in a single line.

4. Give an example of three planes that intersect in a single point.

5. In the picture of the box below, $\overleftrightarrow{AB}$ and $\overleftrightarrow{CD}$ represent parallel lines. Indicate in the picture the plane in which these parallel lines lie.

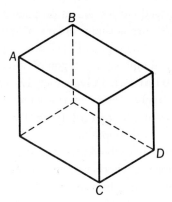

6. If M is a plane and k a line, what three possibilities are there for the intersection set $M \cap k$? Make a drawing showing each possibility.

7. Consider a plane and the surface of an ordinary tin can. Describe positions in which the intersection set of the plane and can will be each of the following:

    a. A circle.   **c.** A rectangle.

    b. A circular region.   **d.** A line segment.

B. 1. Show two segments $\overline{AB}$ and $\overline{CD}$ on the same line so that

    a. $\overline{AB} \cap \overline{CD} = \varnothing$.

    b. $\overline{AB} \cap \overline{CD}$ is a set with exactly one point.

    c. $\overline{AB} \cap \overline{CD} = \overline{CD}$.

    d. $\overline{AB} \cap \overline{CD} = \overline{BC}$.

    e. $\overline{AB} \cup \overline{CD} = \overline{BC}$.

  2. Draw a triangle ABC. By suitable shading show the half plane on the C side of $\overleftrightarrow{AB}$, the half plane on the B side of $\overleftrightarrow{AC}$ and the half plane on the A side of $\overleftrightarrow{BC}$. Indicate the intersection of these three half planes. This intersection set is the **interior** of the triangle.

  3. a. In the adjoining drawing indicate the part of $\angle P$ which is *not* a subset of $\triangle PQR$.

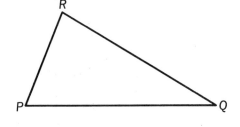

    b. Identify the set of points which is the union $\angle P \cup \angle Q \cup \angle R$.

    c. Identify the set $\angle P \cap \angle Q$.

    d. What relation is there between the interior of $\angle P$ and the interior of $\triangle PQR$?

  4. Looking at the diagram below, give three other names for $\angle AOB$.

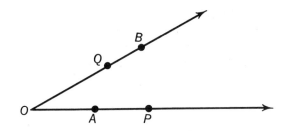

  5. Either give a symbol for or describe in words each of the following sets.

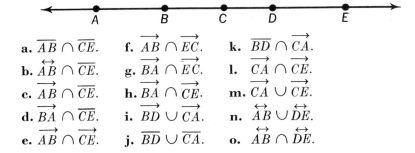

    a. $\overline{AB} \cap \overline{CE}$.   **f.** $\overrightarrow{AB} \cap \overrightarrow{EC}$.   **k.** $\overrightarrow{BD} \cap \overrightarrow{CA}$.

    b. $\overleftrightarrow{AB} \cap \overline{CE}$.   **g.** $\overrightarrow{BA} \cap \overrightarrow{EC}$.   **l.** $\overrightarrow{CA} \cap \overrightarrow{CE}$.

    c. $\overrightarrow{AB} \cap \overline{CE}$.   **h.** $\overrightarrow{BA} \cap \overline{CE}$.   **m.** $\overrightarrow{CA} \cup \overrightarrow{CE}$.

    d. $\overrightarrow{BA} \cap \overline{CE}$.   **i.** $\overrightarrow{BD} \cup \overrightarrow{CA}$.   **n.** $\overleftrightarrow{AB} \cup \overleftrightarrow{DE}$.

    e. $\overrightarrow{AB} \cap \overrightarrow{CE}$.   **j.** $\overline{BD} \cup \overline{CA}$.   **o.** $\overleftrightarrow{AB} \cap \overleftrightarrow{DE}$.

6. Let M denote the shaded region consisting of the union of $\triangle ABC$ and its interior in the figure below. Mark each of the statements below as true or false.

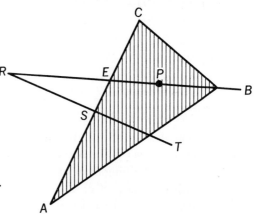

a. $\overleftrightarrow{RP} \cap \triangle ABC = \overline{EB}$.

b. $\overleftrightarrow{RP} \cap M = \overline{EB}$.

c. $\overrightarrow{AT} \cap \overrightarrow{ER} = \{B\}$.

d. $\overline{AT} \cap \overrightarrow{RE} = \varnothing$.

e. $P \in \overrightarrow{ER} \cup \overrightarrow{SR}$.

f. $\overline{ST} \subset M$.

g. $\overline{EB} \subset \triangle ABC$.

h. $\overleftrightarrow{ST} \cap \overleftrightarrow{EB} = \{R\}$.

i. $\overleftrightarrow{ST} \cap \overleftrightarrow{EB} \cap M = \{R\}$.

j. $\overline{EP} \subset \overrightarrow{RE} \cap M$.

C. 1. Make drawings to illustrate each of the following situations.

    a. Two simple closed curves whose intersection set contains just two points.

    b. Two simple closed curves whose intersection set is $\varnothing$.

    c. Two simple closed curves whose intersection contains just one point.

    d. Two simple closed curves whose intersection set contains many points.

  2. Let R be the region bounded by a simple closed curve in a plane M and let k be a line in the plane. Make drawings to illustrate each of the following situations.

    a. $R \cap k$ is a segment.

    b. $R \cap k$ contains exactly one point.

    c. $R \cap k$ contains exactly two points.

    d. $R \cap k$ is the union of two disjoint segments.

    e. $R \cap k$ is the union of a segment and a set with a single point.

  3. Make drawings showing two triangles whose intersection set satisfies the following conditions:

    a. Contains one point.   **d.** Contains four points.

    b. Contains two points.   **e.** Contains five points.

    c. Contains three points.   **f.** Contains six points.

  4. Consider two angles such that the rays lie on four different lines. What is the maximum number of points in the intersection set? Make a drawing illustrating this case.

  5. In the drawing in problem **C4** show the intersection of the interiors of the two angles. This set is the interior of what kind of a curve?

D. The diagram on the next page represents a set lying in a plane. What is the set of possible points P of the plane which do not lie on the curves shown and which can be joined to G, E, and W by curves on the plane not crossing any of those already drawn? Justify your answer.

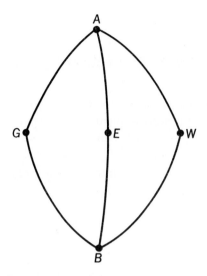

4.8 Axioms and Theorems in Chapter 4

Axiom A1 There are an infinite number of points on a line, an infinite number of lines in a plane and an infinite number of planes in space.

Axiom A2 On any two points there is a line.

Axiom A3 On any three noncollinear points there is a plane.

Axiom A4 The intersection set of two distinct lines is the empty set or a set consisting of a single point.

Axiom A5 The intersection set of two distinct planes is a line or the empty set.

Theorem 4.1 Let k_1 and k_2 be lines and P_1 and P_2 distinct points. If $\{P_1, P_2\} \subset k_1 \cap k_2$, then $k_1 = k_2$.

Theorem 4.2 There is exactly one line containing two distinct points.

Theorem 4.3 Let M_1 and M_2 be planes, and P_1, P_2, P_3 noncollinear points. If $\{P_1, P_2, P_3\} \subset M_1 \cap M_2$, then $M_1 = M_2$.

Theorem 4.4 There is exactly one plane containing three noncollinear points.

Theorem 4.5 If k is a line there is a point not on k.

Theorem 4.6 If k is a line and M a plane there is a point which does not belong to $M \cup k$.

Theorem 4.7 Let P_1 and P_2 be distinct points, k a line, and M a plane. If $\{P_1, P_2\} \subset k \cap M$, then $k \subset M$.

Theorem 4.8 Let P be a point and k a line such that $P \notin k$, i.e., P is not on k. Then there is a plane M such that $k \cup \{P\} \subset M$. Moreover if M, N are planes such that $k \cup \{P\} \subset M \cap N$, then $M = N$.

Theorem **4.9** Let k_1 and k_2 be distinct lines and P a point. If $k_1 \cap k_2 = \{P\}$, then there is a plane M such that $k_1 \cup k_2 \subset M$. Moreover, if M, N are planes such that $k_1 \cup k_2 \subset M \cap N$, then $M = N$.

4.9 Terminal Tasks for Chapter 4

1. To use the following vocabulary correctly in situations involving sets: set, belongs to, is an element of, inclusion relation, subset, empty set, universal set, equal sets, equivalent sets, one-to-one correspondence, intersection, union.

2. To recognize and use the mathematical symbols in situations involving sets: $\in$, $\notin$, $\subset$, $\varnothing$, Ω, $\cup$, $\cap$, $\{\ \}$, and circle diagrams.

3. To show that the system of sets is a mathematical system by identifying the elements, operations, and properties, and performing some simple arithmetic in the system.

4. To describe the elements of a set in English and also in mathematical language, e.g., $E = \{x \mid x = 2y,\ y \text{ is a whole number}\}$, for situations within the algebraic experience of the students.

5. To indicate a deeper insight into the nature of an undefined term in a deductive system by identifying examples in the text in which various interpretations of the undefined terms do not change the structure of the system.

6. To recognize that geometric conjectures are frequently made on the basis of physical experience, by demonstrating the formulation of such a conjecture as a result of an experiment.

7. To state from memory and to illustrate Axioms A1 through A5.

8. To recognize Theorems 4.1 through 4.9 whether written in English or in mathematical symbols.

9. To recognize that Section 4.6 provides an example of a deductive system, by indicating how the assertions in the proofs for Theorems 4.1 through 4.9 depend upon Axioms A1 through A5, defined terms, and previously established theorems.

10. To use the axioms and theorems of this chapter in the solution of exercises requiring simple deductive proofs.

11. To identify, represent geometrically, and (where appropriate) name by mathematical symbols, the following point sets: line, plane, segment, ray, half line, angle, simple closed curve, region, polygon, triangle, vertex.

12. To draw geometric representations which will illustrate the separation properties of a line by a point, a plane by a line, space by a plane, a plane by a simple closed curve and a plane by an angle.

R E V I E W E X E R C I S E S

A. 1. Lines k_1, k_2, k_3, k_4 are distinct lines and M a plane such that $k_1 \cup k_2 \cup k_3 \cup k_4 \subset M$. Set A is the set of all intersections of pairs of these lines. What is the maximum possible number of points in A? What is the minimum number? Draw diagrams representing these cases.

2. Draw diagrams illustrating each of the following situations.
   a. Two angles whose union is two intersecting lines.
   b. Two angles such that the union of the angles and their interiors is the union of a line and a half plane.
   c. An angle and a region whose intersection set is the union of two disjoint segments. Of three disjoint segments.
   d. Two angles whose intersection set is a segment and a point not on it.

3. Plane M contains line k and points A, B, C, D. Points A, B are in one of the half planes determined by k, and C, D are in the other half plane. If Q is the quadrilateral $ABCD$, how many points are in $Q \cap k$? Draw a diagram to represent this situation.

4. The same question as problem **A3** above except that A, C are in one half plane and B, D in the other.

B. 1. If M is a plane such that $\{P, Q\} \subset M$ and $R \notin M$, there is a plane N such that $\{P, Q, R\} \subset N$ and $M \cap N = \overleftrightarrow{PQ}$. Rewrite the sentence above as a verbal statement not using symbolic notation.

2. If M and N are planes with $M \neq N$ and if $P \in M \cap N$, there is a point Q, with $P \neq Q$, such that $M \cap N = \overleftrightarrow{PQ}$. Rewrite the sentence above as a verbal statement, not using symbolic notation.

3. If a line k meets each of two distinct planes in distinct points P, Q, then k is the intersection set of the planes. Rewrite the statement above using symbolic notation.

C. 1. Prove the statement in problem **B1** above.
2. Prove the statement in problem **B2** above.
3. Prove the statement in problem **B3** above.

D. We invent a deductive system in which there are two kinds of undefined elements, inks and anks. It is understood that an ank is a set of inks. They are to satisfy the following axioms.
   (a) There is exactly one ank containing any two distinct inks.
   (b) The intersection of two different anks contains exactly one ink.
   (c) Not all inks belong to the same ank.
   (d) There exists at least one ank.
   (e) Every ank contains exactly two inks.

1. Prove that there are exactly three inks and exactly three anks.

2. Find two examples of situations to which this deductive system applies by suitable identification of the undefined terms ink and ank.

E. 1. A pupil in your class notices that a photographer taking pictures uses a tripod to hold his camera. The pupil asks why he doesn't use something with four legs instead. What did you find in this chapter that would help in answering this question?

2. A set A discussed by your pupils has 5 elements while a second set B has 8 elements. A pupil concludes that $A \cup B$ must have 13 elements. This proves to be incorrect. What did you find in this chapter that would help in explaining this phenomenon?

3. A pupil in your class holds a rectangular card in such a way that only a corner of the card touches the top of his desk. He calls your attention to the fact that he has two planes with only a single point in common (which contradicts Axiom A5). What did you find in this chapter that would help clarify this situation?

4. In discussing sets one of your pupils suggests the set of pianos in the school. When asked for an example of a subset he suggests the set of piano keys. What did you find in this chapter that would help in discussing this (erroneous) suggestion?

5. You have in your classroom a yardstick, somewhat warped with age. A pupil, using it at the chalkboard, notices that when he places the yardstick so that two ends are on the chalkboard the rest of the stick bulges out away from the board. He claims this shows that a line may meet a plane twice without lying in the plane [as claimed by Theorem 4.7 and conjecture (8)]. What did you find in this chapter that would be of assistance in discussing this remark?

6. In discussing the separation of space by a plane you have suggested to your pupils the illustration of the second floor of an apartment house where you must cross the second floor in order to get from the first to the third. A pupil suggests that you could do it by going up the fire escape or climbing a ladder leaning against the building. What did you find in this chapter which would assist in discussing this objection?

5 Congruence

5.1 What Is It All About?   Congruent Segments

In this age of mechanization we are familiar with the interchangeability of parts in the things we buy. If, for example, a bolt is lost from a car it can readily be replaced by another which will exactly fit in the hole left by the old one. This familiar experience depends essentially on the fact that when items are produced in a machine operation they are, to within close limits, the same size and shape. Other illustrations occur if we take two cards from the same deck. We can place one on the other and run our fingers around the edge to satisfy ourselves that one just fits on the other. Similarly two sheets of paper from the same ream, or two pages from this book "just fit," i.e., are the same size and shape. It is this concept which is to be explored in this chapter.

The experiences suggested above with physical objects lead us to try formulating for various point sets the concept of having "the same size and shape." The relationship involved we shall describe by the word *congruence*. Thus, in determining whether one sheet of paper exactly fits on another, we may say we are testing whether these two models of rectangular regions are congruent to each other.

The physical motivations will be strong throughout this chapter and we shall seek to keep this motivation always in mind. However, we shall, as in part of the last chapter, seek to use the physical motivations to formulate axioms and then use the deductive process to obtain consequences of these. That is, we shall seek to build up a small deductive system concerning the idea of congruence.

You saw in Chapter 4 what was meant in a deductive system by an undefined term. It was one for which no definition was given. We might, and often did, associate some intuitive idea with the term but this intuitive idea could never appear in the deductive work. We could not, for example, justify an assertion in a proof by claiming that "a point is a location." In exactly the same way the term congruence will be undefined in this system. That is, in the proofs we shall be able to use only those properties of congruences specifically formulated in the axioms. We cannot justify a step in a proof by claiming "congruence means same size and shape." However, as noted above, we shall keep a close eye on our intuitive experiences as we formulate the axioms.

It is desirable to take the development in stages, so the first discussion will be concerned with congruence of segments. At first sight this may seem such a trivial topic that it needs no special attention. From a naïve point of view we certainly think of all segments as having the same "shape" so they can at all events differ only in "size," by which we presumably mean length. Why then do we not just say that two segments are congruent if they have the same length? This is a very intelligent question. However, the asking of it presumes that we already know what we mean by length and this is a topic we have not yet discussed. Clearly it is an essential topic and will be discussed in a later chapter. However, in our development at that point, we shall introduce the idea of length by relating it to congruence. If we propose to define length by using the idea of congruence we cannot very well define congruence by using the idea of length. It would involve us in the "which came first—the chicken or the egg?" dilemma. Of course, if we should choose to give a treatment of length without using the idea of congruence, then the above suggestion could be used. Indeed, this is not infrequently done. However, as we shall see, the approach to length through congruence is intuitively appealing and seems to be the more desirable point of view in a text for prospective teachers of elementary school pupils. Thus we shall find it necessary to avoid using the word *length* in formally describing congruence.

Let us then be very naïve for the moment and ask what we have in mind in questioning if two segments are congruent. Suppose we wish to compare the segment represented by the edge of the window sill with the segment represented by the edge of the door frame. Without doing damage to the building we cannot place them side by side. In a sense this would not be quite cricket anyway, since segments are sets of points and we have envisioned points as not being moved. How then can we compare these segments? One obvious solution occurs to us. Let us take a piece of string and lay it, pulled taut, along the edge of the window sill. We grasp it at the ends of the window sill and then carry it over to the door frame. If this same piece of string will just fit on the edge of the door frame we will say the segments are congruent. If, on the other hand, the string will not fit, then we will say the segments are not congruent, and we can indeed decide which one is the longer. We have, in effect, made a model of one segment and checked whether this same model would fit on the other.

The process described above is highly suggestive and we will wish to keep it in mind in our discussion of congruence. Clearly, however, it cannot serve as any sort of formal definition. We have seen that no physical object is a perfect model of a segment. In practice the physical operation suggested can be carried out with only approximate accuracy. However, these physical experiments suggest to us properties of an idealized relationship which we will call congruence and whose properties will be described by axioms.

Suppose, then, that two segments are related as just described, in that some model, say a taut string, will exactly fit both of them. Notice that a given point of the first segment is then covered by a position on the string which we could identify by making a mark on the string. When the string is transferred to the other segment this mark on the string covers a certain point of the second segment. Thus each point of the first segment is matched with a unique point of the second. Moreover, since the string exactly covers both segments, the correspondence is one-to-one. Thus we formulate the following: A **congruence** between two segments is a particular kind of one-to-one correspondence. When there is a congruence between two segments we say the segments are **congruent.**

Notice very carefully that not all one-to-one correspondences of segments are congruences. It was suggested in the last chapter that there is a one-to-one correspondence between the points of *any* two segments but we clearly are not envisioning *any* two segments as being congruent. We shall be formulating below as axioms the special properties we require of a one-to-one correspondence in order for it to be a congruence. The first axiom is suggested to us from the fact that if we think of a string as being held up to one of two congruent segments the points where we grasp the string cover the endpoints of this segment. This is equally true for the second segment. Thus if two segments are congruent we expect the endpoints of one to correspond to the endpoints of the other. This is the content of Axiom CS1 below. (The axioms having to do with *congruence* of *segments* are designated as Axiom CS1, CS2, etc., for convenience in reference.)

Axiom CS1 *If two segments are congruent then the endpoints of one are matched with the endpoints of the other.*

This means that if $\overline{AB}$ is congruent to $\overline{CD}$ under a correspondence a, then a either matches A with C and B with D (which we will indicate by $A \underset{a}{\leftrightarrow} C$ and $B \underset{a}{\leftrightarrow} D$) or it matches A with D and B with C (i.e., $A \underset{a}{\leftrightarrow} D, B \underset{a}{\leftrightarrow} C$). It will be very convenient to adopt a shorthand notation. If we wish to say that $\overline{AB}$ is congruent to $\overline{CD}$ with a correspondence a such that $A \underset{a}{\leftrightarrow} C, B \underset{a}{\leftrightarrow} D$ we will write

$$\overline{AB} \underset{a}{\cong} \overline{CD}.$$

Note carefully the agreement that the first point on the left (here A) is to be matched with the first point on the right (here C). Similarly the two second points are matched. If, on the other hand, we write $\overline{AB} \underset{b}{\cong} \overline{DC}$ this says there is a congruence b between the segments such that $A \underset{b}{\leftrightarrow} D$ and $B \underset{b}{\leftrightarrow} C$. It is important to notice this agreement because it means that, while $\overline{AB}$ and $\overline{BA}$ are symbols for the same segment, these symbols are not interchangeable in our congruence notation. When it is not important to name the particular correspondence this will often be omitted.

With this notation it is now possible to write the other axioms more conveniently. For convenience we shall first list them and then consider the intuitive motivation which caused us to adopt them.

Axiom CS2 *If $\overline{AB} \cong \overline{CD}$, then $\overline{CD} \cong \overline{AB}$.*

Axiom CS3 *If $\overline{AB} \cong \overline{CD}$ and $\overline{CD} \cong \overline{EF}$, then $\overline{AB} \cong \overline{EF}$.*

Axiom CS4 *For all segments $\overline{AB}$, it is true that $\overline{AB} \cong \overline{BA}$.*

Axiom CS5 *If $\overline{AB}$ is a segment and $\overrightarrow{PT}$ a ray, there is a unique point S with $S \in \overrightarrow{PT}$ such that $\overline{AB} \cong \overline{PS}$.*

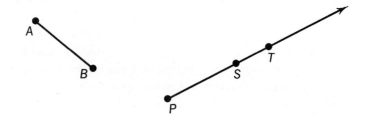

Axiom CS6 *If $\overline{PR} \underset{x}{\cong} \overline{P'R'}$, where x denotes a particular congruence, and if $Q \underset{x}{\leftrightarrow} Q'$, where $Q \in \overline{PR}$, then $\overline{PQ} \cong \overline{P'Q'}$ and $\overline{QR} \cong \overline{Q'R'}$.*

Observe that the notation $Q \underset{x}{\leftrightarrow} Q'$ means that Q and Q' are matching points in the congruence x between $\overline{PR}$ and $\overline{P'R'}$.

Axiom CS7 *Let $P, Q,$ and R be distinct points such that $Q \in \overline{PR}$. If $P', Q',$ and R' are points such that $\overline{PQ} \cong \overline{P'Q'}$, $\overline{QR} \cong \overline{Q'R'}$ and $\overline{PR} \cong \overline{P'R'}$, then $Q' \in \overline{P'R'}$.*

Let us now take time to observe what physical experiences led us to adopt these axioms. If we consider $\overline{AB} \cong \overline{CD}$ we are imagining that if a string is just fitted to $\overline{AB}$ and is then moved to $\overline{CD}$ then it will also just fit on $\overline{CD}$. It is intuitively clear to us that if we begin by fitting a string to $\overline{CD}$ this string should also fit $\overline{AB}$. This is precisely the statement of Axiom CS2. Similarly if $\overline{AB} \cong \overline{CD}$ and $\overline{CD} \cong \overline{EF}$ this should mean that a string fitted to $\overline{CD}$ will fit both $\overline{AB}$ and $\overline{EF}$, so we expect $\overline{AB} \cong \overline{EF}$. This is the claim of Axiom CS3.

For Axiom CS4 imagine that you are holding a string that just fits on $\overline{AB}$ with your left thumb at A and your right thumb at B. It certainly is in accord with our experience that if we now undertake to place the right thumb at A and the left thumb at B, the string will fit in this way also. That is, we seem to observe $\overline{AB} \cong \overline{BA}$, which is Axiom CS4.

Imagine now that you hold a string as above tightly over segment $\overline{AB}$ with your left thumb at A and your right thumb at B. Now move the string over to ray $\overrightarrow{PT}$, placing your left thumb at P. Can you place the string so your right thumb is at some point S of $\overrightarrow{PT}$? Since a ray goes on indefinitely it certainly seems clear that this can be done. You then appear to have $\overline{AB} \cong \overline{PS}$. Can you do this in more than one way? Since we are tacitly assuming a string that will not stretch it seems clear that there is only one possible position for the right thumb on $\overrightarrow{PT}$. This is exactly Axiom CS5.

For Axiom CS6 imagine a string that will just fit on the congruent segments $\overline{PR}$ and $\overline{P'R'}$. Let Q be a point of $\overline{PR}$ and Q' the corresponding point of $\overline{P'R'}$. Thus if we imagine a knot tied in the string above Q, then when the string is moved over to $\overline{P'R'}$ the knot will be above Q'. This means that the piece of string which covered segment $\overline{PQ}$ when the string was fitted over $\overline{PR}$ covers the segment $\overline{P'Q'}$ when it is fitted over $\overline{P'R'}$. Similarly for $\overline{QR}$ and $\overline{Q'R'}$. That is, we seem to observe that, with the same matching of points as at the beginning, $\overline{PQ} \cong \overline{P'Q'}$ and $\overline{QR} \cong \overline{Q'R'}$. This is the statement made in Axiom CS6.

Finally, as before, let Q be a point of segment $\overline{PR}$ and imagine the string stretched on $\overline{PR}$ with the knot above Q. Suppose, in addition, that $\overline{PR} \cong \overline{P'R'}$, $\overline{PQ} \cong \overline{P'Q'}$, $\overline{QR} \cong \overline{Q'R'}$. Is it possible, as indicated in the illustration, that Q'

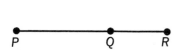
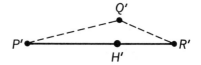

should not be on $\overline{P'R'}$? Since $\overline{PR} \cong \overline{P'R'}$ we know the string will just fit on $\overline{P'R'}$. In this position the knot will be at some point H' of $\overline{P'R'}$. If the diagram were correct it would then be possible to hold the ends at P' and R' but pull the string into a position with the knot at Q'. If a string is pulled tight it is certainly our experience that there is no slack that allows it to be pulled out of line. Thus it seems to us on experimental grounds that the situation in the figure is actually impossible and Q' must be on $\overline{P'R'}$. This is what Axiom CS7 says.

Using out intuitive understanding of congruence we could, of course, conjecture other relationships which we would expect. Some of these are suggested in Problem Set 5.1. We shall discover in the following section that these conjectures can be proved on the basis of the axioms we have already suggested. That is, the conjectures are actually theorems of our deductive system.

Problem Set 5.1

In the following problems various physical experiments are described. In each case you are asked to state the conjecture regarding congruence of segments which it suggests.

   1. You hold a string stretched tightly over a segment $\overline{AB}$. You pick it up and then put it down again just as before. Thus you find a string which will fit

$\overline{AB}$ once, will fit it again. What does this suggest about the congruence of segment $\overline{AB}$ with itself?

2. You have congruent segments $\overline{AB} \cong \overline{A'B'}$, i.e., if you hold a string stretched tightly over $\overline{AB}$ with the left thumb at A and the right thumb at B, then it will fit on $\overline{A'B'}$ with the left thumb at A' and right thumb at B'. Point C is on $\overline{AB}$ and you tie a knot in the string above C. When you move the string you mark the point C' of $\overline{A'B'}$ which is under the knot. Thus in this particular correspondence C matches C'. You repeat the experiment a number of times, perhaps using different strings, but discover the knot always ends up over the same point C'. What does this suggest about the congruence of $\overline{AB}$ with $\overline{A'B'}$?

3. You have segments as shown. You discover the same piece of string will

fit $\overline{AB}$ and $\overline{A'B'}$. You also discover that some other piece of string will fit $\overline{BC}$ and $\overline{B'C'}$. You join these two strings together and discover that the resulting string will just fit both $\overline{AC}$ and $\overline{A'C'}$. What conjecture does this suggest regarding congruence of the segments involved?

4. You have two segments as shown. You discover that the same string will

fit on $\overline{AC}$ and $\overline{A'C'}$. From this you cut off a piece that will just fit on $\overline{AB}$ and discover it also just fits on $\overline{A'B'}$. What relation do you anticipate between the remaining piece of string and segments $\overline{BC}$ and $\overline{B'C'}$? What conjecture does it suggest regarding congruence of the segments involved?

5. In the two fittings of a string on $\overline{AB}$ suggested in the discussion of Axiom CS4, does there seem to be any point of the string that covers the same point of the segment both times? If so, what point does it seem to be?

5.2 Theorems on Congruent Segments

In Section 5.1 we formulated some axioms for the congruence of segments. We now turn to the application of the deductive method to these axioms; i.e., what can be proved from them? In this process, recall that we can use only properties that have been stated as axioms. There are to be no loose pieces of string flapping around in these arguments! This is the crux of the deductive approach—that we make clear what is being assumed. However, most of the results will indeed be things that were conjectured on experimental grounds in the last set of problems.

The first theorem to be proved is the result conjectured in problem **2** of Problem Set 5.1, namely, that there cannot be two different congruences of two segments which match the endpoints in the same way.

Theorem 5.1 *If* $\overline{AB} \underset{a}{\cong} \overline{CD}$ *and* $\overline{AB} \underset{b}{\cong} \overline{CD}$, *then the correspondences* a *and* b
are the same.

Analysis. Before trying to give the proof let us discuss the strategy which we might find useful. If S is any point of $\overline{AB}$ we can let T_a and T_b be the points matched with S under a and b, respectively; i.e., $S \underset{a}{\leftrightarrow} T_a$ and $S \underset{b}{\leftrightarrow} T_b$.

 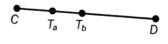

The claim of the theorem is that $T_a = T_b$, i.e., that every point S of $\overline{AB}$ has the same image under a as under b. What equipment do we have that would help us to conclude that two points are identical? A reading of the axioms seems to show only one promising possibility. This is Axiom CS5, which assures us that there is a *unique* point satisfying certain conditions. If we can show that T_a and T_b satisfy the conditions, then we can use Axiom CS5 to conclude that $T_a = T_b$. To apply Axiom CS5 it seems that we need to show that T_a and T_b are on the same ray and that $\overline{CT_a}$ and $\overline{CT_b}$ are congruent to the same segment. After this analysis it should not be hard to write a formal proof. You are asked to supply supporting statements for some of the assertions.

Proof

ASSERTIONS	SUPPORTING STATEMENTS
(1) $T_a \in \overrightarrow{CD}$ and $T_b \in \overrightarrow{CD}$.	(1) Why?
(2) $S \underset{a}{\leftrightarrow} T_a$ and $S \underset{b}{\leftrightarrow} T_b$.	(2) By definition of T_a and T_b.
(3) $\overline{AB} \underset{a}{\cong} \overline{CD}$ and $\overline{AB} \underset{b}{\cong} \overline{CD}$.	(3) Given.
(4) $\overline{AS} \cong \overline{CT_a}$ and $\overline{AS} \cong \overline{CT_b}$.	(4) Why?
(5) $T_a = T_b$.	(5) Why?

By step 5, every point S of $\overline{AB}$ has the same image under a as under b. That is, a and b are the same correspondence. This is what we were seeking to prove.

This theorem really says that a congruence between two segments is entirely determined once we know what it does to the endpoints. For this reason it is generally unnecessary to use a symbol like a or b to indicate the particular correspondence.

You may have questioned the fact that our axioms did not contain a statement that says a segment is always congruent to itself. On the basis of our intuition we would certainly want this to be true. Indeed this was the conjecture intended in problem 1 of Problem Set 5.1. The reason that it was not adopted as an axiom is that it can be readily proved. This is the essential content of the next theorem.

Theorem 5.2 *If $\overline{AB}$ is any segment, then $\overline{AB} \cong \overline{AB}$. Moreover, the correspondence matches every point of $\overline{AB}$ with itself.*

Analysis. For the first part of the theorem we wish to conclude that for any segment $\overline{AB}$ it is true that $\overline{AB} \cong \overline{AB}$. What axioms do we have that permit us to conclude that certain segments are congruent? There are actually four axioms of this nature, namely, Axioms CS2, CS3, CS4, and CS6. Could any of these be used to show $\overline{AB} \cong \overline{AB}$? For this purpose Axiom CS2 seems no help. Moreover, Axiom CS6 seems to require information we do not have in this case. What about Axiom CS3? According to Axiom CS3 we could show $\overline{AB} \cong \overline{AB}$ if we could only dig up a segment $\overline{CD}$ such that $\overline{AB} \cong \overline{CD}$ and $\overline{CD} \cong \overline{AB}$. But can such a segment $\overline{CD}$ always be found? According to Axiom CS4 the answer is "yes," since $\overline{BA}$ is such a segment. The proof of the first half of the theorem can then be readily written as follows:

Proof. For any segment $\overline{AB}$ we know that $\overline{AB} \cong \overline{BA}$ and $\overline{BA} \cong \overline{AB}$ by Axiom CS4. Since $\overline{AB} \cong \overline{BA}$ and $\overline{BA} \cong \overline{AB}$, it follows by Axiom CS3 that $\overline{AB} \cong \overline{AB}$.

For the second half of the theorem let P be any point of $\overline{AB}$ and let P' be its image in the congruence $\overline{AB} \cong \overline{AB}$, i.e., $P \leftrightarrow P'$. The theorem claims that $P = P'$. These points can be proved the same by use of Axiom CS5 just as in Theorem 5.1. The steps could be given as follows. Points P, P' belong to $\overrightarrow{AB}$. $\overline{AP} \cong \overline{AP}$ (why?) and $\overline{AP'} \cong \overline{AP}$ (why?). Thus P, P' are points of ray $\overrightarrow{AB}$ such that $\overline{AP}$ and $\overline{AP'}$ are congruent to the same segment. It follows by Axiom CS5 that $P = P'$. That is, every point P of $\overline{AB}$ is matched with itself.

The conjecture of problem 4 of Problem Set 5.1 concerns the question of what happens if congruent parts are cut from two congruent segments. We shall now show that this conjecture can be proved as a theorem on the basis of the axioms.

Theorem 5.3 *Let $B \in \overline{AC}$ and $B' \in \overrightarrow{A'C'}$. If $\overline{AB} \cong \overline{A'B'}$ and $\overline{AC} \cong \overline{A'C'}$, then $\overline{BC} \cong \overline{B'C'}$. Moreover, $B' \in \overline{A'C'}$, i.e., B' is between A' and C'.*

Analysis. We are given that B' is a point on *ray* $\overrightarrow{A'C'}$ such that $\overline{A'B'} \cong \overline{AB}$. We certainly suspect that B' belongs to *segment* $\overline{A'C'}$, but this is part of what must be proved. What strategy can we adopt in approaching this proof? Is there any axiom that yields information about congruent parts of congruent segments (which is what we are really interested in)? It seems that Axiom CS6 is such an

axiom. What information can we obtain from Axiom CS6? Let a be the congruence of $\overline{AC}$ and $\overline{A'C'}$ so that $\overline{AC} \underset{a}{\cong} \overline{A'C'}$ and let $B \leftrightarrow B''$; i.e., let B'' be the image of B in this congruence. Then by Axiom CS6 we can conclude that $\overline{AB} \cong \overline{A'B''}$ and $\overline{BC} \cong \overline{B''C'}$. It occurs to us that if we could show that $B' = B''$ this would show everything we want since $B'' \in \overline{A'C'}$ and we have just observed that $\overline{BC} \cong \overline{B''C'}$. How could we show $B' = B''$? This is the same problem we solved in the last two proofs by using Axiom CS5. With the hints contained in this analysis, let us try writing a proof.

Proof. We use the notation suggested above where

$$B \underset{a}{\leftrightarrow} B''.$$

ASSERTIONS	SUPPORTING STATEMENTS
(1) $\overline{AC} \underset{a}{\cong} \overline{A'C'}$.	(1) The given congruence of $\overline{AC}$ and $\overline{A'C'}$ is here denoted by a.
(2) $B \underset{a}{\leftrightarrow} B''$.	(2) Definition of B''.
(3) $\overline{AB} \cong \overline{A'B''}$ and $\overline{BC} \cong \overline{B''C'}$.	(3) Why?
(4) $\overline{AB} \cong \overline{A'B'}$.	(4) Given.
(5) B' and B'' belong to $\overrightarrow{A'C'}$.	(5) Why?
(6) $B' = B''$.	(6) Why?
(7) $\overline{B''C'} \cong \overline{B'C'}$.	(7) Step 6.
(8) $\overline{BC} \cong \overline{B'C'}$.	(8) Steps 3 and 7 and Axiom CS3.

Moreover, since $B'' \in \overline{A'C'}$ by its definition, it follows by step 6 that $B' \in \overline{A'C'}$. This completes the proof.

Similarly, the conjecture of problem **3** of Problem Set 5.1 can be proved. In simple terms this conjecture is that if congruent segments are laid end to end the resulting segments are congruent. Formally it may be stated as follows:

Theorem 5.4 *Let* $B \in \overline{AC}$ *and* $B' \in \overline{A'C'}$. *If* $\overline{AB} \cong \overline{A'B'}$ *and* $\overline{BC} \cong \overline{B'C'}$, *then* $\overline{AC} \cong \overline{A'C'}$.

Analysis. As you are aware by now, the analysis of a proof is not a scientific process, but rather an open-minded search for a promising idea. Ultimately we hope to show that $\overline{AC} \cong \overline{A'C'}$. How might this be done? In the last proof we had considerable success in producing a point (namely B'') and showing it was the same as a given point (namely B'). Perhaps this strategy would be worth trying again here. Since we hope to show $\overline{AC} \cong \overline{A'C'}$, let us consider the point C'' (see the figure) on $\overline{A'C'}$ such that $\overline{AC} \cong \overline{A'C''}$. If we can succeed in showing $C' = C''$ we will then have completed the proof. This seems very satisfactory as we have

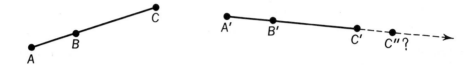

several times used Axiom CS5 to show that two points coincide. There is, however, a slight problem in carrying out this program. We observe at once that $\overline{BC} \cong \overline{B'C'}$ since that was given. Moreover, since $\overline{AB} \cong \overline{A'B'}$ and $\overline{AC} \cong \overline{A'C''}$ it follows from Theorem 5.3 that $\overline{BC} \cong \overline{B'C''}$. Since both $\overline{B'C'}$ and $\overline{B'C''}$ are congruent to $\overline{BC}$ it is a temptation to say that it follows by Axiom CS5 that $C' = C''$. But is this correct? To use Axiom CS5 we must be sure that C' and C'' are on the same ray from B'. Do we actually know this? How do we know that C'' is not on $\overline{A'B'}$? If this were true C' and C'' would be on opposite sides of B' and Axiom CS5 would not apply. Fortunately this case cannot occur. From Theorem 5.3 we know that $B' \in \overline{A'C''}$, i.e., B' is between A' and C''. Thus both C' and C'' are on the ray from B' away from A'. In other words, Axiom CS5 *can* be applied to show $C' = C''$. If read carefully this analysis does constitute a proof of Theorem 5.4. However, it may be helpful to rewrite it below in a more coherently organized form.

ASSERTIONS	SUPPORTING STATEMENTS
(1) There is a point C'' on $\overrightarrow{A'C'}$ such that $\overline{AC} \cong \overline{A'C''}$.	(1) Axiom CS5.
(2) $\overline{AB} \cong \overline{A'B'}$ and $B \in \overline{AC}$.	(2) Given.
(3) $\overline{BC} \cong \overline{B'C''}$.	(3) Steps 1 and 2 and Theorem 5.3.
(4) $B' \in \overline{A'C''}$ so that $C'' \in \overrightarrow{B'C'}$.	(4) Theorem 5.3.
(5) $\overline{BC} \cong \overline{B'C'}$.	(5) Given.
(6) $C'' = C'$.	(6) Steps 3, 4, and 5 and Axiom CS5.
(7) $\overline{AC} \cong \overline{A'C'}$.	(7) Steps 6 and 1.

One additional theorem on subsegments of congruent segments is sometimes useful. It follows from Axiom CS6 and Theorem 5.3.

Theorem 5.5 *If $\overline{AB} \cong_a \overline{A'B'}$ and if $C \leftrightarrow_a C'$ and $D \leftrightarrow_a D'$, then $\overline{CD} \cong \overline{C'D'}$.*

Proof. Let the labels be chosen so that points A, C, D, and B occur in this order on $\overline{AB}$, as shown in the drawing. By Axiom CS6 we know that $\overline{AD} \cong \overline{A'D'}$ and that $\overline{AC} \cong \overline{A'C'}$, while by the choice of labels $C \in \overline{AD}$. It then follows from

Theorem 5.3 that $\overline{CD} \cong \overline{C'D'}$. Incidentally we can also conclude from Theorem 5.3 that $C' \in \overline{A'D'}$, i.e., that points A', C', D', and B' occur in this order on $\overline{A'B'}$.

If you review the conjectures formulated in the last problem set you will observe we have proved them all as theorems except for the last one, which seems to have something to do with midpoints. Actually, the axioms so far adopted do not enable us to prove that midpoints always exist. This is a matter to which we shall return later. For reference, however, it will be worthwhile to define midpoints.

> DEFINITION: A point P of a segment $\overline{AB}$ is called a **midpoint** of $\overline{AB}$ if $\overline{AP} \cong \overline{PB}$, i.e., if P divides $\overline{AB}$ into congruent segments.

As just observed, we are not yet able to prove that every segment has a midpoint. It would be possible for us to show that a segment cannot have two midpoints, but we shall not take time to give the proof. We could, of course, adopt a new axiom stating that every segment has a midpoint. However, since some of our later work will imply this we will not consider it further here.

You may have noticed that in the discussion so far no use at all has been made of Axiom CS7. Thus everything done so far would be entirely valid if we omitted this axiom. However, we shall need it for some of the developments of the next section.

The concept of congruence permits us to make meaningful comparisons of segments. Thus if $\overline{AB}$ and $\overline{CD}$ are any segments, let X be the point of $\overrightarrow{CD}$ (guaranteed by Axiom CS5) such that $\overline{CX} \cong \overline{AB}$. If X is between C and D (as shown

in the drawing), we say that $\overline{AB}$ is *shorter than* $\overline{CD}$. If X is on the extension of $\overline{CD}$ (i.e., if D is between C and X), then we say that $\overline{AB}$ is *longer than* $\overline{CD}$. Finally, if

$X = D$, then, of course, $\overline{AB} \cong \overline{CD}$. It is to be noted that this is a purely geometric relationship. We have as yet introduced no numbers as measures for these segments. This will be done in a later chapter. At that point these geometric comparisons will be reflected by inequalities in the measures. We could now give formal proofs of such intuitively plausible statements as the following: (1) If $\overline{AB}$ is shorter than $\overline{CD}$, then $\overline{CD}$ is longer than $\overline{AB}$. (2) If $\overline{AB}$ is shorter than $\overline{CD}$, and $\overline{CD}$ is shorter than $\overline{EF}$, then $\overline{AB}$ is shorter than $\overline{EF}$. It is not actually necessary to do so, as such properties come out incidentally later in our discussion of measurement. However, one of them is included in the following set of problems.

Here, as elsewhere, when you are asked for a proof you are strongly urged to construct an analysis *before* trying to give the proof.

Problem Set 5.2

A. Prove:
    1. If $\overline{PQ} \cong \overline{RS}$, then $\overline{PQ} \cong \overline{SR}$.
    2. If $\overline{PQ} \cong \overline{RS}$ and $\overline{SR} = \overline{TU}$, then $\overline{PQ} \cong \overline{TU}$.
B. 1. If $\overline{AB} \cong \overline{BC} \cong \overline{CD} \cong \overline{PQ} \cong \overline{QR} \cong \overline{RS}$, prove that $\overline{AD} \cong \overline{PS}$.

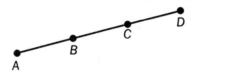 

    2. If $\overline{AB} \cong \overline{CD}$ and if $\overline{AS} \cong \overline{ST} \cong \overline{CU} \cong \overline{UV}$, show that $\overline{TB} \cong \overline{VD}$.

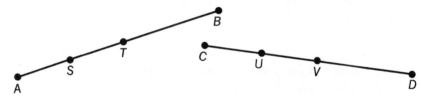

    3. In the following diagram it is given that $\overline{AB} \cong \overline{QR}$ and $\overline{BC} \cong \overline{PQ}$. Show

that $\overline{AC} \cong \overline{PR}$. Be very sure in this proof that you do not use anything not justified by the axioms and theorems. It is easy to jump to conclusions that have not been established.

C. 1. By Axiom CS6 if $\overline{AC} \underset{x}{\cong} \overline{A'C'}$ and if $B \underset{x}{\leftrightarrow} B'$, then $\overline{AB} \cong \overline{A'B'}$ and $\overline{BC} \cong \overline{B'C'}$. Let the correspondences for these last two congruences be y and z so that we may write $\overline{AB} \underset{y}{\cong} \overline{A'B'}$, $\overline{BC} \underset{z}{\cong} \overline{B'C'}$. Let P be any point of $\overline{AB}$ and let P'_x and P'_y be the images of P under x and y. *Prove that* $P'_x = P'_y$. When this is proved, it shows that x and y do the same

thing to all points of $\overline{AB}$. Similarly, x and z do the same thing to all points of $\overline{BC}$. That is, y and z are simply the result of applying x to the sub-segments $\overline{AB}$ and $\overline{BC}$. We often indicate this by omitting any separate symbols y and z and writing $\overline{AB} \underset{x}{\cong} \overline{A'B'}$, $\overline{BC} \underset{x}{\cong} \overline{B'C'}$.

2. By Axiom CS3 if $\overline{AB} \underset{a}{\cong} \overline{CD}$ and if $\overline{CD} \underset{b}{\cong} \overline{EF}$, there is a congruence c such that $\overline{AB} \underset{c}{\cong} \overline{EF}$. If P is any point of $\overline{AB}$ let Q and R be such that $P \underset{a}{\leftrightarrow} Q$ and $Q \underset{b}{\leftrightarrow} R$.

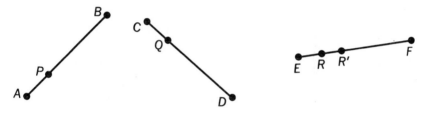

Prove that $P \underset{c}{\leftrightarrow} R$. [HINT: Let R' be the point of $\overline{EF}$ such that $P \underset{c}{\leftrightarrow} R'$ and prove that $R = R'$.]

3. In the diagram $\overline{AB} \cong \overline{PQ}$, $\overline{BC} \cong \overline{RS}$, and $\overline{CD} \cong \overline{QR}$. Prove that $\overline{AD} \cong \overline{PS}$.

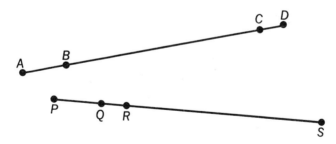

D. Prove that if $\overline{AB}$ is shorter than $\overline{CD}$, and $\overline{CD}$ is shorter than $\overline{EF}$, then $\overline{AB}$ is shorter than $\overline{EF}$.

5.3 Congruence in General

We have discussed now in some detail the idea of congruence for segments. As a motivation for defining congruence for other sets of points consider the following experiment. Imagine two sets of points S and S′ (as shown in the drawing below) which for convenience we assume in a plane. For definiteness consider S and S′ to be the curves rather than the regions.

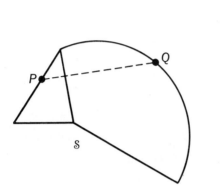
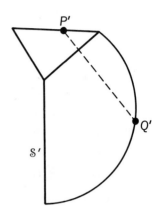

Suppose now that a sheet of tracing paper is placed over S and a careful tracing made of this set. The tracing is then moved over and we attempt to fit this tracing on S′. If the tracing exactly fits S′ we would like to say that the two sets are congruent; i.e., they are "just alike," they have "the same size and shape." As in the case of segments this experiment cannot serve as a formal definition but it suggests to us the essential properties we seek to describe.

Suppose first that P is any point of S as shown. We may imagine a dot made on the tracing to mark the point of the tracing covering P. When the tracing is fitted to S′ this dot covers point $P′$ of S′. Moreover, if the tracing exactly fits both S and S′, every point of S′ is in this way matched with exactly one point of S. That is, we are considering a one-to-one correspondence of the points of S with those of S′. What special properties does this one-to-one correspondence possess?

Let Q and $Q′$ be another pair of corresponding points. Let us consider the line segment $\overline{PQ}$. This is shown as a dashed line to indicate that it need not be a subset of S. In fact, in the case shown $\overline{PQ}$ is not contained in S. If this line segment is copied on the tracing paper, then when the tracing is fitted on S′ the same part of the drawing fits exactly on $\overline{P′Q′}$. In other words, a model of $\overline{PQ}$ fits on $\overline{P′Q′}$ so we should like to regard $\overline{PQ}$ and $\overline{P′Q′}$ as congruent segments. It is this simple observation which motivates the following definition of congruence for general sets of points.

> DEFINITION: If S and S′ are sets of points, a one-to-one correspondence c between them is called a **congruence** if and only if for any points P, Q of S, and the corresponding points $P′$, $Q′$ of S′ it is true that $\overline{PQ} \cong \overline{P′Q′}$. Two sets are **congruent** if there is a congruence between them.

If c is a congruence between S and S' we write $S \underset{c}{\cong} S'$. If it is not important to name the congruence we write simply $S \cong S'$.

It should be observed that if two segments are congruent as discussed in the last section, it follows from Theorem 5.5 that they are also congruent under this more general definition. Thus this definition does no violence to the work we have already done with segments.

It is important to emphasize again that the definition of congruence $S \cong S'$ requires the congruence $\overline{PQ} \cong \overline{P'Q'}$ for *every* pair of points $P, Q \in S$ and their image points $P', Q' \in S'$. It is not necessary for the segment $\overline{PQ}$ to be a subset of S. For example, in the following diagram imagine that the eight segments $\overline{AB}$, $\overline{BC}$, $\overline{CD}$, $\overline{DA}$, $\overline{A'B'}$, $\overline{B'C'}$, $\overline{C'D'}$, $\overline{D'A'}$ are all congruent. It is easy to set up a

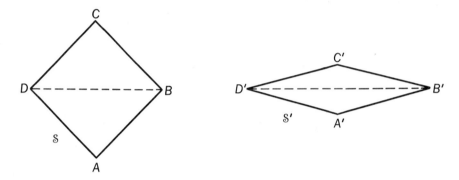

one-to-one correspondence in which A, B, C, and D are matched respectively with A', B', C', and D'. However, such a correspondence would presumably fail to be a congruence since, for example, $\overline{BD}$ and $\overline{B'D'}$ do not fit our intuitive idea of congruent segments.

This displays the interesting fact that two polygons may be formed of congruent sides but not be congruent. Do you think this could happen in the case of two triangles?

Now that congruence of two sets of points has been defined, what properties of it can we discover? One follows immediately from the definition. Since we know by Axiom CS2 that the statements $\overline{PQ} \cong \overline{P'Q'}$ and $\overline{P'Q'} \cong \overline{PQ}$ actually say the same thing, the whole definition of congruence is symmetric. That is, $S \cong S'$ and $S' \cong S$ are actually the same statement so that either one implies the other. (The formal proof of this tends to be confusing because of its triviality.) In one of the problems you will show that for any set S it is true that $S \cong S$. Compare this with Theorem 5.2 for segments.

Suppose now we have three sets S, S', and S'' about which we know that $S \cong S'$ and $S' \cong S''$. Speaking naïvely, the first statement says that a tracing of S' would fit on S while the second says a tracing of S' would fit on S''. It certainly seems that we would then have a tracing that fits both S and S'' and we would conjecture $S \cong S''$. Can this conjecture actually be proved? The following theorem answers this in the affirmative.

Theorem 5.6 *If* $\mathcal{S} \cong \mathcal{S}'$ *and* $\mathcal{S}' \cong \mathcal{S}''$, *then* $\mathcal{S} \cong \mathcal{S}''$.

Proof. Somehow we must produce a one-to-one correspondence between the points of $\mathcal{S}$ and $\mathcal{S}''$ so that if $P, Q \in \mathcal{S}$ and P'', Q'' are the corresponding points of $\mathcal{S}''$, then $\overline{PQ} \cong \overline{P''Q''}$. We produce such a correspondence in the most obvious possible way. For convenience let the given congruences be c and d so we may write $\mathcal{S} \underset{c}{\cong} \mathcal{S}'$ and $\mathcal{S}' \underset{d}{\cong} \mathcal{S}''$. If P is any point of $\mathcal{S}$ there is a point $P' \in \mathcal{S}'$ so that $P \underset{c}{\leftrightarrow} P'$. That is, P' is the image of P under c. Similarly let $P'' \in \mathcal{S}''$ be the image of P' under d so that $P' \underset{d}{\leftrightarrow} P''$. Then we agree to match the points P and P''. Similarly if $Q \in \mathcal{S}$, then $Q \underset{c}{\leftrightarrow} Q'$ and $Q' \underset{d}{\leftrightarrow} Q''$ and we agree to match Q and Q''. This is clearly a one-to-one correspondence of $\mathcal{S}$ and $\mathcal{S}''$. Moreover, $\overline{PQ} \underset{c}{\cong} \overline{P'Q'}$. (Why?) For the same reason $\overline{P'Q'} \underset{d}{\cong} \overline{P''Q''}$. If $\overline{PQ} \cong \overline{P'Q'}$ and $\overline{P'Q'} \cong \overline{P''Q''}$, then we can conclude that $\overline{PQ} \cong \overline{P''Q''}$. (Why?) Since P, Q were *any* points of $\mathcal{S}$ this completes the proof that $\mathcal{S} \cong \mathcal{S}''$.

An intriguing question now presents itself. We know, of course, that a segment can be congruent to another segment, but is it possible that a segment should be congruent to something that is not a segment? Our intuition would cause us to be a little skeptical, but could it be proved impossible? This is what we shall now attempt to do.

Theorem 5.7 *If* $\overline{AB} \cong \mathcal{S}'$ *and if in this congruence* $A \leftrightarrow A'$, $B \leftrightarrow B'$, *then* $\mathcal{S}' = \overline{A'B'}$.

Analysis. Stated verbally, this theorem says that if a segment $\overline{AB}$ is congruent to a set $\mathcal{S}'$ and if A' and B' are the points of $\mathcal{S}'$ corresponding to A and B, respectively, then $\mathcal{S}'$ is nothing but the segment $\overline{A'B'}$; i.e., $\mathcal{S}' = \overline{A'B'}$. How do we go about to prove that two sets are equal? It was suggested in Chapter 4 that this is done by showing that each set is a subset of the other. In other words, we try to establish two statements: (a) $\mathcal{S}' \subset \overline{A'B'}$ and (b) $\overline{A'B'} \subset \mathcal{S}'$.

First let us look for ideas for proving statement (a). If P' is any point of $\mathcal{S}'$,

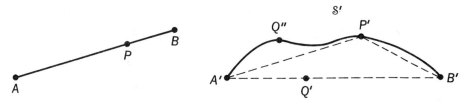

it is incumbent upon us to show that P' is also a point of $\overline{A'B'}$ (in disagreement with the drawing above). The point P' is the image in $\mathcal{S}'$ of a point P of $\overline{AB}$. Since it was given that $\overline{AB} \cong \mathcal{S}'$ we can conclude that $\overline{AP} \cong \overline{A'P'}$, $\overline{PB} \cong \overline{P'B'}$ and $\overline{AB} \cong \overline{A'B'}$. (Why?) Is there any axiom or previously proved theorem which enables us to conclude that three points are collinear? Examination reveals that Axiom CS7 is such a statement and it appears that we can use this to show that

$P' \in \overline{A'B'}$. If this program is carried out it will show that statement (a) holds; i.e., $\mathcal{S}' \subset \overline{A'B'}$. Presently we shall present the proof as a formal step-by-step argument. Meanwhile let us look for ideas as to how statement (b) might be proved.

To establish (b), i.e., that $\overline{A'B'} \subset \mathcal{S}'$, it is necessary to take any point Q' of $\overline{A'B'}$ and show that $Q' \in \mathcal{S}'$. How is this to be done? Notice that we were given that $\overline{AB} \cong \mathcal{S}'$ and we know that $\overline{AB} \cong \overline{A'B'}$. (Why?) By Theorem 5.6 this means that $\overline{A'B'} \cong \mathcal{S}'$. Let $Q'' \in \mathcal{S}'$ be the point matched with Q' by this congruence. If we are smart enough to show that $Q' = Q''$ the proof will be done, since $Q'' \in \mathcal{S}'$. How good are the chances of showing that $Q' = Q''$? Our standard technique for this is to use Axiom CS5. To be able to employ Axiom CS5 it is necessary to know that $\overline{A'Q'} \cong \overline{A'Q''}$ and that Q', Q'' are on the same ray from A'. The first condition, namely, $\overline{A'Q'} \cong \overline{A'Q''}$, is a consequence of the congruence $\overline{A'B'} \cong \mathcal{S}'$. Moreover, by statement (a) we know that $Q'' \in \overline{A'B'}$ so that both Q' and Q'' are on $\overrightarrow{A'B'}$. (Note that the drawing does not show this fact.) Thus it appears we *can* use Axiom CS5 to prove that $Q' = Q''$ so that $Q' \in \mathcal{S}'$. This would complete the proof of statement (b) and hence of Theorem 5.7. Let us verify that we have not overlooked some critical fact in our analysis by writing the full proof of Theorem 5.7 in a formal step by step process.

Proof. We shall use the notation of the above drawing; i.e., P' is any point of $\mathcal{S}'$, P is the corresponding point of $\overline{AB}$, and Q' is any point of $\overline{A'B'}$.

ASSERTIONS	SUPPORTING STATEMENTS
(1) $\overline{AP} \cong \overline{A'P'}$, $\overline{PB} \cong \overline{P'B'}$, $\overline{AB} \cong \overline{A'B'}$.	(1) Why?
(2) $P \in \overline{AB}$.	(2) Given.
(3) $P' \in \overline{A'B'}$.	(3) Steps 1 and 2 and Axiom CS7.
(4) $\mathcal{S}' \subset \overline{A'B'}$.	(4) Step 3, since P' was *any* point of $\mathcal{S}'$.
(5) $\overline{AB} \cong \mathcal{S}'$.	(5) Given.
(6) $\overline{A'B'} \cong \mathcal{S}'$.	(6) Steps 1 and 5 and Theorem 5.6.

Let $Q'' \in \mathcal{S}'$ be the point such that $Q' \leftrightarrow Q''$ in the congruence of step 6.

(7) $\overline{A'Q'} \cong \overline{A'Q''}$.	(7) Definition of congruence in step 6.
(8) $Q' \in \overline{A'B'}$ and hence $Q' \in \overrightarrow{A'B'}$.	(8) Definition of Q'.
(9) $Q'' \in \overline{A'B'}$ and hence $Q'' \in \overrightarrow{A'B'}$.	(9) Step 4.
(10) $Q' = Q''$.	(10) Steps 7, 8, and 9 and Axiom CS5.
(11) $Q' \in \mathcal{S}'$.	(11) Step 10.
(12) $\overline{A'B'} \subset \mathcal{S}'$.	(12) Step 11, since Q' was *any* point of $\overline{A'B'}$.
(13) $\overline{A'B'} = \mathcal{S}'$.	(13) Steps 4 and 12.

It should be noticed that step 3 of the last proof is the first place where use has been made of Axiom CS7.

Sometimes when we have two congruent sets S and S' we find it important to look only at certain matching subsets $\mathfrak{I}$ and $\mathfrak{I}'$. The following theorem assures us of the useful fact that $\mathfrak{I}$ and $\mathfrak{I}'$ are congruent under the same correspondence.

Theorem 5.8 *Let* $S \cong S'$*. If* $\mathfrak{I} \subset S$ *and if* $\mathfrak{I}'$ *is the set of image points of* $\mathfrak{I}$ *in* S'*, then* $\mathfrak{I} \cong \mathfrak{I}'$*.*

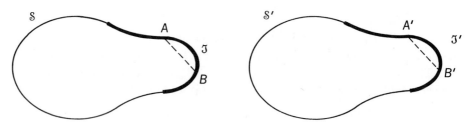

Proof. We need only use the definition of congruence. We already know that the congruence gives a one-to-one correspondence of the points of $\mathfrak{I}$ with those of $\mathfrak{I}'$. Thus if $A, B \in \mathfrak{I}$ and if A', B' are the corresponding points of $\mathfrak{I}'$ we need only show that $\overline{AB} \cong \overline{A'B'}$. The argument could be formally given like this.

ASSERTIONS	SUPPORTING STATEMENTS
(1) $A, B \in \mathfrak{I}$.	(1) Given.
(2) $A \leftrightarrow A', B \leftrightarrow B'$ and $A', B' \in \mathfrak{I}'$.	(2) Definition of $\mathfrak{I}'$.
(3) $A, B \in S$.	(3) Step 1, since $\mathfrak{I} \subset S$.
(4) $A', B' \in S'$.	(4) Step 2, since $S \cong S'$.
(5) $\overline{AB} \cong \overline{A'B'}$.	(5) Step 2, since $S \cong S'$.
(6) $\mathfrak{I} \cong \mathfrak{I}'$.	(6) Definition of congruence.

This result is intuitively plausible. We think of S and S' as being congruent if the same tracing will fit on both of them. If we consider a subset $\mathfrak{I}$ of S this is then covered by a part of the tracing. This part of the tracing then fits exactly on the corresponding part $\mathfrak{I}'$ of S'. Thus we think of subsets $\mathfrak{I}$ and $\mathfrak{I}'$ as congruent.

By using Theorems 5.7 and 5.8 it is easy to show the following theorem, the proof of which is left as an exercise.

Theorem 5.9 *Let* $S \cong S'$ *and* $\overline{AB} \subset S$*. If* $A \leftrightarrow A'$, $B \leftrightarrow B'$*, then* $\overline{A'B'} \subset S'$ *and* $\overline{AB} \cong \overline{A'B'}$*.*

That is, if a set S contains a segment, then S' contains the image segment. Thus, for example, if a set S is a union of segments any congruent set S' must also be a union of the same number of segments.

As will be seen in the next section it will be necessary to adopt some additional axioms before we can obtain some of the intuitively plausible results about such sets of points as angles and triangles. However, one rather simple result will be of use to us and can be shown now.

Theorem 5.10 *If $\overrightarrow{OA}$ and $\overrightarrow{O'A'}$ are any two rays, there is exactly one congruence x such that $\overrightarrow{OA} \underset{x}{\cong} \overrightarrow{O'A'}$. Moreover, $O \underset{x}{\leftrightarrow} O'$.*

Proof. There are really two things to prove. We must show there is a congruence of the two rays and then we must show there is only one. We begin by describing a correspondence x which we hope will prove to be a congruence.

In the first place, let us agree to match the endpoints O and O' so $O \underset{x}{\leftrightarrow} O'$. If P is any point of $\overrightarrow{OA}$ we match it with the point P' of $\overrightarrow{O'A'}$ such that $\overline{OP} \cong \overline{O'P'}$. By Axiom CS5 this is a one-to-one correspondence. Suppose now that P and Q are any points of $\overrightarrow{OA}$ and P' and Q' the corresponding points of $\overrightarrow{O'A'}$ under the correspondence x; i.e., $P \underset{x}{\leftrightarrow} P'$, $Q \underset{x}{\leftrightarrow} Q'$. Thus $\overline{OP} \cong \overline{O'P'}$ and $\overline{OQ} \cong \overline{O'Q'}$. It then follows by Theorem 5.3 that $\overline{PQ} \cong \overline{P'Q'}$. That is, the correspondence x is by definition a congruence. This shows that there is always at least one congruence of two rays.

Suppose now that x and y are both congruences so that $\overrightarrow{OA} \underset{x}{\cong} \overrightarrow{O'A'}$ and $\overrightarrow{OA} \underset{y}{\cong} \overrightarrow{O'A'}$. Can we say anything at all about the image of O under correspondence y? According to Theorem 5.9 any segment contained in $\overrightarrow{OA}$ goes into a segment contained in $\overrightarrow{O'A'}$. In particular, the interior points of one segment go into the interior points of its image. But O is the only point of $\overrightarrow{OA}$ which is not interior to any segment of $\overrightarrow{OA}$. It must then go into a point of $\overrightarrow{O'A'}$ which is not an interior point of segment of $\overrightarrow{O'A'}$. The only such point is O', so we are forced to conclude that $O \underset{y}{\leftrightarrow} O'$. By the same argument $O \underset{x}{\leftrightarrow} O'$. If P is any point of $\overrightarrow{OA}$, let P'_x be its image under x and P'_y its image under y. Then by definition of congruence $\overline{O'P'_x} \cong \overline{OP}$ and $\overline{O'P'_y} \cong \overline{OP}$. By Axiom CS5 it follows that $P'_x = P'_y$. That is, every point P has the same image under x and y, so the two congruences are actually the same. This is what we were to prove.

Notice the physical plausibility of this result. Certainly if we imagine a tracing made of a ray, there seems nothing to prevent this tracing being fitted exactly

on any other ray. Moreover, it seems intuitively clear that this fitting can be
done in only one way. This is precisely the content of the theorem.

A comment on the general idea of congruence may be helpful here. You will
have noticed that any specific examples so far mentioned have been for the case
of sets in a plane. However, no formal restriction to plane sets was made and our
definition of congruence and all our deductive results apply equally well to any
sets. In considering sets which are not necessarily in a plane we might well ask
whether any congruent image of a plane set must be a plane set. As a matter of
fact, if we adopt the axioms in the next section the answer is in the affirmative.
We shall omit the proof, however, as it is a little laborious and we shall have no
specific use for it. In the following sections we shall be concerned almost entirely
with properties of plane sets.

Problem Set 5.3

A. 1. Let S be any point set and let i be the correspondence that matches every
point $P \in S$ with itself. (This is sometimes called the identity correspondence.) Prove that $S \cong_i S$.

2. In problem **A1** it was shown that a set is congruent to itself by the
identity correspondence. Sometimes, however, a set may be congruent
to itself by other correspondences. For example, $\overline{AB} \cong \overline{BA}$ is such a
situation. Give three examples of sets which are congruent to themselves
by correspondences other than the identity. (In answering this, feel free
to be intuitive and draw on any geometric insight you have. No formal
proofs are intended.)

B. 1. The following drawings are intended to represent geometric figures
which are congruent in two different ways. Give the images of A, B, and
C for each of these congruences.

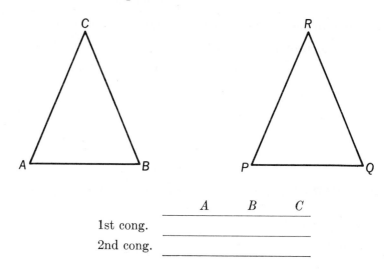

	A	B	C
1st cong.			
2nd cong.			

2. The following drawings are intended to represent geometric figures which are congruent in two different ways. Give the images of $A, B, C,$ and D for each congruence.

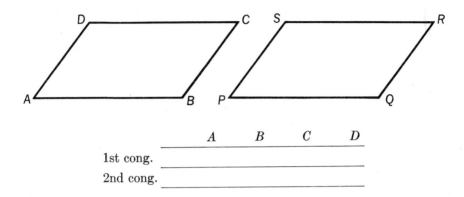

	A	B	C	D
1st cong.				
2nd cong.				

3. The following drawings are intended to represent geometric figures which are congruent in four different ways. Give the images of $A, B, C,$ and D for each such congruence.

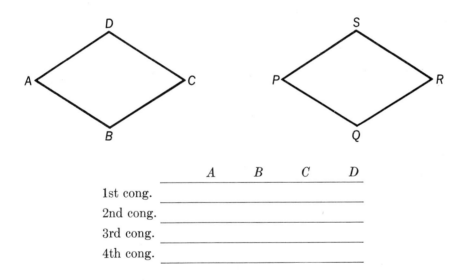

	A	B	C	D
1st cong.				
2nd cong.				
3rd cong.				
4th cong.				

4. Same question as problem **B3** for the following drawings.

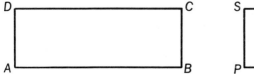 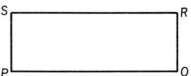

5. The two drawings below are intended to be squares, whose sides are congruent. How many congruences can you find between the squares? Write the images of $A, B, C,$ and D for each such congruence.

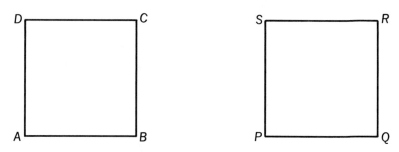

C. 1. $\{A, B, C\}$ and $\{A', B', C'\}$ are sets each of which contain exactly three

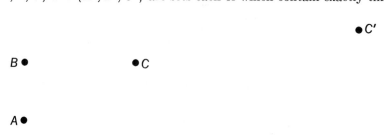

points. Let $\{A, B, C\} \underset{a}{\cong} \{A', B', C'\}$, where we will understand that this means $A \underset{a}{\leftrightarrow} A'$, $B \underset{a}{\leftrightarrow} B'$, $C \underset{a}{\leftrightarrow} C'$, What congruences of segments are implied by the definition of congruence?

2. If $\{A_1, A_2, A_3, A_4\} \underset{c}{\cong} \{B_1, B_2, B_3, B_4\}$ how many different congruences of segments does this imply? We understand this means $A_i \underset{c}{\leftrightarrow} B_i$ for each $i = 1, 2, 3, 4$.

3. Answer the question of problem **C2** for the case
$\{A_1, A_2, \ldots, A_n\} \underset{d}{\cong} \{B_1, B_2, \ldots, B_n\}$.

D. 1. Prove Theorem 5.9.

2. Prove that a congruent image of a polygon is a polygon.

E. 1. Let $A, B, C \in \mathcal{S}$, $B \in \overline{AC}$ and $\mathcal{S} \cong \mathcal{S}'$. If $A \leftrightarrow A'$, $B \leftrightarrow B'$, $C \leftrightarrow C'$ prove that $B' \in \overline{A'C'}$. [HINT: Consider Axiom CS7.] Note carefully there is no assumption that segment $\overline{AC}$ is a subset of $\mathcal{S}$. See the diagram.

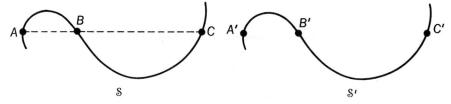

2. If m and m' are lines and if $A \in m$, $A' \in m'$, show that there is a congruence a of these lines such that $A \underset{a}{\leftrightarrow} A'$.

5.4 Axioms for Angles

Now that congruence has been defined for general sets of points we shall wish to consider its application to some additional sets of points with which we are familiar. Suppose the two drawings below represent congruent angles. Notice

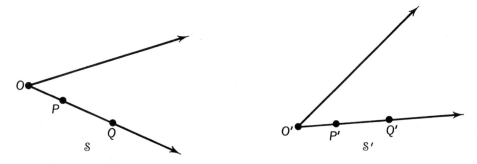

that the vertex of an angle has the interesting property that it is the only point of the angle which is not an interior point of a segment belonging to the angle. According to Theorem 5.9 the image point of the vertex under a congruence must have the same property and therefore must be the vertex of the second angle, i.e., $O \leftrightarrow O'$.

Suppose now that P and Q belong to the same ray of angle $\mathcal{S}$, as shown. Then $\overline{PQ}$ is a subset of the angle. By Theorem 5.9 segment $\overline{P'Q'}$ is a subset of the second angle and so points P', Q' must belong to the same ray of this angle. Thus the points forming one ray of angle $\mathcal{S}$ go into the points of one ray of angle $\mathcal{S}'$. Similarly the second ray of $\mathcal{S}$ goes into the second ray of $\mathcal{S}'$. Indeed the mapping of each ray of $\mathcal{S}$ to a ray of $\mathcal{S}'$ is a congruence (by Theorem 5.8), and so by Theorem 5.10 is completely determined as soon as we know which rays of the angle correspond. Specifically, if $\angle ABC$ is congruent to $\angle PQR$, then either $\overrightarrow{BA}$ is matched with $\overrightarrow{QP}$ and $\overrightarrow{BC}$ with $\overrightarrow{QR}$ or $\overrightarrow{BA}$ is matched with $\overrightarrow{QR}$ and $\overrightarrow{BC}$ with $\overrightarrow{QP}$.

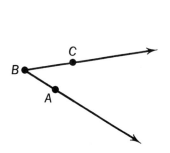

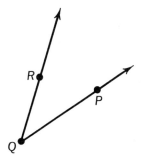

In the first case we express this by writing $\angle ABC \cong \angle PQR$ and in the second case we write $\angle ABC \cong \angle RQP$. In either case $B \leftrightarrow Q$. Note carefully that the notation $\angle ABC \cong \angle PQR$ does not imply that *point P* is the image of *point A*, only that *ray $\overrightarrow{QP}$* is the image of *ray $\overrightarrow{BA}$*.

The discussion above is concerned with conclusions that may be drawn about two angles that are already known to be congruent. A casual reading of it, however, could easily lead us to the conclusion that *any* two angles are congruent (just as Theorem 5.10 states that any two rays are congruent). This is, of course, false but it may be worthwhile to see where the fallacy arises. If $\angle DEF$ and $\angle LMN$ are *any* angles we know by Theorem 5.10 that there is a congruence of

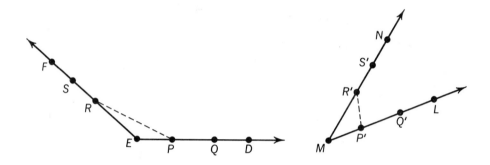

$\overrightarrow{ED}$ with $\overrightarrow{ML}$ and a congruence of $\overrightarrow{EF}$ with $\overrightarrow{MN}$. The combination of these congruences is certainly a one-to-one correspondence of $\angle DEF$ and $\angle LMN$. Moreover, if P, Q are any points of $\overrightarrow{ED}$ and P', Q' the corresponding points of $\overrightarrow{ML}$, then $\overline{PQ} \cong \overline{P'Q'}$. Similarly, if $R, S \in \overrightarrow{EF}$ and R', S' are the corresponding points of $\overrightarrow{MN}$, then $\overline{RS} \cong \overline{R'S'}$. Why does this not show that the correspondence is a congruence? Try to answer this question before reading on.

The difficulty, of course, is that the definition of congruence asks us to consider *any* pair of points in the first set. We have considered above only pairs of points *lying on the same ray*. If we consider the pair P, R and the corresponding pair P', R', there is no assurance whatever that $\overline{PR} \cong \overline{P'R'}$. Indeed, for what it may be worth, this appears to be clearly false for the drawing on the basis of our intuitive understanding of congruent segments.

The discussion above shows that, while we know something about congruent angles on the basis of the general definition of congruent sets, there seem to be serious gaps in our equipment. For example, we seem to have no mechanism for showing that two angles are congruent other than using the definition and looking at all pairs of points on one angle and their images on the other. Since there are an infinite number of such pairs, this is an unpromising situation. Even worse, we have no assurance from the axioms so far adopted that there are such things as congruent angles except for the trivial remark that any set is congruent to itself. (See problem **A1** of Problem Set 5.3.) All our intuitive experience suggests that for a given angle $\angle ABC$ it should be possible to produce a congruent copy of it, $\angle A'B'C'$ with vertex at some other point B'. Moreover, we feel there should be some effective way of deciding when two angles are congruent. This seems to suggest that we may need to adopt some additional axioms concerning angle congruence.

As in the case of segments let us then indulge in a little physical manipulation with representations of angles with the thought that this may suggest appropriate axioms. First, what about the matter of producing a congruent copy of an angle at a new location?

Consider $\angle ABC$ and let $\overrightarrow{QP}$ be a ray in plane π. Imagine a tracing made of

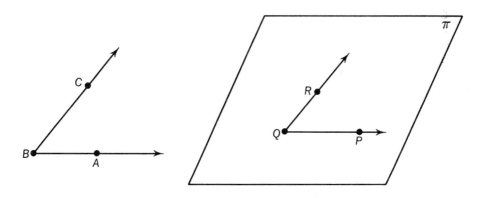

$\angle ABC$ and for convenience let A_0, B_0, and C_0 be the points of the tracing covering A, B, and C, respectively. It is experimentally clear to us that we can place this tracing of $\angle ABC$ on plane π in such a way that B_0 covers Q and $\overrightarrow{B_0A_0}$ covers $\overrightarrow{QP}$. (This is really the experimental meaning of Theorem 5.10.) In this position it appears that $\overrightarrow{B_0C_0}$ covers a ray of $\overrightarrow{QR}$ of π as shown. In other words, we seem to find a ray $\overrightarrow{QR}$ such that $\angle ABC \cong \angle PQR$. It would be very pleasant if we could prove this conjecture about producing a congruent copy of $\angle ABC$. Unfortunately, as noted above, it does not seem possible to prove this on the basis of the axioms so far adopted. We will therefore find it convenient to adopt a new axiom covering this matter. Before doing so, however, let us experiment with a related question.

Is there any other way in which the tracing of $\angle ABC$ could have been placed on plane π so that $\overrightarrow{B_0A_0}$ would cover $\overrightarrow{QP}$? At first sight the answer may appear to be "no," but with a little thought it occurs to us that the tracing could be turned the other side up. In this case $\overrightarrow{B_0C_0}$ covers a different ray of π, say $\overrightarrow{QR'}$. The situation then appears as in the drawing below, with $\overrightarrow{QR}$ and $\overrightarrow{QR'}$ the two possible

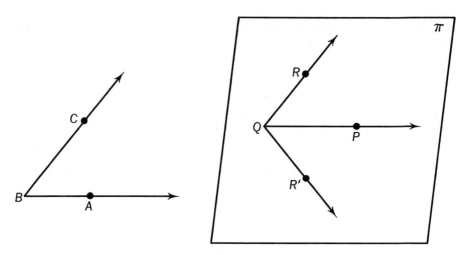

positions of $\overrightarrow{B_0C_0}$. In this drawing $\overrightarrow{QR}$ and $\overrightarrow{QR'}$ seem to be on opposite sides of $\overleftrightarrow{QP}$ in π. That is, $\overrightarrow{QR}$ is in one of the two half planes determined by $\overleftrightarrow{QP}$ in π and $\overrightarrow{QR'}$ in the other. No other placing of the tracing seems possible. The physical experiment suggested above leads us to formulate the following axiom. (The designation CA1 indicates it is the *first* axiom having to do with Congruence of Angles.)

Axiom CA1 *Let $\angle ABC$ be an angle and $\overrightarrow{QP}$ a ray in plane π. Then in π on a given side of $\overleftrightarrow{QP}$ there is exactly one ray $\overrightarrow{QR}$ such that $\angle ABC \cong \angle PQR$.*

A second difficulty noted above in discussing congruence of angles was that we really had no effective criterion for deciding whether two angles are congruent. It will be desirable to adopt an axiom to aid us at this point also. For convenience it will be stated first and the experimental motivation for it explored afterward.

Axiom CA2 *Let P and Q be points, other than the vertex, on the sides $\overrightarrow{BA}$ and $\overrightarrow{BC}$,*

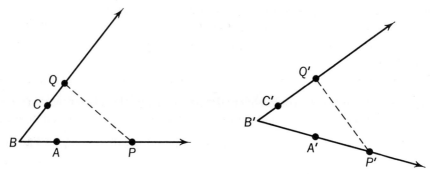

respectively, of $\angle ABC$. *Similarly, let* P' *and* Q' *be points other than the vertex on the sides* $\overrightarrow{B'A'}$ *and* $\overrightarrow{B'C'}$ *of* $\angle A'B'C'$. *If* $\overline{BP} \cong \overline{B'P'}$, $\overline{BQ} \cong \overline{B'Q'}$, *and* $\overline{PQ} \cong \overline{P'Q'}$, *then* $\angle ABC \cong \angle A'B'C'$.

To appreciate the physical significance of this axiom imagine two long strips of wood fastened together at one end by a nail B_0 to form a crude model of an

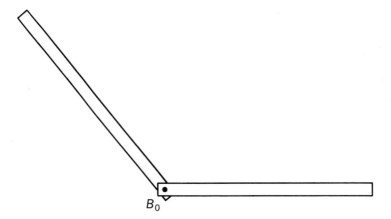

angle. Since the strips rotate freely about B_0, this model can be fitted to any angle we wish. Imagine then that it is fitted to the angle $\angle ABC$ of Axiom CA2 and designate as P_0 and Q_0 the points of the strips that cover P and Q, respectively. If now we take a strip which is a model of segment $\overline{PQ}$, it can be nailed to the other strips at P_0 and Q_0, yielding a framework as shown.

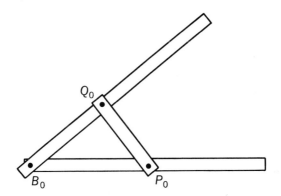

Suppose now that the procedure is carried out again, this time on $\angle A'B'C'$. Since we are given that $\overline{BP} \cong \overline{B'P'}$, the point P_0 which covered P will now cover P'. Similarly Q_0 will cover Q'. Moreover, since $\overline{PQ} \cong \overline{P'Q'}$ the final strip to be nailed on can be the same one as before. We have therefore simply reproduced the framework drawn above. Hence this framework can be fitted on both $\angle ABC$ and $\angle A'B'C'$.

Now we come to the critical observation. As we hold the framework in our hands we find it feels rigid. We can no longer rotate the original strips about B_0. There is no "give" to it at all. It always has the same shape. This means that a model of $\angle ABC$ then fits exactly on $\angle A'B'C'$. That is, we want to conclude that these angles are congruent. This is precisely the statement which is made in Axiom CA2. Notice that in a sense we seem to be observing a fundamental physical fact, namely, that a triangle is a rigid figure.

As we have already remarked, however reasonable the definition of congruence sounds, it can be extremely awkward to apply. In order to show that $S \cong S'$ the definition calls for us to consider *all possible pairs* of points in S and their image points in S'. If, as in the case of an angle, S is an infinite set, this leaves us with infinitely many cases to consider. The real importance of Axiom CA2 is that it permits us to conclude the congruence of two angles by considering only a *single* pair of points other than the vertex, one on each ray of one angle, and their images on the second angle.

In addition to the physical experiences which have led us to formulate Axioms CA1 and CA2, it is easy to describe experiences leading to other conjectures. Some of these are suggested in the problem set below. Some of the conjectures thus suggested will become theorems in the following developments.

Problem Set 5.4

A. 1. Make a tracing of $\angle ABC$. Turn the tracing over and try fitting it again

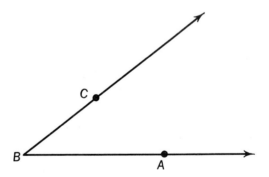

on $\angle ABC$. Does it seem to fit? The part of the tracing which originally covered $\overrightarrow{BA}$ now covers what? What conjecture does this suggest about $\angle ABC$?

2. In the figure shown it is intended that $\overline{AB} \cong \overline{AC}$. Imagine that you make a tracing of $\triangle ABC$ and mark the points covering A, B, and C as A_0, B_0, and C_0. If the tracing is turned over you discover that again it seems to fit on this triangle. In this fitting what points are covered by A_0, B_0, and C_0, respectively? Where is the part of the tracing which was originally on

$\angle B$? What about the part originally on $\angle C$? What conjecture is suggested by this experiment? Write a full statement of the conjecture.

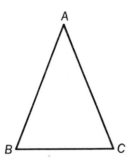

3. Two angles related like $\angle ABC$ and $\angle CBD$ below with B between A and D on $\overleftrightarrow{AD}$ are called **supplementary** and each is called a **supplement**

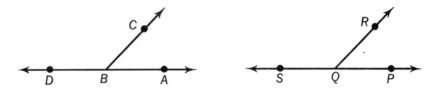

of the other. Similarly $\angle PQR$ and $\angle RQS$ are supplementary. Suppose that $\angle ABC \cong \angle PQR$. Imagine a tracing made of the left-hand figure. Since $\angle ABC \cong PQR$ it should be possible to fit the tracing of $\angle ABC$ onto $\angle PQR$; i.e., the tracing of $\overrightarrow{BA}$ covers $\overrightarrow{QP}$ and the tracing of $\overrightarrow{BC}$ covers $\overrightarrow{QR}$. In this fitting, what seems to become of the tracing of $\overrightarrow{BD}$? What conjecture does this suggest about angles $\angle CBD$ and $\angle RQS$? Write a full statement of the conjecture.

4. Two angles such as $\angle AOB$ and $\angle COD$ are called **vertical** angles. (They

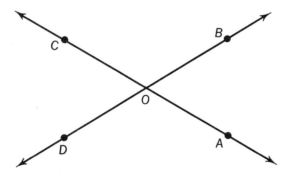

have a common vertex and the union of their rays is two intersecting lines.) Imagine a tracing made of $\angle AOB$. Try placing this tracing on

∠*COD*. Does it seem to fit? State the conjecture suggested by the experiment?

5. In the diagrams B is interior to ∠*AOC* and B' is on the C' side of $\overleftrightarrow{O'A'}$.

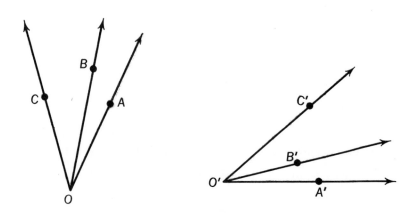

It is intended that ∠*AOC* ≅ ∠*A'O'C'*, and that ∠*AOB* ≅ ∠*A'O'B'*. Imagine that a tracing is made of the left-hand diagram. Then it must be possible to fit the tracing to the right-hand diagram so that the tracing of ∠*AOC* fits on ∠*A'O'C'*. When this is done, what seems to happen to the tracing of $\overrightarrow{OB}$? What seems to happen to the tracing of ∠*BOC*? State completely the conjecture suggested by this experiment.

B. 1. A man was making a gate for his picket fence. He fastened a diagonal brace across it as shown, claiming it would help prevent sagging. Is this

claim correct? If so, explain the principle involved.

2. a. A frame is made as shown using two 2 ft. strips of wood and two 1 ft. strips. Draw two other shapes that this frame could have using the same strips of wood in the same order.

   b. Similarly, a triangular frame is made from three strips of wood as shown. Can you draw other possible shapes for the frame as in **a**? Explain the difference between the situations in **a** and **b**.

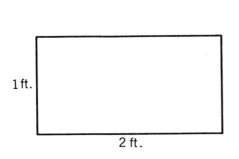

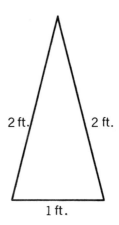

C. Imagine each of the following plane figures formed of strips of wood fastened with a nail at each vertex. Which of these figures are rigid (i.e., cannot
be pushed into a different shape) and which allow distortion into more than
one shape? We assume the figures are to remain in a plane.

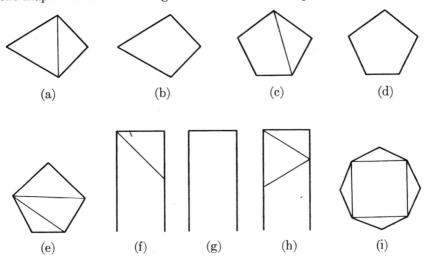

5.5 Deductions on Triangles

Having amused ourselves with physical experiments and making plausible
conjectures based on them let us now return to an application of deduction. Recall that here we are seeking to discover what can be proved on the basis of the
axioms we have so far chosen to adopt. We can use only the axioms and definitions and, of course, previous results we have deduced from these. For the first
time we now have available Axioms CA1 and CA2, which we have just adopted.
It will prove convenient to turn our attention first to the matter of congruence
for triangles.

Suppose $\triangle ABC \underset{c}{\cong} \mathcal{S}'$ and let A', B', C' be the images of A, B, C under congruence c. You may find it helpful to sketch a diagram as you follow this discussion. By Theorem 5.9 the images of $\overline{AB}$, $\overline{BC}$, and $\overline{CA}$ under c are $\overline{A'B'}$, $\overline{B'C'}$, and $\overline{C'A'}$, respectively, so $\mathcal{S}'$ is the union of these three segments. Moreover, A', B', and C' are not collinear, for if they were it would follow by Axiom CS7 that A, B, and C would be collinear also. Thus $\mathcal{S}' = \triangle A'B'C'$. Hence a congruent image of a triangle is always a triangle and the congruence matches the vertices of the triangles. To state that $\triangle ABC$ and $\triangle A'B'C'$ are congruent in such a way that $A \leftrightarrow A'$, $B \leftrightarrow B'$ and $C \leftrightarrow C'$, we write

$$\triangle ABC \cong \triangle A'B'C'.$$

Note carefully the convention that the first-named point on the left is to be matched with the first-named point on the right (i.e., $A \leftrightarrow A'$) and, similarly, for the second- and third-named points ($B \leftrightarrow B'$, $C \leftrightarrow C'$). If we wished to say that the same two triangles are congruent by a correspondence such that $A \leftrightarrow B'$, $B \leftrightarrow C'$, $C \leftrightarrow A'$, this would be written $\triangle ABC \cong \triangle B'C'A'$.

A triangle $\triangle ABC$, as we know, is the union of the three segments $\overline{AB}$, $\overline{BC}$, and $\overline{CA}$, which are called the **sides** of the triangle. There are also associated with $\triangle ABC$ three angles, namely $\angle ABC$, $\angle BCA$, and $\angle CAB$, which we call the **angles** of the triangle. It should be recalled, as we noted in the last chapter, that the angles of a triangle (which consist of *rays*) are not subsets of the triangle (which is a union of *segments*). However, the angles are determined by the triangle.

The notation used above in which A' is used for the image of A, B' for the image of B, etc., is very convenient and we shall frequently use it. Be sure, however, that you do not become hypnotized by the notation. For example, if we write

$$\triangle TVA \cong \triangle PDQ,$$

this indicates a congruence in which $T \leftrightarrow P$, $V \leftrightarrow D$, $A \leftrightarrow Q$. It would then follow from the definition of congruence that

$$\overline{TV} \cong \overline{PD}, \qquad \overline{TA} \cong \overline{PQ}, \qquad \text{and} \qquad \overline{VA} \cong \overline{DQ}.$$

We now examine the relationships between congruences of triangles, congruences of angles and congruences of segments. The first such result is almost immediate.

Theorem 5.11 *If $\triangle ABC \cong \triangle A'B'C'$, then*
  (a) $\overline{AB} \cong \overline{A'B'}$, $\overline{BC} \cong \overline{B'C'}$, $\overline{CA} \cong \overline{C'A'}$.
  (b) $\angle ABC \cong \angle A'B'C'$, $\angle BCA \cong \angle B'C'A'$, $\angle CAB \cong \angle C'A'B'$.

Proof. The three statements in line (a) follow from the definition of congruence. The three statements in line (b) follow from Axiom CA2 and line (a).

The more interesting question is whether, from a combination of some of the relations in (a) and (b), it is possible to conclude that $\triangle ABC \cong \triangle A'B'C'$. This we proceed to consider.

Theorem 5.12 *If $\triangle ABC$ and $\triangle A'B'C'$ are such that $\overline{AB} \cong \overline{A'B'}$, $\overline{BC} \cong \overline{B'C'}$, and $\overline{CA} \cong \overline{C'A'}$, then $\triangle ABC \cong \triangle A'B'C'$.*

Analysis. We are supposed to show that $\triangle ABC \cong \triangle A'B'C'$. What strategy can we adopt in seeking to prove this? Frankly there is very little choice. So far we know nothing at all about congruence of triangles except the definition. Thus it will be necessary for us to fall back on the definition. This means the program will be to set up a one-to-one correspondence between $\triangle ABC$ and $\triangle A'B'C'$ and then try to prove this correspondence is a congruence.

There seems a fairly obvious way of setting up a correspondence. Since $\overline{AB} \cong \overline{A'B'}$, this already gives a one-to-one correspondence of the points on $\overline{AB}$ with those on $\overline{A'B'}$. Similarly, the given congruences $\overline{BC} \cong \overline{B'C'}$ and $\overline{CA} \cong \overline{C'A'}$ provide one-to-one correspondences for the other two pairs of sides. Moreover, since these congruences agree on the vertices A, B, and C, the combination of them provides a one-to-one correspondence of $\triangle ABC$ with $\triangle A'B'C'$. It remains to apply the definition to show that this correspondence is really a congruence. That is, we must consider *any pair of points P, Q* of $\triangle ABC$ and their images P', Q' of $\triangle A'B'C'$ and prove that $\overline{PQ} \cong \overline{P'Q'}$. Since the general direction of the proposed proof is now clear, let us try actually to produce it.

Proof. We will use the correspondence described above in the analysis. Let P, Q be any points of $\triangle ABC$ and P', Q' the corresponding points of $\triangle A'B'C'$. Of course, P, Q may lie on the same side of $\triangle ABC$ or may lie on different sides, and since we must consider *all* possible pairs P, Q, it will be necessary to consider both cases.

Case 1. P and Q are on the same side of $\triangle ABC$. For definiteness suppose $P, Q \in \overline{AB}$ as shown. By the definition of the correspondence $P', Q' \in \overline{A'B'}$.

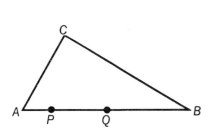
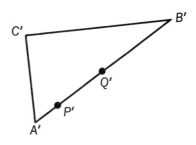

In fact, $P \leftrightarrow P'$ and $Q \leftrightarrow Q'$ in the given congruence $\overline{AB} \cong \overline{A'B'}$. But by Theorem 5.5 this means that $\overline{PQ} \cong \overline{P'Q'}$. This takes care of Case 1.

Case 2.   *P* and *Q* are on different sides of $\triangle ABC$. For definiteness suppose $P \in \overline{AB}$ and $Q \in \overline{AC}$ as shown. Then $P' \in \overline{A'B'}$ and $Q' \in \overline{A'C'}$. How can we hope to show

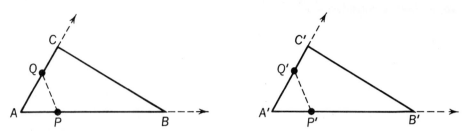

that $\overline{PQ} \cong \overline{P'Q'}$? Since P, Q are points on the sides of $\angle BAC$ it seems that information about congruence of angle $\angle BAC$ and $\angle B'A'C'$ may be of importance. With this hint we make the following observations.

Since $\overline{AB} \cong \overline{A'B'}$, $\overline{BC} \cong \overline{B'C'}$, $\overline{CA} \cong \overline{C'A'}$, it follows from Axiom CA2 that $\angle BAC \underset{x}{\cong} \angle B'A'C'$. (We have chosen to denote this congruence by x.) Since $\overline{AP} \cong \overline{A'P'}$ and $\overline{AQ} \cong \overline{A'Q'}$ (why?), it follows from problem **A2** of Problem Set 5.5 that $P \underset{x}{\leftrightarrow} P'$ and $Q \underset{x}{\leftrightarrow} Q'$. Since x is a congruence, this means by definition that $\overline{PQ} \cong \overline{P'Q'}$.

Thus, in both cases $\overline{PQ} \cong \overline{P'Q'}$, so the correspondence between $\triangle ABC$ and $\triangle A'B'C'$ is indeed a congruence and the proof of Theorem 5.12 is complete.

Notice that Theorem 5.12 allows us to conclude the congruence of two triangles by examining the three sides. For this reason it is frequently referred to as the **sss** theorem.

There are other combinations of data from which it is possible to deduce the congruence of two triangles. Both the next two theorems are of this nature.

Theorem 5.13 *If $\triangle ABC$ and $\triangle A'B'C'$ are such that $\overline{AB} \cong \overline{A'B'}$, $\overline{AC} \cong \overline{A'C'}$ and $\angle BAC \cong B'A'C'$, then $\triangle ABC \cong \triangle A'B'C'$.*

Analysis. A discussion of strategy may be helpful here. Just as in Theorem 5.12 we are asked to show that $\triangle ABC \cong \triangle A'B'C'$. Presumably we could use the same tactics as before and use directly the definition of congruence. This setting up of a one-to-one correspondence and proving it is a congruence is rather laborious, as we have just seen, and is to be avoided if possible. It probably would be much neater if we could prove the desired congruence by using the result of Theorem 5.12. Could we, perhaps, prove from the given information in Theorem 5.13 that $\overline{AB} \cong \overline{A'B'}$, $\overline{BC} \cong \overline{B'C'}$, $\overline{AC} \cong \overline{A'C'}$? If so, the congruence of $\triangle ABC$ and $\triangle A'B'C'$ would follow from Theorem 5.12. This possibility seems worth investigating.

Notice that we are given already two congruences for the sides, namely, $\overline{AB} \cong \overline{A'B'}$ and $\overline{AC} \cong \overline{A'C'}$. All we need is to be sure that $\overline{BC} \cong \overline{B'C'}$. What means do we have to show this? Of course we know that $\angle BAC \underset{x}{\cong} \angle B'A'C'$, where we have chosen to denote the congruence by x. Since $\overline{AC} \cong \overline{A'C'}$, this means (by problem **A2**, p. 181) that $C \underset{x}{\leftrightarrow} C'$. Similarly, $B \underset{x}{\leftrightarrow} B'$. Because x is a congruence, this means that $\overline{BC} \cong \overline{B'C'}$, which is all we need to know.

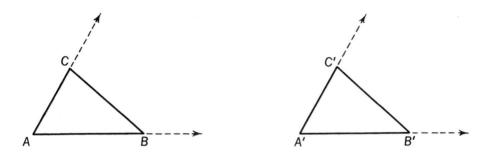

Actually the discussion above *is* a proof of Theorem 5.13, but it may be well to rewrite it without all the excess verbiage.

Proof. It is given that $\angle BAC \underset{x}{\cong} B'A'C'$ by a congruence we may label x. Since $\overline{AC} \cong \overline{A'C'}$, it follows by problem **A2** (page 181) that $C \underset{x}{\leftrightarrow} C'$. Similarly $B \underset{x}{\leftrightarrow} B'$. Because x is a congruence, $\overline{BC} \cong \overline{B'C'}$. This fact that $\overline{BC} \cong \overline{B'C'}$, together with the given information that $\overline{AB} \cong \overline{A'B'}$ and $\overline{AC} \cong \overline{A'C'}$, means that $\triangle ABC \cong \triangle A'B'C'$ by Theorem 5.12.

Since the hypothesis in Theorem 5.13 concerns two sides of a triangle and the angle containing them, it is familiarly called the **sas** theorem. It can be stated verbally in some such form as the following: If two sides and the angle containing them in one triangle are congruent, respectively, to two sides and the angle containing them in a second triangle, the triangles are congruent.

Theorem 5.14 *If $\triangle ABC$ and $\triangle A'B'C'$ are such that $\angle ABC \cong \angle A'B'C'$, $\angle BAC \cong \angle B'A'C'$ and $\overline{AB} \cong \overline{A'B'}$, then $\triangle ABC \cong \triangle A'B'C'$.*

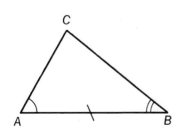
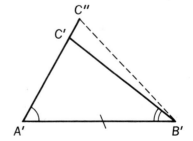

(Note that to serve as a reminder the parts given as congruent have been similarly marked in the drawing.)

Proof. A little subtlety is useful here rather than a direct frontal attack. We shall try to invent a triangle congruent to $\triangle ABC$ and then show it is really $\triangle A'B'C'$. The steps of the proof are given below and you are asked to supply missing supporting statements.

ASSERTIONS	SUPPORTING STATEMENTS
(1) There is a point C'' on $\overrightarrow{A'C'}$ so that $\overline{A'C''} \cong \overline{AC}$. (Draw $\overline{B'C''}$.)	(1) Why?
(2) $\overline{AB} \cong \overline{A'B'}$ and $\angle BAC \cong \angle B'A'C'$.	(2) Why?
(3) $\triangle ABC \cong \triangle A'B'C''$.	(3) Why?
(4) $\angle ABC \cong \angle A'B'C''$.	(4) Why?
(5) $\angle ABC \cong \angle A'B'C'$.	(5) Why?
(6) $\overrightarrow{B'C'} = \overrightarrow{B'C''}$.	(6) Why? (Notice C' and C'' are on the same side of $\overleftrightarrow{A'B'}$.)
(7) $C' = C''$.	(7) Why?
(8) $\triangle ABC \cong \triangle A'B'C'$.	(8) Steps 7 and 3.

This theorem is often called the **asa** theorem, since its hypothesis is concerned with two angles and the side between their vertices. It can be stated verbally as: If two angles and the side between their vertices in one triangle are congruent to the corresponding parts of a second triangle the triangles are congruent. The side in question might also be described as the side *on* the two given angles, since it is the only side contained in the intersection set of the angles.

Theorems 5.12, 5.13, and 5.14 have given us an **sss** congruence theorem, an **sas** congruence theorem and an **asa** congruence theorem. These successes suggest that there may be some other theorems still to discover. Can we, for example, prove an **aas** congruence theorem (i.e., two angles and a side opposite one of their vertices)? And what about the **ssa** case and the **aaa** case? There is indeed an **aas** congruence theorem. Its proof is suggested as problem **D1** of Problem Set 5.6. Curiously, however, there is no **ssa** congruence theorem. In this connection you may find it instructive to examine this drawing of $\triangle ABC$ and $\triangle A'B'C'$, with $\angle A \cong \angle A'$, $\overline{AC} \cong \overline{A'C'}$, and $\overline{BC} \cong \overline{B'C'}$, but where the triangles are not congruent. Thus, knowing that two sides and an angle with vertex opposite one of them in one triangle are congruent to the corresponding parts of a second apparently is not enough to imply congruence of the triangles. The remaining case, namely, the **aaa** case, also does not yield a congruence theorem.

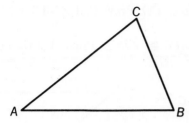 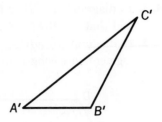

This is formally proved when similar triangles are discussed in Chapter 10. Meanwhile it is easy to draw two triangles where angles appear to be congruent but whose sides are not. Such a drawing is suggested in problem **C1** of Problem Set 5.5.

So far we have considered the possibility of proving congruence of triangles from the congruence of *three* parts of one triangle with the corresponding three parts of a second. Would it ever be possible to prove congruence of triangles from the congruence of *two* parts of one triangle with the corresponding two parts of a second. As you may guess, this is never enough information. In problem **C2** below you are asked to make diagrams showing that in no case is the congruence of two parts sufficient to imply congruence of the triangles.

Finally, what about the possibility of obtaining congruence theorems for triangles by considering congruence of four or more corresponding parts of the triangles? The answer here is that it is correct but unnecessary to look at more than three parts. This may be seen as follows. If the four parts considered include the three sides we already have congruence by the **sss** theorem. If the four parts include the three angles, then there is also one side and congruence follows from the **asa** theorem. The only remaining case is that of two sides and two angles. In this case we can always conclude congruence either by **sas** or **aas**. Thus it is never necessary to use more than three corresponding parts.

Problem Set 5.5

A. 1. Let $\mathcal{S} \underset{a}{\cong} \mathcal{S}'$ and let A, B, and C be three noncollinear points of $\mathcal{S}$. If $A \underset{a}{\leftrightarrow} A'$, $B \underset{a}{\leftrightarrow} B'$, $C \underset{a}{\leftrightarrow} C'$, prove that $\angle ABC \cong \angle A'B'C'$. [NOTE: Observe that there is no assumption that these angles are subsets of $\mathcal{S}$ and $\mathcal{S}'$.]

   2. Let $\angle ABC \underset{x}{\cong} \angle A'B'C'$. If $P \in \overrightarrow{BA}$ and $P' \in \overrightarrow{B'A'}$ are such that $\overline{BP} \cong \overline{B'P'}$, prove that $P \underset{x}{\leftrightarrow} P'$. [HINT: Let P'' be the image of P under x and try to show that $P' = P''$.]

   3. Let $\angle ABC \underset{x}{\cong} \angle A'B'C'$ and $\overrightarrow{BA} \underset{y}{\cong} \overrightarrow{B'A'}$. If $P \in \overrightarrow{BA}$ and if P', P'' are such that $P \underset{x}{\leftrightarrow} P'$, $P \underset{y}{\leftrightarrow} P''$, prove that $P' = P''$.

B. 1. In diagram (a) $\overline{AD} \cong \overline{CB}$ and $\overline{AB} \cong \overline{CD}$. Prove that $\angle BAD \cong \angle DCB$ and that $\angle ABD \cong \angle CDB$.

2. In diagram (b) $\overline{AB} \cong \overline{CD}$ and $\angle ABC \cong \angle DCB$. Prove that the dashed segments are congruent, i.e., $\overline{AC} \cong \overline{BD}$.

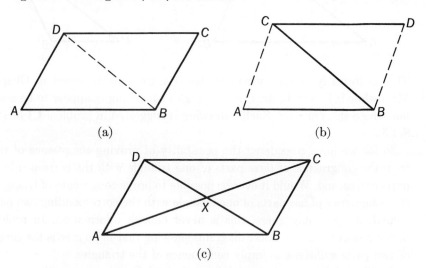

(a)   (b)

(c)

3. In diagram (c) $\overline{AD} \cong \overline{CB}$ and $\overline{AB} \cong \overline{CD}$. Prove that $\overline{AX} \cong \overline{CX}$ and $\overline{BX} \cong \overline{DX}$. [HINT: Begin by using problem **B1** to show that $\angle ABD \cong \angle CDB$ and $\angle BAC \cong \angle DCA$.]

C. 1. Draw a triangle ABC and let B' and C' be the midpoints of $\overline{AB}$ and $\overline{AC}$, respectively. Make a tracing of $\triangle AB'C'$ and use this to satisfy yourself that the angles of $\triangle AB'C'$ seem to be congruent to those of $\triangle ABC$. If this is correct, then $\triangle ABC$ and $\triangle AB'C'$ are noncongruent triangles with congruent angles. Hence we should not expect an **aaa** congruence theorem.

2. In each of the following cases draw two noncongruent triangles $\triangle ABC$ and $\triangle A'B'C'$ satisfying each of the following conditions.

    a. $\overline{AB} \cong \overline{A'B'}$, $\overline{AC} \cong \overline{A'C'}$.   **b.** $\overline{AB} \cong \overline{A'B'}$, $\angle A \cong \angle A'$.

    c. $\overline{AB} \cong \overline{A'B'}$, $\angle C \cong \angle C'$.   **d.** $\angle A \cong \angle A'$, $\angle B \cong \angle B'$.

These four examples cover all possible cases, i.e., two sides, a side and an angle containing the side, a side and an angle not containing the side, and two angles. These drawings then indicate that we cannot expect to show congruence of two triangles by comparing only two parts.

5.6 Angles and Triangles

In Problem Set 5.4 we were led to formulate certain conjectures purely on the basis of simple manipulations with models and drawings. With the machinery developed above, most of these ideas can now be made a part of our deductive system. These conjectures and some closely related topics will occupy us in this section.

The conjecture of problem **A1** of Problem Set 5.4 was the following, which we now prove as a theorem.

Theorem 5.15 *For any angle* $\angle ABC$ *it is true that* $\angle ABC \cong \angle CBA$.

Proof. Let P be any point of $\overrightarrow{BA}$ and let Q be the unique point of $\overrightarrow{BC}$ such that $\overline{BP} \cong \overline{BQ}$. We then make the following remarks:

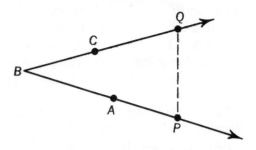

$\overline{BP} \cong \overline{BQ}$ by definition of Q.
$\overline{BQ} \cong \overline{BP}$ by Axiom CS2.
$\overline{PQ} \cong \overline{QP}$ by Axiom CS4.

Therefore by Axiom CA2 it follows that $\angle ABC \cong CBA$, which is what we were asked to show.

The last step above almost certainly leaves you cold, as most readers do not see at once that Axiom CA2 has anything to do with the situation. However, go back to Axiom CA2 and read it carefully. The $A, B, C, P,$ and Q of the statement of Axiom CA2 are to be identified with the points above with the same labels. The points $A', B', C', P',$ and Q' of Axiom CA2 are to be identified, respectively, with points $C, B, A, Q,$ and P. By writing out Axiom CA2 with these substitutions convince yourself that the hypotheses are satisfied and that Axiom CA2 does guarantee the truth of the theorem as stated above.

Consider any side, say $\overline{AB}$, of $\triangle ABC$. There is exactly one vertex of the tri-

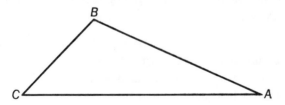

angle, here C, which does not lie on side $\overline{AB}$. This vertex of the triangle is frequently called the vertex **opposite** $\overline{AB}$. The angle of the triangle having this point C as a vertex, i.e., $\angle ACB$, may then be described as the angle whose vertex is opposite $\overline{AB}$. Another way of describing $\angle ACB$ is to observe that it is the one angle of the triangle whose interior contains segment $\overline{AB}$ (except for its endpoints). Some one of these terminologies will be useful in the next theorem.

Theorem 5.16 *If, in a triangle, two sides are congruent, the angles with vertices opposite these sides are congruent.*

[Alternatively this could have been written: *If, in a triangle, two sides are congruent, the angles whose interiors contain these sides are congruent.*]

Proof. Let $\triangle ABC$ in the diagram be the given triangle and let $\overline{AC} \cong \overline{BC}$ be the given congruent sides. Then we are to show that $\angle ABC \cong \angle BAC$. The proof is then readily given as follows:

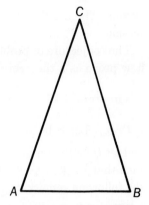

ASSERTIONS	SUPPORTING STATEMENTS
(1) $\overline{AC} \cong \overline{BC}$.	(1) Given.
(2) $\overline{BC} \cong \overline{AC}$.	(2) Given.
(3) $\overline{AB} \cong \overline{BA}$.	(3) Axiom CS4.
(4) $\triangle ABC \cong \triangle BAC$.	(4) Theorem 5.12 (**sss**).
(5) $\angle ABC \cong \angle BAC$.	(5) Theorem 5.11.

Again it may seem that some skullduggery is going on, particularly at step 4. However, if you consider what facts you must know to prove the congruence in step 4 by the **sss** Theorem, they are precisely the statements in steps 1, 2, and 3. The confusing thing is that we are showing that this particular type of triangle is congruent *to itself* by a correspondence other than the identity. Note that this theorem is precisely what was conjectured in problem **A2** of Problem Set 5.4. Compare also problems **B1** through **B5** of Problem Set 5.3.

It is natural at this point to ask whether the converse of the last theorem is true; i.e., if we are told that two angles in a triangle are congruent can we conclude the sides opposite their vertices are congruent? This converse does indeed prove to be true.

Theorem 5.17 *If two angles of a triangle are congruent, the sides opposite their vertices are congruent.*

[Alternatively this could be written: *If two angles of a triangle are congruent, the sides in the interiors of these angles are congruent.*]

Analysis. Let $\triangle ABC$ be the given triangle. We are given that $\angle A \cong \angle B$, and are asked to prove that $\overline{AC} \cong \overline{BC}$. Notice that in both of the last two theorems we have used the idea that a set may be congruent to itself by a correspondence other than the identity. Intuitively we have thought of a set as being "turned over" and fitted back on itself. The drawing makes it very appealing that this should be true here also. What would this mean? Presumably it means we are guessing that there is a congruence of $\triangle ABC$ with itself such that $A \leftrightarrow B$, $B \leftrightarrow A$ and $C \leftrightarrow C$. That is, it looks very plausible that we shall find $\triangle ABC \cong \triangle BAC$. If this turns out to be true we could at once conclude that $\overline{AC} \cong \overline{BC}$. (Why?) Thus, the theorem will be proved if we can succeed in showing that $\triangle ABC \cong \triangle BAC$.

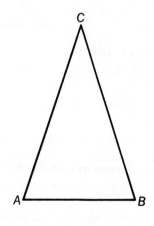

What means do we have of proving this congruence? There are three theorems that we know for showing congruence of triangles, namely, the **sss** Theorem (5.12), the **sas** Theorem (5.13), and the **asa** Theorem (5.14). Since we seem to know nothing so far about sides $\overline{AC}$ and $\overline{BC}$, the first two theorems do not seem promising, but could we use the **asa** Theorem to prove $\triangle ABC \cong \triangle BAC$? If we could show that $\angle A$, $\angle B$, and side $\overline{AB}$ of $\triangle ABC$ are congruent to the corresponding parts of $\triangle BAC$ this would serve the purpose. What are these corresponding parts; i.e., what must be shown? It must be shown that $\angle A \cong \angle B$, $\angle B \cong \angle A$, and $\overline{AB} \cong \overline{BA}$. The first and second statements are given in the hypotheses and the third is guaranteed by Axiom CS4. Thus it appears that the proof does indeed go through. It may be well to write down below the formal steps of the argument, though all the essential reasoning actually appears above.

Proof. (The notation refers to the figure on page 184.)

ASSERTIONS	SUPPORTING STATEMENTS
(1) $\angle BAC \cong \angle ABC$.	(1) Given.
(2) $\angle ABC \cong \angle BAC$.	(2) Given.
(3) $\overline{AB} \cong \overline{BA}$.	(3) Axiom CS4.
(4) $\triangle ABC \cong \triangle BAC$.	(4) Theorem 5.14 (**asa**).
(5) $\overline{AC} \cong \overline{BC}$.	(5) Theorem 5.11.

Notice that this proof is almost identical with that of Theorem 5.16 except that the **asa** Theorem was used instead of the **sss** Theorem to prove the triangles congruent.

If a triangle has at least two congruent sides it is called *isosceles*. If, in particular, all three sides are congruent it is *equilateral*. Note that the set of equilateral triangles is a subset of the set of isosceles triangles. The last two theorems are then really theorems about isosceles triangles. They could be restated as follows using this language.

Theorem 5.16 *In an isosceles triangle the angles with vertices opposite the congruent sides are congruent.*

Theorem 5.17 *If two angles of a triangle are congruent the triangle is isosceles and the congruent sides are opposite the vertices of the congruent angles.*

The angles $\angle AOB$ and $\angle BOC$ in the drawing have one ray $(\overrightarrow{OB})$ in common

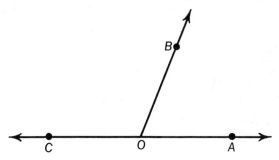

and the union of the remaining rays is a line. Such angles are called **supplementary** and each angle is a supplement of the other. More generally, if two angles are congruent to angles in this relationship they are called **supplementary.** This idea was introduced in problem **A3** of Problem Set 5.4, where an experiment with tracings led us to make the following conjecture which can now be proved.

Theorem 5.18 *If two angles are congruent, their supplements are congruent.*

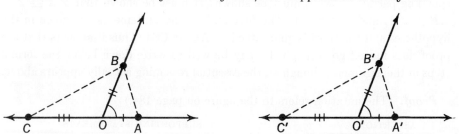

Analysis. Suppose it is given that $\angle AOB \cong \angle A'O'B'$. We are then to prove that $\angle BOC \cong \angle B'O'C'$. With the idea of trying to make capital of what has been learned about congruent triangles, let us suppose the points of A', B', and C' are chosen such that $\overline{OA} \cong \overline{O'A'}$, $\overline{OB} \cong \overline{O'B'}$, $\overline{OC} \cong \overline{O'C'}$. Observe these congruent segments have been indicated in the drawing. If the dotted segments $\overline{AB}$, $\overline{BC}$, $\overline{A'B'}$, and $\overline{B'C'}$ are drawn there appear three triangles that look as if they should be congruent.

The desired conclusion $\angle BOC \cong \angle B'O'C'$ would follow at once if we could only show that $\triangle OBC \cong \triangle O'B'C'$. How might this be proved? The most likely method would seem to be the **sss** Theorem. To apply this it would first be necessary to show that $\overline{BC} \cong \overline{B'C'}$. This, in turn, would follow if we only knew that $\triangle ABC \cong \triangle A'B'C'$. Do we have any means of proving this? We know, of course, that $\overline{AC} \cong \overline{A'C'}$. (Why?) We could prove the triangles congruent by **sas** if we knew that $\overline{AB} \cong \overline{A'B'}$ and $\angle A \cong \angle A'$. These last two results, in turn, would follow if we could show that $\triangle AOB \cong \triangle A'O'B'$. However, the last congruence is known to be true. (Why?) The formal proof of Theorem 5.18 can now be written merely by reversing the steps in the analysis. The essential steps are indicated below. You should supply the missing supporting statements and any other missing details.

Proof

ASSERTIONS	SUPPORTING STATEMENTS
(1) $\triangle OAB \cong \triangle O'A'B'$.	(1) Why?
(2) $\overline{AB} \cong \overline{A'B'}$ and $\angle A \cong \angle A'$.	(2) Why?
(3) $\overline{AC} \cong \overline{A'C'}$.	(3) Theorem 5.4.
(4) $\triangle ABC \cong \triangle A'B'C'$.	(4) Why?
(5) $\overline{BC} \cong \overline{B'C'}$.	(5) Why?
(6) $\triangle BOC \cong \triangle B'O'C'$.	(6) Why?
(7) $\angle BOC \cong \angle B'O'C'$.	(7) Why?

If two angles are related like $\angle AOB$ and $\angle COD$ in the following illustration,

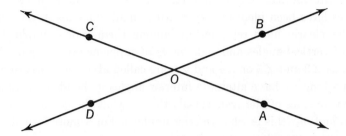

they are called (for some obscure reason) **vertical angles.** That is, two vertical angles have a common vertex and the union of their four rays is two intersecting lines. $\angle BOC$ and $\angle DOA$ in the drawing are also vertical angles. This definition was introduced in problem **A4** of Problem Set 5.4, where it was conjectured that two such angles are congruent. This is formally stated below. The proof is left to be done as an exercise.

Theorem 5.19 *If $\angle AOB$ and $\angle COD$ are vertical angles, then $\angle AOB \cong \angle COD$.*

A somewhat surprising bonus from the work on congruence is that it enables us to do something about a conjecture made in the last chapter. You will recall that two lines were said to be parallel if they were contained in a plane but had an empty intersection set; i.e., they have no points in common. Our physical experience seemed to suggest that such lines do exist, but we remarked that the axioms adopted at that time did not enable us to prove it. With the additional axioms on congruence now at our disposal we shall be able to do so.

As a preliminary we introduce some convenient terminology. Let coplanar lines m_1 and m_2 be met by a third line l at distinct points A and B as shown. Since

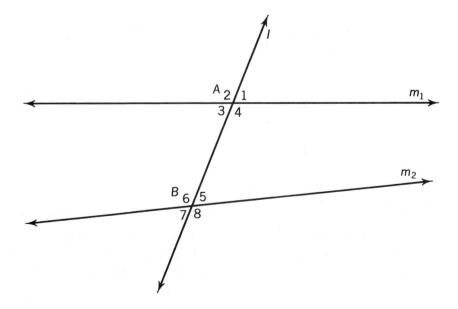

l meets m_1 and m_2 it is sometimes called a **transversal** of m_1 and m_2. In this way eight angles are formed, four with vertices at A and four with vertices at B. These angles have been identified by writing small numerals in their interiors. These angles clearly have relationships among them. For example, there are four pairs of vertical angles and eight pairs of supplementary angles. A pair of angles such as $\angle 3$ and $\angle 5$ or $\angle 4$ and $\angle 6$ are called **alternate interior angles.** Roughly speaking we have alternate interior angles if the identifying numerals are on opposite sides of the transversal (that is what the *alternate* means) and between m_1 and m_2 (this is what *interior* implies). For a more formal definition we might express the relationship like this:

> DEFINITION: Let two coplanar lines m_1 and m_2 be met by a transversal l at distinct points A and B. A pair of the angles formed are called **alternate interior angles** if (a) they each have a ray on the transversal l and the intersection of these rays is $\overline{AB}$, and (b) the other rays are on opposite sides of l.

In terms of this definition the following theorem can be stated:

Theorem 5.20 *If lines m_1 and m_2 in a plane are met by transversal l in such a way that a pair of alternate interior angles are congruent, then $m_1 \parallel m_2$.*

Before attempting to devise a proof, let us consider some intuitive ideas that might have led us to guess that this theorem is true. Suppose in the figure that $\angle 3 \cong \angle 5$. Then we know also that $\angle 4 \cong \angle 6$. (Why?)

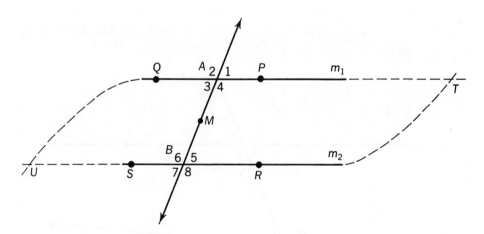

For this intuitive discussion let us assume the existence of a midpoint M for $\overline{AB}$. Let us imagine a tracing of $\overline{AB}$ and rays $\overrightarrow{AP}$ and $\overrightarrow{BR}$ and let the dots on the tracing over A, B, P, R be denoted by $A_0, B_0, P_0,$ and R_0, respectively. Imagine this tracing rotated about M so that A_0 now covers B and B_0 covers A. What would be the effect of such a rotation? Evidently $\overline{A_0M}$ now covers $\overline{BM}$. What happens to $\overrightarrow{A_0P_0}$? Since $\angle 4 \cong \angle 6$ it seems clear that $\overrightarrow{A_0P_0}$ will now cover $\overrightarrow{BS}$. Similarly, it seems clear that $\overrightarrow{B_0R_0}$ now covers $\overrightarrow{AQ}$ since $\angle 3 \cong \angle 5$. In other words, by this rotation the tracing which covers the two rays of m_1 and m_2 on one side of l now is made to cover the rays of m_1 and m_2 on the other side of l.

Suppose now that rays $\overrightarrow{AP}$ and $\overrightarrow{BR}$ have a point of intersection T as indicated in the illustration. In the original tracing T would be covered by a dot T_0 on $\overrightarrow{A_0P_0}$ and $\overrightarrow{B_0R_0}$. After the rotation it appears that T_0 would cover a point U on the other side of l which would be the intersection of $\overrightarrow{BS}$ and $\overrightarrow{AQ}$. This would mean that the distinct lines m_1 and m_2 would have two common points, T and U, violating Theorem 4.2. Thus it appears there can be no intersection T of m_1 and m_2 and the lines must be parallel.

This is actually quite a convincing argument. We cannot look upon it as a proof in our deductive system because our axioms do not say anything about the idea of rotation. The basic idea of the argument, however, is that if m_1 and m_2 intersect once they would intersect again and this would contradict Theorem 4.2. This idea can be used to give an honest proof of Theorem 5.20, that is, a proof based on our axioms.

Proof. It is given that $\angle 3 \cong \angle 5$ and we hope to prove that $m_1 \parallel m_2$. Note that also $\angle 4 \cong \angle 6$. (Why?) We propose to use a contradiction proof (as suggested in the discussion above). Let us assume therefore that m_1 and m_2 have an

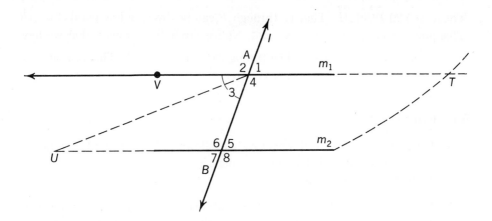

intersection point T. There is a point U of m_2 on the other side of $\overleftrightarrow{AB}$ such that $\overline{AT} \cong \overline{BU}$. (Why?) Draw $\overline{AU}$. It follows that $\triangle ABT \cong \triangle BAU$. (Why?) What can you conclude about $\angle BAU$? Justify each statement in the following line:

$$\angle BAU \cong \angle ABT \cong \angle BAV.$$

This means that $\overrightarrow{AU}$ and $\overrightarrow{AV}$ lie on the same side of l and form congruent angles with $\overrightarrow{AB}$. According to Axiom CA1 this means that $\overrightarrow{AU} = \overrightarrow{AV}$. That is, $U \in m_1$ since $\overrightarrow{AU}$ is the ray of m_1 opposite to $\overrightarrow{AT}$. This would mean there are two distinct lines, m_1 and m_2, on T and U. This is impossible. (Why?) Thus the assumption that there is a point in $m_1 \cap m_2$ leads to a contradiction and we must conclude that $m_1 \cap m_2 = \varnothing$, i.e., that $m_1 \parallel m_2$.

Notice that we have here chosen to give the proof in paragraph form rather than use the rigid format of assertions and supporting statements.

Suppose now that P is a point not on line $\overleftrightarrow{AB}$, as shown. By Axiom CA1 there

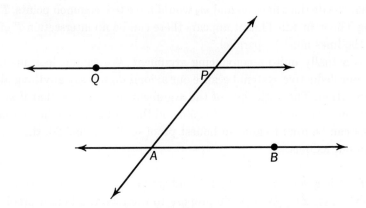

is a ray $\overrightarrow{PQ}$ on the opposite side of $\overleftrightarrow{AP}$ from B such that $\angle APQ \cong \angle PAB$. By Theorem 5.20 $\overleftrightarrow{PQ} \parallel \overleftrightarrow{AB}$. That is, through P can be drawn a line parallel to $\overleftrightarrow{AB}$. This proves a conjecture of Chapter 4. Notice carefully, however, that we have *not* shown that this is the *only* line through P parallel to $\overleftrightarrow{AB}$. This is a question to which we shall return in a later chapter.

Problem Set 5.6

A. 1. Carry out the procedure suggested following the proof of Theorem 5.15 to satisfy yourself that the argument is valid.

2. Prove Theorem 5.19.

B. 1. Prove that if a triangle is equilateral then its three angles are congruent.

2. Prove that if the three angles of a triangle are congruent then the triangle is equilateral.

C. From the figure at the top of page 191:

1. List all pairs of vertical angles.

2. List all pairs of supplementary angles.

3. If $\angle 1 \cong \angle 5$, prove that four of the eight angles are congruent to $\angle 1$ and the other four are congruent to $\angle 2$. Prove that in this case $m_1 \parallel m_2$.

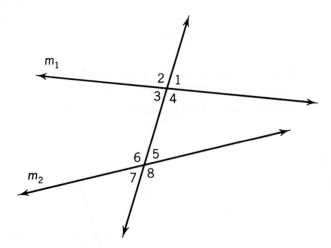

4. If $\angle 4 \cong \angle 5$ prove that four of the eight angles are congruent to $\angle 1$ and the other four to $\angle 2$. Can you conclude in this case that $m_1 \parallel m_2$?

D. In the triangles shown $\angle BAC \cong \angle B'A'C'$, $\angle ABC \cong \angle A'B'C'$ and

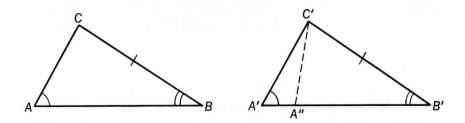

$\overline{BC} \cong \overline{B'C'}$, as indicated. Prove that $\triangle ABC \cong \triangle A'B'C'$. [HINT: Let A'' be the point of $\overrightarrow{B'A'}$ such that $\overline{B'A''} \cong \overline{BA}$. Then try to show $A' = A''$. Theorem 5.20 should prove useful in obtaining this conclusion. This result is often called the **aas** Theorem, since it concerns two angles and a side not between their vertices.]

5.7 Looking Toward Measurement

The choice of congruence as a topic to be developed in some detail was not a purely arbitrary one. In the curriculum of the elementary school the great majority of the geometric considerations cluster around the idea of measurement. Accordingly, it seems appropriate to lay particular emphasis on measurement and the geometric ideas involved in understanding it. In the development of measurement to be given in later chapters, the concept of congruence will be found to play a key role, which accounts for the emphasis on congruence here.

With this in mind we develop here some deductions on angles which will be relevant as we later consider measurement of angles. The first result was essentially conjectured in problem **A5** of Problem Set 5.4.

Theorem 5.21 *Let B be interior to* ∠*AOC and let B′ be on the C′ side of* $\overleftrightarrow{O'A'}$ *in the plane of* ∠*A′O′C′. If* ∠*AOC* ≅ ∠*A′O′C′ and* ∠*AOB* ≅ ∠*A′O′B′, then B′ is interior to* ∠*A′O′C′ and* ∠*BOC* ≅ ∠*B′O′C′.*

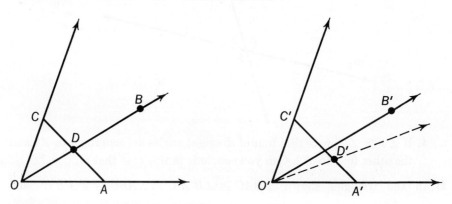

Proof. We may assume for convenience that the points are chosen so that $\overline{OA} \cong \overline{O'A'}$ and $\overline{OC} \cong \overline{O'C'}$. Draw the segment $\overline{CA}$. Since $\overline{CA}$ is (except for endpoints) interior to ∠*AOC* and since *A* and *C* are on opposite sides of $\overleftrightarrow{OB}$, $\overline{AC}$ meets $\overrightarrow{OB}$ in a point *D*.

[NOTE: You will recall that we have agreed, for the purposes of our development, to treat the properties of betweenness, interiors, exteriors, and the like as intuitively known. The theorem above is an example of a situation where these ideas have been used. In a fully axiomatic development of geometry, statements such as the existence of the point *D* would have to be proved and indeed might themselves be quite substantial theorems.]

Draw $\overline{C'A'}$ and let *D′* be the point of $\overrightarrow{A'C'}$ such that $\overline{AD} \cong \overline{A'D'}$. By Theorem 5.3 it follows that $D' \in \overline{A'C'}$; and that $\overline{DC} \cong \overline{D'C'}$. It is now easy to show in succession (1) that △*OAC* ≅ △*O′A′C′* (by **sas**), (2) that △*OAD* ≅ △*O′A′D′* (again by **sas**), and finally (3) that △*ODC* ≅ △*O′D′C′* (by **sss**). It follows by (2) that ∠*AOB* ≅ ∠*A′O′D′* (since ∠*AOB* is the same angle as ∠*AOD*). Thus $\overrightarrow{O'D'}$ is a ray on the *C′* side of $\overleftrightarrow{O'A'}$ such that ∠*A′O′D′* ≅ ∠*AOB*. But $\overrightarrow{O'B'}$ has this same property by hypothesis so by Axiom CA1 $\overrightarrow{OD'} = \overrightarrow{OB'}$. Since *D′* is on $\overline{C'A'}$ it is interior to ∠*A′O′C′*, so it follows that *B′* is also interior to ∠*A′O′C′*. This is one of the things to be proved. Moreover by congruence (3) ∠*D′O′C′* ≅ ∠*DOC*. Since $\overrightarrow{OD} = \overrightarrow{OB}$ and $\overrightarrow{O'D'} = \overrightarrow{O'B'}$ this statement can be written ∠*B′O′C′* ≅ ∠*BAC*. This completes the proof.

Roughly speaking, Theorem 5.21 may be described as follows: Consider the congruent sets consisting of ∠*AOC* and ∠*A′O′C′* and their interiors. If we cut off the congruent sets consisting of ∠*AOB* and ∠*A′O′B′* and their interiors, the

remaining sets are again congruent. For this reason it is sometimes called the
angle subtraction theorem. It is analogous, for angles, to Theorem 5.3 for
segments.

It occurs to us at once that there should also be an "angle addition" theorem.
This is indeed correct and we can establish the following.

Theorem 5.22 *Let B be interior to $\angle AOC$ and B' interior to $\angle A'O'C'$. If*
$\angle AOB \cong \angle A'O'B'$ *and* $\angle BOC \cong \angle B'O'C'$, *then* $\angle AOC \cong \angle A'O'C'$.

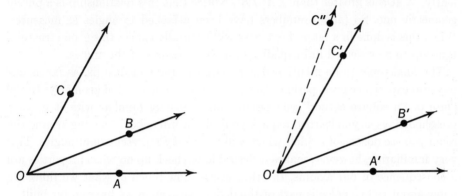

Proof. This result is quite easily obtained by using the last one. Let $\overrightarrow{O'C''}$ be
the ray on the C' side of $\overleftrightarrow{O'A'}$ so that $\angle AOC \cong \angle A'O'C''$. Then by Theorem
5.21, B' is interior to $\angle A'O'C''$ and $\angle B'O'C'' \cong \angle BOC$. We are given that
$\angle B'O'C' \cong \angle BOC$. Since C' and C'' are on the same side of $\overleftrightarrow{O'B'}$, $\overrightarrow{O'C'}$ and
$\overrightarrow{O'C''}$ are therefore rays on the same side of $\overleftrightarrow{O'B'}$ making congruent angles with
$\overrightarrow{O'B'}$. By Axiom CA1 $\overrightarrow{O'C'} = \overrightarrow{O'C''}$. Since $\angle A'O'C'' \cong \angle AOC$ it then follows
that $\angle A'O'C' \cong \angle AOC$.

This result for angles is quite comparable to Theorem 5.4 for segments.

By making use of congruent copies of angles we come quite naturally to the
possibility of comparing angles. Let $\angle AOB$ and $\angle A'O'B'$ be any angles. Accord-
ing to Axiom CA1 there is a unique ray $\overrightarrow{O'B''}$ on the B' side of $\overleftrightarrow{O'A'}$ such that

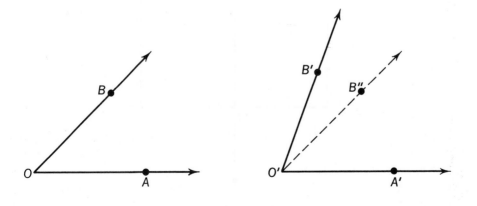

$\angle AOB \cong \angle A'O'B''$. It appears to us that there are three possible cases: (a) $\overrightarrow{O'B''}$ may be (except for point O') interior to $\angle A'O'B'$, as illustrated at the bottom of page 193, or (b) $\overrightarrow{O'B''} = \overrightarrow{O'B'}$, or (c) $\overrightarrow{O'B''}$ is exterior to $\angle A'O'B'$ so that $\overrightarrow{O'B'}$ is interior to $\angle A'O'B''$. [Note that here again we are drawing on our intuitive ideas of exteriors, interiors, etc.] In the first case (the one shown) we say $\angle AOB$ is smaller than $\angle A'O'B'$. In the second case, of course, the angles are congruent, and in the third case $\angle A'O'B'$ is smaller than $\angle AOB$, or equivalently, $\angle AOB$ is greater than $\angle A'O'B'$. Notice that this relationship is a purely geometric one. So far no numbers have been attached to angles as measures. When this is done in a later chapter we will naturally expect this geometric relationship to be reflected in inequalities for the measures of the angles.

The final topic to be mentioned here—that of right angles—is, as far as our physical experience goes, perhaps the most familiar one in all of geometry. In the guise of "a square corner" you became operationally familiar with it in your preschool days as you learned to pack your blocks into a box. Looking around the room you see dozens of models which you would say represent right angles. This very familiarity, however, makes it desirable to check up on what properties are a consequence of our axioms. In other words, how much of what we think we know about right angles is part of the deductive system we have so far built— i.e., how much can be proved from the axioms so far adopted?

The first necessity is to define exactly what is meant by a right angle. A suggestion as to a possible definition may be obtained by looking at an ordinary tile floor. You look at a point where the tiles have been fitted together and you

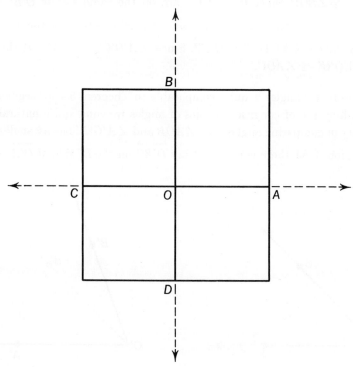

observe that four tiles seem to just fit there and fill up all the floor space around that point. Indeed the edges of the tiles seem to form (parts of) two intersecting lines. Thus two adjacent tiles have angles, say $\angle AOB$ and $\angle COB$, which appear supplementary. On the other hand, we know perfectly well that those tiles originally were just alike; i.e., one would fit exactly on the other. Thus in accord with our intuitive understanding of congruence we think of $\angle AOB$ and $\angle COB$ as congruent. This observation motivates the following formal definition.

> DEFINITION: An angle $\angle AOB$ is called a **right angle** if it is congruent to its supplement.

The first likely question to arise is: Is there such a thing as a right angle? If by this we mean to ask if it can be proved from our axioms that right angles exist, the question is not a stupid one. It is not obvious what the answer is. Since later, in discussing measurement, we shall wish to adopt an axiom which will imply the existence of right angles and quite a lot more besides, it does not seem worth the trouble to make a major production of it here. You may be interested to know, however, that the answer is actually yes. The existence of right angles *can* be proved on the basis of the present axioms. In fact, one of the problems at the end of this section shows how to obtain a right angle if we know that all segments have midpoints. A little judicious playing around with alternate interior angles and congruent triangles would enable us to prove that all segments have midpoints. Thus the existence of right angles *can* be proved, though we shall not trouble to do so.

Having sidestepped the last question, let us look at some of the properties of right angles which are so experimentally familiar that we hardly question them and see whether they can actually be proved. For example, suppose $\angle AOB$ is a right angle and suppose $\angle AOB \cong \angle A'O'B'$. Does it follow that $\angle A'O'B'$ is a right angle? Certainly in our experience a congruent copy of a right angle should be a right angle, but can it be proved from our axioms? Fortunately the answer is yes, as we see below.

Theorem 5.23 *If* $\angle AOB$ *is a right angle and if* $\angle AOB \cong \angle A'O'B'$, *then* $\angle A'O'B'$ *is a right angle.*

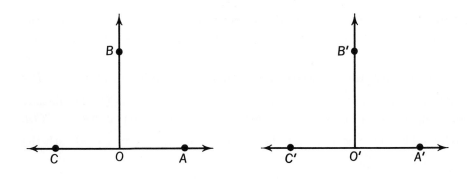

Proof. The proof is quite easy. Notice that what we must show is that $\angle A'O'B' \cong \angle C'O'B'$ since that is the definition of right angle. But we then observe the following:

ASSERTIONS	SUPPORTING STATEMENTS
(1) $A'O'B' \cong \angle AOB$.	(1) Given.
(2) $\angle C'O'B'$ is supplementary to $\angle A'O'B$.	(2) Definition of supplementary.
(3) $\angle COB$ is supplementary to $\angle AOB$.	(3) Definition of supplementary.
(4) $\angle COB \cong \angle C'O'B'$.	(4) Theorem 5.18 and steps 2 and 3.
(5) $\angle AOB \cong \angle COB$.	(5) Definition of right angle.
(6) $\angle A'O'B' \cong \angle C'O'B'$.	(6) Steps 1, 5, and 4 and Theorem 5.6 on transitivity of congruence.

A second conjecture strongly supported by our physical experience is that all right angles are congruent to each other. Thus if you and I each have a carpenter T-square we would be horrified if they would not fit on each other. Let us see if this can be proved.

Theorem 5.24 *Any two right angles are congruent.*

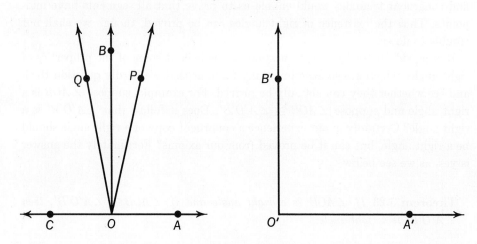

Proof. Let $\angle AOB$ and $\angle A'O'B'$ be right angles. We propose to prove that $\angle AOB \cong \angle A'O'B'$. Let us try a contradiction proof. That is, we assume $\angle AOB$ is *not* congruent to $\angle A'O'B'$ and hope to reach a contradiction. If these angles are not congruent there must be a ray $\overrightarrow{OP}$ different from $\overrightarrow{OB}$ such that $\angle AOP \cong \angle A'O'B'$. This ray $\overrightarrow{OP}$ must be interior to either $\angle AOB$ or $\angle COB$. For definiteness, suppose it is (as shown) interior to $\angle AOB$. We know $\angle AOB \cong \angle COB$. (Why?) Thus by Theorem 5.21 there is a ray $\overrightarrow{OQ}$ interior to $\angle COB$ such that

$\angle AOP \cong \angle COQ$. Both $\angle AOP$ and $\angle COQ$ are right angles. (Why?) We now observe the following sequence of congruences. Give the reason for each one.

$$\angle AOP \cong \angle COQ \cong \angle AOQ.$$

This would say that $\overrightarrow{OP}$ and $\overrightarrow{OQ}$ are distinct rays on the same side of $\overleftrightarrow{OA}$ forming congruent angles with $\overrightarrow{OA}$. This contradicts Axiom CA1 and is therefore impossible. Thus the assumption must be wrong and $\angle AOB$ and $\angle A'O'B'$ must be congruent.

In accord with our usual terminology, if two lines intersect in such a way that at least one (and hence actually all four) of the angles formed is a right angle the lines are said to be **perpendicular.** It is easy to show from the above theorem that if line m lies in a plane π and if $O \in m$ then there is at most one line in π perpendicular to m at O. This proof is given as a problem in the set below.

Problem Set 5.7

A. 1. Two lines intersect at a point O forming four angles. If one of the angles is a right angle show that they are all right angles.

2. Let ABC in drawing (a) be an isosceles triangle with $\overline{AC} \cong \overline{BC}$. Suppose $\overline{AB}$ has midpoint M, i.e., $\overline{AM} \cong \overline{MB}$. Prove that $\angle AMC$ is a right angle. [Note that this shows that right angles exist if we are sure that every segment has a midpoint.]

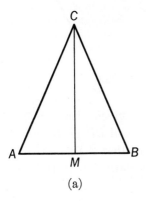

(a)

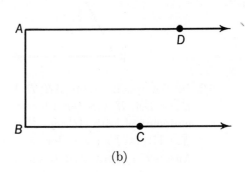

(b)

3. If $\angle DAB$ and $\angle CBA$ in drawing (b) are both right angles, prove that

$$\overleftrightarrow{AD} \parallel \overleftrightarrow{BC}.$$

B. 1. If m is a line in a plane π and $O \in m$, prove that there is at most one line in π which is perpendicular to m at O.

2. If m is a line and P a point not on m, prove there is at most one line through P and perpendicular to m. [HINT: Theorem 5.20 may be of use.]

C. For an alternate proof of Theorem 5.22, let D and D' be chosen as shown in the figure such that O is between A and D and O' between A' and D'. Then

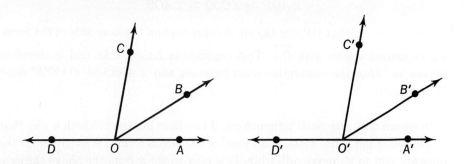

supply the supporting statements for the following assertions, in the order given.

(1) $\angle AOB \cong \angle A'O'B'$.

(2) $\angle BOD \cong \angle B'O'D'$.

(3) $\angle BOC \cong \angle B'O'C'$.

(4) $\angle COD \cong \angle C'O'D'$.

(5) $\angle AOC \cong \angle A'O'C'$.

D. 1. In the quadrilateral $ABCD$ below it is given that $\overline{AB} \cong \overline{CD}$ and $\angle ABD \cong \angle CDB$ as indicated. Prove that $\overline{AD} \cong \overline{CB}$.

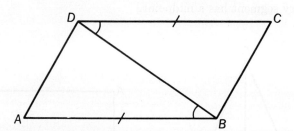

2. In the quadrilateral $ABCD$ below it is given that $\overline{AB} \cong \overline{CD}$ and $\overline{BC} \cong \overline{DA}$. If X is the intersection of $\overline{AC}$ and $\overline{BD}$ prove that X is the midpoint of both $\overline{AC}$ and $\overline{BD}$, i.e., prove that $\overline{AX} \cong \overline{XC}$ and $\overline{BX} \cong \overline{XD}$. [HINT: Can you devise a means to show that $\angle ABD \cong \angle CDB$? Also, what about $\angle ACD$ and $\angle CAB$?]

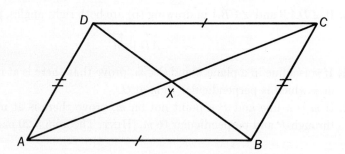

5.8 Axioms and Theorems in Chapter 5

Axiom **CS1** If two segments are congruent, the endpoints of one are matched with the endpoints of the other.

Axiom **CS2** If $\overline{AB} \cong \overline{CD}$, then $\overline{CD} \cong \overline{AB}$.

Axiom **CS3** If $\overline{AB} \cong \overline{CD}$ and $\overline{CD} \cong \overline{EF}$, then $\overline{AB} \cong \overline{EF}$.

Axiom **CS4** For all segments $\overline{AB}$ it is true that $\overline{AB} \cong \overline{BA}$.

Axiom **CS5** If $\overline{AB}$ is a segment and $\overrightarrow{PT}$ a ray there is a unique point S with $S \in \overrightarrow{PT}$ such that $\overline{AB} \cong \overline{PS}$.

Axiom **CS6** If $\overline{PR} \underset{x}{\cong} \overline{P'R'}$, where x denotes a particular congruence, and if $Q \underset{x}{\leftrightarrow} Q'$, where $Q \in \overline{PR}$, then $\overline{PQ} \cong \overline{P'Q'}$ and $\overline{QR} \cong \overline{Q'R'}$.

Axiom **CS7** Let P, Q, R be distinct points such that $Q \in \overline{PR}$. If P', Q', R' are points such that $\overline{PQ} \cong \overline{P'Q'}$, $\overline{QR} \cong \overline{Q'R'}$, $\overline{PR} \cong \overline{P'R'}$, then $Q' \in \overline{P'R'}$.

Axiom **CA1** Let $\angle ABC$ be an angle and $\overrightarrow{QP}$ a ray in plane π. Then in π on a given side of $\overleftrightarrow{QP}$ there is exactly one ray $\overrightarrow{QR}$ such that $\angle ABC \cong \angle PQR$.

Axiom **CA2** Let P and Q be points other than the vertex on the sides $\overrightarrow{BA}$ and $\overrightarrow{BC}$, respectively, of $\angle ABC$. Similarly, let P', Q' be points other than the vertex on sides $\overrightarrow{B'A'}$ and $\overrightarrow{B'C'}$, respectively, of $\angle A'B'C'$. If $\overline{BP} \cong \overline{B'P'}$, $\overline{BQ} \cong \overline{B'Q'}$ and $\overline{PQ} \cong \overline{P'Q'}$, then $\angle ABC \cong \angle A'B'C'$.

Theorem **5.1** If $\overline{AB} \underset{a}{\cong} \overline{CD}$ and $\overline{AB} \underset{b}{\cong} \overline{CD}$, then correspondences a and b are the same.

Theorem **5.2** If $\overline{AB}$ is any segment, then $\overline{AB} \cong \overline{AB}$. Moreover, the correspondence matches every point of $\overline{AB}$ with itself.

Theorem **5.3** Let $B \in \overline{AC}$ and $B' \in \overrightarrow{A'C'}$. If $\overline{AB} \cong \overline{A'B'}$ and $\overline{AC} \cong \overline{A'C'}$, then $\overline{BC} \cong \overline{B'C'}$. Moreover, $B' \in \overline{A'C'}$.

Theorem **5.4** Let $B \in \overline{AC}$ and $B' \in \overline{A'C'}$. If $\overline{AB} \cong \overline{A'B'}$ and $\overline{BC} \cong \overline{B'C'}$, then $\overline{AC} \cong \overline{A'C'}$.

Theorem **5.5** If $\overline{AB} \underset{a}{\cong} \overline{A'B'}$ and if $C \underset{a}{\leftrightarrow} C'$, $D \underset{a}{\leftrightarrow} D'$, then $\overline{CD} \cong \overline{C'D'}$.

Theorem **5.6** If $s \cong s'$ and $s' \cong s''$, then $s \cong s''$.

Theorem **5.7** If $\overline{AB} \cong s'$ and if in this congruence $A \leftrightarrow A'$, $B \leftrightarrow B'$, then $s' = \overline{A'B'}$.

Theorem **5.8** Let $s \cong s'$. If $\mathfrak{I} \subset s$ and if $\mathfrak{I}'$ is the set of image points of $\mathfrak{I}$ in s', then $\mathfrak{I} \cong \mathfrak{I}'$.

Theorem **5.9** Let $s \cong s'$ and $\overline{AB} \subset s$. If $A \leftrightarrow A'$, $B \leftrightarrow B'$, then $\overline{A'B'} \subset s'$ and $\overline{AB} \cong \overline{A'B'}$.

Theorem **5.10** If $\overrightarrow{OA}$ and $\overrightarrow{O'A'}$ are any rays there is exactly one congruence x such that $\overrightarrow{OA} \underset{x}{\cong} \overrightarrow{O'A'}$. Moreover, $O \underset{x}{\leftrightarrow} O'$.

Theorem.5.11. If $\triangle ABC \cong \triangle A'B'C'$, then
  (a) $\overline{AB} \cong \overline{A'B'}$, $\overline{BC} \cong \overline{B'C'}$, $\overline{CA} \cong \overline{C'A'}$.
  (b) $\angle ABC \cong \angle A'B'C'$, $\angle BCA \cong \angle B'C'A'$ and $\angle CAB \cong \angle C'A'B'$.

Theorem **5.12** If $\triangle ABC$ and $\triangle A'B'C'$ are such that $\overline{AB} \cong \overline{A'B'}$, $\overline{BC} \cong \overline{B'C'}$ and $\overline{CA} \cong \overline{C'A'}$, then $\triangle ABC \cong \triangle A'B'C'$.

Theorem **5.13** If $\triangle ABC$ and $\triangle A'B'C'$ are such that $\overline{AB} \cong \overline{A'B'}$, $\overline{AC} \cong \overline{A'C'}$ and $\angle BAC \cong \angle B'A'C'$, then $\triangle ABC \cong \triangle A'B'C'$.

Theorem **5.14** If $\triangle ABC$ and $\triangle A'B'C'$ are such that $\angle ABC \cong \angle A'B'C'$, $\angle BAC \cong \angle B'A'C'$ and $\overline{AB} \cong \overline{A'B'}$, then $\triangle ABC \cong \triangle A'B'C'$.

Theorem **5.15** For any angle $\angle ABC$ it is true that $\angle ABC \cong \angle CBA$.

Theorem **5.16** If, in a triangle, two sides are congruent, the angles with vertices opposite these sides are congruent.

Theorem **5.17** If two angles of a triangle are congruent, the sides opposite their vertices are congruent.

Theorem **5.18** If two angles are congruent their supplements are congruent.

Theorem **5.19** If $\angle AOB$ and $\angle COD$ are vertical angles, then $\angle AOB \cong \angle COD$.

Theorem **5.20** If lines m_1 and m_2 in a plane are met by transversal k in such a way that a pair of alternate interior angles are congruent, the lines are parallel.

Theorem **5.21** Let B be interior to $\angle AOC$ and let B' be on the C' side of $\overleftrightarrow{O'A'}$ in the plane of $\angle A'O'C'$. If $\angle AOC \cong \angle A'O'C'$ and $\angle AOB \cong \angle A'O'B'$, then B' is interior to $\angle A'O'C'$ and $\angle BOC \cong \angle B'O'C'$.

Theorem **5.22** Let B be interior to $\angle AOC$ and B' interior to $\angle A'O'C'$. If $\angle AOB \cong \angle A'O'B'$ and $\angle BOC \cong \angle B'O'C'$, then $\angle AOC \cong \angle A'O'C'$.

Theorem **5.23** If $\angle AOB$ is a right angle and if $\angle AOB \cong \angle A'O'B'$, then $\angle A'O'B'$ is a right angle.

Theorem **5.24** Any two right angles are congruent.

5.9 Terminal Tasks for Chapter 5

1. To use the following vocabulary correctly: isosceles, equilateral, supplementary angles, vertical angles, right angles, perpendicular, alternate interior angles, parallel lines, transversal, congruence, one-to-one correspondence.

2. To demonstrate experimentally with simple models, the intuitive geometric meaning of congruence.

3. To demonstrate familiarity with the axioms for congruence of line segments and congruence of angles by (a) locating in the text any particular axiom to which the student wishes to refer, (b) recognizing the application of the axioms when used as supporting statements for proofs in the text, (c) using the axioms (without necessarily stating them) in simple two- or three-step original proofs.

4. To be able to follow the proofs for theorems concerned with congruent segments, congruent angles, or congruent general point sets, and apply the conclusions in solving simple original exercises. It is not essential that the theorems be quoted verbatim.
5. To identify the strategies used in writing the proofs in the text and apply them in writing proofs for simple original exercises.
6. To interpret the implications of the definition of congruence of general point sets in situations where S is a set of discrete points, or a curve, or a simple closed curve, or a region.
7. To prove the theorems on congruence of triangles in Section 5.5.
8. To select a suitable strategy on the basis of the hypothesis, and to apply the strategy in proving two triangles congruent in simple problems.
9. To recognize the rigidity property of a triangle and to demonstrate the relation of this property to the **sss** congruence theorem for triangles.
10. To differentiate between the physical experiments giving rise to conjectures and the deductive proof for theorems suggested by the conjectures.

REVIEW EXERCISES

A. 1. Imagine the plane quadrilateral at the right to have been formed from wooden strips nailed at the corners. Show two ways of adding one additional strip so that the figure becomes rigid (if kept in the plane). What theorem is involved in asserting the rigidity?

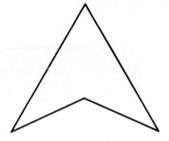

2. As in problem **A1**, consider the following plane figures formed from wooden strips. In each case indicate the smallest number of strips to be added to make it rigid. Show how they could be added.

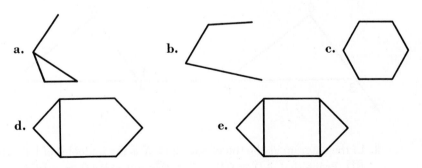

a. b. c.

d. e.

B. Diagrams (1) and (2) are intended to be congruent in more than one way. Give the points which correspond to A, B, C, D, E, and F in each congruence you seem to observe.

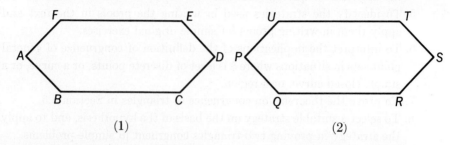

(1)   (2)

C. 1. Two coplanar lines, m_1 and m_2, are met by a transversal k as shown. If $\angle 1 \cong \angle 7$, prove that $m_1 \parallel m_2$.

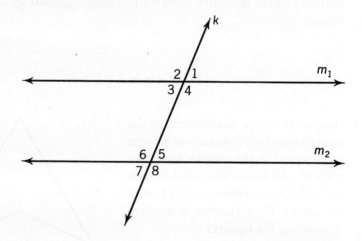

2. In the diagram $\angle 1 \cong \angle 2$, $\angle 3 \cong \angle 4$, and $\overline{AB} \cong \overline{A'B'}$. Prove that $\triangle ABC \cong \triangle A'B'C'$.

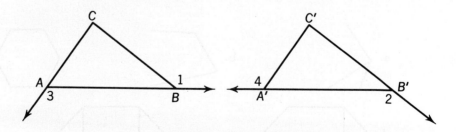

3. In the diagram at the top of page 203, X is the midpoint of both $\overline{AC}$ and $\overline{BD}$. Prove that $\overline{AD} \cong \overline{CB}$, $\overline{AB} \cong \overline{CD}$ and $\angle BAD \cong \angle DCB$.

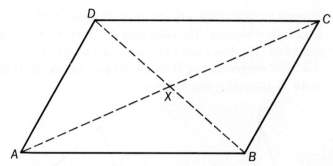

D. 1. Segments $\overline{AB}$ and $\overline{PQ}$ are such that $\overline{AB} \underset{x}{\cong} \overline{PQ}$. Point M is the midpoint of $\overline{AB}$. If $M \underset{x}{\leftrightarrow} N$, prove that N is the midpoint of $\overline{PQ}$.

2. Sets $\mathcal{S}$ and $\mathcal{S}'$ are such that $\mathcal{S} \underset{x}{\cong} \mathcal{S}'$. If $\overrightarrow{AB} \subset \mathcal{S}$ and if $A \underset{x}{\leftrightarrow} A'$, $B \underset{x}{\leftrightarrow} B'$ prove that $\overrightarrow{A'B'} \subset \mathcal{S}'$.

E. 1. Coplanar lines m_1 and m_2 are met by transversal k and $\triangle ABC$ is a triangle. If $\angle 1 \cong \angle A$, $\angle 2 \cong \angle B$ and $\overline{PQ} \cong \overline{AB}$, prove that m_1 and m_2 intersect. [HINT: Consider a point R of m_1 such that $\overline{PR} \cong \overline{AC}$.]

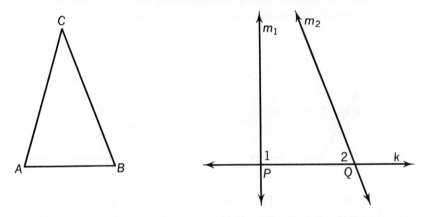

2. Segments $\overline{AC}$ and $\overline{BD}$ below are perpendicular at O. If $\overline{OA} \cong \overline{OB} \cong \overline{OC} \cong \overline{OD}$ prove that $\overline{AB} \cong \overline{BC} \cong \overline{CD} \cong \overline{DA}$ and that $\angle BAD \cong \angle CBA \cong \angle DCB \cong \angle ADC$. What would you conjecture about these four angles? Do you seem able to prove this by using the results of this chapter?

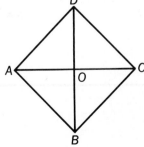

F. 1. A pupil in your class objects that Theorem 5.17 (stating that if two angles are congruent the sides opposite their vertices are congruent) is ridiculous. He shows you the following drawing in which $\angle 1 \cong \angle 2$ but $\overline{AB}$ is *not* congruent to $\overline{CD}$. What did you find in this chapter that would assist in answering this objection?

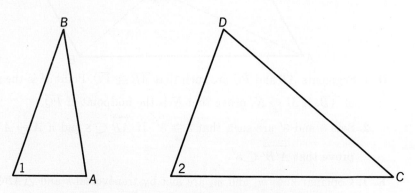

2. One of your pupils objects that it seems unreasonable to say that $\angle PQR$ in the diagram below is larger than $\angle ABC$. What did you find in this chapter that is relevant to this question?

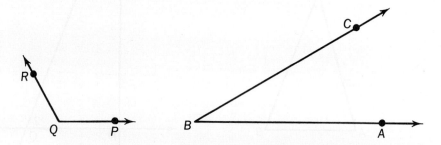

3. One of your fellow students (not a pupil this time) objects to the statement in Section 5.6 that we do not know there is a unique line through P parallel to m. After all, he argues, a parallel to m through P must have a fixed distance from m and there clearly can be at most one such line containing P. What do you find in this chapter which is relevant to this remark?

6 The System
of Integers

6.1 What Next?

In Chapter 2 an effort was made to gather the information we had about whole numbers and organize it in a deductive system. We decided which pieces of information would be definitions, which pieces of information would be used as axioms and which we would prove as theorems in the system. The approach was highly intuitive and there was frequent dependence upon your experiences in the arithmetic you learned for the system of whole numbers. We did not try to define what was meant by a "whole number" or by the operations of addition and multiplication of whole numbers. It was assumed that you had been adding and multiplying whole numbers for years and the development of the system was based upon this familiarity. In the course of our studies we observed that subtraction and division could be performed in W only under limited circumstances.

What we would like to do now is to try to build a new number system which would have the structure of a field. Then we could do all the arithmetic we could perform in W and also *always* subtract and *always* divide (except by the additive identity, i_1). This is a pretty big order so we will split it into two parts. First, we will set up a number system which will have closure with respect to addition, multiplication, and subtraction along with the other properties of W. If this number system fulfills the eleven properties of a field, we will have achieved our goal. If it does not have all these properties, then we will consider those properties which are absent and think about how we might create a new system so that it will have the structure of a field.

We no longer need to lean so heavily upon your experiences in elementary arithmetic. In this chapter we will want to describe the elements in our number system and define the operations we wish to use on these elements. In order to do this we must digress to examine some new ideas and to become acquainted with the language mathematicians use to discuss these ideas.

6.2 Equivalence Relations and Equivalence Classes

When we say "Nancy is the daughter of Mrs. Jones," we are indicating a relation between Nancy and Mrs. Jones: "is the daughter of." If we declare that "Every house on this block belongs to Mr. Smith," then we are applying the relation "belongs to." Mathematical relations with which you are familiar are = (equals), > (is greater than), < (is less than). Those of you who have studied geometry recognize the symbols || (is parallel to), ⊥ (is perpendicular to), ≅ is congruent to), which name relations used extensively in that course.

Some relations have very special properties. We accept the fact that $a = a$. When a relation has this property we say it is **reflexive**. However ">" is not reflexive because 3 is not greater than 3. "Is the daughter of" also is not reflexive since it doesn't make sense to say "Nancy is the daughter of herself."

The equality relation is said to be **symmetric** because we agree that if $a = b$, then $b = a$. The relation "<" is not symmetric since if $7 < 12$, it is not true that $12 < 7$. "Is an element of" is also not a symmetric relation since $10 \in W$ does not imply that $W \in 10$. However, the relation "is perpendicular to" is symmetric, for if line $m \perp$ line n, then it is also true that line $n \perp$ line m.

The equality relation also has the property of **transitivity** because we accept the fact that if $a = b$ and $b = c$, then $a = c$. The relation ">" is also transitive and this is illustrated by: $7 > 5, 5 > 1$, and, obviously, $7 > 1$. "Is perpendicular to" is not transitive, as demonstrated by the diagram. Here line $a \perp$ line c and

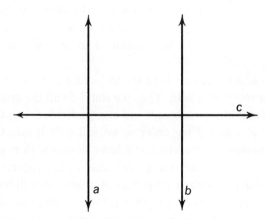

line $c \perp$ line b but line a is not perpendicular to line b. "Is the mother of" is not a transitive relation: If Mrs. Lee is the mother of Mrs. Jones and Mrs. Jones is the mother of Nancy, then it does not hold that Mrs. Lee is the mother of Nancy.

A relation is called an **equivalence relation** if it is reflexive, symmetric, and transitive. An equivalence relation is important to us because it separates all the elements of a set on which it is defined into classes which are mutually exclusive. (For this text we will regard this theorem as true without demonstrating the proof.) This means that if we use the equivalence relation on the elements of the set then every element of the set appears in some class and no element appears in two classes. As an example, let us consider the set of all United States' coins under one dollar and the relation "has the same denomination as." The relation is an equivalence relation:

> *Reflexive:* Any coin has the same denomination as itself.
> *Symmetric:* If one coin has the same denomination as a second coin, then the second coin has the same denomination as the first.
> *Transitive:* If coin A has the same denomination as coin B, and coin B has the same denomination as coin C, then coin A has the same denomination as coin C.

This equivalence relation will partition the set of coins into five equivalence classes: cent, nickel, dime, quarter, and half-dollar. Every coin under one dollar will be in one of these five classes and no coin will be in more than one class. The classes are mutually exclusive and exhaust all the elements in the set.

As an example from arithmetic, let us take the set of all whole numbers and the relation: "has the same remainder when divided by 3 as." The relation is an equivalence relation:

> *Reflexive:* n has the same remainder when divided by 3 as n.
> *Symmetric:* If n has the same remainder when divided by 3 as m, then m has the same remainder when divided by 3 as n.
> *Transitive:* If l has the same remainder when divided by 3 as m, and m has the same remainder when divided by 3 as n, then l has the same remainder when divided by 3 as n.

This equivalence relation partitions the set of whole numbers into 3 equivalence classes which we will name $\bar{0}$, $\bar{1}$, $\bar{2}$. Into the class $\bar{0}$ go all those whole numbers which have a remainder of 0 when divided by 3: i.e., $3 \cdot q + 0$. Into class $\bar{1}$ go all those whole numbers which have a remainder of 1 when divided by 3: i.e., $3 \cdot q + 1$. Into class $\bar{2}$ go all whole numbers which may be written $3 \cdot q + 2$, i.e., which have a remainder of 2 when divided by 3. No other remainders are possible when division of a whole number by 3 is completed. Every whole number will appear in one and only one equivalence class:

$$\bar{0}: \quad 0, \quad 3, \quad 6, \quad 9, \quad 12, \ldots$$
$$\bar{1}: \quad 1, \quad 4, \quad 7, \quad 10, \quad 13, \ldots$$
$$\bar{2}: \quad 2, \quad 5, \quad 8, \quad 11, \quad 14, \ldots$$

The elements of the new number system we are planning to develop are equivalence classes of the elements of the set J which we will consider in the next section.

Problem Set 6.2

A. Each of the following relations is defined on the set indicated. Decide whether the relations are reflexive, symmetric, and/or transitive.

   1. "is a cousin of"—people.
   2. "is at war with"—nations.
   3. "belongs to the same club as"—people.
   4. "is a sister of"—all women.
   5. "is a sister of"—people.
   6. "is more expensive than"—coats.
   7. "has the same truth value as"—implications.
   8. "is two inches away from"—slats of a venetian blind.
   9. "has the same mathematical background as"—students in this class.
  10. "fits tighter than"—shoes tried on the same person.

B. Decide whether each of the following relations is an equivalence relation.

   1. "is a multiple of"—whole numbers.
   2. "is a factor of"—whole numbers.
   3. "is exactly as long as"—line segments.
   4. "is prime to"—whole numbers.
   5. "is not prime to"—whole numbers.
   6. "is divisible by"—whole numbers.
   7. "is named by the same numeral as"—whole numbers.
   8. "is parallel to"—line segments.
   9. "is 5 more than"—whole numbers.
  10. "is not less than"—whole numbers.

C. Set up the equivalence classes into which the relation "has the same remainder when divided by 10 as" separates (or partitions) the set of whole numbers. Show that the classes are mutually exclusive and exhaustive.

6.3 The Set *J*

Sometimes it takes two pieces of information to identify an object or a location. There are many illustrations of this in the physical world. To locate a building we usually give the street and the number; a theater ticket is marked with the row and seat number; a signature usually has a given name and a family name. Frequently the order in which the two pieces of information are given makes a difference. Number 12 on 13th street is a different building from number 13 on 12th street; the first seat in the 10th row is different from the 10th seat in the first row; and the woman's name, Meredith John, might be mistaken for that of a man if written John Meredith. It takes a pair of numerals, one for the numerator and one for the denominator, to form a fraction. We might decide to use the symbol (2, 5) as a substitute for $\frac{2}{5}$. Then, if we were to change the order of the number pair to get (5, 2) the new fraction named would be $\frac{5}{2}$. Since $\frac{5}{2}$ is not the same as $\frac{2}{5}$, (5, 2) is not meant to be the same as (2, 5). When we use two numbers to describe an element and the order in which the numbers are given is significant, then we call the two numbers an **ordered pair.**

Now we are ready to describe the elements of a new system, J, which we wish to create. Recall that when we studied the set of whole numbers we did not make any effort to define what we meant by the concept "one" or "four" or "ten" or any of the elements of the set of whole numbers. We simply wrote names for the elements of W (such as 1, 4, and 10) and proceeded to rely on your previous experience to add, subtract, multiply, and divide the elements. On this basis we examined the properties of the mathematical system of whole numbers. In this chapter we will describe more carefully the numbers we create. For the elements of J we will consider an ordered pair of any whole numbers, a and b, which we will symbolize as "$(a - b)$," read "a dash b." The words "ordered pair" mean that we intend that $(a - b)$ shall be an element different from the element $(b - a)$. The notation has been deliberately chosen so that in certain cases you will associate the pair with a whole number. Since the dash looks like a subtraction sign you are meant to associate the pair $(5 - 2)$ with the whole number 3 and the pair $(12 - 7)$ with the whole number 5. Whenever $a \geq b$, the pair $(a - b)$ is thus said to be associated with or to resemble a whole number. It should be understood that the pairs $(9 - 3)$, $(14 - 8)$, $(6 - 0)$, $(27 - 21)$ which resemble the same whole number are by definition **different** elements of J.

The symbol $(a - b)$ with $a < b$ will name some element which we do not associate with any number we already know, and which we arbitrarily put in J. We must keep in mind that the ordered pair which we write as $(a - b)$ is an element of J with no restrictions placed on a and b other than that they be whole numbers. This means that $\left(\frac{4}{5} - \frac{1}{3}\right)$ is not in J, nor is $(2.67 - 2)$. However $(7469 - 23) \in J$ and $(0 - 3) \in J$.

We will want the equal relation, $=$, for elements in J to conform with the notion that equality means two names for the same element. This requires that two ordered pairs in J must have the same first component and the same second component in order to be equal. That is, we shall want to say:

> If $(p - q) \in J$ and $(r - s) \in J$, then $(p - q) = (r - s)$ if and only if $p = r$ and $q = s$.

Since $(a - b)$ is associated with a whole number when $a \geq b$ we may refer to definitions and theorems established in the system of whole numbers to suggest clues for possible definitions and theorems that might be useful for J. If you look back at problems **B4** and **B5** of Problem Set 2.8 you will recall that these exercises provided us with certain circumstances under which we had two names for the same whole number. Observe that it was established that if a, b, c, $d \in W$ with $a \geq b$, $c \geq d$, then $a - b = c - d$ if and only if $a + d = b + c$.

We would like to define a corresponding relation on the elements of J. We have already given meaning to the equality relation for elements of J and that meaning will not fit in with the above statement for W. Therefore we will define a new relation, $\sim$ (called tilde), on the elements of J in accordance with the suggestion above:

> If $(a - b)$ and $(c - d)$ are elements in J, then $(a - b) \sim (c - d)$ if and only if $a + d = b + c$ in W.

Observe that $(a - b) \sim (c - d)$ is a sentence in J while $a + d = b + c$ is a sentence in W. Recall that if $(a - b) \in J$, then a and b must be in W. It is of interest to us to examine this relation to see if it is an equivalence relation, for then it would separate J into mutually exclusive and exhaustive classes.

> *Reflexive:* We know that $(a - b) \sim (a - b)$ if and only if $a + b = b + a$. Since $a + b = b + a$ is true in W, $(a - b) \sim (a - b)$ is true in J by our definition of $\sim$.
>
> *Symmetric:* We wish to show that if $(a - b) \sim (c - d)$, then $(c - d) \sim (a - b)$. If $(a - b) \sim (c - d)$, then we have $a + d = b + c$ in W. In order to have $(c - d) \sim (a - b)$ we need to show that $c + b = d + a$.
>
> It is clear that $a + d = b + c$ and $c + b = d + a$ are two equivalent sentences. What properties of W under addition would you need to use to establish this? Hence $(c - d) \sim (a - b)$ and we have demonstrated the symmetric property for the relation $\sim$.
>
> *Transitive:* Here we want to prove that if $(a - b) \sim (c - d)$ and $(c - d) \sim (e - f)$, then $(a - b) \sim (e - f)$.
>
> Since $(a - b) \sim (c - d)$ we have $a + d = b + c$ in W.
>
> Since $(c - d) \sim (e - f)$ we have $c + f = d + e$ in W.
>
> Then $(a + d) + (c + f) = (b + c) + (d + e)$ by closure under addition in W.
>
> By commutativity, associativity, and the Cancellation Law for Addition in W we can get $a + f = b + e$.
>
> Our definition of the relation $\sim$ says that if $a + f = b + e$ in W, then $(a - b) \sim (e - f)$ in J.

The presence of these three properties indicates that $\sim$ is an equivalence relation and when used on J, it partitions J into equivalence classes. Thus, every element of J is in one and only one equivalence class, and $(a - b)$ is in the same equivalence class as $(c - d)$ if and only if $(a - b) \sim (c - d)$.

We see that $(9 - 2) \sim (12 - 5)$ because $9 + 5 = 2 + 12$. Hence $(9 - 2)$ and $(12 - 5)$ are in the same equivalence class. The element $(17 - 10)$ is also in that equivalence class. However $(11 - 6)$ is not in the same equivalence class as $(9 - 2)$, since $(11 - 6) \not\sim (9 - 2)$, for $11 + 2 \neq 6 + 9$.

Suppose we chose an element of J, such as $(0 - 0)$, and wished to know which elements of J belonged to the same class as $(0 - 0)$. Because we are assuming that we do not know these elements, let us represent them by $(x - y)$ where we do not know the whole numbers x and y. If $(0 - 0)$ and $(x - y)$ are to be in the same equivalence class, then

$$(0 - 0) \sim (x - y)$$

and

$$0 + y = 0 + x \text{ in } W$$

and

$$y = x.$$

This tells us that when the elements of J are in the same class as $(0 - 0)$, the two components of the ordered pair are the same. Thus $(0 - 0)$, $(1 - 1)$, $(2 - 2)$, $(3 - 3)$, $(4 - 4)$, ..., $(n - n)$ are all in the same class.

Which elements of J belong to the same class as $(1 - 0)$? If

$$(1 - 0) \sim (x - y)$$

then

$$1 + y = 0 + x \text{ in } W$$

and

$$1 + y = x.$$

This tells us that the first component "x" is to be 1 more than the second component "y." Hence $(1 - 0)$, $(2 - 1)$, $(3 - 2)$, $(4 - 3)$, ..., $([n + 1] - n)$ ... are all in the same class.

If $(a - b) \in J$, then a and b are in W. Hence $a = b$ or $a > b$ or $a < b$. If $a = b$, then $(a - b)$ is $(a - a)$ and $(a - a) \sim (0 - 0)$ in J. If $a > b$, then $a = b + k$ so that $(a - b)$ is $([b + k] - b)$ and $([b + k] - b) \sim (k - 0)$ in J. If $a < b$, then $b = a + k$ so that $(a - b)$ is $(a - [a + k])$, and $(a - [a + k]) \sim (0 - k)$ in J. Hence any element of J belongs to a class which will also have as a member $(0 - k)$ or $(k - 0)$ for some whole number k.

Table 6.1, on page 212, shows the partitioning of J, by the relation $\sim$, into equivalence classes.

Each row contains the elements of an equivalence class. Why can't we write out all the elements of J? Can you recognize any patterns in this table? Can you tell in which row each of the following elements of J would appear: $(23 - 22)$? $(15 - 12)$? $(a - a)$? $(9 - 11)$? $(33 - 21)$? What would be the first element of the row in which $(11 - 6)$ would appear? Can you show that every element of J will surely appear in some row? Since the relation $\sim$ partitions J into equivalence classes such that $(a - b)$ belongs to the same class as $(c - d)$

Table 6.1

⋮	⋮	⋮	⋮	⋮	⋮	⋮	⋮	⋮	⋮	⋮
$(0-0)$	$(1-1)$	$(2-2)$	$(3-3)$	$(4-4)$	$(5-5)$	$(6-6)$	$(7-7)$	$(8-8)$	...	$(n-n)$
$(1-0)$	$(2-1)$	$(3-2)$	$(4-3)$	$(5-4)$	$(6-5)$	$(7-6)$	$(8-7)$	$(9-8)$	...	$([n+1]-n)$
$(0-1)$	$(1-2)$	$(2-3)$	$(3-4)$	$(4-5)$	$(5-6)$	$(6-7)$	$(7-8)$	$(8-9)$	...	$(n-[n+1])$
$(2-0)$	$(3-1)$	$(4-2)$	$(5-3)$	$(6-4)$	$(7-5)$	$(8-6)$	$(9-7)$	$(10-8)$	...	$([n+2]-n)$
$(0-2)$	$(1-3)$	$(2-4)$	$(3-5)$	$(4-6)$	$(5-7)$	$(6-8)$	$(7-9)$	$(8-10)$	...	$(n-[n+2])$
$(3-0)$	$(4-1)$	$(5-2)$	$(6-3)$	$(7-4)$	$(8-5)$	$(9-6)$	$(10-7)$	$(11-8)$	...	$([n+3]-n)$
$(0-3)$	$(1-4)$	$(2-5)$	$(3-6)$	$(4-7)$	$(5-8)$	$(6-9)$	$(7-10)$	$(8-11)$	...	$(n-[n+3])$
$(4-0)$	$(5-1)$	$(6-2)$	$(7-3)$	$(8-4)$	$(9-5)$	$(10-6)$	$(11-7)$	$(12-8)$	...	$([n+4]-n)$
$(0-4)$	$(1-5)$	$(2-6)$	$(3-7)$	$(4-8)$	$(5-9)$	$(6-10)$	$(7-11)$	$(8-12)$	...	$(n-[n+4])$
⋮	⋮	⋮	⋮	⋮	⋮	⋮	⋮	⋮		⋮
$(12-0)$	$(13-1)$	$(14-2)$	$(15-3)$	$(16-4)$	$(17-5)$	$(18-6)$	$(19-7)$	$(20-8)$	...	$([n+12]-n)$
$(0-12)$	$(1-13)$	$(2-14)$	$(3-15)$	$(4-16)$	$(5-17)$	$(6-18)$	$(7-19)$	$(8-20)$		$(n-[n+12])$

if and only if $(a - b) \sim (c - d)$, we will henceforth read $(a - b) \sim (c - d)$ as "*a* dash *b* belongs to the same equivalence class as *c* dash *d*."

Any element of an equivalence class may be used to name the class. Thus $(0 - 0), (1 - 0), (0 - 1), (158 - 0)$ may be used as the names for four of the equivalence classes into which *J* is partitioned. Each of the equivalence classes created above will be a number in the new number system we planned to develop. The new system will be called the system of integers. Each **integer** is a number which is one of the equivalence classes into which *J* was partitioned by the relation $\sim$. To differentiate between the ordered pair of whole numbers $(a - b) \in J$ and the equivalence class to which it belongs we will use boldface type for the parentheses around the symbol for the integer. Thus $\boldsymbol{(}a - b\boldsymbol{)}$ names the equivalence class to which $(a - b)$ belongs. Also $\boldsymbol{(}a - b\boldsymbol{)}$ names a number, an element of the system of integers which we will denote by *I*.

Now that we have defined the elements of *I* we shall want to make an agreement about the equality relation between any two elements. Recall that there are an infinite number of elements of *J* in each equivalence class of *I*. Any one of these elements of *J* may be used to name the equivalence class of *I*. Since $(5 - 2) \sim (4 - 1)$, both of these elements of *J* are in the same equivalence class. This equivalence class, which is an element of *I*, may be named $\boldsymbol{(}5 - 2\boldsymbol{)}$ or $\boldsymbol{(}4 - 1\boldsymbol{)}$. Since $\boldsymbol{(}5 - 2\boldsymbol{)}$ and $\boldsymbol{(}4 - 1\boldsymbol{)}$ are two names for the same element of *I*, we will want to say $\boldsymbol{(}5 - 2\boldsymbol{)} = \boldsymbol{(}4 - 1\boldsymbol{)}$. Therefore we will make the following definition:

If $a, b, c, d \in W$, then $\boldsymbol{(}a - b\boldsymbol{)} = \boldsymbol{(}c - d\boldsymbol{)}$ if and only if $(a - b) \sim (c - d)$.

It is obvious that $\boldsymbol{(}a - b\boldsymbol{)} = \boldsymbol{(}c - d\boldsymbol{)}$ if $a = c$ and $b = d$. We leave this proof to you.

Problem Set 6.3

A. Decide whether each of the following suggests the idea of an ordered pair.

1. In giving directions, the policeman said, "Turn left at the traffic light and then make the first right turn after that."
2. The book was 10 inches wide and 2 inches thick.
3. The first two directions for opening a safe which has a combination lock are "5 to the right and then 20 to the left."
4. The rug was 9 feet by 12 feet.
5. Write a two digit number using 7 and 8.
6. Your dental appointment is at 3 o'clock on the 10th.
7. The reference was in volume 4, page 9.
8. The three hourly exams for the autumn semester were scheduled for 10/12, 11/9, and 12/4.
9. Two factors of the number are 5 and 7.
10. They had stateroom B, deck C.

B. Examine the set of ordered pairs

(1) $(0-4)$.	(6) $(0-3)$.	(11) $(13-17)$
(2) $(7-6)$.	(7) $(0-0)$.	(12) $(9-12)$.
(3) $(39-15)$.	(8) $(6-5)$.	(13) $(1.5-.5)$.
(4) $(17-17)$.	(9) $(12-15)$.	(14) $(124-123)$.
(5) $(6-5)$.	(10) $\left(\dfrac{10}{3}-\dfrac{1}{3}\right)$.	(15) $(15-39)$.

1. Pick out the elements of J.
2. Pick out equal elements of J.
3. Pick out elements of J which belong to the same equivalence class.

C. Use the definition of the $\sim$ relation to complete each statement so that it will be true.
   1. If $(x-y) \sim (z-w)$ in J, then _____ in W.
   2. If $(t-p) \sim (q-r)$ in J, then _____ in W.
   3. If $a+b = b+c$ in W, then _____ in J.
   4. If $k+m = n+r$ in W, then _____ in J.
   5. If $([a+b]-c) \sim ([d+e]-f)$ in J, then _____ in W.
   6. If $(g-[h+k]) \sim (l-[m+n])$ in J, then _____ in W.
   7. If $(r+s)+t = (p+q)+m$ in W, then _____ in J.
   8. If $(a+b)+(c+d) = (c+d)+(a+b)$ in W, then_____ in J.
   9. If $([n+k]-n) \sim (5-3)$ in J, then _____ in W.
   10. If $(n-[n+k]) \sim (7-10)$ in J, then _____ in W.

D. Use the definition of the tilde relation to determine a general expression for the elements of J which will be in the same equivalence class as each of the following. Then give 10 elements in each equivalence class.
   1. $(0-2)$.   **4.** $(11-4)$.
   2. $(5-0)$.   **5.** $(9-17)$.
   3. $(10-0)$.

E. Prove each of the following.
   1. $(x-y) = (r-s)$, if $x+s = y+r$ in W.
   2. $((x+a)-(y+a)) = (x-y)$ for all a, x, y in W.
   3. If $(x-y) = (r-s)$, then $((x+a)-y) = ((r+a)-s)$.
   4. If $(x-y) = (r-s)$, then $(x-(y+a)) = (r-(s+a))$.
   5. If $a \leq x$ and y, then $((x-a)-(y-a)) = (x-y)$.
   6. If $(x-y) = (r-s)$, then $((x+a)-(y+b)) = ((r+a)-(s+b))$.
   7. If $(x-y) = (r-s)$, then for $a \leq x$ and r, $((x-a)-y) = ((r-a)-s)$.
   8. If $(x-y) = (r-s)$, then for $b \leq y$ and s, $(x-(y-b)) = (r-(s-b))$.
   9. Use one of the above statements to show that each of the following is true.
      a. $3+5 = 2+6$, so $(3-2) = (6-5)$.

b. $(7 - 11) = (12 - 16)$; hence $(7 - 16) = (12 - 21)$.

c. $(7 - 11) = (12 - 16)$; hence $(13 - 11) = (18 - 16)$.

d. If $(p - q) = (17 - 8)$, then $(p - (q - 4)) = (17 - 4)$ for $4 \leq q$.

e. $(20 - 21) = (10 - 11)$; hence $(22 - 22) = (12 - 12)$.

6.4 The System of Integers under Addition

We must not lose sight of the fact that we are trying to build a number system whose structure is that of a field. All this preparatory material was needed to define the elements of the system we are devising. Now we need to decide on a definition for the operation of addition on these elements. In seeking a suggestion for this definition you may recall problem **C** in Problem Set 2.8. This problem indicates that we might try the following definition for **addition in I:**

If $a, b, c, d \in W$, then $(a - b) + (c - d) = ((a + c) - (b + d))$.

Now we want to see whether this definition has the properties which will make I a commutative group under addition.

First we must be sure that I is closed under addition. The definition makes $((a + c) - (b + d))$ an equivalence class but whether or not it is an equivalence class in I is the question. It will be in I if the two components $(a + c)$ and $(b + d)$ are in W. Since W is closed under addition, $(a + c) \in W$ and $(b + d) \in W$. Hence $((a + c) - (b + d)) \in I$.

We would like to be sure that this definition yields the same sum no matter which elements of J we choose for naming the equivalence classes of I that are to be added. For example, it is clear at once that

$$(7 - 5) \sim (6 - 4)$$

and

$$(8 - 2) \sim (11 - 5).$$

Then, using the definition of addition given above,

$$(7 - 5) + (8 - 2) = ((7 + 8) - (5 + 2)) = (15 - 7).$$

The question we are considering is this: We could have named the equivalence classes by the symbols $(6 - 4)$ and $(11 - 5)$ instead of $(7 - 5)$ and $(8 - 2)$. Would the sum of $(6 - 4)$ and $(11 - 5)$ be the same equivalence class $(15 - 7)$? Let us see:

$$(6 - 4) + (11 - 5) = ((6 + 11) - (4 + 5)) = (17 - 9).$$

Now $(15 - 7)$ will equal $(17 - 9)$ if $(15 - 7) \sim (17 - 9)$, which will hold if

$$15 + 9 = 17 + 7.$$
$$24 = 24.$$

This example suggests that the sum of two elements of I is unique no matter what elements of J are used to name the equivalence classes of I. You will have an opportunity to write a proof for this in the next set of problems. We now have

Theorem 6.1 *I is closed under addition.*

Our road is clear. We will try to prove

Theorem 6.2 *Addition is commutative in* I.

This means we must show that $(a - b) + (c - d) = (c - d) + (a - b)$.

Since we have to compare sums let us add and see what we get. We wish to show

$$(a - b) + (c - d) = (c - d) + (a - b).$$

This will be true if

$$((a + c) - (b + d)) = ((c + a) - (d + b)).$$

Because $a, b, c, d \in W$ we know that $a + c = c + a$ and $b + d = d + b$. Then the first and second components of the ordered pairs which name our equivalence classes are the same and this is a condition for equality of two equivalence classes.

Complete the following proof:

ASSERTIONS	SUPPORTING STATEMENTS
(1) $a, b, c, d \in W$.	(1)
(2) $a + c = c + a$ $\quad b + d = d + b$.	(2)
(3) $((a + c) - (b + d)) =$ $\quad ((c + a) - (d + b))$.	(3)
(4) $(a - b) + (c - d) =$ $\quad (c - d) + (a - b)$.	(4) Definition of addition in I.

Next we will show

Theorem 6.3 *Addition is associative in* I.

If we stated this theorem using mathematical symbols it would look like this:

If $a, b, c, d \in W$, then $[(a - b) + (c - d)] + (e - f) = (a - b) + [(c - d) + (e - f)]$.

The technique we used in searching for clues to the steps of the proof for Theorem 6.2 suggests that we work backward, perform all the indicated additions, and compare the components of the resulting elements in I. If we do this we see that the result above is true if

$$((a+c) - (b+d)) + (e-f) = (a-b) + ((c+e) - (d+f)),$$

and this in turn holds if

$$([(a+c)+e] - [(b+d)+f]) = ([a+(c+e)] - [b+(d+f)]).$$

We observe that $(a+c)+e = a+(c+e)$ in W and
$$(b+d)+f = b+(d+f) \text{ in } W.$$

Hence the ordered pairs for which these equal sums are the first and second components must name the same equivalence class. Try to write up this proof by yourself.

Everything seems to be going swimmingly. Now all we have to do is produce an identity element for addition and then see how we stand with additive inverses in I.

Since 0 is the additive identity in W, a first calculated guess for a candidate to serve as the additive identity in I is clearly $(0-0)$. If $(0-0)$ is to be an additive identity, then $(a-b) + (0-0) = (a-b)$. This equality is what we would like to have as the last step in our argument. Our success in the previous theorems leads us once again to work backward; perform the addition and compare the resulting integers. Thus we would have

$$(a-b) + (0-0) = (a-b)$$

if

$$((a+0) - (b+0)) = (a-b).$$

Clearly $a+0 = a$ and $b+0 = b$ in W.

You have enough hints to try to write a proof for

Theorem 6.4 *An additive identity in I is* $(0-0)$.

In the problem set you will be asked to prove that for any whole number n, $(n-n)$ is another name for an additive identity in I.

The question of the existence of additive inverses in I is somewhat more challenging because we can't get any clues from W about what the inverses might look like. Only 0 has an additive inverse in W. No other element of W has an additive inverse in W. Of course if it turns out that every element of I does have an additive inverse in I, then we have it made. The system of integers will be a commutative group under addition, and in a group where the given operation is addition we can *always* subtract because we proved that in such a group subtraction gives the same result as adding the additive inverse.

Let us look for a possible candidate for the additive inverse of $(a-b) \in I$, assuming it exists. Let $(x-y)$ be the additive inverse of $(a-b)$, which we may write $^-(a - b)$. Then $(a - b) + (x - y) = (0 - 0)$. If we add as indicated we get $((a + x) - (b + y)) = (0 - 0)$,

whence

$$(a + x) - (b + y) \sim (0 - 0),$$
$$(a + x) + 0 = (b + y) + 0,$$

and

$$a + x = b + y.$$

Since we are interested in some candidate for $(x - y)$ we will rewrite the last sentence as

$$x + a = y + b.$$

Then $(x - y) \sim (b - a)$ and by the definition of equality of two equivalence classes $(x - y) = (b - a)$. The candidate suggested for the additive inverse of $(a - b)$ is $(b - a)$, which must be in I since $b, a \in W$.

Now we can try to prove

Theorem 6.5 *Every element in I has an additive inverse in I.*

We will show that if $(a - b) \in I$ then $(b - a)$ is the additive inverse of $(a - b)$ in I. To show that $(b - a) = {}^-(a - b)$ we need to establish that $(a - b) + (b - a) = (0 - 0)$. Make an analysis by performing the indicated addition and using the definitions of $=$ in I and $\sim$ in J. You will arrive at $a + b = b + a$. Why is this true in W? Use your analysis to provide clues for writing a proof for Theorem 6.5.

The proofs of Theorems 6.1 through 6.5 establish that the system of integers I under addition has the structure of a commutative group.

Problem Set 6.4

    A. Prove: Addition is well defined in I. To establish this you should show: If $(a - b) = (c - d)$ and $(e - f) = (g - h)$, then $(a - b) + (e - f) = (c - d) + (g - h)$.

    B. Prove:
        1. In I, $(0 - 0) = (n - n)$.
        2. In I, $(a - b) + (n - n) = (a - b)$.
        3. Write five different names for an additive identity in I. May we say "the" additive identity in I?

    C. Prove: In I, if $(a - b) = (c - d)$, then $(b - a) = (d - c)$.

    D. Identify the property or properties of I under addition, being applied in each of the following calculations.

1. $(8 - 15) + (7 - 7) = (8 - 15)$.
2. $(5 - 2) + (2 - 5) = (0 - 0)$.
3. $[(6 - 10) + (4 - 2) + (11 - 7)] \in I$.
4. $(12 - 9) + [(9 - 12) + (13 - 6)] = (13 - 6)$.
5. $[(3 - 4) + (14 - 6)] + (4 - 3) = (14 - 6)$.

6.5 Theorems in *I* under Addition

As soon as we realize that I is a group under addition we know that we have a set of six additional theorems which must be true in I. These are the six theorems proved for a group in Chapter 3. Stated for I, these theorems are as follows:

Theroem 6.6 *If a, b, c, d, e, $f \in W$ and $(a - b) + (c - d) = (e - f) + (c - d)$, then $(a - b) = (e - f)$ in I.*

Theorem 6.7 *If $a, b \in W$, then $^-(^-(a - b))$ is $(a - b)$ in I.*

Theorem 6.8 *In I, $^-(0 - 0)$ is $(0 - 0)$.*

Theorem 6.9 *If a, b, c, $d \in W$, then $(x - y) + (a - b) = (c - d)$ in I has the unique solution $(x - y) = (c - d) + {}^-(a - b) = (c - d) + (b - a)$ in I.*

Theorem 6.10 *If a, b, c, $d \in W$, then $^-((a - b) + (c - d)) = {}^-(a - b) + {}^-(c - d) = (b - a) + (d - c)$ in I.*

Before stating the next theorem we shall want to define subtraction in I. In W we defined subtraction in terms of addition. Thus we said $a - b = c$ if and only if there exists $c \in W$ such that $a = c + b$. Similarly we will say in I, $(a - b) - (c - d) = (e - f)$ if and only if there exists an element $(e - f)$ in I such that $(a - b) = (e - f) + (c - d)$. By Theorem 6.9 the last equation can always be solved for $(e - f)$. Hence in I subtraction is always possible. Notice how different this is from the situation in W. An example may make this definition seem more familiar:

$(12 - 5) - (5 - 1) = (e - f)$ if and only if $(12 - 5) = (e - f) + (5 - 1)$

Let us add and try to simplify:

$$(12 - 5) = ((e + 5) - (f + 1)).$$
$$(12 - 5) \sim ([e + 5] - [f + 1]).$$
$$12 + (f + 1) = 5 + (e + 5).$$
$$13 + f = 10 + e.$$
$$(13 - 10) \sim (e - f).$$
$$(13 - 10) = (e - f).$$

Now check this work by observing that $(12 - 5) = (13 - 10) + (5 - 1)$. Go through all the steps to demonstrate this. Hence by the definition of subtraction:

$$(12 - 5) - (5 - 1) = (13 - 10).$$

We are ready for

Theorem 6.11 *If* a, b, c, $d \in W$, *then* $(a - b) - (c - d) = (a - b) + {}^-(c - d) = (a - b) + (d - c)$.

We know that we do not have to provide proofs for Theorems 6.6 through 6.11, but we will choose one theorem and write out the proof for it just to see how it goes. Let us choose

Theorem 6.6 *If* a, b, c, d, e, $f \in W$ *and* $(a - b) + (c - d) = (e - f) + (c - d)$, *then* $(a - b) = (e - f)$.

Of course, we could add $(d - c)$, the additive inverse of $(c - d)$, to the elements on each side of the = sign in the given equation. Then, using the associative property and definitions of additive inverse and identity in I, we would arrive at the equivalent equation: $(a - b) = (e - f)$. This is the same outline we used to prove the theorem in Chapter 3. Or, we could add as indicated and apply the definitions for $\sim$ in J and = in I. This would give us:

(1) $(a - b) + (c - d) = (e - f) + (c - d)$.
(2) $((a + c) - (b + d)) = ((e + c) - (f + d))$.
(3) $([a + c] - [b + d]) \sim ([e + c] - [f + d])$.
(4) $(a + c) + (f + d) = (b + d) + (e + c)$.

Using the commutative and associative properties and the Cancellation Law for Addition in W:

(5) $a + f = b + e$.
(6) $(a - b) \sim (e - f)$.
(7) $(a - b) = (e - f)$.

Rewrite this proof, filling in the steps assumed between steps 4 and 5. Provide the required supporting statements.

Problem Set 6.5

A. Prove each of the following theorems.

    1. Theorem 6.7   **4.** Theorem 6.10.
    2. Theorem 6.8.   **5.** Theorem 6.11.
    3. Theorem 6.9.

B. Perform the indicated calculations in I and name the results by symbols of the form $(0 - n)$ or $(n - 0)$.

1. $^-(8 - 2) + (6 - 0) = $ _____.

2. $^-(5 - 5) + {}^-(1 - 16) = $ _____.

3. $(12 - 15) + (9 - 10) = $ _____.

4. $(3 - 11) + (4 - 8) = $ _____.

5. $(29 - 15) - (2 - 4) = $ _____.

6. $^-((7 - 12) + (30 - 15)) = $ _____.

7. $^-(6 - 9) + (6 - 9) = $ _____.

8. $^-(6 - 9) + {}^-(9 - 6) = $ _____.

9. $^-(6 - 9) - (9 - 6) = $ _____.

10. $(14 - 5) - {}^-(25 - 17) = $ _____.

C. Solve in I.

1. $(x - y) + (8 - 3) = (7 - 2)$.

2. $(11 - 6) + (p - q) = (23 - 19)$.

3. $(r - s) + (5 - 13) = (4 - 7) + (5 - 13)$.

4. $(t - w) - (16 - 9) = (18 - 29)$.

5. $^-(2 - 1) + (m - n) = (4 - 0)$.

D. Prove: The additive identity in I is unique. [Let $(x - y)$ and $(r - s)$ each serve as an additive identity and show that $(x - y) = (r - s)$.]

6.6 The System of Integers under Multiplication

Since we are striving for a field we shall need a second operation, and we choose multiplication. Just as we did in addition, we will seek a suggestion for a definition from our work in W. Keep in mind that we do this because $(a - b)$ resembles a whole number if $a \geqq b$. Look back at problem **D** of Problem Set 2.8. There you were to have proved that in W:

$$(a - b) \cdot (c - d) = (a \cdot c + b \cdot d) - (b \cdot c + a \cdot d).$$

This provides a clue for the definition of multiplication in I and, accordingly, we shall say:

If $a, b, c, d \in W$, then $(a - b) \cdot (c - d) = ((a \cdot c + b \cdot d) - (a \cdot d + b \cdot c))$.

Now we want to investigate the properties of closure, commutativity, associativity, identity, inverses for every element, except $(0 - 0)$, and distributivity of multiplication over addition.

To establish closure for I under multiplication we will need to show that $((a \cdot c + b \cdot d) - (a \cdot d + b \cdot c)) \in I$. We may do this by proving that $(a \cdot c + b \cdot d) \in W$ and $(a \cdot d + b \cdot c) \in W$. What properties of W under addition and multiplication assure us that the two components of the equivalence class belong to W?

We will consider an example to illustrate that the product of two elements in I is the same no matter which elements of J are chosen to name them. Suppose we select $(5 - 2)$ and $(7 - 3)$ in J. Then

$$\begin{aligned}(5 - 2) \cdot (7 - 3) &= ((5 \cdot 7 + 2 \cdot 3) - (5 \cdot 3 + 2 \cdot 7)) \\ &= ((35 + 6) - (15 + 14)) \\ &= (41 - 29).\end{aligned}$$

Since $(5 - 2) \sim (6 - 3)$ and $(7 - 3) \sim (8 - 4)$ we may use $(6 - 3)$ as another name for $(5 - 2)$ and $(8 - 4)$ as another name for $(7 - 3)$. Then

$$(6 - 3) \cdot (8 - 4) = ((6 \cdot 8 + 3 \cdot 4) - (6 \cdot 4 + 3 \cdot 8))$$
$$= ((48 + 12) - (24 + 24))$$
$$= (60 - 48).$$

Applying the definition for $=$ in I, we wish to show:

$$(41 - 29) = (60 - 48).$$

This will be so if

$$(41 - 29) \sim (60 - 48).$$

This in turn is true if

$$41 + 48 = 29 + 60$$

and

$$89 = 89.$$

This example suggests the general statement: No matter which elements in J are used to name any two equivalence classes in I, the product of the two classes in I will be the same. This will appear in the problem set for those who wish to write a formal proof. We now have:

Theorem 6.12 *I is closed under multiplication.*

The techniques used in trying to establish the commutative, associative, and distributive properties are those we used in studying I under addition. In general, when seeking clues for a proof, we will make an analysis by working backward, perform the indicated operations and examine the resulting elements in I to see if they can be shown to be equal.

To prove that multiplication is commutative in I we will need to show that

$$(a - b) \cdot (c - d) = (c - d) \cdot (a - b).$$

Our analysis (now a familiar procedure to you) may proceed as follows. First, we will multiply as indicated; i.e., the desired result will be true if

$$((a \cdot c + b \cdot d) - (a \cdot d + b \cdot c)) = ((c \cdot a + d \cdot b) - (c \cdot b + d \cdot a)).$$

The two equivalence classes will be equal if the first components are equal and the second components are equal. We need to show that

$$a \cdot c + b \cdot d = c \cdot a + d \cdot b \text{ in } W$$

and

$$a \cdot d + b \cdot c = c \cdot b + d \cdot a \text{ in } W.$$

What properties of the system of whole numbers under addition and multiplication make the two statements W true? We are ready to write a proof for

Theorem 6.13 *Multiplication is commutative in I.*

The discussion above should help you write the theorem in mathematical symbols.

Proof

ASSERTIONS	SUPPORTING STATEMENTS
(1) $a, b, c, d \in W$.	(1)
(2) $a \cdot c,\ b \cdot d,\ c \cdot a,\ d \cdot b,\ a \cdot d,$ $b \cdot c, c \cdot b, d \cdot a$ are all in W.	(2)
(3) $a \cdot c + b \cdot d,\ c \cdot a + d \cdot b,\ a \cdot d + b \cdot c, c \cdot b + d \cdot a$ are all in W.	(3)
(4) $a \cdot c + b \cdot d = c \cdot a + d \cdot b$.	(4)
(5) $a \cdot d + b \cdot c = c \cdot b + d \cdot a$.	(5)
(6) $((a \cdot c + b \cdot d) - (a \cdot d + b \cdot c)) = ((c \cdot a + d \cdot b) - (c \cdot b + d \cdot a))$.	(6)
(7) $(a - b) \cdot (c - d) = (c - d) \cdot (a - b)$.	(7) Definition of multiplication in I.

Complete the proof by filling in the missing supporting statements.

It is hoped that by now the general procedure for writing an analysis and eventually a proof will enable those who enjoy algebraic manipulation to proceed independently to establish the following two theorems.

Theorem 6.14 *Multiplication is associative in I.*

Theorem 6.15 *Multiplication is distributive over addition in I.*

We shall want to try to identify the multiplicative identity if it exists. The multiplicative identity in W was 1 and you may possible guess that either $(1 - 0)$ or $(0 - 1)$ might serve as a multiplicative identity in I. You can check this conjecture readily by examining the statements

$$(a - b) \cdot (1 - 0) = (a - b)$$

and

$$(a - b) \cdot (0 - 1) = (a - b)$$

to see if they are true or false. What do you find? Do you think either one or both will fill the bill?

Suppose we didn't have any inkling of the form of an element of I which might serve as a multiplicative identity. In that case how might we maneuver to arrive at a sensible suggestion? We might proceed, using the same strategy we employed to investigate the possible existence and form of an additive identity. We might assume $(x - y)$ is the multiplicative identity and examine the equation $(a - b) \cdot (x - y) = (a - b)$. If we multiply, we get $((a \cdot x + b \cdot y) - (a \cdot y + b \cdot x)) = (a - b)$. This will hold if

$$([a \cdot x + b \cdot y] - [a \cdot y + b \cdot x]) \sim (a - b),$$

which is true if

$$(a \cdot x + b \cdot y) + b = (a \cdot y + b \cdot x) + a.$$

Since the last equation is in W we may use the commutative and associative properties under addition and the distributive property of multiplication over addition to write:

$$a \cdot x + (b \cdot y + b) = b \cdot x + (a \cdot y + a)$$

and

$$a \cdot x + b \cdot (y + 1) = b \cdot x + a \cdot (y + 1).$$

A good, hard look at this last equation suggests that the left- and right-hand members of this equation would be equal if $x = y + 1$. This tells us that a calculated guess for the form of $(x - y)$, if it is to serve as a multiplicative identity, is $((y + 1) - y)$. Any element of J for which the first component is 1 more than the second is in the same equivalence class of I. Since any member of an equivalence class may be used to name it, our original conjecture of using $(1 - 0)$ was a good one. To prove that $(1 - 0)$ is a multiplicative identity we could use clues from the work we did when we tested to see whether $(a - b) \cdot (x - y)$ gave a product of $(a - b)$. You should have no trouble proving:

Theorem 6.16 *The element* $(1 - 0)$ *in I is a multiplicative identity.*

If we stop a moment and review what we have done, we soon realize that we have described a number system which does have 10 of the 11 properties of a field. We are interested in developing a number system whose structure is that of a field for then we may always add, subtract, multiply, and divide (except by i_1) in that system. The arithmetic of such a number system constitutes a major part of the mathematics experience of an elementary school child. All that we need do now to complete our investigation of the field properties of I is to determine whether there exist multiplicative inverses in I for every element in I. If they do exist, we shall want to decide how to name them.

The strategy for investigating the existence of a particular element in I should be fairly familiar by now. First—guess! Guess, on the basis of past experience. Test your guess to see if it performs the intended function. If your past experience yields no sensible candidate, then assume $(x - y)$ is the element and maneuver mathematically within the system to see if some $(x - y)$ can fulfill the intended function. If so, what is its form in I? It is obvious at once that we cannot depend upon our experiences in W to suggest a candidate for a multiplicative inverse in I, since only 1 has a multiplicative inverse in W. Hence we shall proceed as follows: Let $(x - y)$ serve as a multiplicative inverse of $(a - b)$.

Then
$$(a - b) \cdot (x - y) = (1 - 0).$$

Multiplying, we get
$$((a \cdot x + b \cdot y) - (a \cdot y + b \cdot x)) = (1 - 0),$$

whence
$$([a \cdot x + b \cdot y] - [a \cdot y + b \cdot x]) \sim (1 - 0),$$
$$(a \cdot x + b \cdot y) + 0 = (a \cdot y + b \cdot x) + 1.$$

This sentence will obviously be false if $a = b$, no matter what x and y are. From this we surmise that $(a - a)$ or $(0 - 0)$ does not have a multiplicative inverse in I. This fits in with our properties for a field. Now let us try some other whole numbers for a and b and examine the sentence above with suitable substitutions. Suppose we choose $(11 - 4)$ for $(a - b)$:

$$11 \cdot x + 4 \cdot y = (11 \cdot y + 4 \cdot x) + 1.$$

Since this is a sentence in W, it may be rewritten:

$$7 \cdot x = 7 \cdot y + 1.$$

The sentence is clearly false since $7 \cdot x$ has a factor of 7 and $(7 \cdot y + 1)$ does not have a factor of 7. Hence there is no x and y which will make the sentence $(11 - 4) \cdot (x - y) = (1 - 0)$ true. There is no multiplicative inverse for $(11 - 4)$ in I.

We now face the disappointing conclusion that not every element other than i_1 has a multiplicative inverse in I. The system of integers does not have the structure of a field.

Problem Set 6.6

A. Prove: Multiplication is well defined in I. To establish this you should show: If $(a - b) = (c - d)$ and $(e - f) = (g - h)$, then $(a - b) \cdot (e - f) = (c - d) \cdot (g - h)$.

B. Prove:
1. Multiplication is associative in I.
2. Multiplication is distributive over addition, in I.

C. Prove:
1. $((y + 1) - y) = (1 - 0)$.
2. $((y + 1) - y) = ((x + 1) - x)$.
3. Write five different names for a multiplicative identity in I. May we say "the" multiplicative identity in I?

D. 1. Show that $(1 - 0)$ has a multiplicative inverse in I.
2. Show that $(0 - 1)$ has a multiplicative inverse in I.

E. Perform the calculations.

1. $(8 - 5) \cdot (1 - 0) =$ _____.   6. $(5 - 0) \cdot (2 - 0) =$ _____.
2. $(1 - 0) \cdot (1 - 0) =$ _____.   7. $(5 - 0) \cdot (0 - 2) =$ _____.
3. $(1 - 0) \cdot (0 - 1) =$ _____.   8. $(8 - 0) \cdot (4 - 0) =$ _____.
4. $(0 - 1) \cdot (0 - 1) =$ _____.   9. $(8 - 0) \cdot (0 - 4) =$ _____.
5. $(3 - 0) \cdot (0 - 1) =$ _____.   10. $(0 - 3) \cdot (0 - 2) =$ _____.

6.7 Theorems in *I* under Multiplication

Since the system of integers does not have multiplicative inverses for every element in the set, we cannot automatically assert that the theorems we proved for a group or a field are true for I under multiplication. However, those theorems, proofs of which did not involve multiplicative inverses, may be accepted as true without further proof in I under multiplication, since I does have other properties of a field under the second operation. Thus the following familiar theorems may be accepted as true in I without further proof.

Theorem 6.17 *If* $a, b \in W$, *then* $(a - b) \cdot (0 - 0) = (0 - 0)$ *in I.*

Theorem 6.18 *If* $a, b, c, d \in W$, *then the product of* $(a - b)$ *and* $^-(c - d)$ *is* $^-((a - b) \cdot (c - d))$ *in I.*

Recalling that $(d - c)$ is the additive inverse of $(c - d)$ and that $(a - b) \cdot (c - d) = ((a \cdot c + b \cdot d) - (a \cdot d + b \cdot c))$ the statement to be proved may be written symbolically as:

$$(a - b) \cdot (d - c) = ((a \cdot d + b \cdot c) - (a \cdot c + b \cdot d)).$$

Theorem 6.19 *If* $a, b, c, d \in W$, *then the product of* $^-(a - b)$ *and* $^-(c - d)$ *is* $(a - b) \cdot (c - d)$ *in I.*

Once again, this might be written:

$$(b - a) \cdot (d - c) = (a - b) \cdot (c - d).$$

The above three theorems correspond to Theorems 3.13, 3.20, and 3.21 for a field. Theorem 3.22 is one we would like to have in I, but since the proof given in Chapter 3 depends upon the presence of multiplicative inverses we shall try to establish a corresponding theorem in I by another approach.

If $a, b, c, d \in W$ and $(a - b) \cdot (c - d) = (0 - 0)$, then either $(a - b) = (0 - 0)$ or $(c - d) = (0 - 0)$.

If $(a - b) = (0 - 0)$, then the theorem is already true. If $(a - b) \neq (0 - 0)$, then we must show that $(c - d) = (0 - 0)$. Since $(a - b) \cdot (c - d) = (0 - 0)$ is given and $(a - b) \cdot (0 - 0) = (0 - 0)$ by Theorem 6.17, we may write $(a - b) \cdot (c - d) = (a - b) \cdot (0 - 0)$.

We would like to be able to say that $(c - d) = (0 - 0)$. But we cannot do this unless we have a Cancellation Law for Multiplication in I. The proof of a Cancellation Law for Multiplication in I is somewhat more laborious than we wish to undertake. However, since we feel its need and recognize its usefulness we shall state and use the following theorem, omitting the proof:

Theorem 6.20 *If a, b, c, d, e, f $\in W$ and $(a - b) \cdot (c - d) = (e - f) \cdot$ $(c - d)$, then $(a - b) = (e - f)$ for $(c - d) \neq (0 - 0)$ in I.*

The restriction on $(c - d)$ is necessary, for if we omitted it we would be faced with a situation like the following:

$(7 - 2) \cdot (0 - 0) = (0 - 0)$ by Theorem 6.17.
$(1 - 4) \cdot (0 - 0) = (0 - 0)$ by Theorem 6.17.
$(7 - 2) \cdot (0 - 0) = (1 - 4) \cdot (0 - 0)$, closure under multiplication.

Applying the Cancellation Law for Multiplication:

$$(7 - 2) = (1 - 4).$$

The last sentence is not true in I, for

$$7 + 4 \neq 2 + 1 \text{ in } W.$$

Thus, unless we place the restriction that $(c - d)$ may not be the additive identity in I, in the statement of the Cancellation Law for Multiplication, we arrive at an unacceptable conclusion which contradicts previous agreements.

Now that we have included a Cancellation Law for Multiplication in our system of integers we may complete the proof of Theorem 6.21.

Theorem 6.21 *If a, b, c, d $\in W$ and $(a - b) \cdot (c - d) = (0 - 0)$, then either $(a - b) = (0 - 0)$ or $(c - d) = (0 - 0)$ in I.*

Rewrite the proof of Theorem 6.21 assuming $(c - d) \neq (0 - 0)$ and show that $(a - b)$ must be $(0 - 0)$. Will the theorem be true if both $(a - b)$ and $(c - d)$ are equal to $(0 - 0)$?

In a field, the inverse operation, division, was shown to be the same as multiplying by the multiplicative inverse. Thus $p \div q = p \cdot q^{-1}$ and division was always possible in F, except for $q = i_1$. This situation is, disappointingly, not true in I. We may not always divide, and remain within the set of integers, even if the divisor is not $(0 - 0)$.

Recalling the previous definition for division in W we will define division in I as follows:

$(a - b) \div (c - d) = (e - f)$ in I if and only if there exists an $(e - f)$ such that $(a - b) = (e - f) \cdot (c - d)$ for $(c - d) \neq (0 - 0)$.

Accordingly, $(8 - 2)$ is divisible by $(5 - 3)$ if we can produce an $(e - f)$ such that $(8 - 2) = (e - f) \cdot (5 - 3)$. Let us investigate this possibility. We will multiply and examine the equation we eventually get in W:

$$(8 - 2) = ((5 \cdot e + 3 \cdot f) - (5 \cdot f + 3 \cdot e)).$$
$$8 + (5 \cdot f + 3 \cdot e) = (5 \cdot e + 3 \cdot f) + 2.$$
$$6 + 2 \cdot f = 2 \cdot e.$$
$$3 + f = e.$$

The last equation indicates that an element of I whose first component is 3 more than its second component should be a suitable candidate for $(e - f)$. Show that

$$(8 - 2) = (3 - 0) \cdot (5 - 3).$$

Then $(8 - 2)$ is divisible by $(5 - 3)$ and the quotient is $(3 - 0)$.

On the other hand, it is not difficult to demonstrate that $(8 - 2)$ is not divisible by $(6 - 1)$. Let us assume that there does exist an element $(e - f)$ such that

$$(8 - 2) = (e - f) \cdot (6 - 1),$$

and show that this leads to a contradiction.

$$(8 - 2) = ((6 \cdot e + 1 \cdot f) - (6 \cdot f + 1 \cdot e)).$$
$$8 + (6 \cdot f + e) = (6 \cdot e + f) + 2.$$
$$6 + 5 \cdot f = 5 \cdot e.$$

The last sentence cannot be true in W, since $5 \cdot e$ has a factor of 5 and $(6 + 5 \cdot f)$ does not have a factor of 5. Hence $(8 - 2)$ is not divisible by $(6 - 1)$ in I.

According to our definition of division above, the equation $(a - b) \cdot (x - y) = (c - d)$ will have a solution for $(x - y)$ in I if and only if $(c - d)$ is divisible by $(a - b)$. Using the procedures indicated above we can show that $(12 - 9) \cdot (x - y) = (30 - 45)$ has a solution $(0 - 5)$ in I, while $(3 - 5) \cdot (x - y) = (11 - 4)$ has no solution in I.

The absence of multiplicative inverses in I for every element makes it necessary to test every equation of the form $(a - b) \cdot (x - y) = (c - d)$ to determine whether or not it has a solution set in I. The absence of the same property limits the conditions under which division may be performed in I.

Problem Set 6.7

A. Write out a proof for each of the following theorems.

    1. Theorem 6.17.   **3.** Theorem 6.19.

    2. Theorem 6.18.

B. Perform the indicated operations in I and write the answers in the form
$(n - 0)$ or $(0 - n)$.

1. $(6 - 3) \cdot (2 - 7) = $ _____.
2. $(5 - 9) \cdot (0 - 0) = $ _____.
3. $(4 - 2) \cdot {}^-(4 - 2) = $ _____.
4. ${}^-(8 - 4) \cdot {}^-(10 - 2) = $ _____.
5. ${}^-(9 - 3) \cdot (0 - 7) = $ _____.

6. $(13 - 5) \cdot (1 - 0) = $ _____.
7. $(7 - 1) \cdot (1 - 7) = $ _____.
8. ${}^-(0 - 0) \cdot (23 - 11) = $ _____.
9. ${}^-(2 - 11) \cdot {}^-(6 - 8) = $ _____.
10. $(20 - 10) \cdot {}^-(9 - 6) = $ _____.

C. Decide whether each of the following names an element in I.

1. $(18 - 2) \div (9 - 5) = $ _____.
2. $(18 - 2) \div (9 - 6) = $ _____.
3. ${}^-(15 - 3) \div (4 - 0) = $ _____.

4. ${}^-(15 - 3) \div {}^-(3 - 0) = $ _____.
5. $(15 - 3) \div {}^-(6 - 0) = $ _____.

D. Solve, when possible, in I.

1. $(32 - 16) \cdot (a - b) = (0 - 0)$.
2. $(4 - 1) \cdot (x - y) = (12 - 3)$.
3. $(2 - 0) \cdot (r - s) = (13 - 2)$.
4. $(m - n) \cdot (7 - 3) = (11 - 6) \cdot (7 - 3)$.
5. $(c - d) \cdot {}^-(5 - 0) = (10 - 0)$.

6.8 Familiar Names for Elements in *I*

The ordered pairs of I, $(a - b)$, were written in this form so that you would
keep in mind that $(a - b)$ can be associated with a whole number only if $a \geq b$,
while $(a - b)$ is always an element in I regardless of whether $a \gtreqless b$. This means
that I contains elements some of which are associated with elements in W and
others which are not associated with elements in W.

At no time, anywhere in the chapter, is the symbol separating the a and b in
$(a - b)$ actually used as a subtraction symbol. We could have used (a, b) or
$(a * b)$ or any other mark to separate the ordered pair. Since we could not always
subtract in W and were interested in developing a system in which the set was
closed under subtraction, we decided to use $(a - b)$ to keep this goal in mind.
Furthermore, this notation suggested to us that we seek clues and hunches for
definitions and theorems in I by referring to our study of subtraction in W.

While this notation is helpful in developing the properties and other theorems
in I, it is a clumsy one for purposes of rapid calculation. We will, therefore, rename each equivalence class in I by a single numeral. Recall that every element
of I has a name of the form $(n - 0)$ or $(0 - n)$. Thus

$(5 - 0)$ will be named $^+5$ (positive 5), and its additive inverse $(0 - 5)$
will be named $^-5$ (negative five).

Similarly,

$(10 - 0)$ will be named $^+10$ (positive ten), and its additive inverse
$(0 - 10)$ will be named $^-10$ (negative ten).

Since $(10 - 0)$ may be named by any element of J in the equivalence class, $^+10$ is also the name for $(11 - 1)$, $(12 - 2)$, $(13 - 3)$, $(14 - 4)$, $(15 - 5)$, $((k + 10) - k)$, . . . and $^-10$ is the name for $(1 - 11)$, $(2 - 12)$, $(3 - 13)$, $(4 - 14)$, $(5 - 15)$, $(p - (p + 10))$. . . . Do you observe a pattern for associating an equivalence class in I with its more familiar name? What will we call $(0 - 0)$? The set of integers is now

$$\{. . . {}^-8, {}^-7, {}^-6, {}^-5, {}^-4, {}^-3, {}^-2, {}^-1, 0 \; {}^+1, {}^+2, {}^+3, {}^+4, {}^+5, . . .\}.$$

Of all the integers, it is the positive integers $^+1$, $^+2$, $^+3$, $^+4$, . . . and 0 which are meant to resemble the whole numbers. This means that if $3 + 4 = 7$ in W, we expect $^+3 + {}^+4 = {}^+7$ in I; and if $3 \cdot 4 = 12$ in W, then we expect $^+3 \cdot {}^+4 = {}^+12$ in I. Actually, this was arranged when we chose our definitions for addition and multiplication in I. Just for emphasis we will demonstrate that if ^+n, $^+r \in I$ correspond respectively to n, $r \in W$, then the integer $^+n + {}^+r$ corresponds to the whole number $n + r$.

$(n - 0) = {}^+n$, which corresponds to n; $(r - 0) = {}^+r$, which corresponds to r; $^+n + {}^+r = (n - 0) + (r - 0) = ((n + r) - (0 - 0)) = ((n + r) - 0)$, which may be named $^+(n + r) \in I$.

The positive integer $^+(n + r)$ corresponds to the whole number $n + r$. Thus, $^+n + {}^+r \in I$ corresponds to $(n + r) \in W$. A similar proof to show $^+n \cdot {}^+r \in I$ corresponds to $n \cdot r \in W$ will be required in the problem set.

We now know that the addition and multiplication facts we learned in W may be applied to the positive integers and zero in I. If $6 + 9 = 15$ in W, then $^+6 + {}^+9 = {}^+15$ in I. If $9 \cdot 3 = 27$ in W, then $^+9 \cdot {}^+3 = {}^+27$ in I. For the sake of efficiency and speed in computation we will agree, due to this correspondence, to drop the raised "$+$" mark when we name positive integers. Thus, when you encounter an example like $12 + 4 = \square$, the computation may take place either in W or I, depending upon the circumstances out of which the problem arose. In either case the sum will be 16.

Problem Set 6.8

A. Prove if ^+n and ^+r in I correspond, respectively, to n and r in W, then the integer $^+n \cdot {}^+r$ corresponds to the whole number $n \cdot r$.

B. 1. Prove: In I, $((k + n) - k) = (n - 0) = {}^+n$.

2. Prove: In I, $(p - (p + m)) = (0 - m) = {}^-m$.

3. Prove: If $a > b$ in W, then there exists $c \in W$ such that $(a - b) = (c - 0)$ in I.

4. Prove: If $a < b$ in W, then there exists $c \in W$ such that $(a - b) = (0 - c)$ in I.

C. Match.

    (1) $(0 - 9)$ (a) 0

    (2) $(9 - 0)$ (b) x

(3) $(37 - 15)$ (c) 1
(4) $(15 - 37)$ (d) 9
(5) $((6 + x) - 6)$ (e) $^-4$
(6) $((x + 7) - x)$ (f) 22
(7) $((y + 7) - (y + 6))$ (g) $^-9$
(8) $(p - p)$ (h) 7
(9) $(7 - (t + 7))$ (i) ^-t
(10) $(t - (t + 4))$ (j) $^-22$

D. For each set of equivalence classes select those which name the indicated integer.

1. 4: $(12 - 8)$, $(16 - 20)$, $(0 - 4)$, $(4 - 0)$, $(125 - 122)$.
2. $^-6$: $(6 - 0)$, $(0 - 6)$, $(134 - 128)$, $(10 - 4)$, $(2 - 8)$.
3. 0: $(437 - 437)$, $(1 - 0)$, $(0 - 1)$, $(0 - 0)$, $(1 - 1)$.
4. $^-13$: $(0 - 13)$, $(27 - 14)$, $(14 - 27)$, $(226 - 239)$, $(2 - 15)$.
5. 11: $(0 - 11)$, $(1 - 12)$, $(11 - 0)$, $(20 - 11)$, $(119 - 109)$.

E. Name each equivalence class by a more familiar numeral for the integer.

1. $(6 - 19)$.   9. $(144 - 144)$.
2. $(18 - 24)$.   10. $(207 - 119)$.
3. $(31 - 17)$.   11. $(17 - 106)$.
4. $(125 - 25)$.   12. $(623 - 509)$.
5. $(14 - 16)$.   13. $(509 - 623)$.
6. $(12 - 29)$.   14. $(58 - 100)$.
7. $(38 - 46)$.   15. $(301 - 156)$.
8. $(28 - 8)$.

6.9 Arithmetic in *I*

Recall that "$=$" means two names for the same number and we may write $(7 - 0) = 7$ and $(0 - 7) = ^-7$. Thus $^-7$ is the additive inverse of 7. In general, in I, ^-n and n are the additive inverses of each other. So now the arithmetic in I may include statements like: $^-8 + 8 = 0$ and $135 + ^-135 = 0$.

We, of course, would like an efficient way to add two negative integers or a negative and a positive integer. Theorem 6.10 tells us that if x and y are two integers, then $^-x + ^-y = ^-(x + y)$. If x and y are two positive integers, then their inverses are the two negative integers, ^-x and ^-y. Thus, if $x = 13$ and $y = 17$, then $^-13 + ^-17 = ^-(13 + 17) = ^-30$.

If we wish to add $y + ^-x$ we would have $17 + ^-13$, which we know from Theorem 6.11 is $17 - 13$. Our definition for subtraction tells us that $17 - 13 = p$ if there exists p in I such that $17 = p + 13$. Clearly $p = 4$. Then $17 - 13 = 4$.

Suppose, however, we are asked to add $x + ^-y$ or $13 + ^-17$. Let $r = 13 + ^-17$. Then $^-r = ^-(13 + ^-17) = ^-13 + ^-(^-17) = ^-13 + 17 = 17 + ^-13 = 17 - 13 = 4$. If $^-r = 4$ then $r = ^-4$. Thus $13 + ^-17 = ^-4$. Note that $17 + ^-13 = 17 - $

13 = 4, which resembles subtraction in the system of whole numbers. However, 13 + ⁻17 = 13 − 17 = ⁻4, which is not meaningful in W, certainly names an element of I. In each case the sum of a positive and negative integer may be written as a difference, and the examples above suggest a procedure for finding this difference in I.

We also wish to see what multiplication in I looks like when we use the more familiar numerals. By Theorem 6.17, if $x \in I$ then $x \cdot 0 = 0$. Thus $15 \cdot 0 = 0$ and ⁻12 $\cdot 0 = 0$. Theorems 6.18 and 6.19 tell us how to multiply a positive and a negative integer or two negative integers. If m and n are two positive integers, then ⁻m and ⁻n are negative integers. Our theorems tell us that $m \cdot {}^-n = {}^-(m \cdot n)$ and ⁻$m \cdot {}^-n = (m \cdot n)$. Specifically, $9 \cdot {}^-3 = {}^-(9 \cdot 3) = {}^-27$ and ⁻13 $\cdot$ ⁻5 $= (13 \cdot 5) = 65$.

We saw that division could be performed in I only under certain circumstances. If $x, y \in I$, then $x \div y = z$ if and only if there exists an element z in I such that $x = z \cdot y$. If p and q are two positive integers such that p is divisible by q, we expect the quotient to be the same as that which we would have if p and q were whole numbers. Also ⁻$p \div q = k$ if ⁻$p = k \cdot q$. Our theorems for multiplication in I indicate that either k or q must be a negative integer. Since we took q as a positive integer, k must be a negative integer. Similarly, ⁻$p \div {}^-q = j$ if ⁻$p = {}^-q \cdot j$, whence j must be a positive integer. If we used the fractional form (with which you are familiar) to represent division, examples of the conclusions we reached above might be written:

$$\frac{16}{8} = 2.$$

$$\frac{{}^-16}{8} = {}^-2.$$

$$\frac{{}^-16}{{}^-8} = 2.$$

What will be the quotient, if we have $\dfrac{16}{{}^-8}$? Justify your answer.

Surely you must have observed that the symbol " − " has been given four interpretations in the course of this chapter. It has been used to denote the operation, subtraction: $21 - 16$. It has been used to name certain elements of I: ⁻19 (negative nineteen). It has been used to indicate the additive inverse: ⁻$a + a = i_1$. It has been used to name the elements of J: $(a - b)$. If $a \in I$, it may be positive or negative. If a is positive, the inverse of a is negative; if a is negative, the inverse of a is positive. It takes a bit of ingenuity and some discrimination to decide when " − " means what, but the context in which the " − " appears will determine the interpretation that is intended. The raised " − " to indicate "negative" and "inverse" is used to help in making the distinction among the meanings of " − ."

In W we said $a > b$ if and only if there exists $c \neq 0$ such that $a = b + c$. So that $7 > 5$ if there exists an element $c \in W$ such that $7 = 5 + c$. Our knowledge of the addition facts in W indicate that $c = 2$. Hence $7 > 5$. We also decided that $2 \not> 3$ because there is no whole number x such that $2 = 3 + x$. Hence $2 < 3$.

We will try to apply this definition to the elements of I to see if it provides a reasonable way to tell whether $12 > 4$? $^-12 > 4$? $^-12 > {}^-4$? $12 > {}^-4$? Applying the definition we would say $12 > 4$ if there exists $r \in I$ such that $12 = 4 + r$. Clearly r is 8 and $12 > 4$.

However, using this same definition for "is greater than," we realize suddenly that we could show $3 > 4$ since there exists $s \in I$ such that $3 = 4 + s$. Here $s = {}^-1$. The definition used for "is greater than" in W will need some modification if we are to maintain the order relations we accepted for W. We do not want $3 > 4$ in I because we wish the positive integers and zero to resemble the whole numbers. If we observe the two examples above, we see that to show $12 > 4$ we produced the positive integer 8 such that $12 = 4 + 8$. However, when we considered the relation between 3 and 4 we found that we added a negative integer to 4 to get 3. Since we want 3 to be less than 4 we will make the following definition of order for the integers:

> $a > b$ if and only if there exists a positive integer c such that
> $$a = b + c.$$
> It follows that $a < b$ if there exists a negative integer c such that
> $$a = b + c.$$

Now let us refer back to our four examples:

Which is larger, 12 or 4?
Which is larger, $^-12$ or 4?
Which is larger, $^-12$ or $^-4$?
Which is larger, 12 or $^-4$?

Since

$12 = 4 + 8,$	$12 > 4$ or $4 < 12.$
$^-12 = 4 + {}^-16,$	$^-12 < 4$ or $4 > {}^-12.$
$^-12 = {}^-4 + {}^-8,$	$^-12 < {}^-4$ or $^-4 > {}^-12.$
$12 = {}^-4 + 16,$	$12 > {}^-4$ or $^-4 < 12.$

Which is larger, $^-14$ or $^-15$?

$$^-14 = {}^-15 + 1, \qquad ^-14 > {}^-15 \text{ or } {}^-15 < {}^-14.$$

If we wish to order the integers by these rules, listing them so that they are increasing to the right, it is clear that $^-14$ is to the right of $^-15$.

$$\ldots {}^-15, \, {}^-14, \, {}^-13, \, {}^-12, \, \ldots .$$

Is 0 to the right or left of $^-1$? $0 = {}^-1 + 1$; $0 > {}^-1$;   0 is to the right of $^-1$. Therefore

$$\ldots {}^-15, {}^-14, {}^-13, {}^-12, \ldots , {}^-1, 0, 1, 2, 3, 4, 5, \ldots .$$

Problem Set 6.9

A. Add in I.

1. $16 + 12 = $ ____.
2. $^-9 + 4 = $ ____.
3. $^-9 + 18 = $ ____.
4. $3 + {}^-4 = $ ____.
5. $3 + {}^-2 = $ ____.

6. $^-15 + {}^-17 = $ ____.
7. $32 + {}^-19 = $ ____.
8. $0 + {}^-5 = $ ____.
9. $^-50 + 16 = $ ____.
10. $^-18 + {}^-6 = $ ____.

B. Subtract in I. Recall that in I, subtraction is the same as adding the additive inverse.

1. $15 - 18 = $ ____.
2. $15 - {}^-18 = $ ____.
3. $^-15 - 18 = $ ____.
4. $^-15 - {}^-18 = $ ____.
5. $^-27 - 14 = $ ____.

6. $38 - 15 = $ ____.
7. $0 - 9 = $ ____.
8. $0 - {}^-9 = $ ____.
9. $116 - 57 = $ ____.
10. $^-29 - {}^-8 = $ ____.

C. Multiply in I.

1. $5 \cdot 8 = $ ____.
2. $^-6 \cdot 0 = $ ____.
3. $^-3 \cdot 7 = $ ____.
4. $14 \cdot {}^-2 = $ ____.
5. $^-8 \cdot {}^-7 = $ ____.

6. $23 \cdot {}^-1 = $ ____.
7. $^-23 \cdot {}^-1 = $ ____.
8. $11 \cdot 13 = $ ____.
9. $^-16 \cdot 5 = $ ____.
10. $^-9 \cdot {}^-7 = $ ____.

D. Divide in I.

1. $24 \div 6 = $ ____.

2. $36 \div {}^-9 = $ ____.

3. $^-16 \div 4 = $ ____.

4. $^-48 \div {}^-12 = $ ____.

5. $15 \div {}^-3 = $ ____.

6. $\dfrac{^-18}{2} = $ ____

7. $\dfrac{21}{^-7} = $ ____.

8. $\dfrac{14}{2} = $ ____.

9. $\dfrac{^-55}{^-11} = $ ____.

10. $\dfrac{^-10}{5} = $ ____.

E. Solve in I.

1. $x + 7 = {}^-9$.
2. $y - {}^-3 = 6$.
3. $2 \cdot t = {}^-18$.
4. $^-5 \cdot m = 20$.
5. $17 \cdot k = 51$.

6. $p + {}^-11 = 4$.
7. $3 \cdot s + 5 = {}^-10$.
8. $^-6 \cdot n = {}^-78$.
9. $9 \cdot r - 6 = 57$.
10. $11 - 4 \cdot b = 27$.

F. Prove:
  1. In I, if $a = b$, then $^-a = ^-b$.
  2. In I, if $^-a = ^-b$, then $a = b$.
  3. In I, if $^-a = b$, then $a = ^-b$.
  4. In I, if $a = ^-b$, then $^-a = b$.

G. Prove: In I, if $r \neq i_1$, $\dfrac{r \cdot s}{r} = s$.

H. 1. Show that $^-\left(\dfrac{16}{8}\right) = \dfrac{^-16}{8} = \dfrac{16}{^-8}$ in I.

  2. Prove: In I, if m is divisible by n and $n \neq i_1$, then
$$^-\left(\frac{m}{n}\right) = \frac{^-m}{n} = \frac{m}{^-n}.$$

I. 1. Use mathematical symbols to write a sentence showing which is larger:
$^-23$ or $^-25$? $^-10$ or 2? $^-2$ or 1?   8 or 3?   0 or $^-3$?

  2. With the same pairs of integers use mathematical symbols and write sentences showing which is smaller.

  3. Write the following set of integers so that they will increase toward the right.

$^-23$, 5, 8, $^-11$, 0, $^-1$, 32, $^-15$, 3, $^-100$, 100, 48, $^-39$, $^-16$, $^-17$.

6.10 Theorems in Chapter 6

Theorem 6.1 I is closed under addition.

Theorem 6.2 Addition is commutative in I.

Theorem 6.3 Addition is associative in I.

Theorem 6.4 An additive identity in I is $(0 - 0)$.

Theorem 6.5 Every element in I has an additive inverse in I.

Theorem 6.6 If $a, b, c, d, e, f \in W$ and $(a - b) + (c - d) = (e - f) + (c - d)$, then $(a - b) = (e - f)$ in I.

Theorem 6.7 If $a, b \in W$, then $^-(^-(a - b)) = (a - b)$ in I.

Theorem 6.8 In I, $^-(0 - 0)$ is $(0 - 0)$.

Theorem 6.9 If $a, b, c, d \in W$, then $(x - y) + (a - b) = (c - d)$ in I has the unique solution $(x - y) = (c - d) + ^-(a - b) = (c - d) + (b - a)$ in I.

Theorem 6.10 If $a, b, c, d \in W$, then $^-((a - b) + (c - d)) = ^-(a - b) + ^-(c - d) = (b - a) + (d - c)$ in I.

Theorem 6.11 If $a, b, c, d \in W$, then $(a - b) - (c - d) = (a - b) + ^-(c - d) = (a - b) + (d - c)$.

Theorem 6.12 I is closed under multiplication.

Theorem 6.13 Multiplication is commutative in I.

Theorem 6.14 Multiplication is associative in I.

Theorem **6.15** Multiplication is distributive over addition in I.

Theorem **6.16** The element $(1 - 0)$ in I is a multiplicative identity.

Theorem **6.17** If $a, b \in W$, then $(a - b) \cdot (0 - 0) = (0 - 0)$ in I.

Theorem **6.18** If $a, b, c, d \in W$, then the product of $(a - b)$ and $^-(c - d)$ is $^-((a - b) \cdot (c - d))$ in I.

Theorem **6.19** If $a, b, c, d \in W$, then the product of $^-(a - b)$ and $^-(c - d)$ is $(a - b) \cdot (c - d)$ in I.

Theorem **6.20** If $a, b, c, d, e, f \in W$ and $(a - b) \cdot (c - d) = (e - f) \cdot (c - d)$, then $(a - b) = (e - f)$ for $(c - d) \neq (0 - 0)$ in I.

Theorem **6.21** If $a, b, c, d \in W$ and $(a - b) \cdot (c - d) = (0 - 0)$, then either $(a - b) = (0 - 0)$ or $(c - d) = (0 - 0)$ in I.

6.11 Terminal Tasks for Chapter 6

1. To be able to describe algebraically the reflexive, symmetric, and transitive properties of an equivalence relation.

2. To be able to illustrate that the "$=$" relation is an equivalence relation.

3. To be able to follow the text discussion establishing "$\sim$" as an equivalence relation.

4. To recognize the three equivalent sentences:

$$(a - b) = (c - d) \text{ in } I,$$
$$(a - b) \sim (c - d) \text{ in } J,$$
$$a + d = b + c \text{ in } W,$$

and given any one of the sentences, to be able to write the other two.

5. To recognize the dependence of the development of the structure of I upon the structure of W.

6. To identify the structure of I under addition as a commutative group.

7. To apply the previously proved theorems establishing the arithmetic of a commutative group, to I under addition.

8. To observe that I does not have the structure of a field.

9. To be able to perform the arithmetic of I under multiplication.

10. To associate a given equivalence class which is an element of I with a positive or a negative integer.

11. To recognize that the arithmetic of the positive integers and zero has the same form as the arithmetic of the whole numbers.

12. To be able to perform the arithmetic involving negative numbers in I.

13. To use the concept of equivalence classes in the interpretation of the "$=$" symbol as "two names for the same number."

14. To be able to do a simple proof in I, applying the theorems established for I in the text.

15. To be able to "order" the integers in accordance with the definition for "greater than."

16. To be able to make some sensible conjecture about the form of the

ordered pair we would need to expand to a new number system in which we could always divide (except by 0).

R E V I E W   E X E R C I S E S

A. Perform the indicated calculations in I:

1. $17 + {}^-9 = $ _____.
2. ${}^-30 \div 6 = $ _____.
3. $19 + 43 = $ _____.
4. $({}^-12 + 5) \cdot 1 = $ _____.
5. $54 \cdot {}^-3 = $ _____.
6. $0 - 8 = $ _____.
7. $243 \div 1 = $ _____.
8. $243 \div {}^-1 = $ _____.
9. $40 \cdot {}^-5 = $ _____.
10. ${}^-13 + {}^-17 = $ _____.

11. ${}^-23 \cdot 0 = $ _____.
12. ${}^-7 - 24 = $ _____.
13. $24 - ({}^-7) = $ _____.
14. $0 \div 11 = $ _____.
15. $(8 \cdot {}^-7) \div 4 = $ _____.
16. ${}^-90 \cdot {}^-90 = $ _____.
17. ${}^-14 \div {}^-2 = $ _____.
18. ${}^-7 + 4 - 5 = $ _____.
19. $(15 + 4) - (15 - 4) = $ _____.
20. $8 - 1 - 3 = $ _____.

B. Solve in I. In each case indicate whether the problem could be solved in W.

1. $4 \cdot k + 36 = 0$.
2. $3 \cdot x - 5 \cdot x = {}^-12$.
3. $2 \cdot y = 13 + y$.
4. $7 \cdot m + 12 = 42 - 3 \cdot m$.
5. The rectangle shown below has a perimeter of 80 inches; find its length and width.

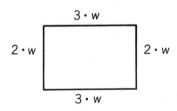

C. 1. Select the equivalence relations.

(a) "is the husband of" defined on the set of people.
(b) "is a divisor of" defined on elements of I.
(c) "is a member of the same political party as" defined on the set of people.
(d) "is equivalent to" defined on the set of mathematical sentences.
(e) "is congruent to" defined on sets of points.

2. Consider the set Q whose elements are the ordered pairs of integers $\dfrac{a}{b}$ (read "a bar b"). We define the following relation "$\frown$" on the elements of Q:

$$\frac{a}{b} \frown \frac{c}{d} \text{ if and only if } a \cdot d = b \cdot c \text{ in } I.$$

Prove "$\frown$" is an equivalence relation.

D. Prove:
1. $(a + b) - c = a + (b - c)$ for $a, b, c \in I$.
2. $a - (b - c) = (a - b) + c$ for $a, b, c \in I$.
3. $a - (b + c) = (a - b) - c$ for $a, b, c \in I$.
4. If $a - b = c - b$, then $a = c$ for $a, b, c \in I$.

E. Examine the following proof. Answer the questions listed below.

If $x \div (p^{-1} \cdot q) + r = i_1$, then $x = {}^{-}r \cdot (p^{-1} \cdot q)$.

(1) ${}^{-}r \cdot (p^{-1} \cdot q) \div (p^{-1} \cdot q) + r = i_1$.   (1) Substitution.

(2) ${}^{-}r \cdot (p^{-1} \cdot q) \cdot (p^{-1} \cdot q)^{-1} + r = i_1$.   (2) $a \div b = a \cdot b^{-1}$.

(3) ${}^{-}r \cdot (p^{-1} \cdot q) \cdot (p \cdot q^{-1}) + r = i_1$.   (3) $(a \cdot b)^{-1} = a^{-1}b^{-1}$; $(a^{-1})^{-1} = a$.

(4) ${}^{-}r \cdot [p^{-1} \cdot (q \cdot p) \cdot q^{-1}] + r = i_1$.   (4) Associativity under multiplication.

(5) ${}^{-}r \cdot [p^{-1} \cdot (p \cdot q) \cdot q^{-1}] + r = i_1$.   (5) Commutativity under multiplication.

(6) ${}^{-}r \cdot [(p^{-1} \cdot p) \cdot (q \cdot q^{-1})] + r = i_1$.   (6) Associativity under multiplication.

(7) ${}^{-}r \cdot (i_2 \cdot i_2) + r = i_1$.   (7) Definition of multiplicative inverse.

(8) ${}^{-}r + r = i_1$.   (8) Definition of multiplicative identity.

(9) $i_1 = i_1$.   (9) Definition of additive inverse.

1. Would this proof hold if p, q, r were elements of a group?
2. Would this proof hold if p, q, r were elements of a field?
3. List the restrictions which we would need to place on $p, q,$ or r in order for this proof to hold in I.
4. List the restrictions which we would need to place on $p, q,$ or r in order for the proof to hold in W.

F. Prove each of the following in I. If you need a hint, recall how similar exercises were done in W.
1. If a and b are each divisible by c, then $(a + b)$ is divisible by c.
2. If a and b are each divisible by c, then

$$\frac{a}{c} + \frac{b}{c} = \frac{a + b}{c}.$$

Do we need to note the restriction $c \neq 0$ in this example?
3. If a and b are each divisible by c, then

$$(a + b) \div c = (a \div c) + (b \div c).$$

(Right distributivity of division over addition.)

4. If a is divisible by b, and c is divisible by d, then

$$\frac{a}{b} \cdot \frac{c}{d} = \frac{a \cdot c}{b \cdot d}.$$

5. If a is divisible by b, and c is divisible by d, then

$$\frac{a}{b} + \frac{c}{d} = \frac{a \cdot d + b \cdot c}{b \cdot d}.$$

G. Identify some fact or facts learned in this chapter which might help you cope with the following hypothetical elementary classroom situations:

1. "My big sister is taking algebra. She says two minuses give a plus. What is she talking about?"

2. "If □ = 5, can we say 5 = □? Doesn't the □ have to be on the left side of the equal sign?"

3. "In keeping score we're using $\overset{\uparrow}{3}$ to show points we win and $\overset{\downarrow}{10}$ to show points we lose in each game. But now we're not sure who has more points after six games."

4. "You can never subtract 7 from 3."

5. "The big number must always be on top in a subtraction example."

6. "The integers are 0, 1, 2, 3, 4, 5, 6, 7, 8, 9."

7. "I know that 25 is more than 20. So my guess is that $^-25$ is more than $^-20$."

8. You are using the number line to teach addition and subtraction of whole numbers. A child wonders why you never move to the left of the point that is associated with zero.

9. In studying about weather the class is seeking an efficient way to record, for comparison, the lowest known temperatures in each state, for the preceding year.

10. "If the 4 you have written on the board is not a number, then what *is* a number?"

11. You and the class list as many physical situations as you can think of, for which the system of integers may serve as a mathematical model.

7 The System of Rational Numbers

7.1 Now What?

The system of integers was created so that we would have a number system in which we could always add, multiply, and also subtract. As the development proceeded and property after property of a field was established for I, we began to hope that we had indeed created a number system with the structure of a field. You realize this is a worthwhile goal, for in a field we can always add, subtract, multiply and divide (except by i_1).

You know now, of course, that we did not succeed, for the definitions of the elements and operations of I were such that we do not have a multiplicative inverse for every element (except 0) in the set. This means that we cannot always divide in I. (Let us acknowledge once and for all the restriction that we may not divide by 0 in W or I so that we need not repeat it continuously.) While it was a blow to have missed the field by one property, we should not concentrate on our failure. Rather let us focus on the fact that we did create a number system in which we could solve all the problems we could handle in W, and in addition, we could solve problems which would have been meaningless in W, namely, problems involving $x - y$ with $x < y$.

Since the structure of I was such that we could not always divide, it occurs to us that we should attempt to create a new number system. In this new system we will want to be able to solve the problems we could handle in I and, in addition, always be able to divide (except by 0). Since the concept of the equivalence class served not only to clarify the nature of a number in I, but also facilitated working out the proofs of the properties of the system, we shall employ that device in defining the elements of the new number system to be developed in this chapter, the system of rational numbers.

Our study of the structure of the system of rational numbers will parallel our development of I. Occasionally a student will carry through the work of this chapter not only independently of the instructor, but also of the text. We will choose the elements of the system of rationals so that they will, under special circumstances, be associated with integers. This means not only that they will have symbols which will look like integers, but also that the sum, product, difference, and quotient of such rational numbers will also be associated with integers. Further, we shall refer to our work in I in searching for definitions for the operations and relations.

7.2 The Set Q

Just as we created the set J whose elements comprised the members of the equivalence classes which were the integers, so we shall create a set Q whose elements we hope to be able to partition into equivalence classes which will be the rational numbers.

Let a and b be integers. Then the ordered pair $\dfrac{a}{b}$ (read "a bar b") will be an element of Q. This symbol was selected because it looks like "a divided by b" in I. If a is divisible by b, then $\dfrac{a}{b} \in Q$ will be associated with an integer. If a is not divisible by b, then the ordered pair $\dfrac{a}{b}$ is still in Q, although we are not able to associate it with any number we have considered up to this point. Since $\dfrac{a}{b}$ is an ordered pair, it is intended that $\dfrac{a}{b}$ and $\dfrac{b}{a}$ shall be two different elements of Q. We shall call a the "first component" and b the "second component" of the ordered pair $\dfrac{a}{b}$. It should be clear that although the ordered pairs $\dfrac{10}{2}, \dfrac{25}{5}, \dfrac{35}{7}$, and $\dfrac{-60}{-12}$ all are associated with the same integer, they are different elements of Q.

Since the symbol we are using for an element in Q is meant to call to mind "a divided by b" where $a, b \in I$, it occurs to us that perhaps we ought to consider the special situation in which the second component of the ordered pair is zero. In I the symbol $\dfrac{x}{0}$ or $x \div 0$ is not meaningful, in accordance with our definition of division.

Since $\dfrac{x}{0}$ is not meaningful in I, the symbol $\dfrac{x}{0} \in Q$ could not be associated with any integer. We will realize as the system of rational numbers unfolds that the symbol $\dfrac{x}{0}$ is not meaningful in that system either. We will find that if we permit the second component of the ordered pair to be zero, we will reach conclusions contrary to agreements we shall want to make. Some of these conflicting situations will be pointed out when they arise. In the meantime we will redefine the elements of Q so that we exclude all those ordered pairs with zero as the second component.

If $a, b \in I$ with $b \neq 0$, then $\dfrac{a}{b} \in Q$.

Two elements of Q shall be equal if and only if their first and second components are equal. Thus $\dfrac{a}{b} = \dfrac{c}{d}$ in Q if and only if $a = c$ and $b = d$. In I we showed that if $\dfrac{a}{b}$ and $\dfrac{c}{d}$ are elements of I, then $\dfrac{a}{b} = \dfrac{c}{d}$ if and only if $a \cdot d = b \cdot c$. Since we have already defined the equality relation for Q, we will define a new relation on the elements of Q, which will correspond to that described above for I. We will say: If $\dfrac{a}{b}, \dfrac{c}{d} \in Q$, then $\dfrac{a}{b} \frown \dfrac{c}{d}$ if and only if $a \cdot d = b \cdot c$ in I. (We might read $\dfrac{a}{b} \frown \dfrac{c}{d}$ as "$\dfrac{a}{b}$ lid $\dfrac{c}{d}$.") Note that $\dfrac{a}{b} \frown \dfrac{c}{d}$ is a sentence in Q and $a \cdot d = b \cdot c$ is a sentence in I. Let us see whether $\dfrac{-2}{5} \frown \dfrac{10}{-25}$ in Q. According to our definition, $\dfrac{-2}{5} \frown \dfrac{10}{-25}$ if $-2 \cdot -25 = 5 \cdot 10$ in I. Since both these products are 50, our sentence in Q is true. Also, if we know that $4 \cdot 6 = 3 \cdot 8$ in I, we may write $\dfrac{4}{3} \frown \dfrac{8}{6}$ in Q.

Of primary interest, with our new relation, is whether or not it is an equivalence relation. Let us determine this at once by examining the relation to decide whether it is reflexive, symmetric, and transitive.

Reflexive: $a \cdot b = b \cdot a$ in I; hence $\dfrac{a}{b} \frown \dfrac{a}{b}$ in Q.

Symmetric: $\dfrac{a}{b} \frown \dfrac{c}{d}$ in Q; $a \cdot d = b \cdot c$ in I; $b \cdot c = a \cdot d$; $c \cdot b = d \cdot a$;

$\dfrac{c}{d} \frown \dfrac{a}{b}$ in Q.

Transitive: $\dfrac{a}{b} \frown \dfrac{c}{d}$ and $\dfrac{c}{d} \frown \dfrac{e}{f}$ in Q; $a \cdot d = b \cdot c$; $c \cdot f = d \cdot e$;

$(a \cdot d) \cdot f = (b \cdot c) \cdot f$; $(c \cdot f) \cdot b = (d \cdot e) \cdot b$. Then $(a \cdot d) \cdot f = (d \cdot e) \cdot b$; $(a \cdot f) \cdot d = (b \cdot e) \cdot d$; $a \cdot f = b \cdot e$ and finally $\dfrac{a}{b} \frown \dfrac{e}{f}$.

Having established that "$\frown$" is an equivalence relation, we know it will partition Q into equivalence classes which are mutually exclusive and exhaustive. Each of these equivalence classes will be an element of the system of rational numbers R.

Let us look at some specific examples to illustrate how we know which elements of Q belong to the same equivalence class. Suppose we consider $\frac{1}{1} \in Q$. If $\frac{x}{y} \in Q$, then $\frac{x}{y}$ and $\frac{1}{1}$ will be in the same equivalence class if $\frac{1}{1} \frown \frac{x}{y}$ or $1 \cdot y = 1 \cdot x$ in I. This tells us that if the first and second components are the same integers, the ordered pairs belong to the same equivalence class. Thus $\frac{1}{1}, \frac{-1}{-1}, \frac{2}{2}, \frac{-2}{-2}, \frac{3}{3}, \frac{-3}{-3}, \frac{4}{4}, \frac{-4}{-4}$, $\frac{5}{5}, \frac{-5}{-5}, \frac{-6}{-6}, \cdots, \frac{n}{n} \cdots$ are in the same equivalence class, which is a rational number. Since n is divisible by n, this particular rational number is associated with an integer, in this case the integer 1.

Now we will choose $\frac{5}{8} \in Q$, and try to find elements of Q in the same equivalence class as "5 bar 8." If $\frac{5}{8} \frown \frac{x}{y}$, then $5 \cdot y = 8 \cdot x$ in I. Since $5 \cdot y = 8 \cdot x$ and 5 and 8 are prime to each other, x must be a multiple of 5 and y must be a multiple of 8. Let $x = 5 \cdot p$ and $y = 8 \cdot q$. This gives us $5 \cdot 8 \cdot q = 8 \cdot 5 \cdot p$, whence $q = p$. This means if $x = 5 \cdot 3$, then $y = 8 \cdot 3$; if $x = 5 \cdot 9$, then $y = 8 \cdot 9$; if $x = 5 \cdot n$, then $y = 8 \cdot n$. So we may write $\frac{5}{8} \frown \frac{5 \cdot n}{8 \cdot n}$. Thus $\frac{5}{8}, \frac{-5}{-8}, \frac{5 \cdot 2}{8 \cdot 2}, \frac{5 \cdot -2}{8 \cdot -2}, \frac{5 \cdot 3}{8 \cdot 3}$, $\frac{5 \cdot -3}{8 \cdot -3}, \frac{5 \cdot 4}{8 \cdot 4}, \frac{5 \cdot -4}{8 \cdot -4}, \cdots, \frac{5 \cdot n}{8 \cdot n}, \cdots$ are in the same equivalence class, which is a rational number. Since 5 is not divisible by 8 this rational number is not associated with any number of I. We may select any member of the equivalence class to name the class. In order to differentiate between $\frac{5}{8} \in Q$, and "5 bar 8" when we want it to be an element of R, we shall write $\mathbf{\frac{5}{8}}$ (with a boldface bar) to name the equivalence class which contains the element $\frac{5}{8}$ of Q.

If the first and second components of the equivalence class, which is an element of R, are positive integers, then the rational number is defined as a **positive rational number.** If the first component of the equivalence class is a negative integer and the second component is a positive integer, then the rational number is defined as a **negative rational number.** Thus, by definition, $\mathbf{\frac{7}{8}}$ is a positive rational number and $\mathbf{\frac{-7}{8}}$ is a negative rational number.

We shall define the equality relation in R as follows: $\frac{a}{b} = \frac{c}{d}$ in R if and only if

$\dfrac{a}{b} \frown \dfrac{c}{d}$ in Q. Since $\dfrac{a}{b} \frown \dfrac{c}{d}$ in Q if and only if $a \cdot d = b \cdot c$ in I, we have three equivalent sentences:

$$\frac{a}{b} = \frac{c}{d} \text{ in } R.$$

$$\frac{a}{b} \frown \frac{c}{d} \text{ in } Q.$$

$$a \cdot d = b \cdot c \text{ in } I.$$

Keep in mind that $\dfrac{a}{b} = \dfrac{c}{d}$ means that we have two names for the same equivalence class. In our work we go back and forth from R to I as the need arises, skipping the intermediate equivalent sentence in Q. We are interested in restating this equality by its equivalent sentence in I because we know the properties and theorems for multiplication in I and can employ many arithmetic procedures in that system.

Problem Set 7.2

A. Identify elements of Q which are in the same equivalence class as each of the following. Write ten elements in each class.

1. $\dfrac{16}{2}$.

2. $\dfrac{-3}{7}$.

3. $\dfrac{4}{-8}$.

4. $\dfrac{-5}{-9}$.

5. $\dfrac{m}{p}$.

B. Show that if we were to permit $\dfrac{0}{0}$ to be an element of Q, then for every element $\dfrac{x}{y}$ of Q, $\dfrac{x}{y} \frown \dfrac{0}{0}$.

C. Write equivalent sentences in the indicated systems.

1. If $\dfrac{r}{s} = \dfrac{p}{q}$ in R, then _____ in I.

2. If $\dfrac{3}{t} = \dfrac{k}{m}$ in R, then _____ in I.

3. If $10 \cdot 3 = 6 \cdot 5$ in I, then _____ in R.

4. If $7 \cdot y = 8 \cdot x$ in I with $x \neq 0$, $y \neq 0$, then _____ in R.

5. If $\dfrac{a}{b} \frown \dfrac{r}{s}$ in Q, then _____ in R.

D. Prove: If $a \cdot b = r \cdot s$ in I with $a, b, r, s \neq 0$, then in R:

1. $\dfrac{a}{r} = \dfrac{s}{b}$.

2. $\dfrac{a}{s} = \dfrac{r}{b}$.

3. $\dfrac{r}{a} = \dfrac{b}{s}$.

4. $\dfrac{s}{a} = \dfrac{b}{r}$.

E. Prove: In R, $\dfrac{a}{b} = \dfrac{c}{d}$ if $a = c$ and $b = d \neq 0$ in I.

F. Prove in R:

1. If $\dfrac{x}{y}$ is a positive rational number, then $\dfrac{^-x}{^-y}$ names the same positive rational number.

2. If $\dfrac{^-x}{y}$ is a negative rational number, then $\dfrac{x}{^-y}$ names the same negative rational number.

3. $\dfrac{0}{x} = \dfrac{0}{y}$. There is only one rational number whose first component is zero.

7.3 The System of Rationals under Addition

Now that we have our elements of R we will define the first operation, addition, and examine our system to see if it has the structure of a commutative group under addition. In accordance with our plan we will refer to our work on integers for a suggestion for the definition. In **G5** of the Review Exercises, Chapter 6, we were asked to prove:

$$\frac{a}{b} + \frac{c}{d} = \frac{a \cdot d + b \cdot c}{b \cdot d},$$

where $\dfrac{a}{b}$ and $\dfrac{c}{d}$ were integers. This appears to be a likely recommendation. Hence we define addition in R as follows:

$$\frac{a}{b} + \frac{c}{d} = \frac{a \cdot d + b \cdot c}{b \cdot d}.$$

Since $a, b, c, d \in I$ and I is closed under addition and multiplication, $a \cdot d + b \cdot c \in I$ and $b \cdot d \neq 0 \in I$. The components of the ordered pair which name the sum are therefore integers and thus the equivalence class is an element of R.

Let us take a single example to illustrate that addition is well defined in R. We will select $\dfrac{7}{8} \frown \dfrac{14}{16}$ and $\dfrac{-2}{3} \frown \dfrac{10}{-15}$.

$$\frac{7}{8} + \frac{-2}{3} = \frac{7 \cdot 3 + 8 \cdot {}^-2}{8 \cdot 3} = \frac{21 + {}^-16}{24} = \frac{5}{24}.$$

$$\frac{14}{16} + \frac{10}{-15} = \frac{14 \cdot {}^-15 + 16 \cdot 10}{16 \cdot {}^-15} = \frac{{}^-210 + 160}{{}^-240} = \frac{{}^-50}{{}^-240}.$$

Since $\dfrac{5}{24} \frown \dfrac{-50}{-240}$, addition is well defined for the rational numbers we chose. A general proof that addition is well defined will be left to you, in the problem set. Then we have

Theorem 7.1 R *is closed under addition.*

To establish commutativity we need to prove

Theorem 7.2 *If* $a, b, c, d \in I$, *then* $\dfrac{a}{b} + \dfrac{c}{d} = \dfrac{c}{d} + \dfrac{a}{b}$ *in* R.

The strategy for the analysis is the same as that which we used in the corresponding proofs in I. Work backward performing the indicated operations until you have a sentence in R with one equivalence class on each side of the $=$ sign. Then write an equivalent sentence in I. Apply the properties and theorems of I to arrive at a statement you know to be true. To get clues for the proof of Theorem 7.2, the analysis might proceed as follows:

$$\frac{a}{b} + \frac{c}{d} = \frac{c}{d} + \frac{a}{b},$$

which is true if

$$\frac{a \cdot d + b \cdot c}{b \cdot d} = \frac{c \cdot b + d \cdot a}{d \cdot b},$$

which is true if

$$a \cdot d + b \cdot c = c \cdot b + d \cdot a \quad \text{and} \quad b \cdot d = d \cdot b \text{ in } I.$$

The last two sentences are true in I because we have closure and commutativity under addition and multiplication in I. You should now be able to write a proof for Theorem 7.2.

The proof for associativity under addition is left entirely to you. Prove

Theorem 7.3 *If* $a, b, c, d, e, f \in I$, *then* $\left(\dfrac{a}{b} + \dfrac{c}{d}\right) + \dfrac{e}{f} = \dfrac{a}{b} + \left(\dfrac{c}{d} + \dfrac{e}{f}\right)$ *in* R.

Now we would like to produce an additive identity in R. Since 0 is the additive identity in I, we might guess that an ordered pair involving a zero ought to be a good first try for an additive identity in R. We can't use $\dfrac{0}{0}$ or $\dfrac{a}{0}$ because we have agreed to omit them from Q, so they are not in any equivalence class of R. All that is left is $\dfrac{0}{a}$. Test $\dfrac{0}{a}$ to see if it functions as an additive identity in R.

Suppose you were not able to make a successful conjecture as to the existence or form of an additive identity in R. Do you recall how we proceeded to make such an investigation in I? The strategy is the same here. Assume $\dfrac{x}{y}$ is an additive identity. Then assume

$$\frac{a}{b} + \frac{x}{y} = \frac{a}{b},$$

which is true if

$$\frac{a \cdot y + b \cdot x}{b \cdot y} = \frac{a}{b},$$

which is true if

$$(a \cdot y + b \cdot x) \cdot b = a \cdot (b \cdot y) \text{ in } I,$$

which is true if

$$(a \cdot y) \cdot b + (b \cdot x) \cdot b = a \cdot (b \cdot y).$$

This sentence is true if $(b \cdot x) \cdot b = 0$. Since $b \neq 0$, x must be 0 in order for $(b \cdot x) \cdot b = 0$ to be true. Our conjecture for a candidate to serve as an additive identity is $\frac{0}{y}$. Thus:

Theorem 7.4 *In R, $\frac{0}{y}$ is an additive identity.*

To prove this theorem, you must show that $\frac{a}{b} + \frac{0}{y} = \frac{a}{b}$. Write the proof in full. Since, for any $y \neq 0$, $\frac{0}{y} = \frac{0}{1}$, we can simplify calculations by using $\frac{0}{1}$ to name the class.

   To complete our investigation of the structure of R under addition we must explore the existence and form of additive inverses. By now the procedure for such a study should be familiar to you. We will record the analysis and leave the proof to you. Assume $\frac{x}{y}$ is to function as the additive inverse of $\frac{a}{b}$ in R: $\frac{x}{y} = {}^{-}\!\left(\frac{a}{b}\right)$.
Then

$$\frac{a}{b} + \frac{x}{y} = \frac{0}{1},$$

which is true if

$$\frac{a \cdot y + b \cdot x}{b \cdot y} = \frac{0}{1},$$

which is true if

$$a \cdot y + b \cdot x = 0 \text{ in } I.$$

There are two circumstances which interest us and in which the sentence $a \cdot y + b \cdot x = 0$ is true:

   (1) $a \cdot y = {}^{-}(b \cdot x) = {}^{-}b \cdot x$, whence

$$\frac{a}{{}^{-}b} = \frac{x}{y}.$$

(2) $b \cdot x = {}^-(a \cdot y) = {}^-a \cdot y$, whence

$$\frac{x}{y} = \frac{{}^-a}{b}.$$

It appears that we have two candidates for the additive inverse of $\frac{a}{b}$. However, since

$$\frac{a}{{}^-b} = \frac{{}^-a}{b}$$

we really have one candidate which may be named two ways. Thus

$$^-\left(\frac{a}{b}\right) = \frac{{}^-a}{b} = \frac{a}{{}^-b}.$$

Theorem 7.5 *If $\frac{a}{b} \in R$, then its additive inverse in R is $\frac{{}^-a}{b}$.*

Theorems 7.1 through 7.5 show that the system of rational numbers under addition is a commutative group.

Problem Set 7.3

A. Consider the following suggested definition of addition in R:

$$\frac{a}{b} + \frac{c}{d} = \frac{a + c}{b + d} \qquad \text{where } b + d \neq 0.$$

Give an example to illustrate that the operation is not well defined.

B. Use the definition for addition in R to write another name for each sum.

1. $\dfrac{2}{3} + \dfrac{1}{5} = \underline{\quad}$.

6. $\dfrac{8}{3} + \dfrac{{}^-4}{3} = \underline{\quad}$.

2. $\dfrac{10}{2} + \dfrac{9}{3} = \underline{\quad}$.

7. $\dfrac{2}{13} + \dfrac{12}{{}^-10} = \underline{\quad}$.

3. $\dfrac{4}{7} + \dfrac{5}{6} = \underline{\quad}$.

8. $\dfrac{{}^-6}{{}^-15} + \dfrac{3}{5} = \underline{\quad}$.

4. $\dfrac{{}^-9}{10} + \dfrac{7}{10} = \underline{\quad}$.

9. $\dfrac{11}{t} + \dfrac{7}{r} = \underline{\quad}$.

5. $^-\left(\dfrac{12}{11}\right) + \dfrac{2}{11} = \underline{\quad}$.

10. $\dfrac{s}{9} + \dfrac{k}{10} = \underline{\quad}$.

C. 1. Prove: In R, $\dfrac{a}{c} + \dfrac{b}{c} = \dfrac{a + b}{c}$.

  2. Apply this theorem to problems **B4, B5,** and **B6**.

D. Perform the indicated calculations. Use the properties of R under addition to simplify the work wherever possible.

1. $\dfrac{6}{11} + \left(\dfrac{2}{11} + \dfrac{1}{5}\right) = $ _____.

4. $\left(\dfrac{3}{4} + \dfrac{7}{8}\right) + \dfrac{-3}{4} = $ _____.

2. $\dfrac{0}{13} + \dfrac{12}{19} = $ _____.

5. $\left(\dfrac{5}{8} + \dfrac{7}{9}\right) + \left(\dfrac{-5}{8} + \dfrac{7}{-9}\right) = $ _____.

3. $\left(\dfrac{5}{9} + \dfrac{5}{-9}\right) + \dfrac{5}{9} = $ _____.

E. 1. Prove addition is well defined in R. Show that if $\dfrac{a}{b} = \dfrac{c}{d}, \dfrac{e}{f} = \dfrac{m}{n}$, then

$$\frac{a}{b} + \frac{e}{f} = \frac{c}{d} + \frac{m}{n}.$$

2. In problem **B**, Problem Set 7.2, you showed why it was decided to discard $\dfrac{0}{0}$ as a member of R. Now show that if $\dfrac{x}{0}$ were an element of R, then

$\dfrac{a}{0} + \dfrac{b}{0}$ would be meaningless.

F. Show that if $\dfrac{a}{0}$ were an element of R, there would be no unique additive

identity of $\dfrac{a}{0}$ in R. (Show that for any $\dfrac{x}{y} \in R, \dfrac{a}{0} + \dfrac{x}{y} = \dfrac{a}{0}$.)

G. Use the appropriate properties of R under addition to give meaning to

$\dfrac{x}{y} + \dfrac{u}{w} + \dfrac{p}{q}$.

H. Let P be the set of all positive rational numbers. (Recall that we defined addition for all rational numbers.) Show that if $\dfrac{m}{n}$ and $\dfrac{r}{s}$ are any two positive

rational numbers, then $\dfrac{m}{n} + \dfrac{r}{s}$ is a positive rational number. You will have

proved that P is closed under addition.

7.4 Theorems in *R* under Addition

Since R under addition is a commutative group, we know from our study of groups that the following theorems are true:

Theorem 7.6 *If* $\dfrac{a}{b}, \dfrac{c}{d}, \dfrac{e}{f} \in R$ *and* $\dfrac{a}{b} + \dfrac{e}{f} = \dfrac{c}{d} + \dfrac{e}{f},$ *then* $\dfrac{a}{b} = \dfrac{c}{d}.$

This is the Cancellation Law for Addition.

Theorem 7.7 *If* $\dfrac{a}{b} \in R$, *then* $^{-}\left[^{-}\left(\dfrac{a}{b}\right)\right] = \dfrac{a}{b}.$

Theorem 7.8 *If* $b \in I$ *with* $b \neq 0,$ *then* $^{-}\left(\dfrac{0}{b}\right) = \dfrac{0}{b}$ *in* $R.$

Theorem 7.9 *If* $\frac{a}{b}, \frac{c}{d} \in R$, *then the equation* $\frac{x}{y} + \frac{a}{b} = \frac{c}{d}$ *has the unique solution*

$\frac{x}{y} = \frac{c}{d} + {}^{-}\!\left(\frac{a}{b}\right)$ *in R.*

Theorem 7.10 *If* $\frac{a}{b}, \frac{c}{d} \in R$, *then* ${}^{-}\!\left(\frac{a}{b}\right) + {}^{-}\!\left(\frac{c}{d}\right) = {}^{-}\!\left(\frac{a}{b} + \frac{c}{d}\right)$.

Just for the sake of the exercise let us prove Theorem 7.10. We must show that
${}^{-}\!\left(\frac{a}{b}\right) + {}^{-}\!\left(\frac{c}{d}\right) = {}^{-}\!\left(\frac{a}{b} + \frac{c}{d}\right)$. We might proceed as follows:

ASSERTIONS	SUPPORTING STATEMENTS
(1) ${}^{-}\!\left(\frac{a}{b}\right) + {}^{-}\!\left(\frac{c}{d}\right) = \frac{{}^{-}a}{b} + \frac{{}^{-}c}{d}$.	(1) Theorem 7.5.
(2) $= \frac{{}^{-}a \cdot d + {}^{-}c \cdot b}{b \cdot d}$.	(2) Definition of addition in R.
(3) $= \frac{{}^{-}(a \cdot d) + {}^{-}(c \cdot b)}{b \cdot d}$.	(3) Theorem 6.18.
(4) $= \frac{{}^{-}(a \cdot d + b \cdot c)}{b \cdot d}$.	(4) Theorem 6.10.
(5) $= {}^{-}\!\left(\frac{a \cdot d + b \cdot c}{b \cdot d}\right)$.	(5) Theorem 7.5.
(6) $= {}^{-}\!\left(\frac{a}{b} + \frac{c}{d}\right)$.	(6) Definition of addition in R.

Of course we could prove Theorem 7.10 by the method of the proof given for the corresponding theorem in our study of groups.

The definition of subtraction will follow that given in W and also in I:

If $\frac{a}{b}, \frac{c}{d} \in R$, then $\frac{a}{b} - \frac{c}{d} = \frac{e}{f}$ if and only if $\frac{a}{b} = \frac{e}{f} + \frac{c}{d}$.

We may now state another theorem that we know to be true in R:

Theorem 7.11 *If* $\frac{a}{b}, \frac{c}{d} \in R$, *then* $\frac{a}{b} - \frac{c}{d} = \frac{a}{b} + {}^{-}\!\left(\frac{c}{d}\right)$.

Problem Set 7.4

A. Write a proof for each of the following.
   1. Theorem 7.6.   4. Theorem 7.9.
   2. Theorem 7.7.   5. Theorem 7.11.
   3. Theorem 7.8.

B. Perform the indicated computations in R.

1. $^-\!\left(\dfrac{2}{9}\right) + {}^-\!\left(\dfrac{5}{8}\right) = $ _____.

2. $^-\!\left(\dfrac{2}{9} + \dfrac{5}{8}\right) = $ _____.

3. $^-\!\left(\dfrac{^-3}{4} + \dfrac{10}{7}\right) = $ _____.

4. $\dfrac{1}{6} + \dfrac{1}{7} + {}^-\!\left(\dfrac{13}{42}\right) = $ _____.

5. $\dfrac{4}{9} + \dfrac{5}{9} = $ _____.

6. $\dfrac{15}{8} - \dfrac{4}{3} = $ _____.

7. $^-\!\left(\dfrac{0}{11} + \dfrac{^-9}{11}\right) = $ _____.

8. $\dfrac{11}{12} - \dfrac{5}{6} + \dfrac{1}{3} = $ _____.

9. $\dfrac{18}{25} - \dfrac{2}{5} = $ _____.

10. $\dfrac{17}{24} + \dfrac{1}{8} - \dfrac{1}{2} = $ _____.

C. Find, in each case, a candidate for the solution set in R.

1. $\dfrac{x}{y} + \dfrac{3}{4} = \dfrac{5}{6}$.

2. $\dfrac{7}{8} + \dfrac{p}{q} = \dfrac{1}{4}$.

3. $\dfrac{1}{2} - \dfrac{m}{n} = \dfrac{3}{1}$.

4. $\dfrac{r}{s} - \left(\dfrac{8}{9} + \dfrac{2}{3}\right) = \dfrac{0}{27}$.

5. $\dfrac{a}{b} + \dfrac{11}{12} = \dfrac{7}{12} + \dfrac{5}{12}$.

D. Prove in R:

1. $\left(\dfrac{a}{b} + \dfrac{c}{d}\right) - \dfrac{e}{f} = \dfrac{a}{b} + \left(\dfrac{c}{d} - \dfrac{e}{f}\right)$.

2. $\left(\dfrac{a}{b} - \dfrac{c}{d}\right) + \dfrac{e}{f} = \left(\dfrac{a}{b} + \dfrac{e}{f}\right) - \dfrac{c}{d} = \dfrac{a}{b} + \left(\dfrac{e}{f} - \dfrac{c}{d}\right)$.

3. $\dfrac{a}{b} - \left(\dfrac{c}{d} - \dfrac{e}{f}\right) = \left(\dfrac{a}{b} - \dfrac{c}{d}\right) + \dfrac{e}{f} = \left(\dfrac{a}{b} + \dfrac{e}{f}\right) - \dfrac{c}{d}$.

4. $\dfrac{x}{y} = \left(\dfrac{c}{d} - \dfrac{a}{b}\right)$ is a suitable candidate for the solution set of the equation

$\left(\dfrac{x}{y} + \dfrac{a}{b}\right) - \dfrac{c}{d} = \dfrac{0}{m}$.

E. Prove: The additive identity in R is unique.

7.5 The System of Rationals under Multiplication

In the Review Exercise **G4**, Chapter 6, you proved that in $I, \dfrac{a}{b} \cdot \dfrac{c}{d} = \dfrac{a \cdot c}{b \cdot d}$.

This is our clue for a definition for multiplication in R:

$$\frac{a}{b} \cdot \frac{c}{d} = \frac{a \cdot c}{b \cdot d}.$$

By now you should be able to prove with no difficulty that $\dfrac{a \cdot c}{b \cdot d} \in R$, since $a \cdot c,\, b \cdot d \in I$, and $b \cdot d \neq 0$.

Once again we will illustrate that multiplication is well defined and leave the proof as an exercise in Problem Set 7.5. Let us choose $\dfrac{8}{10} = \dfrac{4}{5}$ and $\dfrac{1}{3} = \dfrac{3}{9}$. We must show $\dfrac{8}{10} \cdot \dfrac{1}{3} = \dfrac{4}{5} \cdot \dfrac{3}{9}$.

$$\frac{8}{10} \cdot \frac{1}{3} = \frac{8 \cdot 1}{10 \cdot 3} = \frac{8}{30}.$$

$$\frac{4}{5} \cdot \frac{3}{9} = \frac{4 \cdot 3}{5 \cdot 9} = \frac{12}{45}.$$

$$\frac{8}{30} = \frac{12}{45} \text{ because } 8 \cdot 45 = 30 \cdot 12.$$

Theorem 7.12 *R is closed under multiplication.*

The proofs for commutativity, associativity, and distributivity of multiplication over addition will be left to you.

Theorem 7.13 *If* $\dfrac{a}{b}, \dfrac{c}{d} \in R$, *then* $\dfrac{a}{b} \cdot \dfrac{c}{d} = \dfrac{c}{d} \cdot \dfrac{a}{b}$.

Theorem 7.14 *If* $\dfrac{a}{b}, \dfrac{c}{d}, \dfrac{e}{f} \in R$, *then* $\left(\dfrac{a}{b} \cdot \dfrac{c}{d}\right) \cdot \dfrac{e}{f} = \dfrac{a}{b} \cdot \left(\dfrac{c}{d} \cdot \dfrac{e}{f}\right)$.

Theorem 7.15 *If* $\dfrac{a}{b}, \dfrac{c}{d}, \dfrac{e}{f} \in R$, *then* $\dfrac{a}{b} \cdot \left(\dfrac{c}{d} + \dfrac{e}{f}\right) = \dfrac{a}{b} \cdot \dfrac{c}{d} + \dfrac{a}{b} \cdot \dfrac{e}{f}$.

You would more than likely guess that $\dfrac{x}{x}$ is a suitable candidate for a multiplicative identity in R. If you didn't guess it, then you could find a candidate if you proceeded as follows: Let $\dfrac{x}{y}$ represent a multiplicative identity:

$$\frac{a}{b} \cdot \frac{x}{y} = \frac{a}{b}.$$

$$\frac{a \cdot x}{b \cdot y} = \frac{a}{b}.$$

$$(a \cdot x) \cdot b = a \cdot (b \cdot y) \text{ in } I.$$

For all $a \neq 0$, $b \neq 0$, $x = y$.

Use this analysis to help you with a proof for

Theorem 7.16 *In* R, $\dfrac{n}{n}$ *is a multiplicative identity.*

To simplify calculations we will use $\dfrac{1}{1}$ to name the class $\dfrac{n}{n}$.

Now if multiplicative inverses for every element in $R \left(\text{except } \dfrac{0}{n} \right)$ exist, we will have created a number system whose structure is a field. All the theorems we proved describing the arithmetic permissible in a field will be applicable to the system of rational numbers. With no more delay we will allow $\dfrac{x}{y}$ to function as a multiplicative inverse for $\dfrac{a}{b}$ in the following sentence in R:

$$\frac{a}{b} \cdot \frac{x}{y} = \frac{1}{1},$$

$$\frac{a \cdot x}{b \cdot y} = \frac{1}{1},$$

$$(a \cdot x) \cdot 1 = (b \cdot y) \cdot 1 \text{ in } I,$$

$$a \cdot x = b \cdot y,$$

$$\frac{x}{y} = \frac{b}{a} \text{ in } R.$$

It appears that so long as $a \neq 0$ (i.e., we exclude $\dfrac{0}{n}$ from the elements which may have multiplicative inverses in R), then $\dfrac{a}{b} \in R$ seems to have a multiplicative inverse, $\dfrac{b}{a} \in R$. We shall write the multiplicative inverse of $\dfrac{a}{b}$ as $\left(\dfrac{a}{b} \right)^{-1}$. Then $\left(\dfrac{a}{b} \right)^{-1} = \dfrac{b}{a}$. Prove:

Theorem 7.17 *Every element in* R, *except the additive identity, has a multiplicative inverse in* R.

In symbols you may show: If $\dfrac{a}{b} \in R$ with $a \neq 0$, then $\left(\dfrac{a}{b} \right)^{-1} = \dfrac{b}{a}$.

We have a field!

Problem Set 7.5

A. Suppose we decided to try the following definition of multiplication in R:

$$\frac{a}{b} \cdot \frac{c}{d} = \frac{a \cdot d}{b \cdot c} \qquad \text{where } a \neq 0, \, c \neq 0.$$

Since this operation is well defined, it is in order to consider these questions:
1. Is R closed under this definition of multiplication?
2. Is multiplication commutative?
3. Is multiplication associative?
4. Is multiplication distributive over addition?
5. Is there a multiplicative identity in R?

6. Does every element of R except $\dfrac{0}{n}$ have a multiplicative inverse in R?

Why don't we use this definition?

B. Use the appropriate properties of R under multiplication to give meaning to

$\dfrac{m}{n} \cdot \dfrac{p}{q} \cdot \dfrac{x}{y}$.

C. Prove multiplication is well defined in R. Show that if $\dfrac{a}{b} = \dfrac{m}{n}$ and $\dfrac{c}{d} = \dfrac{p}{q}$,

then $\dfrac{a}{b} \cdot \dfrac{c}{d} = \dfrac{m}{n} \cdot \dfrac{p}{q}$.

D. 1. Why do we make the restriction that $\dfrac{0}{n}$ shall not have a multiplicative inverse in R?

2. What's wrong with the following reasoning? $\left(\dfrac{a}{b}\right)^{-1} = \dfrac{b}{a}$; hence $\left(\dfrac{n}{0}\right)^{-1} =$

$\dfrac{0}{n}$ and $\dfrac{n}{0} \cdot \dfrac{0}{n}$ must equal $\dfrac{1}{1}$. If $\dfrac{n \cdot 0}{0 \cdot n} = \dfrac{1}{1}$, then $\dfrac{0}{0} = \dfrac{1}{1}$.

E. Where possible use the properties of multiplication in R to simplify the calculations:

1. $\dfrac{2}{3} \cdot \dfrac{5}{6} + \dfrac{1}{3} \cdot \dfrac{5}{6} =$ _____.   **4.** $\dfrac{-1}{7} \cdot \left(\dfrac{7}{-1} \cdot \dfrac{4}{21}\right) =$ _____.

2. $\left(\dfrac{2}{5} \cdot \dfrac{19}{3}\right) \cdot \dfrac{5}{2} =$ _____.   **5.** $\dfrac{-3}{-11} \cdot \left(\dfrac{12}{19} \cdot \dfrac{11}{3}\right) =$ _____.

3. $\dfrac{15}{6} \cdot \dfrac{4}{10} =$ _____.

F. Prove: If P is the set of positive rational numbers and $\dfrac{m}{n}$ and $\dfrac{r}{s}$ are any two

positive rational numbers, then $\dfrac{m}{n} \cdot \dfrac{r}{s}$ is an element of P.

G. Using the definition of multiplication and the multiplicative identity property, rewrite each rational number so that the first and second components of each ordered pair will have only the factor 1 in common.

Example. $\dfrac{10}{12} = \dfrac{5 \cdot 2}{6 \cdot 2} = \dfrac{5}{6} \cdot \dfrac{2}{2} = \dfrac{5}{6}.$

1. $\dfrac{36}{120} = \underline{\quad}.$

2. $\dfrac{24}{56} = \underline{\quad}.$

3. $\dfrac{125}{300} = \underline{\quad}.$

4. $\dfrac{70}{28} = \underline{\quad}.$

5. $\dfrac{16}{32} = \underline{\quad}.$

6. $\dfrac{65}{85} = \underline{\quad}.$

7. $\dfrac{45}{105} = \underline{\quad}.$

8. $\dfrac{56}{63} = \underline{\quad}.$

9. $\dfrac{220}{200} = \underline{\quad}.$

10. $\dfrac{1000}{1,000,000} = \underline{\quad}.$

H. Using the multiplicative identity property, rewrite each addend so that the second components are the same. Then add, using problem **C1**, Problem Set 7.3.

Example. $\dfrac{1}{3} + \dfrac{2}{7} = \dfrac{1}{3} \cdot \dfrac{7}{7} + \dfrac{2}{7} \cdot \dfrac{3}{3} = \dfrac{7}{21} + \dfrac{6}{21} = \dfrac{13}{21}.$

1. $\dfrac{1}{2} + \dfrac{2}{3}$

2. $\dfrac{3}{5} + \dfrac{4}{7}$

3. $\dfrac{^-7}{10} + \dfrac{2}{5}$

4. $\dfrac{3}{8} + \dfrac{^-1}{4}$

5. $\dfrac{5}{6} + \dfrac{7}{12} + \dfrac{1}{3}$

6. $\dfrac{3}{4} + \left(\dfrac{^-7}{6} \right)$

7. $\dfrac{4}{15} + \dfrac{1}{2} + \dfrac{3}{10}$

8. $\left(\dfrac{1}{6} + \dfrac{2}{9} \right) + \left(\dfrac{5}{16} + \dfrac{^-1}{4} \right)$

9. $\left(\dfrac{1}{3} + \dfrac{1}{4} \right) + \left(\dfrac{1}{5} + \dfrac{1}{6} \right)$

10. $\dfrac{5}{6} + \dfrac{3}{8} + \dfrac{1}{3}$

I. 1. Prove: If $\dfrac{a}{b}, \dfrac{b}{c} \in R$, then $\dfrac{a}{b} \cdot \dfrac{b}{c} = \dfrac{a}{c}.$

2. Multiply and write products so that the first and second components of the ordered pairs are prime to each other.

a. $\dfrac{5}{6} \cdot \dfrac{6}{25}$

b. $\dfrac{3}{10} \cdot \dfrac{11}{4} \cdot \dfrac{10}{11}$

c. $\dfrac{9}{2} \cdot \dfrac{2}{7} \cdot \dfrac{7}{9}$

d. $\dfrac{6}{10} \cdot \dfrac{2}{7} \cdot \dfrac{5}{2}$

e. $\dfrac{10}{3} \cdot \dfrac{3}{2} \cdot \dfrac{4}{4}$

J. Prove in R: $\dfrac{a}{b} \cdot \dfrac{0}{n} = \dfrac{0}{n}$.

7.6 Theorems in *R* under Multiplication

Since R is a field, the theorems we established for a field under multiplication must hold without further proof in R. Thus the following theorems are true in R.

Theorem 7.18 *If* $\dfrac{a}{b}, \dfrac{c}{d}, \dfrac{e}{f} \in R$ *with* $e \neq 0$ *and* $\dfrac{a}{b} \cdot \dfrac{e}{f} = \dfrac{c}{d} \cdot \dfrac{e}{f}$, *then* $\dfrac{a}{b} = \dfrac{c}{d}$.

This is the Cancellation Law for Multiplication in R.

Theorem 7.19 *If* $\dfrac{a}{b} \in R$ *with* $a \neq 0$, *then* $\left[\left(\dfrac{a}{b} \right)^{-1} \right]^{-1} = \dfrac{a}{b}$.

Theorem 7.20 *In* R, $\left(\dfrac{n}{n} \right)^{-1} = \dfrac{n}{n}$.

Why don't we have to add the restriction that $n \neq 0$?

Theorem 7.21 *If* $\dfrac{a}{b}, \dfrac{c}{d} \in R$ *with* $a \neq 0$, *then* $\dfrac{x}{y} \cdot \dfrac{a}{b} = \dfrac{c}{d}$ *has the unique solution* $\dfrac{x}{y} = \dfrac{c}{d} \cdot \left(\dfrac{a}{b} \right)^{-1}$ *in* R.

Theorem 7.22 *If* $\dfrac{a}{b}, \dfrac{c}{d} \in R$ *with* $a \neq 0, c \neq 0$, *then* $\left(\dfrac{a}{b} \right)^{-1} \cdot \left(\dfrac{c}{d} \right)^{-1} = \left(\dfrac{a}{b} \cdot \dfrac{c}{d} \right)^{-1}$.

For the next theorem we shall need a definition for division. In accordance with the definition used in W and in I we shall say:

If $\dfrac{a}{b}, \dfrac{c}{d} \in R$, then $\dfrac{a}{b} \div \dfrac{c}{d} = \dfrac{e}{f}$ if and only if $\dfrac{e}{f} \in R$ such that $\dfrac{a}{b} = \dfrac{e}{f} \cdot \dfrac{c}{d}$.

Theorem 7.23 *If* $\dfrac{a}{b}, \dfrac{c}{d} \in R$ *with* $c \neq 0$, *then* $\dfrac{a}{b} \div \dfrac{c}{d} = \dfrac{a}{b} \cdot \left(\dfrac{c}{d} \right)^{-1}$.

Theorem 7.24 *If* $\dfrac{a}{b}, \dfrac{c}{d} \in R$, *then* $\dfrac{a}{b} \cdot {}^{-}\!\left(\dfrac{c}{d} \right) = {}^{-}\!\left(\dfrac{a}{b} \cdot \dfrac{c}{d} \right)$.

Theorem 7.25 *If* $\dfrac{a}{b}, \dfrac{c}{d} \in R$, *then* ${}^{-}\!\left(\dfrac{a}{b} \right) \cdot {}^{-}\!\left(\dfrac{c}{d} \right) = \dfrac{a}{b} \cdot \dfrac{c}{d}$.

Theorem 7.26 If $\frac{a}{b}, \frac{c}{d} \in R$ and $\frac{a}{b} \cdot \frac{c}{d} = \frac{0}{n}$, then either $\frac{a}{b} = \frac{0}{n}$ or $\frac{c}{d} = \frac{0}{n}$.

Let us see how the proof of one of these theorems would look in R. Suppose we choose Theorem 7.22. We must prove that if $a \neq 0$, $c \neq 0$,

$$\left(\frac{a}{b}\right)^{-1} \cdot \left(\frac{c}{d}\right)^{-1} = \left(\frac{a}{b} \cdot \frac{c}{d}\right)^{-1}.$$

ASSERTIONS	SUPPORTING STATEMENTS
(1) $\left(\frac{a}{b} \cdot \frac{c}{d}\right)^{-1} = \left(\frac{a \cdot c}{b \cdot d}\right)^{-1}.$	(1) Definition of multiplication in R.
(2) $\left(\frac{a \cdot c}{b \cdot d}\right)^{-1} = \frac{b \cdot d}{a \cdot c}.$	(2) Theorem 7.17.
(3) $\frac{b \cdot d}{a \cdot c} = \frac{b}{a} \cdot \frac{d}{c}.$	(3) Definition of multiplication in R.
(4) $\frac{b}{a} = \left(\frac{a}{b}\right)^{-1}, \frac{d}{c} = \left(\frac{c}{d}\right)^{-1}.$	(4) Theorem 7.17.
(5) $\left(\frac{a}{b} \cdot \frac{c}{d}\right)^{-1} = \left(\frac{a}{b}\right)^{-1} \cdot \left(\frac{c}{d}\right)^{-1}.$	(5) Steps 1–4.

Problem Set 7.6

A. Prove:

1. Theorem 7.18.	**5.** Theorem 7.23.
2. Theorem 7.19.	**6.** Theorem 7.24.
3. Theorem 7.20.	**7.** Theorem 7.25.
4. Theorem 7.21.	**8.** Theorem 7.26.

B. Apply the theorems of Section 7.6 to perform the following calculations in R.

1. $^{-}\left(\frac{2}{3}\right) \cdot {}^{-}\left(\frac{4}{9}\right) = \underline{\quad}.$

6. $^{-}\left(\frac{5}{5}\right) \cdot {}^{-}\left(\frac{4}{4}\right) = \underline{\quad}.$

2. $\left[\left(\frac{6}{11}\right)^{-1}\right]^{-1} = \underline{\quad}.$

7. $\dfrac{6}{-19} \div \dfrac{-7}{38} = \underline{\quad}.$

3. $\left(\frac{5}{8}\right)^{-1} \cdot \left(\frac{8}{5}\right)^{-1} = \underline{\quad}.$

8. $\dfrac{12}{3} \cdot {}^{-}\left(\frac{1}{4}\right) = \underline{\quad}.$

4. $\dfrac{1}{3} \div \dfrac{7}{9} = \underline{\quad}.$

9. $\left(\frac{5}{5}\right)^{-1} \cdot \dfrac{243}{242} = \underline{\quad}.$

5. $\dfrac{10}{13} \cdot \dfrac{0}{1} = \underline{\quad}.$

10. $\left(\frac{1}{10}\right)^{-1} \div \left(\frac{1}{2}\right)^{-1} = \underline{\quad}.$

C. Solve in R.

1. $\dfrac{x}{y} \cdot \dfrac{2}{3} = \dfrac{6}{7}.$ $\dfrac{x}{y} = \underline{\quad}.$

2. $\dfrac{5}{9} \cdot \dfrac{a}{b} = \dfrac{10}{1}.$ $\dfrac{a}{b} = \underline{\quad}.$

3. $\dfrac{m}{n} \cdot \dfrac{4}{15} = \dfrac{7}{15} \cdot \dfrac{4}{15}.$ $\dfrac{m}{n} = \underline{\quad}.$

4. $\dfrac{p}{q} \cdot \dfrac{11}{12} = \dfrac{0}{1}.$ $\dfrac{p}{q} = \underline{\quad}.$

5. $-\left(\dfrac{r}{s}\right) \cdot \dfrac{8}{4} = \dfrac{-12}{2}.$ $\dfrac{r}{s} = \underline{\quad}.$

D. Prove in R if $a, b, c, d, e, f \neq 0$.

1. $\dfrac{a}{b} \cdot \left(\dfrac{c}{d} \div \dfrac{e}{f}\right) = \left(\dfrac{a}{b} \div \dfrac{e}{f}\right) \cdot \dfrac{c}{d}.$

4. $\left(\dfrac{a}{b} \cdot \dfrac{c}{d}\right) \div \dfrac{e}{f} = \dfrac{a}{b} \cdot \left(\dfrac{c}{d} \div \dfrac{e}{f}\right).$

2. $\dfrac{a}{b} \div \left(\dfrac{c}{d} \cdot \dfrac{e}{f}\right) = \left(\dfrac{a}{b} \div \dfrac{c}{d}\right) \cdot \dfrac{f}{e}.$

5. $\left(\dfrac{a}{b} \div \dfrac{c}{d}\right) \cdot \dfrac{e}{f} = \left(\dfrac{a}{b} \cdot \dfrac{e}{f}\right) \div \dfrac{c}{d}.$

3. $\left(\dfrac{a}{b} \div \dfrac{c}{d}\right) \div \dfrac{e}{f} = \dfrac{a \cdot d \cdot f}{b \cdot c \cdot e}.$

E. Find a candidate for the solution set of the equation $\dfrac{a}{b} \cdot \dfrac{x}{y} + \dfrac{c}{d} = \dfrac{e}{f}$ in R, if $a \neq 0$. Show that your candidate for $\dfrac{x}{y}$ is a unique solution of the equation.

7.7 Familiar Names for Elements in *R*

Those elements of R in which the second component is a factor of the first component, such as $\dfrac{10}{2}, \dfrac{-8}{4}, \dfrac{0}{6}, \dfrac{-24}{-3},$ and $\dfrac{5}{1},$ were meant to be associated with the integers. Each of these particular elements of R may be written $\dfrac{a \cdot b}{a \cdot 1},$ which is equal to $\dfrac{b}{1}.$ Thus $\dfrac{10}{2} = \dfrac{2 \cdot 5}{2 \cdot 1} = \dfrac{5}{1}; \dfrac{-8}{4} = \dfrac{4 \cdot -2}{4 \cdot 1} = \dfrac{-2}{1}; \dfrac{0}{6} = \dfrac{6 \cdot 0}{6 \cdot 1} = \dfrac{0}{1}; \dfrac{-24}{-3} = \dfrac{-3 \cdot 8}{-3 \cdot 1} = \dfrac{8}{1};$ and $\dfrac{5}{1} = \dfrac{1 \cdot 5}{1 \cdot 1} = \dfrac{5}{1}.$ It is evident that every rational number which is associated with an integer may be written in the form $\dfrac{n}{1}$ where $n \in I.$ With each of these elements $\dfrac{n}{1}$ of R we will associate the integer $n.$ Then $\dfrac{10}{2} = \dfrac{5}{1},$ which is associated with the integer 5; $\dfrac{^-8}{4} = \dfrac{^-2}{1}$, which is associated with the integer $^-2$;

$\dfrac{0}{6} = \dfrac{0}{1}$, which is associated with the integer 0; and so forth.

This association would be very useful if the sum $\dfrac{10}{2} + \dfrac{^-8}{4}$ were the rational

number that we would associate with $5 + {^-2}$ in I, and the product $\dfrac{10}{2} \cdot \dfrac{^-8}{4}$ were

the rational number that we would associate with $5 \cdot {^-2}$ in I. Let us see whether

this is so.

$$\frac{10}{2} + \frac{^-8}{4} = \frac{10 \cdot 4 + {^-8} \cdot 2}{2 \cdot 4} = \frac{40 + {^-16}}{8} = \frac{24}{8} = \frac{3}{1} \text{ in } R.$$

$5 + {^-2} = 5 - 2 = 3$ in I.

$\dfrac{3}{1}$ in R is, in fact, associated with 3 in I.

Also: $\dfrac{10}{2} \cdot \dfrac{^-8}{4} = \dfrac{10 \cdot {^-8}}{2 \cdot 4} = \dfrac{^-80}{8} = \dfrac{^-10}{1}$ in R.

$5 \cdot {^-2} = {^-(5 \cdot 2)} = {^-10}$ in I.

$\dfrac{^-10}{1}$ in R is, in fact, associated with $^-10$ in I.

In general, $\dfrac{a}{1} + \dfrac{b}{1} = \dfrac{a \cdot 1 + b \cdot 1}{1 \cdot 1} = \dfrac{a + b}{1}$, which is associated with $a + b$ in I.

Also, $\dfrac{a}{1} \cdot \dfrac{b}{1} = \dfrac{a \cdot b}{1}$, which is associated with $a \cdot b$ in I.

In elementary arithmetic the rational numbers are frequently referred to as

"the positive and negative fractions and zero." The fraction written $\dfrac{m}{n}$ is com-

monly given one of the following interpretations, in accordance with the physical

situation out of which the number arose:

(a) $\dfrac{2}{3}$ indicates a ratio of 2 to 3 which we might use to signify 2 heads for

every 3 flips of a coin, or 2 yards of material for every $3, or 2 feet of for-

ward movement observed every 3 hours.

(b) $\dfrac{2}{3}$ indicates two parts of a single unit that has been separated into three

congruent parts.

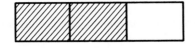

(c) $\dfrac{2}{3}$ indicates $\dfrac{1}{3}$ of 2 units. Since $\dfrac{1}{3} \cdot 2 = 2 \cdot \dfrac{1}{3} = 2 \div 3$, we may regard $\dfrac{2}{3}$ as $2 \div 3$.

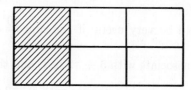

We chose the symbol $\dfrac{a}{b}$ to name an element of R because we wished the symbol to remind you that we were seeking a system in which we could always divide, just as we chose $(a - b) \in I$ because we wanted you to be reminded that we were seeking a system in which we could always subtract. We will associate the famil‐ iar fraction $\dfrac{a}{b}$ with $\dfrac{a}{b}$. Accordingly,

$\dfrac{2}{3}$ will name $\dfrac{2}{3}$, $\dfrac{4}{6}$ will name $\dfrac{4}{6}$; $\dfrac{2 \cdot n}{3 \cdot n}$ will name $\dfrac{2 \cdot n}{3 \cdot n}$.

Since $\dfrac{2}{3} = \dfrac{4}{6} = \dfrac{2 \cdot n}{3 \cdot n}$, their new names will name the same rational number.

Whence $\dfrac{2}{3} = \dfrac{4}{6} = \dfrac{2 \cdot n}{3 \cdot n}$. Similarly, $\dfrac{-1}{5}$ will name $\dfrac{-1}{5}$ and $\dfrac{-2}{10}$ will name $\dfrac{-2}{10}$. Since $\dfrac{-1}{5} = \dfrac{-2}{10}$, their new names will name the same rational number and $\dfrac{-1}{5} = \dfrac{-2}{10}$.

This transition to the familiar fractional names is so simple in our development that it is almost trivial.

Decimals for rational numbers are also very useful. You know that in our decimal system of numeration, we use the device of a decimal point to separate that part of the rational number which is integral from that which is fractional. Thus 6.7 is read "six and seven tenths"; 15.32 is read "fifteen and thirty-two hundredths"; 489.621 is read "four hundred eighty-nine and six hundred twenty-one thousandths." The expanded numeral for 489.621 might look like: $4 \cdot 100 + 8 \cdot 10 + 9 \cdot 1 + \dfrac{6}{10} + \dfrac{2}{100} + \dfrac{1}{1000}$. If we agreed to write $1000 = 10 \cdot 10 \cdot 10 = 10^3$; $100 = 10 \cdot 10 = 10^2$; $10 = 10^1$ where the "3," "2," and "1" are called **exponents,** then our expanded numeral might be written:

$$4 \cdot 10^2 + 8 \cdot 10^1 + 9 \cdot 1 + \dfrac{6}{10^1} + \dfrac{2}{10^2} + \dfrac{1}{10^3}.$$

To maintain the pattern of the exponent decreasing toward the right, we may further define 1 as 10^0, $\dfrac{1}{10^1}$ as 10^{-1}, $\dfrac{1}{10^2}$ as 10^{-2}, and $\dfrac{1}{10^3}$ as 10^{-3}. Finally, we may rewrite the expanded numeral as

$$4 \cdot 10^2 + 8 \cdot 10^1 + 9 \cdot 10^0 + 6 \cdot 10^{-1} + 2 \cdot 10^{-2} + 1 \cdot 10^{-3}.$$

Observe that each addend in the expanded numeral, representing a specific place value in the numeral 489.621, is written as a multiple of a power of ten. This is characteristic of our decimal system of numeration. For the integral part of the rational number (489) the exponents of 10 are positive or zero; for the decimal fractional part (621) the exponents are negative.

It should be clear that 73 may be named 73.000 if we choose, since the latter numeral means 73 and no tenths, no hundredths, no thousandths. While 73.000 may be given a special interpretation in the physical world, different from that given to 73, for our computational purposes we may use them interchangeably. Thus we may write

$$\frac{73}{6} = \frac{73.000}{6} = \frac{73.00000}{6}.$$

The algorithm you learned in elementary arithmetic for writing the decimal numeral for a rational named by a fractional numeral consisted simply of performing the indicated division. The procedure looked like the following:

$$
\begin{array}{r}
12.166 \\
6\,\overline{)\,73.000} \\
6 \\
\overline{13} \\
12 \\
\overline{10} \\
6 \\
\overline{40} \\
36 \\
\overline{40} \\
\end{array}
$$

and $\dfrac{73}{6} = 12.16\underline{6}$, the underlined 6 indicating that in this instance the 6 would keep repeating forever. Sometimes this is written $\dfrac{73}{6} = 12.16666.\ldots$. This repeating decimal numeral $12.1\underline{6}$, which goes on and on forever, is called an infinite decimal numeral and is intended as a new kind of numeral which completely identifies the rational number named by $\dfrac{73}{6}$. We will not consider here the concepts underlying arithmetic manipulations with infinite decimal numerals. We shall lean heavily on your past experiences and intuitive insight in performing the arithmetic of the system of rational numbers when using infinite decimal numerals to name the numbers. For example:

$$\frac{1}{3} + \frac{1}{6} = \frac{2}{6} + \frac{1}{6} = \frac{3}{6} = \frac{1}{2} = .5.$$

We have agreed to write $\frac{1}{3} = .\underline{3}$ and $\frac{1}{6} = .1\underline{6}$. Hence $.3333\ldots + .1666\ldots$ must name the sum $\frac{1}{2}$ or $.5$. This means that we have agreed that in the following addition:

$$
\begin{array}{r}
.3333\ldots \\
.1666\ldots \\
\hline
.4999\ldots
\end{array}
$$

$.4999\ldots$ is another name for $.5$. This is not an "obvious" result, but it will be clarified in Chapter 8 where a more detailed study of the relation between a rational number and its decimal numeral will be made. What little calculation we will perform using decimal numerals will, we hope, be intuitively acceptable to you.

In computing the decimal numeral for $\frac{1}{8}$ we eventually get a remainder of 0 so that all subsequent digits in the decimal numeral are zero. We find that $\frac{1}{8} = .125000000\ldots$ or $.125\underline{0}$. We agreed that for our purposes $.125\underline{0} = .125$ so that we may write $\frac{1}{8}$ as $.125$ and describe $.125$ as a terminating decimal. Other rational numbers whose decimal numerals are terminating are: $\frac{1}{2} = .5$; $\frac{1}{4} = .25$; $\frac{3}{5} = .6$; $\frac{1}{10} = .1$; $\frac{9}{4} = 2.25$; $\frac{10}{8} = 1.25$; $\frac{49,672}{100} = 496.72$; $\frac{25,367}{1000} = 25.367$.

You are aware, however, that if we perform the division to find the decimal numeral for $\frac{1}{3}$, we would get $.\underline{3}$, a repeating, rather than a terminal decimal. Similarly, $\frac{1}{6} = .1\underline{6}$; $\frac{2}{9} = .\underline{2}$; $\frac{3}{11} = .\underline{27}$; $\frac{1}{7} = .\underline{142857}$. You might wonder if all rational numbers have decimal numerals that are terminating or repeating, or if we could produce a decimal numeral which is terminating or repeating and does not represent a rational number.

We can guess at the answers to these questions by considering some examples. First let us look more clearly at the algorithm for finding the decimal numeral for the rational number $\frac{1}{7}$.

$$
\begin{array}{r}
.1428571428 \\
7\overline{\smash{\big)}\,1.0000000000} \\
\underline{7} \\
\mathbf{30} \\
\underline{28} \\
\mathbf{20} \\
\underline{14} \\
\mathbf{60} \\
\underline{56} \\
\mathbf{40} \\
\underline{35} \\
\mathbf{50} \\
\underline{49} \\
\mathbf{10} \\
\underline{7} \\
\mathbf{30} \\
\underline{28} \\
\mathbf{20} \\
\underline{14} \\
\mathbf{60} \\
\underline{56} \\
\mathbf{40}
\end{array}
$$

Observe the remainders, in boldface. Each of the remainders is less than 7, for if a remainder were greater than or equal to 7, it would mean the quotient we had used was too small. Since the remainders must be less than 7, they must be one of the numbers: 0, 1, 2, 3, 4, 5, 6. If the remainder is 0, the decimal numeral will be terminal. If the remainder is not zero, then it must be one of the counting numbers less than the divisor. In our example the remainders are 3, 2, 6, 4, 5 before the 1 (which appeared in the dividend) is repeated. As soon as a remainder is repeated the digits in the quotient begin to repeat. For $\frac{1}{7}$ the maximum possible number of digits in the quotient before the pattern repeats is 6, since there are only six possible remainders (other than 0) that can arise.

Of course, the decimal numeral may begin to repeat before all possible remainders are exhausted. For instance, $\frac{2}{13} = .\underline{153846}$, which repeats after the sixth digit although there are 13 possible remainders when dividing by 13: 0, 1, 2, . . ., 12. Since every rational number may be named by $\frac{x}{y}$ when $x, y \in I$ and $y \neq 0$, there will always be a finite number of counting numbers less than y which are possible remainders, when computing the decimal numerals. Hence there are a finite number (less than y) of digits in the decimal numeral before it terminates, or repeats. Any rational number may be named by a repeating or terminal decimal number. Thus $\frac{1}{16} = .0625$ and terminates when the subsequent remainder is 0, while $\frac{7}{6} = 1.1\underline{6}$ and repeats when the remainder 4 keeps recurring.

It is simple enough to write fractional numerals for rationals named by terminating decimals. You learned to do this in the elementary grades. For instance, $.5 = \frac{5}{10}$ or $\frac{1}{2}$; $.27 = \frac{27}{100}$; $.89643 = \frac{89,643}{100,000}$; $.275 = \frac{275}{1000}$ or $\frac{11}{40}$. It is reasonable to conjecture that there should be some procedure for writing a fractional numeral for a rational named by a repeating decimal. Consider $.\underline{23}$:

$$.\underline{23} = .232323\ldots$$

Let $r = .232323\ldots$ and observe that the repetition occurs after every two digits. We will multiply by 100

to get $\qquad\qquad\qquad\qquad 100 \cdot r = 23.232323\ldots$
and subtract $\qquad\qquad\qquad\qquad r = \quad .232323\ldots$

This gives $\qquad\qquad\qquad\quad 99 \cdot r = 23,$

$$\frac{1}{99} \cdot 99 \cdot r = \frac{1}{99} \cdot 23,$$

$$r = \frac{23}{99},$$

and $\qquad\qquad\qquad\qquad\qquad .\underline{23} = \frac{23}{99}.$

We will try another example:

Let $\qquad\qquad\qquad s = \quad 6.523523\ldots \qquad$ and multiply by 1000
$$1000 \cdot s = 6523.523523523\ldots$$
Subtract $\qquad\qquad\quad s = \quad 6.523523\ldots$

$$999 \cdot s = 6517,$$

$$s = \frac{6517}{999},$$

$$6.\underline{523} = \frac{6517}{999}.$$

Finally let us show that $4.999\ldots$ is another name for 5.

Let $\qquad\qquad\qquad\quad x = \quad 4.999\ldots \qquad$ and multiply by 10
$$10 \cdot x = 49.9999\ldots$$
Subtract $\qquad\qquad\qquad x = \quad 4.9999\ldots$
$$9 \cdot x = 45$$
$$x = 5$$
$$4.\underline{9} = 5.$$

The examples above suggest two theorems which we will state without proof:

Theorem 7.27 *Every rational number may be written as a repeating decimal numeral.*

Theorem 7.28 *Every repeating decimal numeral names a rational number.*

Do not fall into the trap of thinking that every infinite decimal numeral names a rational number. The fact that there exist infinite decimal numerals which do not name rational numbers means that we will want to expand our number system once more. This is considered in the next chapter.

Problem Set 7.7

A. Using ordered pair notation show that

    1. $^-2 \cdot 3 = {}^-6$ in I.   **3.** $7 + 0 = 7$ in I.

    2. $^-2 \cdot 3 = {}^-6$ in R.   **4.** $7 + 0 = 7$ in R.

B. Perform the calculations in R and write the answers so that the numerators and denominators of the fractional numerals have no common factors other than 1.

    1. $\left(\dfrac{2}{11} + \dfrac{1}{8}\right) + \dfrac{5}{6}$ **6.** $\left[{}^-\!\left(\dfrac{2}{3}\right) + \dfrac{7}{10}\right] + \dfrac{8}{12}$

    2. $\dfrac{^-23}{114} + \dfrac{6}{57}$ **7.** $\dfrac{15}{18} \cdot \dfrac{^-2}{3} \cdot \dfrac{9}{^-5}$

    3. $\dfrac{0}{6} \cdot \dfrac{10}{1000}$ **8.** $\dfrac{12}{25} \div \dfrac{4}{5}$

    4. $\left(\dfrac{20}{35} + \dfrac{^-9}{7}\right) - \dfrac{3}{5}$ **9.** $\dfrac{20}{21} \cdot \left(\dfrac{7}{10} + \dfrac{3}{5}\right)$

    5. $\dfrac{0}{6} + \dfrac{10}{^-1000}$ **10.** $\left(\dfrac{9}{16} \cdot \dfrac{16}{9}\right) \div \dfrac{3}{4}$

C. **1.** Write expanded numerals for each rational number.

    a. 6243   **d.** 26.0048

    b. 15.9   **e.** 5.1<u>6</u>

    c. 327.296

2. Write decimal numerals for each rational number.

    a. $\dfrac{10}{7}$ **d.** $\dfrac{31}{15}$

    b. $\dfrac{7}{16}$ **e.** $\dfrac{19}{24}$

    c. $\dfrac{9}{14}$

3. Rename each rational number as a fractional numeral whose denominator is a power of ten. Then write an equivalent decimal numeral.

Example. $\dfrac{3}{25} = \dfrac{3}{25} \cdot \dfrac{4}{4} = \dfrac{12}{100} = .12.$

a. $\dfrac{2}{5}$ **f.** $\dfrac{11}{50}$

b. $\dfrac{1}{4}$ **g.** $\dfrac{1}{8}$

c. $\dfrac{7}{25}$ **h.** $\dfrac{251}{50}$

d. $\dfrac{3}{2}$ **i.** $\dfrac{16}{125}$

e. $\dfrac{19}{20}$ **j.** $\dfrac{1}{16}$

4. Write fractional numerals for each rational number.

a. .25   **f.** 4.3$\underline{8}$
b. .125   **g.** .$\underline{509}$
c. .7   **h.** 6.999. . .
d. .500   **i.** .1$\underline{6}$
e. .$\underline{3}$ **j.** .32$\underline{7}$

D. Match. (You should know these facts by heart.)

(1) $\dfrac{1}{2}$ (a) .1$\underline{6}$

(2) $\dfrac{1}{5}$ (b) .625

(3) $\dfrac{1}{6}$ (c) .5

(4) $\dfrac{1}{8}$ (d) .25

(5) $\dfrac{3}{8}$ (e) .$\underline{3}$

(6) $\dfrac{1}{3}$ (f) .2

(7) $\dfrac{2}{5}$ (g) .125

(8) $\dfrac{5}{6}$ (h) .02

(9) $\dfrac{5}{8}$ (i) .6

(10) $\dfrac{1}{10}$ (j) .8

(11) $\dfrac{1}{4}$ (k) .375

(12) $\dfrac{2}{3}$ (l) .875

(13) $\dfrac{1}{20}$ (m) .8$\underline{3}$

(14) $\dfrac{1}{25}$ (n) .05

(15) $\dfrac{7}{8}$ (o) .4

(16) $\dfrac{1}{50}$ (p) .01

(17) $\dfrac{3}{4}$ (q) .008

(18) $\dfrac{3}{5}$ (r) .001

(19) $\dfrac{7}{20}$ (s) .75

(20) $\dfrac{4}{5}$ (t) .1

(21) $\dfrac{3}{25}$ (u) .$\underline{6}$

(22) $\dfrac{1}{100}$ (v) .35

(23) $\dfrac{1}{125}$ (w) .12

(24) $\dfrac{1}{1000}$ (x) .04

7.8 Less Familiar Names for Rational Numbers, in Bases Other Than Ten

The Hindu-Arabic system of numeration which we use has two characteristics already so well known to you that we will just mention them without any elaboration. They are place value, and ten digits: 0, 1, 2, 3, 4, 5, 6, 7, 8, 9. The fact that there are ten digits indicates that the place value will be designated by powers of ten. The following diagram is a common one.

$$486{,}197.245$$

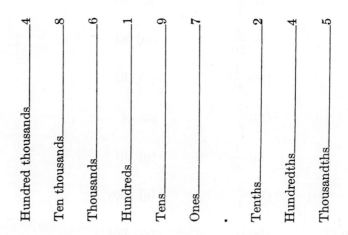

We may write the corresponding expanded numeral:

$$4 \cdot 10^5 + 8 \cdot 10^4 + 6 \cdot 10^3 + 1 \cdot 10^2 + 9 \cdot 10^1 + 7 \cdot 10^0 +$$
$$2 \cdot 10^{-1} + 4 \cdot 10^{-2} + 5 \cdot 10^{-3}.$$

We say we are using the decimal system of numeration or, in other words, we are naming the rational numbers *in base ten*. In counting in the base ten, every time we reach a higher power of the base we switch one place to the left. Thus: 1, 2, 3, . . ., 8, 9, <u>10</u>, 11, 12, 13, . . ., 95, 96, 97, 98, 99, <u>100</u>, 101, 102, . . ., 998, 999, <u>1000</u>, . . ., where $10 = 10^1$, $100 = 10^2$, $1000 = 10^3$.

The use of the base ten in naming the rationals is not essential; it is just convenient. We still have vestiges of the use of base sixty (60 seconds in a minute, 60 minutes in an hour) and the base twelve (12 inches in a foot, 12 items in a dozen). Numbers are often written in base two in programming for a high-speed computer. Regardless of the base in which a number is named, the place-value property of our system of numeration is maintained. In counting, in any base, we switch one place to the left as we reach a higher power of the base. The powers of 2 are 2, 4, 8, 16, 32, 64, . . ., and a place-value chart in base two would look like this:

|Sixteens|Eights|Fours|Twos|Ones| . |Halves|Fourths|Eighths|Sixteenths|

where the dot(.) is not a decimal point (as in base ten) but might be called a "dosimal" point. The powers of 3 are 3, 9, 27, 81, 243, . . ., and a place-value chart in base three would look like this:

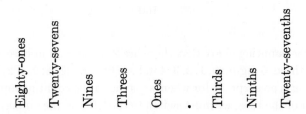

where the dot (.) might be called a "tresimal" point. You can prepare a place-value chart for any base.

Study the following chart listing some counting numbers in different bases. Note that the same numbers sometimes have different names or numerals in the different bases. Observe also that the place-value property is retained and for the counting numbers we have switched one place to the left as we reached the next higher power of the base.

Counting Numbers	Base Ten	Base Eight	Base Five	Base Three	Base Two
One	1	1	1	1	1
Two	2	2	2	2	10
Three	3	3	3	10	11
Four	4	4	4	11	100
Five	5	5	10	12	101
Six	6	6	11	20	110
Seven	7	7	12	21	111
Eight	8	10	13	22	1000
Nine	9	11	14	100	1001
Ten	10	12	20	101	1010
.	.	.	.	.	.
.	.	.	.	.	.
.	.	.	.	.	.
One hundred	100	144	400	10,201	1,100,100

Consider $(144)_{eight}$, which is listed as another name for one hundred: $(144)_{eight}$ is read "one-four-four in base eight," *not* "one hundred forty-four." The numeral tells us that we have:

$$
\begin{array}{lll}
\text{4 groups of one or } 4 \cdot 1 & = & 4 \\
\text{4 groups of eight or } 4 \cdot 8 & = & 32 \\
\text{1 group of sixty-four or } 1 \cdot 64 & = & \underline{64} \\
& & 100
\end{array}
$$

Similarly $(10,201)_{three}$ tells us that we have

1 group of one or $1 \cdot 1$	$=$	1
2 groups of nine or $2 \cdot 9$	$=$	18
1 group of eighty-one or $1 \cdot 81$	$=$	81
		$\overline{100}$

Notice from the counting chart that there are 2 digits: 0, 1 in base two; 3 digits: 0, 1, 2 in base three; 5 digits: 0, 1, 2, 3, 4 in base five; 8 digits: 0, 1, 2, 3, 4, 5, 6, 7 in base eight. This is no surprise, for when we come to the counting number which is the first power of the base, we must switch to the left and the numeral for the base is always "10." Hence in base four, the numeral for four is 10 and the only digits needed to write any number are 0, 1, 2, 3; in base six the numeral for six is 10 and the only digits needed to write any number are 0, 1, 2, 3, 4, 5. In base twelve, the numeral for twelve is 10 and twelve digits will be required to name the numbers from zero to twelve. We may use 0, 1, 2, 3, 4, 5, 6, 7, 8, 9 as the first ten digits but we will need additional symbols for the digits which name ten and eleven. Frequently "t" is used for ten and "e" for eleven. Thus $(1t2)_{twelve}$ names $(266)_{ten}$ since $(1t2)_{twelve}$ tells us that we have

2 groups of 1 or $2 \cdot 1$	$=$	2
t groups of 12 or $10 \cdot 12$	$=$	120
1 group of 144 or $1 \cdot 144$	$=$	144
		$\overline{266}$

Any fractional numeral may be rewritten in any base. Thus

$$\left(\frac{2}{3}\right)_{ten} = \left(\frac{10}{11}\right)_{two} = \left(\frac{2}{10}\right)_{three} = \left(\frac{2}{3}\right)_{four};$$

$$\left(\frac{7}{8}\right)_{ten} = \left(\frac{111}{1000}\right)_{two} = \left(\frac{12}{13}\right)_{five} = \left(\frac{11}{12}\right)_{six} = \left(\frac{7}{8}\right)_{twelve}.$$

Recall that every rational number has a decimal numeral which terminates or repeats. Thus $\left(\frac{1}{2}\right)_{ten} = (.5)_{ten}$. Will $\frac{1}{2}$ terminate or repeat if we write a corresponding numeral in other bases? Examine $(.5)_{ten}$; $(.3)_{six}$; $(.2)_{four}$; $(.6)_{twelve}$. They are all names for $\frac{1}{2}$ and all four terminate. Surely you must have wondered why we did not use base three or five or seven or nine. If we wish to rename $\left(\frac{1}{2}\right)_{ten}$ as a "pentamal" numeral we will want to know how many fifths, twenty-fifths, one-hundred-twenty-fifths, . . ., there are in one-half:

$$\left(\frac{1}{2}\right)_{ten} = (. \qquad\qquad)_{five}.$$

Fifths

Twenty-fifths

One-hundred-twenty-fifths

The following algorithm gives a simple technique for fulfilling the requirements of this problem:

$$\frac{1}{2}\cdot\frac{\dfrac{5}{2}}{\dfrac{5}{2}} = \frac{\dfrac{5}{2}}{5} = \frac{2+\dfrac{1}{2}}{5} = \frac{2}{5}+\frac{\dfrac{1}{2}}{5}.$$

Thus the first digit to the right of the pentamal point is 2. Now we wish to calculate the number of twenty-fifths in $\dfrac{\dfrac{1}{2}}{5}$:

$$\frac{\dfrac{1}{2}}{5}\cdot\frac{5}{5} = \frac{\dfrac{5}{2}}{25} = \frac{2+\dfrac{1}{2}}{25} = \frac{2}{25}+\frac{\dfrac{1}{2}}{25}.$$

The second digit to the right of the pentamal point is also 2. Can you see that the digit 2 will repeat forever? Thus we have a repeating pentamal numeral:

$$\left(\frac{1}{2}\right)_{ten} = (.\underline{2})_{five}.$$

Observe the following calculation:

$$\left(\frac{1}{7}\right)_{ten} = (. \quad)_{six}$$

$$\left(\frac{1}{7}\right)\cdot\frac{\dfrac{6}{7}}{\dfrac{6}{7}} = \frac{\dfrac{6}{7}}{6} = \frac{0}{6}+\frac{\dfrac{6}{7}}{6}.$$

$$\frac{\dfrac{6}{7}}{6}\cdot\frac{6}{6} = \frac{\dfrac{36}{7}}{36} = \frac{5+\dfrac{1}{7}}{36} = \frac{5}{36}+\frac{\left(\dfrac{1}{7}\right)}{36}.$$

As soon as the ringed remainder repeats, the heximal numeral will repeat, so that

$$\left(\frac{1}{7}\right)_{\text{ten}} = (.0\underline{5})_{\text{six}}.$$

The counting we have done in other bases indicates clearly that when the rational number is associated with a whole number, it may be named in any base. If the rational number is small the problem is simple enough. Suppose we wish to write $(28)_{\text{ten}}$ in base eight. We will want to know how many ones and how many eights there are in $(28)_{\text{ten}}$. (Why don't we wish to know how many 8^2 or sixty-fours there are in $(28)_{\text{ten}}$?) If we divide 28 by 8 we find:

$$
\begin{array}{r}
3 \\
8\overline{\smash{\big)}\,28} \\
24 \\
\hline
4
\end{array}
$$

This tells us that there are 3 eights and 4 ones in $(28)_{\text{ten}}$. Hence $(28)_{\text{ten}} = (34)_{\text{eight}}$.

Should we wish to write $(1897)_{\text{ten}}$ in base eight we anticipate a somewhat more complicated calculation. We will need to find out how many ones, how many eights, how many 8^2 or sixty-fours, how many 8^3 or five-hundred-twelves there are in 1897. We can perform the necessary divisions:

$$
\begin{array}{cccc}
3 & 5 & 5 & 1 \\
512\overline{\smash{\big)}\,1897} & 64\overline{\smash{\big)}\,361} & 8\overline{\smash{\big)}\,41} & 1\overline{\smash{\big)}\,1} \\
1536 & 320 & 40 & 1 \\
\hline
361 & 41 & 1 & 0
\end{array}
$$

Hence $(1897)_{\text{ten}} = (3551)_{\text{eight}}$.

An algorithm which eliminates the necessity for memorizing the powers of the base while rewriting an integer in any given base will be demonstrated for the same example as above: $(1897)_{\text{ten}} = (\quad)_{\text{eight}}$

$$
\begin{array}{l}
8\,\underline{\big|\,1897} \\
\quad 8\,\underline{\big|\,237}\ \text{and a remainder of 1} \\
\qquad 8\,\underline{\big|\,29}\ \text{and a remainder of 5} \\
\qquad\quad 3\ \text{and a remainder of 5}
\end{array}
$$

Dividing by 8 we find that 1897 contains 237 eights and 1 left over. We have the ones' digit, 1. When we divide 237 by 8 we find that we have 29 sixty-fours and 5 eights left over. We have the eights' digit, 5. Dividing 29 by 8 we find that we have 3 five-hundred-twelves and 5 sixty-fours left over. Now we have the sixty-fours' digit, 5, and the five-hundred-twelves' digit, 3. This agrees with our first calculation and $(1897)_{\text{ten}} = (3551)_{\text{eight}}$. For the second method we did not need to know the powers of 8. We simply performed successive division by 8 and recorded the remainders.

Two important reasons for considering the naming of rational numbers in bases other than ten have been considered in this section. One is the opportunity it provides to demonstrate vividly the place value property: each position in the numeral represents some power of the base, with the exponents decreasing to the right. The second purpose is to make you aware that a property of a number does not depend upon the system of numeration in which we name the number. We can illustrate the first of these purposes by observing the expanded numerals for a sequence of digits in several different bases:

$$(312)_{\text{ten}} = 3 \cdot 10^2 + 1 \cdot 10^1 + 2 \cdot 10^0, \text{ where 10 names the base ten.}$$
$$(312)_{\text{six}} = 3 \cdot 10^2 + 1 \cdot 10^1 + 2 \cdot 10^0, \text{ where 10 names the base six.}$$
$$(312)_{\text{four}} = 3 \cdot 10^2 + 1 \cdot 10^1 + 2 \cdot 10^0, \text{ where 10 names the base four.}$$

In each case the position of the digit 2 indicates that we have 2 groups of ones; the position of the 1 indicates that we have 1 group of the first power of the base; the position of the 3 indicates that we have 3 groups of the second power of the base. This example exhibits the core of the place value property.

The second purpose we have in mind was demonstrated when we showed that a rational number may be named by a terminating or repeating numeral in any base. An example to show that a definition of a number should not depend upon the system of numeration in which it is named is the following: Children often define an even number as a number which "ends in 0, 2, 4, 6, 8." We all agree that twelve is an even number. However, in base seven we write twelve as $(15)_{\text{seven}}$. Even though $(15)_{\text{seven}}$ does not "end in 0, 2, 4, 6, 8" it still names twelve and definitely is even. We might better say:

A number is even if it has a factor of two.

Problem Set 7.8

A. Write the first twenty-five counting numbers in

1. Base seven.   4. Base nine.
2. Base six.   5. Base twelve.
3. Base four.

B. Rename as indicated.

1. $(212)_{\text{three}} = ($ $)_{\text{ten}}$.   6. $(111)_{\text{eleven}} = ($ $)_{\text{ten}}$.
2. $(56)_{\text{seven}} = ($ $)_{\text{ten}}$.   7. $(.1)_{\text{two}} = ($ $)_{\text{ten}}$.
3. $(11,001)_{\text{two}} = ($ $)_{\text{ten}}$.   8. $(.13)_{\text{five}} = ($ $)_{\text{ten}}$.
4. $(111)_{\text{four}} = ($ $)_{\text{ten}}$.   9. $(2.4)_{\text{five}} = ($ $)_{\text{ten}}$.
5. $(111)_{\text{nine}} = ($ $)_{\text{ten}}$.   10. $(10.3)_{\text{five}} = ($ $)_{\text{ten}}$.

C. Rename as indicated.

1. $(675)_{\text{ten}} = ($ $)_{\text{nine}}$.   6. $(.25)_{\text{ten}} = ($ $)_{\text{two}}$.
2. $(11,235)_{\text{ten}} = ($ $)_{\text{seven}}$.   7. $(.6\underline{6})_{\text{ten}} = ($ $)_{\text{three}}$.
3. $(.75)_{\text{ten}} = ($ $)_{\text{four}}$.   8. $(8.5)_{\text{ten}} = ($ $)_{\text{seven}}$.
4. $(.125)_{\text{ten}} = ($ $)_{\text{eight}}$.   9. $(27)_{\text{ten}} = ($ $)_{\text{two}}$.
5. $(.8\underline{3})_{\text{ten}} = ($ $)_{\text{six}}$.   10. $(27)_{\text{ten}} = ($ $)_{\text{three}}$.

D. 1. Find the base b if

    a. $(10)_{\text{ten}} = (13)_b$.   **c.** $(101)_{\text{two}} = (12)_b$.

    b. $(54)_b = (34)_{\text{ten}}$.

2. Consider the following situation:

"I am 20 years old. My mother is 112 years old, but her age is only 2 more than 3 times my age."

    a. In what base are the numbers named?

    b. How old (base ten) are the mother and child?

E. Review rules for divisibility developed in Chapter 2.

    1. Show that if we rewrite the number in base nine then the number is divisible by 9 if the ones' digit is 0.

    2. Suggest a corresponding rule for divisibility by 7. Why does it work?

    3. Is it possible to write a corresponding rule for divisibility by 11? What might it be? Does it work? Always?

    4. Why aren't these rules efficient?

7.9 Order in *R*

When we studied order for the integers we made the following definition:

If a, $b \in I$, then $a > b$ if and only if there exists a positive integer c such that $a = b + c$.

Let us see if we can apply this to R and get results that fit in with our experiences. Of course, for those elements of R which are associated with integers, we expect this definition of order to hold. And it does. For example, $\dfrac{5}{1}$ is associated with the integer 5, and $\dfrac{8}{1}$ with the integer 8. We know $8 > 5$ and we expect $\dfrac{8}{1} > \dfrac{5}{1}$. The definition, if applied to R, requires that there exists a positive rational number $\dfrac{c}{d}$ such that

$$\frac{8}{1} = \frac{5}{1} + \frac{c}{d}.$$

We may use $\dfrac{3}{1}$ or $\dfrac{6}{2}$ or $\dfrac{9}{3}$ or $\dfrac{3 \cdot n}{n}$ (all of which are equal) for $\dfrac{c}{d}$ and the condition will be fulfilled. Hence $\dfrac{8}{1} > \dfrac{5}{1}$.

Our experience with the integers leads us to guess that $\frac{-1}{3} < \frac{1}{3}$ or $\frac{1}{3} > \frac{-1}{3}$. If we apply the order definition above to R we must produce a positive rational number $\frac{c}{d}$ such that $\frac{1}{3} = \frac{-1}{3} + \frac{c}{d}$. We can produce $\frac{2}{3}$ or $\frac{2 \cdot n}{3 \cdot n}$ (all of which are equal) for $\frac{c}{d}$ and consequently $\frac{1}{3} > \frac{-1}{3}$.

The definition appears to be applicable in R so we will agree:

> If a, $b \in R$, then $a > b$ if and only if there exists a positive rational c such that $a = b + c$.

Three important theorems concerning the inequality relation defined in R are essential for the ensuing work on measurement.

The simplified notation a, b, c, for elements of R, is introduced here to facilitate recording the following three proofs.

Theorem 7.29 *If a, b, $c \in R$ such that $a > b$ and $b > c$, then $a > c$.*

We will be proving that the "is greater than" relation defined in R has the transitive property. Can you see that once this has been established for R, it will also be true for elements of I and of W?

ASSERTIONS	SUPPORTING STATEMENTS
(1) $a > b$, $b > c$	(1) Given premise.
(2) $a = b + k$ and $b = c + m$ where k and m are positive rational numbers.	(2) Definition of ">" on R.
(3) $a = (c + m) + k$.	(3) Step 2 and substitution.
(4) $a = c + (m + k)$.	(4) Addition is associative in R.
(5) $m + k$ is a positive rational number.	(5) Problem **H**, Problem Set 7.3.
(6) $a > c$.	(6) Definition of ">" on R.

Observe that the strategy we employ here involves using the definition of ">" to transform the inequality into an equation in R. Now we may use the theorems of R that are applicable (always keeping an eye on what we want to prove) and finally apply the definition of ">" again to arrive at the desired inequality. We will use this procedure to prove two more useful theorems.

Theorem 7.30 *If a, b, c, $d \in R$ with $a > b$, $c > d$, then $a + c > b + d$.*

ASSERTIONS	SUPPORTING STATEMENTS
(1) $a > b,\ c > d$.	(1) Given premise.
(2) $a = b + k,\ c = d + m$ where k and m are positive rational numbers.	(2) Definition of ">" on R.
(3) $a + c = (b + k) + (d + m)$.	(3) Step 2, R is closed under addition.
(4) $a + c = (b + d) + (k + m)$.	(4) Closure, commutativity and associativity under addition in R.
(5) $a + c > b + d$.	(5) Definition of ">" in R.

Theorem 7.31 *If $a,\ b,\ k \in R$ with k a positive rational number and $a > b$, then $k \cdot a > k \cdot b$.*

ASSERTIONS	SUPPORTING STATEMENTS
(1) $a > b$, k a positive rational number.	(1) Given premise.
(2) $a = b + c$, with c a positive rational number.	(2) Definition of ">" on R.
(3) $k \cdot a = k \cdot (b + c)$.	(3) R is closed under multiplication.
(4) $k \cdot a = k \cdot b + k \cdot c$.	(4) Multiplication is distributive over addition.
(5) $k \cdot c$ is a positive rational number.	(5) Problem **F**, Problem Set 7.5.
(6) $k \cdot a > k \cdot b$.	(6) Definition of ">" on R.

The system of rationals has not only order but also has a property, which none of the other number systems we studied had. The rational numbers are *dense*. This means that between any two rational numbers we will always find another rational number. Between 0 and 1, there is $\frac{1}{2}$. Of course there are more rational numbers than we can count between 0 and 1; we just chose $\frac{1}{2}$ to demonstrate that there was surely one rational number between 0 and 1. We recognize at once that $\frac{1}{4}$ is between 0 and $\frac{1}{2}$; $\frac{1}{8}$ is between 0 and $\frac{1}{4}$; $\frac{1}{16}$ is between 0 and $\frac{1}{8}$. How long can we keep this up? Forever. Will we ever be able to produce the rational number closest to 0? No, indeed. For no matter what number you name different from 0, we can find a rational number closer to 0, simply by taking $\frac{1}{2}$ of the number you named.

A simple procedure for finding a rational number between any two given rational numbers is to calculate the average of the two numbers. Thus x will be between 5 and 8 if $x = \frac{5 + 8}{2} = \frac{13}{2}$. Similarly, if

$$t = \frac{\frac{2}{3} + \frac{1}{4}}{2} = \frac{\frac{8+3}{12}}{2} = \frac{11}{12} \div \frac{2}{1} = \frac{11}{12} \cdot \frac{1}{2} = \frac{11}{24},$$

then $\frac{11}{24}$ is a rational number between $\frac{2}{3}$ and $\frac{1}{4}$. Order the fractions $\frac{2}{3}, \frac{1}{4}, \frac{11}{24}$.

Let us observe that, in general, if a and b are two rational numbers such that $a > b$, then $a > \frac{a+b}{2} > b$. If $a > b$, then $a = b + c$ and $a + a = (a+b) + c$ or $2a = (a+b) + c$. If we multiply by $\frac{1}{2}$ we get the equivalent equation:

$a = \frac{a+b}{2} + \frac{c}{2}$. Since c and $\frac{1}{2}$ are positive rational numbers, their product is also

a positive rational number. Hence $a > \frac{a+b}{2}$. Similarly, if $a > b$, then $a = b + c$

and $b + a = (b+b) + c$ or $b + a = 2b + c$. If we multiply by $\frac{1}{2}$ we get the

equivalent equation $\frac{b+a}{2} = b + \frac{c}{2}$. Since $\frac{c}{2}$ is a positive rational number,

$\frac{b+a}{2} > b$. Thus we have shown that $a > \frac{a+b}{2} > b$.

Problem Set 7.9

A. 1. Determine which of each pair of rational numbers is the larger.

   a. $\frac{5}{7}, \frac{59}{84}$.

   b. $\frac{38}{75}, \frac{8}{15}$.

   c. $\frac{7}{10}, \frac{15}{21}$.

   d. $\frac{-4}{45}, \frac{-1}{15}$.

   e. $\frac{-3}{4}, \frac{7}{-9}$.

  2. Order the following rational numbers so that they will decrease to the right:

$$-2\frac{1}{2}, \frac{5}{2}, -2, \frac{51}{20}, \frac{9}{4}, \frac{12}{5}, \frac{10}{-6}, \frac{26}{10}, \frac{-26}{10}, \frac{253}{100}.$$

B. 1. Find a rational number between each pair of rational numbers in problem **A1.**

  2. Show by a counterexample that the following rule for calculation is unsatisfactory:

"If you add any two rational numbers and divide the sum by different rational numbers associated with whole numbers (other than 0), then you will have a set of rational numbers between the two given rational numbers."

C. Explain why there is no rational number closest to 4.

D. 1. Prove: If $a + c > b + c$, then $a > b$ for $a, b, c \in R$.

 2. Prove: If $a \cdot k > b \cdot k$, then $a > b$ for $a, b, k \in R$ and k a positive rational number.

 3. Write equivalent sentences to find candidates for $x \in R$ which will make the given open sentences true statements.

a. $x + 3 > 5 + 3$.   **d.** $5 \cdot x + 7 < 37$.

b. $x + 12 > 19$.   **e.** $\dfrac{3 \cdot x}{4} < \dfrac{7}{8}$.

c. $2 \cdot x < 22$.

7.10 Theorems in Chapter 7

Theorem 7.1 R is closed under addition.

Theorem 7.2 If $a, b, c, d \in I$, then $\dfrac{a}{b} + \dfrac{c}{d} = \dfrac{c}{d} + \dfrac{a}{b}$ in R.

Theorem 7.3 If $a, b, c, d, e, f \in I$, then $\left(\dfrac{a}{b} + \dfrac{c}{d}\right) + \dfrac{e}{f} = \dfrac{a}{b} + \left(\dfrac{c}{d} + \dfrac{e}{f}\right)$ in R.

Theorem 7.4 In R, $\dfrac{0}{y}$ is an additive identity.

Theorem 7.5 If $\dfrac{a}{b} \in R$, then its additive inverse in R is $\dfrac{^-a}{b}$.

Theorem 7.6 If $\dfrac{a}{b}, \dfrac{c}{d}, \dfrac{e}{f} \in R$, and $\dfrac{a}{b} + \dfrac{e}{f} = \dfrac{c}{d} + \dfrac{e}{f}$, then $\dfrac{a}{b} = \dfrac{c}{d}$.

Theorem 7.7 If $\dfrac{a}{b} \in R$, then $^-\left[^-\left(\dfrac{a}{b}\right)\right] = \dfrac{a}{b}$.

Theorem 7.8 If $b \in I$ with $b \neq 0$, then $^-\left(\dfrac{0}{b}\right) = \dfrac{0}{b}$ in R.

Theorem 7.9 If $\dfrac{a}{b}, \dfrac{c}{d} \in R$, then the equation $\dfrac{x}{y} + \dfrac{a}{b} = \dfrac{c}{d}$ has the unique solution $\dfrac{x}{y} = \dfrac{c}{d} + {}^-\left(\dfrac{a}{b}\right)$ in R.

Theorem 7.10 If $\dfrac{a}{b}, \dfrac{c}{d} \in R$, then $^-\left(\dfrac{a}{b}\right) + {}^-\left(\dfrac{c}{d}\right) = {}^-\left(\dfrac{a}{b} + \dfrac{c}{d}\right)$.

Theorem 7.11 If $\dfrac{a}{b}, \dfrac{c}{d} \in R$, then $\dfrac{a}{b} - \dfrac{c}{d} = \dfrac{a}{b} + {}^-\left(\dfrac{c}{d}\right)$.

Theorem 7.12 R is closed under multiplication.

Theorem 7.13 If $\dfrac{a}{b}, \dfrac{c}{d} \in R$, then $\dfrac{a}{b} \cdot \dfrac{c}{d} = \dfrac{c}{d} \cdot \dfrac{a}{b}$.

Theorem 7.14 If $\dfrac{a}{b}, \dfrac{c}{d}, \dfrac{e}{f} \in R$, then $\left(\dfrac{a}{b} \cdot \dfrac{c}{d}\right) \cdot \dfrac{e}{f} = \dfrac{a}{b} \cdot \left(\dfrac{c}{d} \cdot \dfrac{e}{f}\right)$.

Theorem 7.15 If $\frac{a}{b}, \frac{c}{d}, \frac{e}{f} \in R$, then $\frac{a}{b} \cdot \left(\frac{c}{d} + \frac{e}{f}\right) = \frac{a}{b} \cdot \frac{c}{d} + \frac{a}{b} \cdot \frac{e}{f}$.

Theorem 7.16 In R, $\frac{n}{n}$ is a multiplicative identity.

Theorem 7.17 If $\frac{a}{b} \in R$ with $a \neq 0$, then $\left(\frac{a}{b}\right)^{-1} = \frac{b}{a}$.

Theorem 7.18 If $\frac{a}{b}, \frac{c}{d}, \frac{e}{f} \in R$ with $e \neq 0$ and $\frac{a}{b} \cdot \frac{e}{f} = \frac{c}{d} \cdot \frac{e}{f}$, then $\frac{a}{b} = \frac{c}{d}$.

Theorem 7.19 If $\frac{a}{b} \in R$ with $a \neq 0$, then $\left[\left(\frac{a}{b}\right)^{-1}\right]^{-1} = \frac{a}{b}$.

Theorem 7.20 In R, $\left(\frac{n}{n}\right)^{-1} = \frac{n}{n}$.

Theorem 7.21 If $\frac{a}{b}, \frac{c}{d} \in R$ with $a \neq 0$, then $\frac{x}{y} \cdot \frac{a}{b} = \frac{c}{d}$ has the unique solution $\frac{x}{y} = \frac{c}{d} \cdot \left(\frac{a}{b}\right)^{-1}$ in R.

Theorem 7.22 If $\frac{a}{b}, \frac{c}{d} \in R$ with $a \neq 0$ and $c \neq 0$, then $\left(\frac{a}{b}\right)^{-1} \cdot \left(\frac{c}{d}\right)^{-1} = \left(\frac{a}{b} \cdot \frac{c}{d}\right)^{-1}$.

Theorem 7.23 If $\frac{a}{b}, \frac{c}{d} \in R$ with $c \neq 0$, then $\frac{a}{b} \div \frac{c}{d} = \frac{a}{b} \cdot \left(\frac{c}{d}\right)^{-1}$.

Theorem 7.24 If $\frac{a}{b}, \frac{c}{d} \in R$, then $\frac{a}{b} \cdot {}^{-}\!\left(\frac{c}{d}\right) = {}^{-}\!\left(\frac{a}{b} \cdot \frac{c}{d}\right)$.

Theorem 7.25 If $\frac{a}{b}, \frac{c}{d} \in R$, then ${}^{-}\!\left(\frac{a}{b}\right) \cdot {}^{-}\!\left(\frac{c}{d}\right) = \frac{a}{b} \cdot \frac{c}{d}$.

Theorem 7.26 If $\frac{a}{b}, \frac{c}{d} \in R$ and $\frac{a}{b} \cdot \frac{c}{d} = \frac{0}{n}$, then either $\frac{a}{b} = \frac{0}{n}$ or $\frac{c}{d} = \frac{0}{n}$.

Theorem 7.27 Every rational number may be written as a repeating decimal numeral.

Theorem 7.28 Every repeating decimal numeral names a rational number.

Theorem 7.29 If $a, b, c \in R$ such that $a > b$ and $b > c$, then $a > c$.

Theorem 7.30 If $a, b, c, d \in R$ with $a > b$ and $c > d$, then $a + c > b + d$.

Theorem 7.31 If $a, b, k \in R$ with k a positive rational number and $a > b$, then $k \cdot a > k \cdot b$.

7.11 Terminal Tasks for Chapter 7

1. To be able to identify elements of a specific equivalence class when given the elements of a system and an equivalence relation defined on them.
2. To be able to differentiate between the equivalence class which is the rational number and the different names for it.
3. To identify those rational numbers which are associated with elements of I.

4. To be able to point out specifically when and how the development of the system of rational numbers depends upon the system of integers.

5. To recognize the field structure of the system of rationals.

6. To indicate comprehension of the implications of the field structure of R by listing appropriate field theorems applicable in R.

7. To perform addition, subtraction, multiplication, and division in R.

8. To write the decimal numeral for any given rational number.

9. To identify rational numbers when named by their decimal numerals and to write an equivalent fractional numeral.

10. To be able to write a rational number less than one hundred in any given base.

11. To be able to order a given set of rational numbers.

12. To demonstrate the ability to use the strategy of making an analysis to seek clues for a proof.

13. To be able to write a simple three-step or four-step proof for an original exercise concerning structure in R.

REVIEW   EXERCISES

A. Consider the system whose elements in set A consist of the ordered pairs (a, b) where $a, b \in W$ and $b \neq 0$. The following relation is defined on A: $(a, b) \wr\wr (c, d)$ if and only if $a \cdot d = b \cdot c$ in W.

1. Prove the relation is an equivalence relation.

2. Let $(\overline{a, b})$ denote the equivalence class of which (a, b) is a member, and $(\overline{a, b}) = (\overline{c, d})$ if and only if $a \cdot d = b \cdot c$ in W. List 10 members of each of the following equivalence classes.

   a. $(\overline{1, 2})$ d. $(\overline{n, n + 3})$
   b. $(\overline{0, 5})$ e. $(\overline{q, q})$
   c. $(\overline{3, 7})$

B. Consider the following sentences in R or Q. Complete only those which have meaning in R or Q.

1. $\dfrac{a}{b} \wedge \dfrac{c}{d}$ if and only if_____.   5. $\dfrac{a}{b} \in R$ if and only if_____.

2. $\dfrac{a}{b} \wedge \dfrac{c}{d}$ if and only if_____.   6. $\dfrac{a}{b} \in Q$ if and only if_____.

3. $\dfrac{a}{b} = \dfrac{c}{d}$ if and only if_____.   7. $\dfrac{a}{b} \in R$ if and only if_____.

4. $\dfrac{a}{b} = \dfrac{c}{d}$ if and only if_____.   8. $\dfrac{a}{b} \in Q$ if and only if_____.

C. 1. Show that if x is a factor of y, then $\frac{y}{x}$ is equal to an equivalence class of the form $\frac{n}{1}$.

2. Show that if y is a factor of x, then $\frac{y}{x}$ is equal to an equivalence class of the form $\frac{1}{n}$.

3. Show that $\frac{y}{x}$ is equal to an equivalence class $\frac{p}{q}$ where p and q have no factor in common except 1.

D. 1. Indicate five definitions or theorems in R which were suggested to us by the development of I.

2. Place a check in the appropriate box if the statement is always true in the indicated system. Otherwise leave blank.

	W	I	R
a. $k \cdot 0 = 0$			
b. $(r + s) \div t = (r \div t) + (s \div t)$			
c. $^-m \cdot \,^-n = m \cdot n$			
d. $a \cdot (c - d) = b \cdot (c - d) \rightarrow a = b$			
e. $p - q = r$ if and only if $p = q + r$			

E. Match. All fractional and decimal numerals name elements in R.

(1) $\dfrac{k}{m} \cdot \left(\dfrac{k}{m}\right)^{-1}$ (a) 0

(2) $\dfrac{s}{^-r} \cdot \dfrac{^-s}{r}$ (b) $\dfrac{f \cdot g + t \cdot \,^-j}{t \cdot g}$

(3) $\dfrac{^-p}{q} \div \dfrac{p}{q}$ (c) $\dfrac{5}{6}$

(4) $\dfrac{a}{b} + \dfrac{0}{b}$ (d) $\dfrac{c}{d}$

(5) $\dfrac{a}{b} \cdot \dfrac{0}{b}$ (e) $\left(\dfrac{v}{u}\right)^{-1}$

(6) $\left(\dfrac{f}{t} + \dfrac{j}{g}\right)^{-1}$ (f) $\dfrac{r^2}{2}$

(7) $.5 + .\underline{3}$ (g) $\dfrac{t \cdot j - f \cdot g}{t \cdot g}$

(continued on next page)

(8) $\dfrac{t}{f} - {}^{-}\left(\dfrac{g}{j}\right)$ (h) 1

(9) $\dfrac{c}{d} \cdot \dfrac{1}{c}$ (i) $\dfrac{t \cdot g}{f \cdot g + t \cdot j}$

(10) ${}^{-}\left(\dfrac{{}^{-}c}{d}\right)$ (j) $\dfrac{8}{1}$

(11) $\left(\dfrac{x}{y} + \dfrac{u}{v}\right) + \dfrac{{}^{-}x}{y}$ (k) $\dfrac{{}^{-}a}{{}^{-}b}$

(12) $\dfrac{2}{3} + \dfrac{3}{6}$ (l) $\dfrac{7}{6}$

(13) $\left(\dfrac{s}{{}^{-}r}\right)^{-1} \div \dfrac{s}{{}^{-}r}$ (m) ${}^{-}1$

(14) $\left(\dfrac{t}{f}\right)^{-1} - \left(\dfrac{g}{j}\right)^{-1}$ (n) $\dfrac{s^2}{r^2}$

(15) 7.$\underline{9}$ (o) $\dfrac{t \cdot j + f \cdot g}{f \cdot j}$

(p) None of the above.

F. 1. Let P be the set of equivalence classes set up in exercise **A** above. We will define operation $*$ for P as follows: $(\overline{a, b}) * (\overline{c, d}) = (\overline{a \cdot c, b \cdot d})$. Keep in mind the definition in problem **A2** (above) of the $=$ relation for elements of P. Is P a group under operation $*$?

2. If $G = \{5, 6, 7, 8, 9, 10, 11, \ldots\}$, which of the following two suggested definitions for operation Δ will provide for an identity element in G:

(a) If $x,\ y \in G$, then $x \Delta y = x + y$ in W.   *Example:* $8 \Delta 9 = 8 + 9 = 17$.

(b) If $x,\ y \in G$, then $x \Delta y = (x + y) - 5$ in W.   *Example:* $8 \Delta 9 = (8 + 9) - 5 = 12$.

G. 1. If $\dfrac{3}{4} + \dfrac{1}{2} = \dfrac{5}{4}$ in R, then we expect $.75 + .5$ to equal 1.25. Verify that the algorithm for addition of rational numbers named by decimal numerals does yield this result.

2. If $\dfrac{1}{2} \cdot \dfrac{2}{5} = \dfrac{1}{5}$ in R, then we expect $.5 \cdot .4$ to be equal to $.2$. Verify that the algorithm for multiplication of rational numbers named by decimal numerals does yield this result.

3. If $\dfrac{7}{8} - \dfrac{1}{4} = \dfrac{5}{8}$, what do you expect will be the difference between $.875$ and $.25$? Verify your answer.

4. If $\dfrac{9}{10} \div \dfrac{3}{5} = \dfrac{3}{2}$, what do you expect will be the quotient of $.9 \div .6$? Verify your answer.

5. Select a sixth grade arithmetic text from your curriculum library and review the algorithms for addition, subtraction, multiplication, and division of rational numbers named by decimal numerals.

H. Solve in R. Indicate whether the equation may also be solved in W or I.

1. $3 \cdot t + 4 = 10.$

2. $\dfrac{1}{3} \cdot k = 6.$

3. $4 - s = 5.$

4. $\dfrac{2 \cdot m}{7} - 3 = 5.$

5. $4 \cdot b - 11 = 15 - 9 \cdot b.$

I. Perform the indicated calculations.

1. Write a fractional numeral for $.426$.

2. Write a fractional numeral for $.2\underline{3}$.

3. Write the decimal numeral for $\dfrac{7}{18}$.

4. $(324)_{\text{five}} = (\quad)_{\text{ten}}.$

5. $(72)_{\text{ten}} = (\quad)_{\text{eight}}.$

6. $(.7)_{\text{ten}} = (\quad)_{\text{five}}.$

7. $\left(\dfrac{3}{4}\right)_{\text{ten}} = (\quad)_{\text{six}}.$

8. $(t7)_{\text{twelve}} = (\quad)_{\text{ten}}.$

9. $(10101)_{\text{two}} = (\quad)_{\text{three}}.$

10. $(.5)_{\text{six}} = (\quad)_{\text{twelve}}.$

J. If $p, q, r \in R$ with $p, q, r \neq 0$, prove:

1. $(p \cdot q)^{-1} = p^{-1} \cdot q^{-1}.$

2. $p \div (q \cdot r) = (p \cdot r^{-1}) \cdot q^{-1}.$

3. $(p \cdot q) \div r = (p \div r) \cdot q.$

4. $(p \cdot q) \div r = (q \div r) \cdot p.$

5. $p \div (q \div r) = (p \cdot r) \div q.$

6. $(p - q) \div r = (p \div r) - (q \div r).$

K. Not all the numbers we need are rational numbers. If a square of side s has an area of 2 square units, the measure of the side s is not a rational number. Search the whole text to see if you can find the discussion in which it is demonstrated that $\sqrt{2}$ cannot be written as an ordered pair of integers, $\dfrac{a}{b}$.

L. Identify some fact, or facts, which you learned in this chapter and which might help you meet the following hypothetical classroom situations:

1. "My father says all you have to do to divide fractions is invert and multiply."

2. "Why is it that the value of the fraction doesn't change when you multiply the numerator and denominator by the same number?"

3. A preschool child complains: "You gave him the bigger half of the apple."

4. You decide to explain the algorithm for division of fractions as follows:

$$\frac{\dfrac{1}{3}}{\dfrac{2}{7}} = \frac{\dfrac{1}{3} \cdot \dfrac{7}{2}}{\dfrac{2}{7} \cdot \dfrac{7}{2}} = \frac{\dfrac{1}{3} \cdot \dfrac{7}{2}}{1} = \frac{1}{3} \cdot \frac{7}{2}.$$

5. You present another method for division of fractions:

$$\frac{\dfrac{1}{3}}{\dfrac{2}{7}} \cdot \frac{21}{21} = \frac{\dfrac{1}{3} \cdot \dfrac{21}{1}}{\dfrac{2}{7} \cdot \dfrac{21}{1}} = \frac{7}{6}.$$

6. "Why is it that $\dfrac{2 \cdot 7}{3 \cdot 7} = \dfrac{2}{3}$ but $\dfrac{2+7}{3+7} \neq \dfrac{2}{3}$?"

7. A student makes the following error:

$$\frac{4 \cdot 3}{\cancel{8} \cdot \cancel{6}}_{\cancel{2}} = 12.$$

8. "Seven divided by zero is seven because you're not dividing by anything so it remains the same."

9. "Zero divided by five is a silly idea. How can you divide nothing into five equal parts?"

10. You need to plan remedial work for a child who adds two fractions as follows: $\dfrac{3}{5} + \dfrac{4}{9} = \dfrac{7}{14}$.

11. "What's wrong with what I'm doing? How can $1 = 4$?

$$1 = \frac{24}{24} = \frac{24}{12+12} = \frac{24}{12} + \frac{24}{12} = 2 + 2 = 4.\text{"}$$

12. If I hit four bullseyes out of six tries, it is different from hitting two bullseyes out of three tries. So why do we say $\dfrac{4}{6} = \dfrac{2}{3}$?

8 Linear Measurement and Coordinates

8.1 What Is Measurement?

The ideas of measurement have always been an integral part of the elementary school program. We find lengths of segments (or other curves), areas of plane regions, volumes of solid regions, and weights of objects. We measure angles, time, speed, and many other things. It therefore becomes important to develop the necessary understandings of the process. Here we shall restrict attention to the geometric measurements, i.e., to the measurement of angles and the determination of length, area, and volume. Thus we have in this topic the wedding of the two main strands of thinking which we have so far developed independently, namely, number systems and geometry. As we shall see, this interweaving of ideas on geometry and number will be helpful to both. We shall not only devise meaningful ways of associating numbers with geometric figures, but shall also observe useful geometric interpretations of operations with numbers.

Rather than starting with a general philosophical discussion of what measurement means, let us instead turn directly to the discussion of the questions that arise in trying to measure line segments. It is hoped that the general picture will be clearer in retrospect as we look back on several specific measurement situations than it is likely to be if stated in vague generalities at the beginning.

Since measurement arises out of concrete needs in dealing with our physical environment, let us consider a problem arising from a physical situation. Suppose that a class of elementary school pupils is presented with the following problem. They are to go to the store and get a strip of wood molding long enough to go along the edge of the chalk rail at the front of the room. The only equipment available for them to use in determining the amount to buy is a box of soda straws. The suggestion that they pretend that rulers haven't been invented yet may elicit an interested response as well as forestalling an obvious suggestion.

After a little reflection some child gets the idea of placing enough of the straws end to end to stretch along the entire edge of the chalk rail. The number of straws needed can then be counted, say eight. Of course, if the youngster is bright he will be more likely to take one straw and use it repeatedly, counting the number of times he uses it. However, with a little persuasion he can probably be talked into putting the straws all down. There is some virtue in doing this, as one then visually sees the edge of the chalk rail covered and the class can verify the count. In any case, it is now clear that a pupil could take a straw to the store and tell the clerk he wanted as much molding as eight of these straws placed end to end.

This simple example contains within it all the essential facets of measurement of segments. The edge of the chalk rail is a model of a segment, like $\overline{AB}$. The

straws likewise appear as models of segments, and indeed they appear congruent to each other. Thus they may all be considered as models of some segment $\overline{PQ}$.

Placing the straws end to end along the chalk rail amounts to marking congruent copies of $\overline{PQ}$ on $\overline{AB}$ until $\overline{AB}$ is covered, as shown. Finally, the counting of the

straws is equivalent to counting the number of congruent copies of $\overline{PQ}$ needed to cover $\overline{AB}$ exactly.

If $\overline{AB}$ is a segment to be measured, the measurement process, as suggested by the above, may be formally stated as follows:

(1) Select any segment $\overline{PQ}$ to serve as a *unit segment*.
(2) Starting at A, mark on $\overline{AB}$ congruent copies of $\overline{PQ}$ such that consecutive copies have only an endpoint in common.
(3) If the union of r of these congruent copies equals $\overline{AB}$ (i.e., is the same set of points as $\overline{AB}$), we say the measure of $\overline{AB}$ with respect to $\overline{PQ}$ as a unit segment is r. This is written

$$m(\overline{AB}) = r.$$

Notice that these statements define what is meant by the *measure of a segment*. The drawing is intended to illustrate the case $m(\overline{AB}) = 8$.

According to this convention the measure of a segment, $m(\overline{AB})$, is simply a *number*. However, in order to describe the length of a segment, one must indicate both the measure, i.e., the number, and *the unit being used*. Thus, in the illustration above, it will do no good to tell the clerk we want a piece of molding eight straws long unless we produce the straw to indicate what unit was used. In practice, of course, we commonly use standardized units like foot or meter to avoid carrying around models of the units selected, but this is a matter of convenience rather than theoretical necessity. In theory any segment could be selected as a unit. If we speak of segment $\overline{AB}$ as having a length of 4 feet, we mean that the measure is 4, i.e., $m(\overline{AB}) = 4$, if we use the foot as a unit.

What difficulties can we expect to encounter in the procedure outlined above? Our hypothetical class will immediately discover one—namely, that in practice it is not possible to place the straws accurately enough to be sure whether they *exactly* cover the segment in question. This clearly is a difficulty arising from actual manipulative techniques of applying the measurement process. A little thought will show that this is really a profound matter. While it is clear that we can devise more satisfactory methods of procedure than placing straws, it is equally clear that any procedure will involve some manipulative error. Thus, in its application, measurement is an inherently approximate process.

We shall return to this question of the approximate character of measurement as an applied process at a later point in the chapter. For the next few sections we shall look instead at the theoretical questions involved in seeking to assign measures to segments. For example, are the axioms on congruence of segments sufficient to justify the process of measurement as it is stated above, or do we need to supplement them? Certainly Axiom CS5 assures us of the possibility of laying off from A on $\overrightarrow{AB}$ a congruent copy of the chosen unit segment $\overline{PQ}$, and there is nothing to prevent the process being repeated as often as desired. Will this set of congruent copies ever actually reach B? To put it naïvely, is there a possibility that $\overline{PQ}$ could be so short or $\overline{AB}$ so long that no number of these congruent copies of $\overline{PQ}$ would contain $\overline{AB}$? Our intuition says no, but nothing in our former axioms assures us of this. It thus is desirable to adopt a new axiom. Observe that we require the endpoints of a segment to be distinct so that $P \neq Q$. (The notation used, MS1, indicates that this is the *first* axiom we have adopted concerning Measurement of Segments.)

Axiom MS1 *If $\overline{AB}$ and $\overline{PQ}$ are any segments, there exists on $\overrightarrow{AB}$ a sequence of $n + 1$ points $P_0 = A, P_1, P_2, \ldots, P_n$ such that $\overline{PQ} \cong \overline{P_0P_1} \cong \overline{P_1P_2} \cong \cdots \cong \overline{P_{n-1}P_n}$ where each two consecutive segments on $\overline{AB}$ have only an endpoint in common and such that*

$$\overline{AB} \subset \overline{P_0P_n} = \bigcup_{i=1}^{i=n} \overline{P_{i-1}P_i}.$$

[NOTE: The notation $\bigcup_{i=1}^{i=n} \overline{P_{i-1}P_i}$ indicates the union of the indicated segments, i.e., $\overline{P_0P_1} \cup \overline{P_1P_2} \cup \overline{P_2P_3} \cup \cdots \cup \overline{P_{n-1}P_n}$, which in this case is precisely the segment $\overline{P_0P_n}$.]

A much more troublesome difficulty with the measurement process is that, once a unit segment is chosen, most segments cannot be measured. This also our class of school children would discover. In laying off congruent copies of $\overline{PQ}$ on $\overline{AB}$ it is, of course, possible that one of the points P_k of Axiom MS1 will coincide with B. In this case $\overline{AB} = \overline{P_0P_k}$ and $m(\overline{AB}) = k$. A much more common situation will be the one shown in the drawing below, in which no P_k equals B.

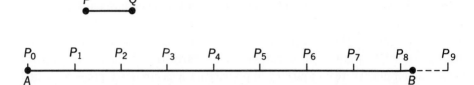

Here, B lies between P_8 and P_9. Thus $\overline{AB} \supset \overline{P_0P_8}$ and $\overline{AB} \subset \overline{P_0P_9}$ but $\overline{AB}$ is not equal to either of these sets. Thus, the stated measurement procedure assigns no meaning to $m(\overline{AB})$. This is not to say that we have not obtained some useful information about $\overline{AB}$. We have discovered that it is longer than a segment whose measure is 8 and shorter than one whose measure is 9. (Recall the discussion of "longer than" and "shorter than" for segments in Section 5.2.) The fact remains, however, that we have not assigned a number as a measure for $\overline{AB}$.

Thus the measurement procedure actually assigns measures to a limited class of segments and for other segments leaves us only the possibility of describing them somewhat vaguely by comparing them with these "measurable" segments. This state of affairs may seem highly unsatisfactory. Indeed it seems downright undemocratic that there should be a special privileged class of segments which have measures while others do not. We shall indeed eventually wish to establish equal rights for all segments but it will take a bit of work. Meanwhile in Section 8.2 we will examine what can be said about segments which *do* have measures.

Problem Set 8.1

A. 1. Find the measure of $\overline{AB}$ with respect to each of the other segments as unit segments.

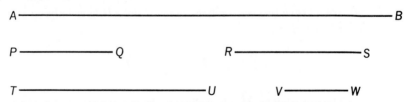

2. A segment $\overline{AB}$ is composed of points. Explain why we do not find a measure for $\overline{AB}$ merely by counting its points.

B. 1. If $\overline{AB}$ and $\overline{CD}$ are segments such that $m(\overline{AB}) = m(\overline{CD}) = 1$, use the properties of congruent segments to show that $\overline{AB} \cong \overline{CD}$.

2. If $\overline{AB}$ and $\overline{CD}$ are segments such that $m(\overline{AB}) = m(\overline{CD}) = 2$, use the properties of congruent segments to show that $\overline{AB} \cong \overline{CD}$.

3. If $\overline{AB}$ and $\overline{CD}$ are segments such that $m(\overline{AB}) = m(\overline{CD}) = 3$, use the properties of congruent segments to show that $\overline{AB} \cong \overline{CD}$.

C. 1. Segment $\overline{AB}$ is measured by two different persons. One finds that $m(\overline{AB}) = 12$ while the other finds $m(\overline{AB}) = 15$. An impartial umpire rules they are both correct. Explain how this could be.

2. A segment measured by one observer is found to have a length between 1 mile and 2 miles. The same segment, measured by a second observer, is found to have a length between 2264 yards and 2265 yards. Which result gives more precise information (assuming both are correct)? Discuss the effect of using different units. Why do we not measure the distance to the sun in millimeters to provide more exact information?

8.2 Measurable Segments

As suggested at the end of Section 8.1, let us investigate the properties of the "measurable" segments. It is understood here that all measures are with respect to some fixed unit segment.

Theorem 8.1 *If $B \in \overline{AC}$ and if $\overline{AB}$ and $\overline{BC}$ are segments having measures, then $\overline{AC}$ has a measure and $m(\overline{AC}) = m(\overline{AB}) + m(\overline{BC})$.*

Proof. The result is an immediate consequence of our definition of measure since $\overline{AC} = \overline{AB} \cup \overline{BC}$. For if $\overline{AB}$ is exactly covered by $m(\overline{AB})$ congruent copies of the unit segment, and if $\overline{BC}$ is exactly covered by $m(\overline{BC})$ copies, then their union $\overline{AC}$ is exactly covered by $m(\overline{AB}) + m(\overline{BC})$ congruent copies of the unit segment. Thus, by definition $m(\overline{AC}) = m(\overline{AB}) + m(\overline{BC})$.

A similar argument will establish the following, which is a kind of converse of Theorem 8.1.

Theorem 8.2 *If $B \in \overline{AC}$ and if $\overline{AB}$ and $\overline{AC}$ are segments having measures, then $\overline{BC}$ has a measure and $m(\overline{BC}) = m(\overline{AC}) - m(\overline{AB})$.*

In both the last two theorems it has been tacitly assumed that B is actually an interior point of $\overline{AC}$, since if B is an endpoint, one of the segments degenerates into a single point. However, if we agree that such a degenerate segment (i.e., single point) shall have measure zero, both theorems are still valid. From now on we shall agree to accept this convention.

The close relation between measure and congruence for measurable segments becomes clear in the next two results.

Theorem 8.3 *If $\overline{AB}$ has a measure and if $\overline{AB} \cong \overline{CD}$, then $\overline{CD}$ has a measure and $m(\overline{CD}) = m(\overline{AB})$.*

Proof. Let $k = m(\overline{AB})$. Then, according to the definition of measure, there are $k + 1$ points $P_0 = A, P_1, P_2, \ldots, P_k = B$ dividing $\overline{AB}$ into k segments, each congruent to the unit segment. It is given that $AB \cong CD$. Let $Q_0, Q_1, \ldots, Q_k$

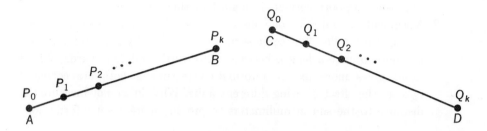

be the images of $P_0, P_1, P_2, \ldots, P_k$ in this congruence. Then by Theorem 5.5 on congruent segments each segment $\overline{Q_i Q_{i+1}}$ is congruent to $\overline{P_i P_{i+1}}$ and hence (by Axiom CS3) to the unit segment. Thus, $\overline{CD}$ is exactly covered by k congruent copies of the unit segment, so by definition $m(\overline{CD}) = k = m(\overline{AB})$.

Theorem 8.4 *If $\overline{AB}$ and $\overline{CD}$ are segments having measures and if $m(\overline{AB}) = m(\overline{CD})$, then $\overline{AB} \cong \overline{CD}$.*

Proof. This calls simply for repeated application of Theorem 5.4. (Compare problems **B1, B2,** and **B3** of Problem Set 8.1 above.) Let $m(\overline{AB}) = m(\overline{CD}) = k$ and let $P_0, P_1, \ldots, P_k$ and $Q_0, Q_1, \ldots, Q_k$ be the points dividing $\overline{AB}$ and $\overline{CD}$ into k congruent copies of the unit segment. Then we know that $\overline{P_0 P_1} \cong \overline{Q_0 Q_1}$ and $\overline{P_1 P_2} \cong \overline{Q_1 Q_2}$, so by Theorem 5.4 $\overline{P_0 P_2} \cong \overline{Q_0 Q_2}$. But from $\overline{P_0 P_2} \cong \overline{Q_0 Q_2}$ and $\overline{P_2 P_3} \cong \overline{Q_2 Q_3}$ it follows by the same theorem that $\overline{P_0 P_3} \cong \overline{Q_0 Q_3}$. By repeating this argument $k - 1$ times we eventually conclude that $\overline{P_0 P_k} \cong \overline{Q_0 Q_k}$, that is, $\overline{AB} \cong \overline{CD}$.

The last two theorems taken together show that, for segments which have measures with respect to a given unit segment, the statements $\overline{AB} \cong \overline{CD}$ and $m(\overline{AB}) = m(\overline{CD})$ are equivalent; i.e., each one implies the other.

You may have been conscious of a kind of sloppiness in the proof of Theorem 8.4. The phrase "By repeating the argument $k - 1$ times we eventually conclude that . . ." is a little unsatisfying. It is almost the same as "Now that you have seen a few examples, surely you are smart enough to see how it goes on!" It is hoped that you did indeed "see how it goes on" and that the discussion of Theorem 8.4 was convincing to you, but as a formal argument it certainly leaves something to be desired. Basically this is because a theorem like this asking us to show that something is true for all counting numbers k calls for a technique of proof called **mathematical induction.** A formal discussion of mathematical induction has not been included in this text, whence we have been reduced to arguments like that above. If you are familiar with mathematical induction you may find it interesting to give a more legitimate proof of Theorem 8.4. This is suggested as one of the exercises below.

Problem Set 8.2

A. 1. Verify the validity of Theorem 8.1 when B is an endpoint of segment $\overline{AC}$.
   2. Verify the validity of Theorem 8.2 when B is an endpoint of segment $\overline{AC}$.

B. 1. Compare the following segments (without measuring) to find which is longest and which is shortest.

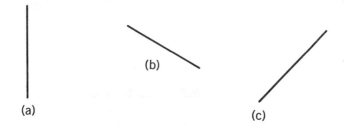

(a)   (b)   (c)

2. Estimate by inspection whether $\overline{AB}$ is longer than, shorter than, or congruent to $\overline{CD}$. Then compare without measuring.

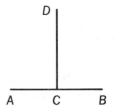

C. In these problems make use of properties of geometric figures familiar to you even though not formally discussed so far in this text.
   1. Quadrilateral $ROME$ is a square. When measured in centimeters $m(\overline{RO}) = 2$. What can be said of $m(\overline{OM})$, $m(\overline{ME})$ and $m(\overline{ER})$?

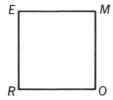 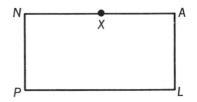

2. Quadrilateral $PLAN$ is a rectangle. X is the midpoint of $\overline{NA}$ and $\overline{PN} \cong \overline{NX}$. In terms of some convenient unit $m(\overline{PN}) = 3$. Find $m(\overline{NA})$, $m(\overline{AL})$ and $m(\overline{PL})$. Indicate clearly what theorems were used in drawing these conclusions and the properties of rectangles you have assumed.

3. The four sides of a quadrilateral each have a measure of 10 in inches. What kind of quadrilateral *must* it be? Be careful not to name just a special case.
4. What names would be used to describe the triangles shown?

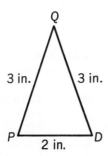 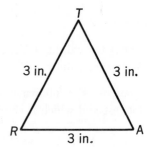

8.3 Coordinates on a Line

One of the really far-reaching ideas in mathematics is that of identifying a point by associating it with one or more numbers. At a very primitive level we are all familiar with this in the form of street addresses. If we send a letter to a friend at 3126 Beech Drive, we anticipate (perhaps optimistically) that the mailman will leave it at the correct house on Beech Drive because we have identified the house by indicating the number associated with it. The discussion of measurement above for segments permits us to begin the development of this idea.

Let Z be a point of a line k and consider the points obtained by laying off congruent copies of some unit segment on one of the rays from Z. Notice that point C as shown is the endpoint of the *fourth* congruent copy of the unit segment

starting at Z. It is therefore quite natural to associate C with the number 4 as indicated. Similarly, D, which is the endpoint of the seventh copy, is associated with the number 7. Using this scheme we may associate a whole number with each of the endpoints of segments indicated on $\overrightarrow{ZC}$. It is reasonable to associate the number 0 with the starting point Z. Any one of the marked points on $\overrightarrow{ZC}$ is completely identified if we indicate the number associated with it. When a number is used in identifying a point it is called a **coordinate** of the point. Thus, above, the coordinate of C is 4, the coordinate of D is 7 and the coordinate of Z is 0. In this way we have a one-to-one correspondence between the marked points and their coordinates.

We may likewise consider the points of k obtained by laying off congruent copies of the unit segment on the other ray of k from Z. If we seek to assign coordinates to these new points a difficulty arises. Since H is the endpoint of the

fourth copy of the unit from Z it would be natural to associate it with the number 4. This would be confusing, since 4 has been used as a coordinate for C. Several obvious solutions suggest themselves. If we imagine k to run east and west we can think of an east ray $\overrightarrow{ZC}$ and a west ray $\overrightarrow{ZH}$. Then we could associate a point with a number and a direction. Thus C might be associated with coordinate $4e$ and H with coordinate $4w$. This scheme is widely used in assigning street addresses. However, it occurs to us that the system of integers furnishes a ready-made set of numbers to use for coordinates. We have used the positive integers as coordinates for points on one ray. Why not use their additive inverses, i.e., the negative integers, as coordinates for points on the other? For example, H may be assigned the coordinate $^-4$. The result would appear as shown in the drawing below. In effect we have designated one of the two rays on k from Z as the positive ray, i.e.,

the ray containing points with positive coordinates and, the other as the negative ray which contains the points with negative coordinates.

This simple assignment of integers to points on a line is certainly familiar to you. It is often referred to, for obvious reasons, as a **number line.** Presently we shall proceed to assign coordinates to a larger class of points on the line. One of the most familiar physical illustrations of number line in which both rays are actually used is the scale on a thermometer.

Although the basic ideas are familiar enough, it may be well to point out specifically some of the features of the number line as here presented. The designation of positive and negative rays on k has, in effect, given positive and negative directions on the line. This lends itself to a geometric interpretation of operations on integers.

Consider the number 4, which is the coordinate of the point C in the following illustration. From the way in which coordinates were assigned, this means that to get from Z to C, one must move four units in the positive direction. Thus the number 4 may be associated with a motion of four units in the positive direction. An equation such as $4 + 5 = 9$ is then subject to the following geometric interpretation. If one starts at Z (often called the **origin** of the coordinate system) and makes a four-unit move in the positive direction, he arrives at point C (whose coordinate is 4). If he then follows this with a motion of five units in the positive direction, he reaches point D, whose coordinate is 9. There is nothing profound in this observation. Indeed it is nothing but an application of Theorem 8.1.

Using the same technique we may associate the number $^-3$ with a motion of three units in the negative direction. The geometric interpretation of addition suggested above is then found to extend readily to all cases of addition of integers. For example, the equation $2 + (^-5) = ^-3$ may be interpreted to read: Starting from Z a motion of two units in the positive direction followed by a motion of five units in the negative direction leads to a point D whose coordinate is $^-3$. This is

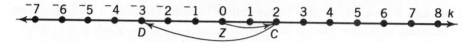

an application of Theorem 8.2, which assures us that $m(\overline{ZD}) = m(\overline{CD}) - m(\overline{ZC}) = 5 - 2 = 3$. Since D is on the negative ray its coordinate is $^-3$. A complete justification would require looking at several different cases, but nothing is involved except Theorems 8.1 and 8.2.

It is to be observed that each negative integer is merely the additive inverse of the corresponding positive integer and conversely. For example, 3 and $^-3$ are additive inverses of each other. With this in mind there is no real necessity of providing a separate geometric interpretation for the operation of subtraction since, as we know, subtracting a number is the same as adding its additive inverse. Thus

$$5 - 3 = 5 + {}^-3 = 2.$$
$$4 - 7 = 4 + {}^-7 = {}^-3.$$
$$5 - (^-3) = 5 + 3 = 8.$$

If, however, as would certainly be done with the lower elementary grades, one works only in the system of whole numbers, the same geometric idea can be employed by associating the addition of a number with motion in the positive direction and subtraction of a number with motion in the negative direction. In fact, this gives geometric meaning to the fact that the whole numbers are not closed under subtraction.

The same concept of positive and negative motion on the line also allows a convenient geometric interpretation of inequalities. Let A and B be the points of a number line which have coordinates a and b, respectively. If $a > b$ this means, as you know, that $a - b$ is positive, i.e., that $a - b = p$ or $a = b + p$

where p is some positive number. This means that the motion from B (the point with coordinate b) to A (the point with coordinate a or $b + p$) must be the motion which corresponds to p and this is in the positive direction. Thus $a > b$ means that on the number line A is in the positive direction from B. As the number line is shown in the accompanying diagram, the positive direction is to

$$^-8 \quad ^-7 \quad ^-6 \quad ^-5 \quad ^-4 \quad ^-3 \quad ^-2 \quad ^-1 \quad 0 \quad 1 \quad 2 \quad 3 \quad 4 \quad 5 \quad 6 \quad 7 \quad 8 \quad 9 \quad 10$$

the right, so the larger of two numbers is the one whose corresponding point is further to the right. Thus we observe $^-1 > {}^-8$, $^-1 < 0$, $^-3 < 9$.

Let A and B be points of a number line whose coordinates are a and b, respectively. If we write $a - b = t$ or equivalently $a = b + t$ then t can be associated with the motion from B to A. Suppose first that t is positive as in the sketch below, where $t = 4$. This means $\overline{AB}$ is exactly covered by t (in this case 4)

$$B \qquad\qquad A$$

congruent copies of the unit segment so that $m(\overline{AB}) = t$.

If, instead, t is a negative integer as shown here, where $t = {}^-3$, it is clear that $\overline{AB}$ is again a measurable segment. However, this time the measure $m(\overline{AB})$ is

$$A \qquad\qquad B$$

not the number t (here $^-3$) associated with the motion but instead its additive inverse, namely, 3 or ^-t. The conclusions we have reached could be written as follows:

$$m(\overline{AB}) = t \text{ if } t \geqq 0.$$
$$m(\overline{AB}) = {}^-t \text{ if } t < 0.$$

It is frequently convenient to introduce the following notation which is suggested by the result above.

> DEFINITION: If x is any integer, then *the absolute value of x*, denoted by $|x|$, is defined as follows:
> $$|x| = \begin{cases} x \text{ if } x \geqq 0. \\ {}^-x \text{ if } x < 0. \end{cases}$$

Using this notation and the fact that $t = a - b$ the conclusion above can be stated as follows.

Theorem 8.5 *If A has coordinate a and B has coordinate b, then $\overline{AB}$ has a measure and $m(\overline{AB}) = |a - b|$.*

A final remark about the number line seems indicated, though in some ways it belongs more to the practice of measurement than its theory. Imagine a model of a line segment, perhaps the edge of a strip of cardboard, and let a part of a number line, including the origin, be laid off along this edge.

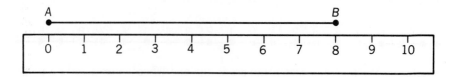

It is at once clear that we now have a very efficient device for measuring segments. If we wish to measure $\overline{AB}$ we may lay this scale along $\overline{AB}$. If this is done in such a way that A is at the origin (zero point) of the scale and B, as in the above diagram, is then at the point with coordinate 8, we may conclude at once that $m(\overline{AB}) = 8$. The instrument here described is, of course, merely the familiar *ruler*, though in common usage the word ruler often implies use of some socially accepted unit like the inch or centimeter as the unit segment. Thus a ruler is simply some movable representation of part of a number line.

Problem Set 8.3

A. 1. Use arrows as in the text to represent each of the following sums on the number line.

   a. $(^-2) + (^-5)$ **c.** $(^-2) + (5)$
   b. $(2) + (^-5)$ **d.** $(2) + (5)$

 2. Change each of the following to an addition problem and use arrows to represent each sum on the number line.

   a. $(^-3) - (^-7)$ **e.** $(^-7) - (^-3)$
   b. $(3) - (^-7)$ **f.** $(7) - (^-3)$
   c. $(^-3) - (7)$ **g.** $(^-7) - (3)$
   d. $(3) - (7)$ **h.** $(7) - (3)$

 3. Express the following by a single numeral and illustrate by arrows on the number line.

$$[(^-5) - (^-3)] + (^-2)$$

B. 1. Insert the correct inequality between each of the following pairs of numbers.

   a. $^-10$ $^-5$.   **f.** 0   3.
   b. 10 $^-5$.   **g.** 0 $^-3$.
   c. 10 $^-10$.   **h.** $^-1$ 5.
   d. 1 $^-5$.   **i.** $^-6$ 5.
   e. $^-1$ $^-5$.   **j.** $^-100$ 2.

 2. When three distinct points lie on a line, exactly one lies between the other two, i.e., exactly one point belongs to the segment having the other two points as endpoints. In the following cases you are given the coordinates of three points. Determine which one lies between the other two.

	A	B	C
a.	⁻1	⁻2	1
b.	2	0	1
c.	⁻8	0	8
d.	5	12	19
e.	⁻5	⁻12	⁻19
f.	⁻1	8	⁻9

3. If A, B, and C are distinct points on a line with coordinates a, b, and c, respectively, state in words how to determine from the coordinates which point lies between the other two.

4. A, B, and C are distinct points on a line such that $A \in \overline{BC}$. If the coordinates of A, B, and C are a, b, and c, respectively, what can be said about the coordinates?

C. 1. Evaluate each of the following.

$$|\ ^-8\ | \quad |\ 15\ | \quad |\ ^-8 - (^-5)\ | \quad |\ 5 + (^-9)\ | \quad |\ 9 + (^-5)\ |$$

2. Find the set of integers satisfying each of the following relations. In each case show the corresponding points on a number line.
   a. $|\ x\ | < 3$.   **d.** $|\ x + 1\ | < 3$.
   b. $|\ x - 5\ | < 4$.   **e.** $2 < |\ x - 1\ | < 5$.
   c. $|\ x - 5\ | > 4$.

3. Show on the number line the points whose coordinates are contained in the following set of integers:

$$\{x \mid x > -1\} \cap \{x \mid x < 6\}.$$

D. 1. Let A, B, C, D, E be points on a number line whose coordinates are 2, 5, ⁻3, 6, ⁻8. If one starts at A and moves in succession to B, C, D, E:
   a. What is the total distance moved?
   b. How far is one from where he started?
   Why are the answers different for parts **a** and **b**?
   Under what circumstances would the answers be the same?

2. In problem **D1** you considered the trip from A to E, going to B, C, D in order on the way. This might be abbreviated A-B-C-D-E. Another trip from A to E visiting all the other points, but in a different order, would be shown by A-C-B-D-E.
   a. Use the notation above to write all possible trips from A to E and stopping at all three of the points B, C, and D.
   b. Find the total distance traveled for each of the routes in **a**.
   c. Which of the routes is the shortest in total distance?

E. 1. If P is a point with coordinate x on a number line, show that $m(\overline{ZP}) = |x|$ where Z is the origin of coordinates.

2. Take a road map of your state and locate the scale of miles shown. Use this (nonstandard) unit to construct a ruler for use on the map. Use this ruler to find the distances between cities shown on the map. Compare your results with those shown on the mileage chart. If your results do not check too closely with those recorded on the chart, can you think of a reason why this might be so?

8.4 Rational Numbers as Measures and Coordinates

So far in our discussion we have assumed that some fixed unit segment was selected and used throughout. Theoretically, of course, one unit is as good as another. In practice different units are in use, among them the centimeter, inch, foot, yard, meter, kilometer, and mile. This is precisely the reason why it is vital for us in describing a length to indicate the unit as well as to give the measure, i.e., to speak of a length of 3 miles or 6 feet or 4 units, where the unit is some known segment $\overline{PQ}$.

The practice of using different units at different times requires us to investigate the relation between the measures in such cases. Suppose that segments $\overline{PQ}$ and $\overline{RS}$ below are so related that it takes two congruent copies of $\overline{RS}$ to cover $\overline{PQ}$.

If a segment $\overline{AB}$ is measurable with respect to $\overline{PQ}$ as a unit we may have, as indicated in the sketch, $m(\overline{AB}) = 5$. What will the situation be if instead we

use $\overline{RS}$ as a unit? Since each congruent copy of $\overline{PQ}$ is covered by two copies of $\overline{RS}$ it follows at once that $\overline{AB}$ is measurable in terms of unit $\overline{RS}$ and, in fact, $m'(\overline{AB}) = 2 \cdot 5 = 10$, where we have used m' to denote measure with respect to $\overline{RS}$. Indeed, it is clear at once that every segment $\overline{CD}$ measurable with respect to $\overline{PQ}$ is also measurable with respect to $\overline{RS}$ and that for such a segment $m'(\overline{CD}) = 2m(\overline{CD})$. On the other hand, if segment $\overline{CD}$ has an odd measure with respect to $\overline{RS}$, it does not have a measure with respect to $\overline{PQ}$, since it is not exactly covered by an integral number of copies of $\overline{PQ}$. Thus by using the smaller segment as the unit we can measure all the segments that could be measured before, and a lot more besides.

It may be useful to compare the number lines formed with respect to the two units. They would appear as shown at the top of the next page.

The use of the smaller unit attaches coordinates to more points, but, unfortu-

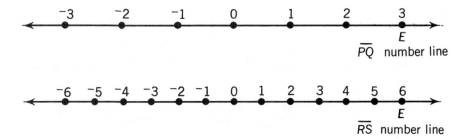

$\overline{PQ}$ number line

$\overline{RS}$ number line

nately, changes the coordinates for those points which already had coordinates on the $\overline{PQ}$ number line. Is there any feasible way of retaining the virtue of having coordinates for more points, as on the $\overline{RS}$ number line, without altering the coordinates that had already been assigned on the $\overline{PQ}$ number line? One such possibility has undoubtedly already occurred to you. Let us, at least nominally, retain $\overline{PQ}$ as a unit segment but agree to abandon the requirement that $m(\overline{AB})$ be a whole number. For example, let us assign to the point marked 3 on the $\overline{RS}$ number line the coordinate $\frac{3}{2}$, and in general to a point marked t on the $\overline{RS}$ number line we assign the coordinate $\frac{t}{2}$. It is to be seen at once that the procedure leaves each of the marked points on the $\overline{PQ}$ number line with its original coordinate. For example, point E would now be assigned the coordinate $\frac{6}{2}$, but this is equal to 3 so E has retained its coordinate of 3. The augmented $\overline{PQ}$ number line then appears as shown in the sketch.

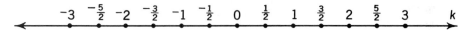

As we agree to allow coordinates of the form $\frac{t}{2}$ we also admit measures of this form. Thus, to say $m(\overline{AB}) = \frac{3}{2}$ will mean that $\overline{AB}$ is exactly covered by three congruent copies of some segment $\overline{RS}$ which is half as long as $\overline{PQ}$, i.e., such that two copies of $\overline{RS}$ just cover $\overline{PQ}$. This is the same as saying that $\overline{AB}$ is congruent to the segment whose endpoints above have coordinates 0 and $\frac{3}{2}$.

If $\overline{TU}$ is a segment such that three copies of it cover $\overline{PQ}$, similar reasoning leads us to introduce coordinates of the form $\frac{t}{3}$ for the points of k which divide the original unit segments in thirds. The line k with the points now assigned coordinates would then appear as in the following drawing.

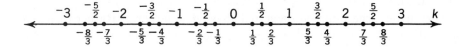

Similarly, every rational number $\dfrac{r}{q}$ is assigned as a coordinate to a point W of k as follows. Assuming $q > 0$, consider a segment $\overline{XY}$ for which q congruent copies cover the basic unit segment $\overline{PQ}$. Then point W of k is assigned the co-

q copies

ordinate $\dfrac{r}{q}$ if segment $\overline{ZW}$ (where Z is the origin) is exactly covered by $|\,r\,|$ congruent copies of $\overline{XY}$ and W is on the positive or negative ray of k according to whether r is positive or negative. Similarly, we write $m(\overline{AB}) = \dfrac{r}{q}$ if r and q are both positive and if $\overline{AB}$ is covered by r congruent copies of $\overline{XY}$.

Two remarks are in order with regard to this procedure of assigning co-ordinates. First, for a given integer $q > 0$, are we sure there is a segment $\overline{XY}$ such that q copies of $\overline{XY}$ exactly cover the unit segment $\overline{PQ}$? The answer is that as far as the axioms so far adopted are concerned, we do not know. Thus, to justify the description above, it is necessary for us to adopt some axiom such as the follow-ing:

Axiom MS2 *If $\overline{AB}$ is any segment and q any positive integer, there exist $q + 1$ points $P_0 = A$, P_1, P_2, . . . , $P_q = B$ of $\overline{AB}$ such that $\overline{P_0P_1} \cong \overline{P_1P_2} \cong \cdots \cong \overline{P_{q-1}P_q}$ and such that each two consecutive segments have only an endpoint in common.*

For the case of $q = 2$ this axiom states that every segment has a midpoint. It was noted in Chapter 5 that such an axiom would eventually be introduced.

The second remark concerns the many different representations of a rational number. In assigning rational coordinates to points of the number line (or measures to segments) we represented the rational number as $\dfrac{r}{q}$. We know that any rational number has infinitely many such fractional representations such as $\dfrac{5}{2}, \dfrac{10}{4}, \dfrac{15}{6}, \dfrac{20}{8}, \dfrac{25}{10}$, etc. Is there a possibility that we might, under our procedure, say that for a certain segment $\overline{AB}$, $m(\overline{AB}) = \dfrac{5}{2}$, but at the same time conclude that $m(\overline{AB}) \neq \dfrac{15}{6}$? This is a horrifying thought. It would mean that in giving a measure for a segment it would not be enough to give a rational number, but that one must give a particular representation of that rational number.

Fortunately, the situation suggested above does not arise. Rather than give a general formal argument, let us consider the specific numerical example above which exhibits all the essential features of the general case. Suppose we are told that $m(\overline{AB}) = \dfrac{5}{2}$. What does this really mean? It says that if the unit segment $\overline{PQ}$ is divided into two congruent parts, then $\overline{AB}$ is exactly covered by five

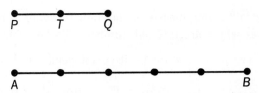

congruent copies of one of these smaller segments $\overline{PT}$. (As always the covering segments can have only endpoints in common.) What would it mean to try to measure $\overline{AB}$ in sixths? It would ask that we consider $\overline{PQ}$ subdivided in six congruent pieces and then see whether $\overline{AB}$ could be covered by congruent copies of one of these smaller segments $\overline{PU}$. If it takes six congruent copies of $\overline{PU}$ to cover

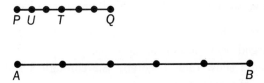

$\overline{PQ}$, it is clear that the segments $\overline{PT}$ and $\overline{TQ}$ are each covered by three congruent copies of $\overline{PU}$. Since it takes five copies of $\overline{PT}$ to cover $\overline{AB}$, and each of these is covered by three copies of $\overline{PU}$, it follows that $\overline{AB}$ is exactly covered by $3 \cdot 5 = 15$ congruent copies of $\overline{PU}$. Thus, by our agreement, $m(\overline{AB}) = \dfrac{15}{6}$. The general case can be dealt with in essentially the same way.

Once this question has been satisfactorily disposed of, we find that we have an immense and gratifying increase in the set of "measurable" segments since we are now admitting not only all segments which can be exactly covered with congruent copies of the unit segment $\overline{PQ}$, but also all those that can be exactly covered with congruent copies of any fractional part of $\overline{PQ}$. Correspondingly, the class of points on the number line to which coordinates have been assigned has been vastly expanded. Indeed there are now so many points with coordinates on any segment that it is no longer feasible to try to indicate them all on a diagram of the number line. Between any two points having coordinates we can find infinitely many other points having coordinates.

A critical question now arises. In admitting a larger class of segments as "measurable" and a larger class of points having coordinates, have we lost the properties indicated in Theorems 8.1 through 8.5? If so, our achievement has been a hollow one since it is largely these properties which make measure and coordinates interesting. Fortunately, these five theorems, without the change of a single word, are valid with our enlarged idea of measure. As an example, consider Theorem 8.1, which we restate for reference.

Theorem 8.1 *If* $B \in \overline{AC}$ *and if* $\overline{AB}$ *and* $\overline{BC}$ *are segments having measures,* *then* $\overline{AC}$ *has a measure and* $m(\overline{AC}) = m(\overline{AB}) + m(\overline{BC})$.

Proof. The words "having measures" are now to be interpreted in the sense of having measures which are rational numbers. To be definite, let $m(\overline{AB}) = \frac{p}{q}$, $m(\overline{BC}) = \frac{r}{s}$, where p, q, r, s are positive integers. As remarked above, we can just as legitimately write $m(\overline{AB}) = \frac{ps}{qs}$, $m(\overline{BC}) = \frac{qr}{qs}$. If $\overline{TU}$ is a segment obtained by dividing the unit segment $\overline{PQ}$ into qs congruent parts, then by our definition of measure it takes ps congruent copies of $\overline{TU}$ to cover $\overline{AB}$ and qr copies to cover $\overline{BC}$. Thus, $\overline{AC}$ is exactly covered by $ps + qr$ congruent copies of $\overline{TU}$, and by the definition of measure with unit $\overline{PQ}$ this means that $m(\overline{AC}) = \frac{ps + qr}{qs}$. According to our work on rational numbers $\frac{ps + qr}{qs} = \frac{p}{q} + \frac{r}{s}$ so we conclude, as desired, that $m(\overline{AC}) = m(\overline{AB}) + m(\overline{BC})$. This proves Theorem 8.1 with our enlarged definition of measurement.

Similar arguments show that Theorems 8.2 through 8.5 still hold with the enlarged definition of measurement.

An interesting question now presents itself. We have used the rational numbers to assign coordinates to a large class of points on the number line. Have we given coordinates to *all* points on the line? It looks very plausible that the answer should be "yes." However, as we shall see below, the answer is really "no" if we want the line to behave in accord with our geometric intuition. The exploration of this question in Section 8.5 will, in fact, lead us toward inventing a larger number system than the rationals in order to have coordinates for all points on a line.

Problem Set 8.4

A. 1. a. If $\frac{p}{q}$ is a rational number, give a definition for the absolute value, $\left|\frac{p}{q}\right|$.

    b. Express each of the following by a single fraction.

$$\left|\frac{-8}{5}\right| \qquad \left|\frac{-3}{-7}\right| \qquad \left|\frac{-8}{3} - \frac{4}{-3}\right| \qquad \left|\frac{4}{-3} - \frac{3}{-4}\right| \qquad \left|\frac{1}{4} - \frac{5}{6}\right|$$

2. Insert the proper inequalities in the following pairs.

    a. $-\left(\frac{5}{6}\right) \qquad \frac{1}{3}$.

    b. $\frac{5}{6} \qquad \frac{-1}{3}$.

    c. $-\left(\frac{5}{6}\right) \qquad \frac{-7}{12}$.

    d. $\frac{5}{6} \qquad \frac{7}{12}$.

    e. $\frac{5}{6} \qquad \frac{11}{14}$.

    f. $\frac{7}{15} \qquad \frac{5}{12}$.

B. 1. In the following cases you are given the coordinates of three distinct points, A, B, and C. In each case name the point which is between the other two.

	A	B	C
a.	$\dfrac{-2}{3}$	$\dfrac{4}{5}$	$\dfrac{11}{15}$
b.	$\dfrac{5}{12}$	$\dfrac{2}{5}$	$\dfrac{7}{15}$
c.	$\dfrac{-2}{5}$	0	$\dfrac{-8}{21}$
d.	$\dfrac{5}{6}$	$\dfrac{11}{14}$	$\dfrac{6}{7}$

2. Find the coordinates of five points which lie between the points with coordinates $\dfrac{1}{2}$ and $\dfrac{3}{5}$.

3. Find the coordinates of eight points between those with coordinates $\dfrac{-1}{3}$ and $\dfrac{1}{4}$.

4. When integral coordinates were first introduced every such point had two closest points having coordinates. For example, the points with coordinates 4 and 6 were closest to the point with coordinate 5. After all rational numbers were used as coordinates was this still true? Explain.

C. 1. Find the measures of the segments whose endpoints have coordinates as given below.

    a. $\dfrac{-5}{2}$ and $\dfrac{3}{4}$ **b.** $\dfrac{-5}{2}$ and $\dfrac{-3}{4}$ **c.** $\dfrac{14}{3}$ and $\dfrac{5}{6}$

2. The coordinates of points A, B, C are 5, $\dfrac{-8}{3}$, $\dfrac{5}{6}$, respectively. Find the total distance traveled in going from A to B to C.

D. 1. If points $A, B, C,$ and D have coordinates $\dfrac{1}{3}, \dfrac{1}{2}, \dfrac{3}{2},$ and $\dfrac{4}{3}$, respectively, find which of the following pairs of segments are congruent: $\overline{AB}$ and $\overline{CD}$; $\overline{AC}$ and $\overline{BD}$; $\overline{AD}$ and $\overline{BC}$.

2. If A and B have coordinates $\dfrac{3}{2}$ and $\dfrac{11}{6}$, respectively, and if C has coordinate $\dfrac{5}{6}$, find the coordinates of all the possible positions of D so that $\overline{AB} \cong \overline{CD}$.

E. 1. Prove Theorem 8.3 for the case of rational measures.

2. Give a discussion to show that if $m(\overline{AB}) = \dfrac{p}{q}$, then it is also correct to write $m(\overline{AB}) = \dfrac{2p}{2q}$, or in general to write $m(\overline{AB}) = \dfrac{kp}{kq}$ where p, q, and k are understood to be positive integers.

8.5 Looking Toward the Real Numbers

In discussing rational numbers in an earlier chapter you considered the representation of rational numbers by decimals. In this connection you may well have been reminded of the remark by the frustrated golfer who described golf as a game in which "the object is to propel a round ball from one place to another with instruments singularly ill-adapted for the purpose." In some ways decimals do seem "singularly ill-adapted" for representing rationals. As simple a rational number as $\dfrac{1}{3}$ cannot be represented as an ordinary decimal, since the division process for $1 \div 3$ never has a remainder of 0. In order to represent it in decimal form at all, one is forced to invent the concept of an "infinite" decimal and write

$$\frac{1}{3} = .3333\ldots$$

where the 3's are understood to continue forever. The introduction of the number line provides a geometric interpretation of this symbolism which makes it worthwhile to re-examine its meaning.

The awkward symbol of the infinite decimal .3333. . . is to be considered as a shorthand for instructions to consider the successive intervals

$$[.3, .4], [.33, .34], [.333, .334], [.3333, .3334], \ldots .$$

(The symbol $[a, b]$ here denotes the set of
numbers x such that $a \leqq x \leqq b$.)

The number $\dfrac{1}{3}$ belongs to all these intervals as we readily find from the division process. Thus $.3 \leqq \dfrac{1}{3} \leqq .4$, $.33 \leqq \dfrac{1}{3} \leqq .34$, $.333 \leqq \dfrac{1}{3} \leqq .334$, etc. Indeed in this case the equality signs could be omitted since $\dfrac{1}{3}$ is actually interior to each interval. Moreover, since the differences of the endpoints of these intervals approach 0 there cannot be two different numbers which belong to all of them. (Why?) Thus $\dfrac{1}{3}$ is the only number which belongs to all the intervals. This is the sense in which we say that .3333. . . represents $\dfrac{1}{3}$. The infinite decimal can be thought of as a trap set to catch a rational number and the number it catches is $\dfrac{1}{3}$.

Let us consider the geometric description of the discussion above on the number line. The first interval, [.3, .4], determines a segment on the number line whose endpoints have coordinates .3 and .4. The point whose coordinate is $\frac{1}{3}$ then

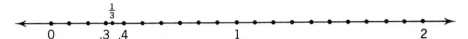

belongs to this segment. Looking at the second interval, [.33, .34], we see that geometrically this means the segment with endpoints .3 and .4 has been sub-divided into 10 congruent pieces and that the point whose coordinate is $\frac{1}{3}$ belongs to the fourth of these pieces. This is indicated in the drawing below, using an

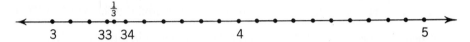

enlarged scale. If we imagine the successive intervals, we may visualize the corresponding segments on the number line, each of which is one tenth as long as the former one, shutting down on the point whose coordinate is $\frac{1}{3}$. Thus, seen from the point of view of the number line, the infinite decimal is a set of instructions which focuses our attention on a certain specific point on the number line, namely, the point with coordinate $\frac{1}{3}$, and in this sense completely describes the point.

This interpretation immediately suggests the question as to whether *every* point P on the number line can be described in such a way, i.e., by an infinite decimal. It is not difficult to see that this is possible. Suppose that P is an arbitrary point of the number line. By Axiom MS1, P must belong to some one of the congruent copies of the unit segment. For definiteness suppose that point P belongs to the segment of the number line whose endpoints have coordinates 7 and 8. If the segment is divided into ten congruent pieces the endpoints will have coordinates 7.0, 7.1, 7.2, 7.3, 7.4, 7.5, 7.6, 7.7, 7.8, 7.9, and 8.0. Then P must belong to some one of these segments, say to the segment whose endpoints are 7.5 and 7.6. If this segment is now divided into ten congruent pieces by the points 7.50, 7.51, 7.52, . . ., 7.59, 7.60, then P must belong to one of these segments, say the one whose endpoints have coordinates 7.52 and 7.53. By continuing this subdivision process it is clear how P can be associated with a set of intervals such as

$$[7, 8], [7.5, 7.6], [7.52, 7.53], \ldots,$$

or, equivalently, P can be associated with an infinite decimal such as 7.52. . . .

Using this process, every point P of the number line can be associated with an infinite decimal

$$a_0.a_1a_2a_3a_4. \ldots,$$

meaning that P belongs to all the segments determined by the intervals

$$[a_0, a_0 + 1], [a_0.a_1, a_0.a_1 + .1], [a_0.a_1a_2, a_0.a_1a_2 + .01], \ldots ,$$

$$\left[a_0.a_1a_2 \cdots a_k, a_0.a_1a_2 \cdots a_k + \frac{1}{10^k} \right], \ldots .$$

To avoid slight difficulties we consider P is on the positive ray. Moreover, it seems intuitively clear that two different points of the number line, P and Q, cannot be associated with the same infinite decimal, for if they are different there should eventually be a subdivision fine enough so that they will belong to different subsegments.

The procedure of associating an infinite decimal with a point is unique except for one situation—namely, when the point P is one of the points of the decimal subdivision. This situation will be illustrated by an example. Suppose that P is the point having the rational coordinate $\frac{6}{5}$. Then it is found to be between 1 and 2 and hence associated with the interval $[1, 2]$. When this interval is divided in tenths as shown in the illustration, P turns out to be one of those division points.

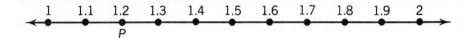

Specifically, it is the point with coordinate 1.2 (which, of course, you already knew).

Here the ambiguity arises since P belongs to two different ones of the small segments, namely, that corresponding to $[1.2, 1.3]$ and that corresponding to $[1.1, 1.2]$. Either of these choices leads to an infinite decimal for P. Consider first the effect of choosing $[1.2, 1.3]$. Then the first two intervals would be

$$[1, 2], [1.2, 1.3].$$

If this second segment is divided into tenths the point P must belong to the first one, i.e., the segment corresponding to $[1.20, 1.21]$. Indeed, no matter how often we continue the process P will always be the left-hand endpoint and so belong to the first interval. Thus, the sequence of intervals would be

$$[1, 2], [1.2, 1.3], [1.20, 1.21], [1.200, 1.201], [1.2000, 1.2001], \ldots$$

and the infinite decimal would be

$$1.2000. \ldots ,$$

where the omitted symbols are all zeros. This says that since the point had a coordinate expressible as a finite decimal 1.2 there really was no need to continue the subdivision process. If you do, you simply get an infinite succession of zeros.

Consider, however, the effect of taking $[1.1, 1.2]$ as the second interval, When this is divided in ten congruent parts the point P being the right-hand endpoint must belong to the last of these segments, namely, that given by [1.19, 1.20]. In fact, no matter how often we repeat the subdivision process P will always belong to the last segment. The sequence of intervals is therefore

$$[1, 2], [1.1, 1.2], [1.19, 1.20], [1.199, 1.200], [1.1999, 1.2000], \ldots$$

and the corresponding infinite decimal is

$$1.1999. \ldots,$$

where the omitted digits are all 9's. Thus, the point P has two corresponding infinite decimals, 1.2000. . . and 1.1999. . . . These are both decimal representations of the rational number $\frac{6}{5}$ or 1.2.

The case described above where P actually is one of the endpoints in the decimal division process is the only one in which a point has two corresponding infinite decimals. These points are those which have rational coordinates that can be written as finite decimals.

We have seen above that every point on the number line can be associated with an infinite decimal and that the decimal may be regarded as a set of directions which completely determine the point; i.e., when the decimal is given the point is completely identified. A related question now occurs to us. Does *every* infinite decimal correspond to a point on the number line? Let us see what this would mean geometrically. Consider, for example, the decimal 2.746. . . where we understand that all the digits are determined though we have written only the first four. The associated sequence of intervals is

$$[2, 3], [2.7, 2.8], [2.74, 2.75], [2.746, 2.747], \ldots.$$

If we examine the segments on the number line corresponding to these intervals as shown below, we see a set of segments, each contained in the last and only

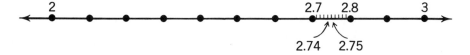

one tenth as long. Our intuition certainly suggests to us that these segments are shutting down on a point of the number line, i.e., that there is a point which belongs to all these segments. Although this intuitively plausible fact does not follow from the axioms we have so far adopted, we shall presently adopt an axiom which will guarantee its truth. As soon as we have done so, we will have, in the infinite decimals, a complete set of symbols which can be used to identify the various points of the number line. Indeed, the relation of points to infinite decimals will be one-to-one except for the cases noted in which a point may be associated with two infinite decimals. Thus, it will be of interest in the next section to examine more fully the set of infinite decimals.

Problem Set 8.5

A. 1. Identify which of the following rational numbers have two infinite decimal representations and in each case find the two:

$$\frac{13}{80} \quad \frac{5}{6} \quad \frac{7}{16} \quad \frac{5}{12} \quad \frac{21}{12} \quad \frac{45}{12} \quad \frac{3}{28}$$

2. For each of the following rational numbers use division to find the infinite decimal representation.

a. $\dfrac{4}{7}$　　　　　　　　　　　**c.** $\dfrac{5}{37}$

b. $\dfrac{13}{74}$　　　　　　　　　　**d.** $\dfrac{23}{13}$

B. 1. Express as a fraction the rational number represented by each of the following repeating decimals:

a. $.1111\ldots = .\overline{1}.$　　　　　　　**c.** $.202020\ldots = .\overline{20}.$

b. $.121212\ldots = .\overline{12}.$　　　　　**d.** $.10222\ldots = .10\overline{2}.$

2. Show that the repeating decimal

$$.1234321234321234321\ldots$$

represents the same rational number as $\dfrac{1112}{9009}$.

8.6 The Real Numbers

Because of the work of the last section, an examination of infinite decimals seems appropriate. We know that all the rational numbers can be expressed as infinite decimals simply by using the division process. Thus, in the last problem set, you discovered, for example, that

$$\frac{4}{7} = .571428571428.\ \ldots$$

$$\frac{13}{74} = .1756756756.\ \ldots$$

Thus, some of the infinite decimals represent rational numbers. It occurs to us then to ask whether *all* the infinite decimals represent rational numbers. This would be a delightful result since it would mean that the infinite decimals are nothing but new names for the rational numbers with which we are already quite familiar.

Unfortunately the conjecture just made turns out to be false. You will recall that in the chapter on rational numbers you noticed an interesting characteristic of the infinite decimals for the rationals. This was that an infinite decimal corresponding to a rational number is always periodic. As a matter of fact, the converse is also true, i.e., every periodic infinite decimal represents a rational number. It then follows that an infinite decimal which is *not* periodic cannot correspond to a rational number. Consider, for example, the infinite decimal .21211211121111. . . where the number of consecutive 1's following the 2's increases by one each time. No matter how far out we go in the decimal there are sequences of consecutive 1's still to come which are longer than any that have yet occurred. Thus, this decimal is not periodic and hence does not correspond to a rational number. The set of infinite decimals contains a subset (the repeating decimals) which corresponds to the rationals but also contains a large set of decimals which do not correspond to rationals.

This presents us with a rather unpalatable situation. If, on the number line, there are indeed to be points corresponding to all the infinite decimals, then we immediately find there are some (i.e., those corresponding to the nonrepeating decimals) to which we have not yet assigned any coordinate. Thus, the rational numbers do not provide coordinates for *all* points of a number line. Yet the use of coordinates for identifying points is a very useful one.

There is, as you have undoubtedly observed, an obvious exit from this impass. Why not use the infinite decimals themselves as coordinates? We certainly know there are enough of them and they provide a numerical means of identifying *all* the points of the number line. There is only one fly in the ointment here. One of the most advantageous things about the rationals as coordinates was that they formed a field, and this field had a nice relationship to congruence and measurement as reflected in Theorems 8.1, 8.2, 8.3, 8.4, and 8.5. Yet so far our infinite decimals are nothing but symbols. We do not even have any operations defined on them.

It thus appears desirable to try to give suitable definitions for addition and multiplication so that the infinite decimals will become a field which will contain the field of rationals. By now this should be a familiar idea. We have already extended our number system from the whole numbers to the integers and from the integers to the rationals, so a further extension should not be an unfamiliar concept (at least in principle). It should be reasonably clear what we would wish to do. We would like to take the set of all infinite decimals and somehow define for them operations of addition and multiplication. We would then proceed to consider the operational properties of this new system. For example, we would investigate whether addition and multiplication are commutative and associative, whether the distributive property holds, and whether there are additive and multiplicative identities and inverses.

The procedure just outlined, as may be imagined, is a fairly laborious one but it is a fact that it can be done. The system which results is called the **field of real numbers.** We shall not attempt to carry out this work in detail, but an example of how one might seek to define addition may be instructive. Consider two infinite decimals

$$A = .31568. \ldots$$
$$B = .43815. \ldots$$

Decimal A is associated with the sequence of intervals

$$[.3, .4], [.31, .32], [.315, .316], [.3156, .3157], [.31568, .31569], \ldots,$$

while B is associated with the sequence

$$[.4, .5], [.43, .44], [.438, .439], [.4381, .4382], [.43815, .43816], \ldots.$$

Consider the sequence of intervals which is obtained by adding the two first numbers and the two second numbers for each corresponding pair of intervals. This would yield the sequence

$$[.7, .9], [.74, .76], [.753, .755], [.7537, .7539], [.75383, .75385], \ldots.$$

This sequence of intervals can then be associated with the infinite decimal .7538..., which is defined to be $A + B$.

The real numbers may be identified with the infinite decimals except, as indicated earlier, decimals such as .41999... and .42000... are to be considered as representing the same real number. For reference we state the following theorem, the proof of which will be omitted. The notation $[a, b]$ is used here to mean the set of all real numbers x such that $a \leqq x \leqq b$.

Theorem 8.6

(a) *The real numbers form a field.*

(b) *The real numbers contain the rational numbers as a subfield.*

(c) *The real numbers have an order relation $>$ having the same properties as for the rationals.*

(d) *For every sequence of closed intervals such that $[a_1, b_1] \supset [a_2, b_2] \supset [a_3, b_3] \supset \cdots$ there is at least one real number belonging to all the intervals.*

(e) *For every real number B with $B \geqq 0$, there is a unique real number $x \geqq 0$ such that $x^2 = B$. This number x is denoted by $\sqrt{B}$.*

It is interesting to notice how the problem of square roots noted in part (e) leads to the idea of infinite decimals. Consider the problem of determining $\sqrt{2}$, i.e., of finding the positive real number x such that $x^2 = 2$. Observe that $1^2 = 1$, which is less than 2, and $2^2 = 4$, which is greater than 2, so that $1^2 < x^2 < 2^2$. According to the inequality properties for positive real numbers [assumed in Theorem 8.6(c)] we can conclude that $1 < x < 2$ so x belongs to the interval $[1, 2]$. Breaking this interval into tenths we find $(1.4)^2 = 1.96 < 2$ and $(1.5)^2 = 2.25 > 2$ so that

$$x \in [1.4, 1.5].$$

Similarly,

$$(1.41)^2 = 1.9881, \quad (1.42)^2 = 2.0164$$

so that $x \in [1.41, 1.42]$. Thus x corresponds to the sequence of intervals

$$[1, 2], [1.4, 1.5], [1.41, 1.42], [1.414, 1.415], \ldots$$

and so is represented by the infinite decimal $x = 1.414. \ldots$

Is this number x a rational number? Since 2 is rational it seems plausible that its square root $\sqrt{2}$ should also be rational. Let us look for such a positive rational number $\frac{p}{q}$. Any positive rational number has infinitely many representations, but we agree to select the one for which p and q are positive integers with no common factor (other than 1). Every positive rational number has exactly one such representation.

If $\left(\frac{p}{q}\right)^2 = 2$, then $p^2 = 2q^2$. If p were odd its square p^2 would also be odd (see problem **D1** below) and hence could not equal the even integer $2q^2$. Thus p is even and $p = 2k$ for some positive integer k. The equation $p^2 = 2q^2$ thus becomes $4k^2 = 2q^2$ or, equivalently, $q^2 = 2k^2$. The same reasoning as before shows that q must be even, so that p and q each have a factor 2. This is impossible, since p and q had no common factor except 1. We are then forced to conclude there is no rational number $\frac{p}{q}$ such that $\frac{p^2}{q^2} = 2$ and hence $\sqrt{2}$ is *not* a rational number. A real number which is not rational is called an **irrational number.** We have here shown that $\sqrt{2}$ is irrational. In a similar way $\sqrt{3}, \sqrt{5}, \sqrt{7}, \sqrt{8}, \sqrt{10}$ are irrational, whereas $\sqrt{1}, \sqrt{4}, \sqrt{9}$, are rational.

If we had stumbled earlier across the fact that there was no rational number $\sqrt{2}$, it would have provided an added incentive to try to expand the rational number system to the reals.

You may be interested to know that the expansion process for number systems need not stop with the field of real numbers. These, in turn, can be extended again to a larger field, called the **complex numbers,** in which *every* number has a square root. We shall not discuss this field, however, as it is not necessary for the topics we wish to develop. Indeed, most of our work will really be done in the familiar field of rationals.

Now that we have invented the field of real numbers, let us return to its application to coordinates and measurement.

Problem Set 8.6

A. 1. Let $A = .21763\ldots$ and $B = .64503\ldots$.
   a. Write the first five members of the interval sequences associated with A and B.
   b. Apply the addition process indicated in the text to the interval sequences for A and B.
   c. Using the result of **b** write the first four digits in the infinite decimal for $A + B$.
   2. Carry out the instructions of problem **A1** for the infinite decimals $A = .09643\ldots$ and $B = .43574\ldots$.
   3. a. If $A = \frac{2}{7}$, find the infinite decimal for A and write the first five

members of the associated sequence of intervals.

b. If $B = \dfrac{1}{6}$ find the infinite decimal for B and write the first five members of the associated sequence of intervals.

c. Find the first five members of the sum sequence for the intervals in **a** and **b** and from this write as many digits as this indicates in the infinite decimal for $A + B$.

d. Verify the correctness of the result in **c** by computing $A + B = \dfrac{2}{7} + \dfrac{1}{6}$ and finding the infinite decimal for $A + B$ by division.

4. Carry out the instructions of problem **A3** for the rational numbers $A = \dfrac{2}{15}$ and $B = \dfrac{3}{13}$.

B. 1. Use an argument like that of the text to show that there is no rational number which equals $\sqrt{6}$, i.e., that $\dfrac{p^2}{q^2} = 6$ is impossible if p, q are positive integers.

2. Use an argument like that of the text to show that there is no rational number which equals $\sqrt{3}$, i.e., that $\dfrac{p^2}{q^2} = 3$ is impossible if p, q are positive integers. [HINT: You may use the fact, proved in **D2**, that if p^2 is divisible by 3, then p is also divisible by 3.]

3. The real numbers which are not rational numbers are called **irrational numbers.**

   a. Show by an example that the product of two irrational numbers may be irrational. Assume the fact proved in **D3**.

   b. Show by an example that the product of two irrational numbers may be rational.

   c. Explain why the product of two rational numbers cannot be irrational.

4. The cube root of a number B, denoted by $\sqrt[3]{B}$, means a number x whose cube equals B, i.e., $x^3 = B$. Show that there is no rational number $\dfrac{p}{q}$ which equals $\sqrt[3]{2}$.

5. Explain why the method of problem **B1** cannot be applied to show there is no rational number $\dfrac{p}{q}$ which equals $\sqrt{4}$.

C. 1. Explain how you would proceed to try to define the product $A \cdot B$ of two infinite decimals A and B.

2. Apply the process in **C1** to find the first three digits in the infinite decimal for $A \cdot B$ if A and B are the two infinite decimals of problem **A1**.

D. 1. Show that if m and n are odd positive integers, then $m \cdot n$ is odd. Notice in particular that the square of an odd integer is odd. [HINT: If m and n are odd, then $m = 2 \cdot k + 1$ and $n = 2 \cdot r + 1$ for some whole numbers k, r.] Show that $m \cdot n$ is also odd, i.e., has remainder 1 if divided by 2.

2. If n is a positive integer such that n^2 is divisible by 3, show that n is divisible by 3. [HINT: Use a contradiction argument. If n is not divisible by 3, then when it is divided by 3 the remainder must be either 1 or 2. In the first case we can write $n = 3 \cdot k + 1$ and in the second $n = 3 \cdot k + 2$.] Show that in both cases n^2 has a remainder 1 and so is not divisible by 3.

3. If A and B are positive real numbers prove that $\sqrt{A} \cdot \sqrt{B} = \sqrt{A \cdot B}$. [HINT: Let $\sqrt{A} = x$, $\sqrt{B} = y$ so that $A = x^2$, $B = y^2$.] Give the proof by justifying each of the following equalities:

$$\sqrt{A \cdot B} = \sqrt{x^2 \cdot y^2} = \sqrt{x \cdot (x \cdot y) \cdot y} = \sqrt{x \cdot (y \cdot x) \cdot y}$$
$$= \sqrt{(x \cdot y) \cdot (x \cdot y)} = x \cdot y = \sqrt{A} \cdot \sqrt{B}.$$

8.7 Measurement for All Segments

In Section 8.5 we noted that every point of a number line could be associated with an infinite decimal. Since the infinite decimals have now been made into the system of real numbers this means that with every point on the number line there is associated a real number, which we may call its **coordinate.** We also observed that it seems highly plausible that every infinite decimal (i.e., every real number) does identify a point on the number line. This would say that there is a one-to-one correspondence of the points on the line with the set of real numbers. Since this does not follow from our previous axioms, we propose now to adopt an axiom stating this one-to-one correspondence and therefore using the real numbers as coordinates. However, we wish this coordinate system not only to permit us to identify points by numbers, but we want the coordinates to have a nice relationship to congruence and measurement comparable to the properties of Theorems 8.1, 8.2, 8.3, 8.4, and 8.5 which are known to hold for the case of rational measures and coordinates. We are thus led to formulate a somewhat forbidding-looking axiom as follows:

Axiom MS3 *Let* $\overline{PQ}$ *be a segment and* Z, U *points of a line* k *such that* $\overline{ZU} \cong \overline{PQ}$. *Then there is a unique one-to-one correspondence of the points of* k *with the real numbers having the following properties:*

(a) *Z has the coordinate 0 and U has the coordinate 1.*

(b) *If P_a, P_b, P_c are points of k having coordinates a, b, c, respectively, then $P_a \in \overline{P_b P_c}$ if and only if $b \leq a \leq c$ or $c \leq a \leq b$.*

(c) *If P_a, P_b, P_c, P_d are points of k with coordinates a, b, c, d, respectively, then $\overline{P_a P_b} \cong \overline{P_c P_d}$ if and only if $|a - b| = |c - d|$.*

At first sight this seems like a horrendous mouthful to swallow. On examination, however, we find that the properties stated in Axiom MS3 are ones that we already know for the case of rational coordinates. For example, consider the points P_a, P_b, P_c on k with rational coordinates a, b, c. If P_a belongs to segment $\overline{P_b P_c}$, it might be one of the endpoints, in which case $a = b$ or $a = c$. If P_a belongs to $\overline{P_b P_c}$ but is not an endpoint, then either P_a is in the positive direction from P_b and the negative direction from P_c (so that $b < a < c$), or it is in the negative direction from P_b and the positive direction from P_c (so that $c < a < b$). Thus in any case either $b \leq a \leq c$ or $c \leq a \leq b$. Conversely, if either of these conditions holds we find $P_a \in \overline{P_b P_c}$. This is precisely the statement made in part (b) of Axiom MS3.

Similarly consider statement (c) for the case of rational coordinates. By Theorem 8.5 segments $\overline{P_a P_b}$ and $\overline{P_c P_d}$ are segments having measures and $m(\overline{P_a P_b}) = |a - b|$, $m(\overline{P_c P_d}) = |c - d|$. Hence the statement $|a - b| = |c - d|$ is the same thing as the statement $m(\overline{P_a P_b}) = m(\overline{P_c P_d})$. By Theorems 8.3 and 8.4, $m(\overline{P_a P_b}) = m(\overline{P_c P_d})$ is equivalent to the statement $\overline{P_a P_b} \cong \overline{P_c P_d}$. Thus property (c) was already known for the case of rational coordinates.

From this point of view Axiom MS3 seems much less of a preposterous leap of faith. In essence, it says only that we assume that, in using real numbers for coordinates, we retain some of the useful properties we had already noticed for the rational coordinates.

Now that we have succeeded in inventing a complete number line, i.e., with coordinates for *all* points, it turns out we can use it to give measures to *all* segments. Indeed, as noted below, we essentially use the number line as a ruler.

Let $\overline{AB}$ be any segment and as usual let $\overline{PQ}$ denote the segment we select as a unit. According to Axiom MS3, coordinates can be assigned to a line k using

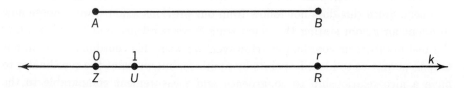

$\overline{PQ}$ as a unit segment. By Axiom CS5 there is a unique point R on the positive ray $\overrightarrow{ZU}$ of k such that $\overline{AB} \cong \overline{ZR}$. The point R has a positive real number r as a coordinate. We *define* the measure $m(\overline{AB})$ of segment $\overline{AB}$ by the equation $m(\overline{AB}) = r$. Notice that we have merely laid off a congruent copy of $\overline{AB}$ from Z on k and examined the coordinate r of the endpoint of this copy.

The procedure of the last paragraph has at last solved the problem of assigning measures to *all* segments. We no longer need to make a painful distinction between segments with measures and segments without measures. A relevant question now arises, however. If we use this enlarged definition of measure for segments, will we still have the nice relationship between congruence and measurement that gave us the results of Theorems 8.1, 8.2, 8.3, 8.4, and 8.5? Fortunately

the answer is in the affirmative. The statements of these theorems are now, however, unnecessarily awkward since *all* segments now have measures. The next
three theorems contain essentially the same information stated in more compact form.

Theorem 8.7 $\overline{AB} \cong \overline{CD}$ *if and only if* $m(\overline{AB}) = m(\overline{CD})$.
(This theorem embraces the results of Theorems 8.3 and 8.4.)

Proof. As usual, the phrase "if and only if" is a warning that there are *two*
things to prove. We must show each of the following two statements:
(a) If $\overline{AB} \cong \overline{CD}$, then $m(\overline{AB}) = m(\overline{CD})$.
(b) If $m(\overline{AB}) = m(\overline{CD})$, then $\overline{AB} \cong \overline{CD}$.

Let us consider these in turn.
(a) We are given that $\overline{AB} \cong \overline{CD}$. To find $m(\overline{AB})$ we find the point R on the
positive ray of the number line k such that $\overline{AB} \cong \overline{ZR}$. Then by definition
$m(\overline{AB}) = r$ where r is the coordinate of R. Since $\overline{CD} \cong \overline{AB}$ and $\overline{AB} \cong \overline{ZR}$ it
follows that $\overline{CD} \cong \overline{ZR}$. (What axiom is used here?) Then by definition $m(\overline{CD}) =$
r also, so $m(\overline{AB}) = m(\overline{CD})$. This proves statement (a).
(b) This time we are given $m(\overline{AB}) = m(\overline{CD})$. Let r be this common value. By
definition of measure, $\overline{AB} \cong \overline{ZR}$ where R is the point of the number line k with
coordinate r. Similarly, $\overline{CD} \cong \overline{ZR}$ so it follows that $\overline{AB} \cong \overline{CD}$. (By what axiom?)
This completes the proof of statement (b) and hence of the theorem.

Theorem 8.8 *If* P_a *and* P_b *are points whose coordinates are a and b, respectively,*
on a number line k, then $m(\overline{P_aP_b}) = |a - b|$.
(This is the equivalent of Theorem 8.5.)

Proof. To find $m(\overline{P_aP_b})$ one locates the point R with positive coordinate r on
k such that $\overline{P_aP_b} \cong \overline{ZR}$. Since Z has coordinate 0 (why?), it then follows by (c)
of MS3 that $|a - b| = |r - 0| = |r| = r$.
Since by definition $m(\overline{P_aP_b}) = r$ this proves the theorem.

Theorem 8.9 *If* $B \in \overline{AC}$, *then* $m(\overline{AC}) = m(\overline{AB}) + m(\overline{BC})$.
(This contains the content of Theorems 8.1 and 8.2.)

Proof. Let $m(\overline{AC}) = r$. If R is the point of the number line k whose coordinate
is r, then $\overline{AC} \cong \overline{ZR}$. In this congruence let T be the image of B and let t be the

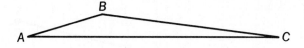

coordinate of T. Then $\overline{AB} \cong \overline{ZT}$ and $\overline{BC} \cong \overline{TR}$. (Why?) According to Theorem 8.8 it follows that $m(\overline{AB}) = |\, t - 0\,| = |\, t\,|$ and $m(\overline{BC}) = |\, r - t\,|$. Since $T \in \overline{ZR}$ we find from statement (b) of Axiom MS3 that $0 \leq t \leq r$ so that $t \geq 0$ and $r - t \geq 0$. Thus by definition of absolute value

$$m(\overline{AB}) = |\, t\,| = t,\ m(\overline{BC}) = |\, r - t\,| = r - t.$$

By substitution we therefore find

$$m(\overline{AB}) + m(\overline{BC}) = t + (r - t) = r = m(\overline{AC}).$$

This proves the theorem.

With the adoption of Axiom MS3 we have indeed achieved our goal of assigning measures to all segments and the results of Theorems 8.7, 8.8, and 8.9 show that this idea of measure does have the manipulative properties that we intuitively expect on the basis of our experiences with the simple case of integral measures.

This actually completes the theoretical aspect of our discussion of measuring segments. You will have noticed that all the results about segment measurement are contained in Theorems 8.7, 8.8, and 8.9 so that from here on there will be no occasion to refer to the earlier partial results stated in Theorems 8.1, 8.2, 8.3, 8.4, and 8.5. You will also notice that the definitions of measure and the proofs of Theorems 8.7, 8.8, and 8.9 depend only on Axiom MS3 and of course the properties of real numbers stated in Theorem 8.6.

Problem Set 8.7

A. The converse of Theorem 8.9 would be the following:

  If $m(\overline{AC}) = m(\overline{AB}) + m(\overline{BC})$, then $B \in \overline{AC}$.

Prove this converse by supplying the missing supporting statements.

On the number line k let T and R be the points with positive coordinates t and r such that $\overline{AB} \cong \overline{ZT}$ and $\overline{AC} \cong \overline{ZR}$.

ASSERTIONS	SUPPORTING STATEMENTS
(1) $m(\overline{AC}) = m(\overline{AB}) + m(\overline{BC})$.	(1) Why?
(2) $m(\overline{AB}) = t$.	(2) Why?
(3) $m(\overline{AC}) = r$.	(3) Why?
(4) $r \geqq t \geqq 0$.	(4) Why?
(5) $T \in \overline{ZR}$.	(5) Why?
(6) $|r - t| = r - t$.	(6) Why?
(7) $m(\overline{TR}) = r - t$.	(7) Why?
(8) $m(\overline{BC}) = r - t$.	(8) Why?
(9) $\overline{BC} \cong \overline{TR}$.	(9) Why?
(10) Thus $\overline{AB} \cong \overline{ZT}$, $\overline{BC} \cong \overline{TR}$, $\overline{AC} \cong \overline{ZR}$ and $T \in \overline{ZR}$. It follows that $B \in \overline{AC}$.	(10) Why?

B. Our Axiom MS2 is as follows (see Section 8.4): If $\overline{AB}$ is any segment and q any positive integer, there exist $q + 1$ points $P_0 = A$, P_1, P_2, ..., $P_q = B$ of $\overline{AB}$ such that $\overline{P_0 P_1} \cong \overline{P_1 P_2} \cong \cdots \cong \overline{P_{q-1} P_q}$ and such that each two consecutive segments have only an endpoint in common. Show that Axiom MS2 can be proved from Axiom MS3 by supplying the missing supporting statements below. Observe that because of Axiom MS3 all segments have measures.

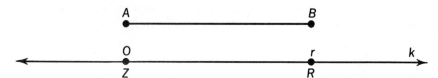

ASSERTIONS	SUPPORTING STATEMENTS
(1) Let $m(\overline{AB}) = r$. Thus, if R is the point of the number line with coordinate r, $\overline{AB} \cong \overline{ZR}$.	(1) Why?
(2) Let $S_0, S_1, S_2, \ldots, S_q$ be the points of k whose coordinates are $0, \dfrac{r}{q}, \dfrac{2r}{q}, \ldots, \dfrac{qr}{q}$. Note that $S_0 = Z$, $S_q = R$.	(2) Why?
(3) Let $P_0, P_1, P_2, \ldots, P_q$ be the points of $\overline{AB}$ which correspond to $S_0, S_1, \ldots, S_q$ in the congruence $\overline{AB} \cong \overline{ZR}$. $m(\overline{S_0 S_1}) = m(\overline{S_1 S_2}) = m(\overline{S_2 S_3}) = \cdots = m(\overline{S_{q-1} S_q})$.	(3) Why?
(4) $\overline{S_0 S_1} \cong \overline{S_1 S_2} \cong \cdots \cong \overline{S_{q-1} S_q}$.	(4) Why?
(5) $\overline{P_0 P_1} \cong \overline{S_0 S_1}$, $\overline{P_1 P_2} \cong \overline{S_1 S_2}$, ..., $\overline{P_{q-1} P_q} \cong \overline{S_{q-1} S_q}$.	(5) Why?
(6) $\overline{P_0 P_1} \cong \overline{P_1 P_2} \cong \cdots \cong \overline{P_{q-1} P_q}$.	(6) Why?

Since by their definition consecutive segments of the sequence $\overline{S_0S_1}$, $\overline{S_1S_2}$, ..., $\overline{S_{q-1}S_q}$ have only endpoints in common and since congruence is a one-to-one correspondence, this is also true of segments $\overline{P_0P_1}$, $\overline{P_1P_2}$, ..., $\overline{P_{q-1}P_q}$. Thus the points P_0, P_1, ..., P_q are the points required in Axiom MS2 and the proof is complete.

C. In the last paragraph before Problem Set 8.7 it was noted that the definition of measure and all the results on measurement—i.e., Theorems 8.7, 8.8, and 8.9—depend only on Axiom MS3 and the properties of real numbers. If this is so, it means that Axioms MS1 and MS2 and the entire discussion of Sections 8.1 through 8.6 are unnecessary except that we need to know the properties of real numbers. Why do you think the development was presented in this way?

8.8 The Practice of Measurement

" 'Yes, indeed,' says the Unicorn, . . . 'What can we measure? . . . We are experts in the theory of measurement, not its practice.' " This excerpt from J. L. Synge* describes with devastating accuracy the present state of our development. We have with almost painful care discussed the theoretical possibility of talking about the measure of a segment but have done almost nothing with considering its application. We shall now turn to this, which is, after all, the way in which measurement really becomes a part of our experience.

We return at once to a remark made in Section 8.1 that, in its application, measurement is always an approximate process. One of the reasons for this is that our theoretical considerations concerned ideal segments, whereas the practical application is made to some physical object which may be only a fair representation of a segment. For example, if you undertake to measure the edge of a desk you will find a certain amount of rounding on the corners and it is by no means clear exactly where the endpoints are. However, the problem lies much deeper than this, as we shall see.

Let us consider the problem of measuring the segment $\overline{AB}$ below. Since we have already "invented" the ruler in Section 8.3, let us apply this instrument as shown in the drawing below. We are immediately aware that the point B does

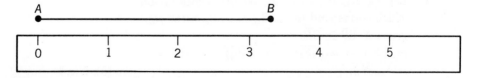

not exactly match any of the marked points on the ruler, so $m(\overline{AB})$ does not equal any of the numbers shown. We note that $m(\overline{AB})$ is between 3 and 4. Of the

* J. L. Synge, *Kandelman's Krim* (London; Jonathan Cape, 1957), p. 51.

points marked it is the one with coordinate 3 which seems closest to $m(\overline{AB})$. When, as here, we have a number which may not be equal to $m(\overline{AB})$ but is a reasonable approximation to it, we write $m(\overline{AB}) \approx 3$. The symbol $\approx$ is used to mean "is approximately equal to." In this case the number 3 is the closest integer to $m(\overline{AB})$ so $m(\overline{AB})$ is closer to 3 than to either 4 or 2. We speak of $\overline{AB}$ as having a length of approximately 3 units. Even in a case like the one shown here, where point D seems opposite one of the marked points, we are conscious

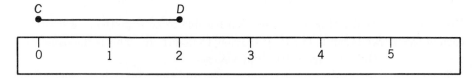

that we cannot honestly say we are sure the length of $\overline{CD}$ is exactly 2 units. The size of the dots used to mark C and D, the thickness of the lines on the ruler, and slight possible variations in laying down the ruler all make it impossible to state with certainty that $m(\overline{CD})$ is *exactly* 2, though we are certainly willing to write, as above, $m(\overline{CD}) \approx 2$.

It has undoubtedly already occurred to you that if we concede that measurement is only approximate it is desirable that the approximation should be a reasonably close one and that the more marked points we put on the ruler, the more closely we can describe the length in question. Thus, instead of using a ruler with points marked only for integral coordinates, let us use one on which are marked the points with coordinates $\dfrac{t}{2}$. Using this ruler it appears that the closest

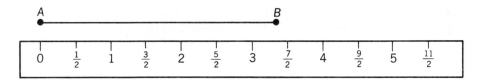

marked point of the ruler is the one with coordinate $\dfrac{7}{2}$. We therefore write $m(\overline{AB}) \approx \dfrac{7}{2}$. Notice, however, that this last approximation is actually to the nearest *half-unit*, whereas the earlier one was to the nearest whole unit. Thus

$$m(\overline{AB}) \approx 3 \text{ to the nearest unit.}$$

$$m(\overline{AB}) \approx \frac{7}{2} \text{ to the nearest half-unit.}$$

Similarly, one might use a ruler on which the quarter-unit points are marked and find

$$m(\overline{AB}) \approx \frac{7}{2} \text{ to the nearest quarter-unit,}$$

or one divided into tenths of a unit and find

$$m(\overline{AB}) \approx 3.4 \text{ to the nearest tenth unit.}$$

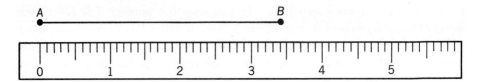

Notice that in the drawing it has not been feasible to indicate the coordinates of each of the marked points, but they are easy to determine. This is the usual procedure used on the ordinary rulers that we use.

The above procedure naturally prompts the question: What is to prevent our using finer and finer subdivisions and so writing an approximation to $m(\overline{AB})$ as close as we wish? The answer is that *in theory* nothing prevents this. Indeed this is precisely the thinking that led us to talk about the exact value of $m(\overline{AB})$. *In practice* there is the question of how fine a scale you can read. It will do no good to have a ruler marked in thousandths of a unit if you are then unable to read the scale and see which of the division points is closest to B. Thus again we find in practice that measurement is approximate.

Of course the discussion above is not intended to imply that a ruler is the ultimate in measuring instruments. Instruments exist which read to thousandths of an inch or less. However, any instrument can be correctly read only to a certain degree of precision. Trying for more with that particular device is futile.

It is clear that in recording an approximate value for a measurement it may become important for us to know how good an approximation is intended. If a length is described as approximately 3 inches, it makes a difference whether this approximation is to the nearest inch, the nearest half-inch or the nearest tenth of an inch.

To clarify this situation let us ask just what information is communicated by the statement that

$$m(\overline{AB}) \approx 3 \text{ to the nearest inch.}$$

It means that $2.5 \leqq m(\overline{AB}) \leqq 3.5$. If we imagine the ruler in position to measure $\overline{AB}$, then B may be any point in the hatched interval. The length of this interval

of uncertainty is 1 unit, which in this case is 1 inch. The length of this interval of uncertainty is often called the **precision** of the measurement. The smaller this interval the more precise the measurement is said to be. Notice that for any possible position of B in this allowed interval the difference between $m(\overline{AB})$ and 3 cannot exceed half the length of the interval, which in this case is $\frac{1}{2}$ inch. Since this difference is the error committed in recording the answer as 3 instead of $m(\overline{AB})$, we describe this by saying that the **greatest possible error** in this measurement is $\frac{1}{2}$ inch.

Similarly, if we are told that a segment $\overline{AB}$ has a length of 3 inches to the nearest half-inch, this must mean that $2\frac{3}{4} \leq m(\overline{AB}) \leq 3\frac{1}{4}$ in inches. For this case the precision—i.e., the length of the interval of uncertainty—is $\frac{1}{2}$ inch and the

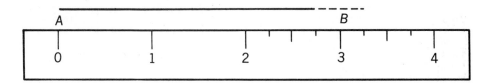

greatest possible error is $\frac{1}{4}$ inch. It is to be noted that the precision in each case is twice the greatest possible error.

There are two ways in which results of measurements are commonly recorded so that they indicate to us how closely the recorded answer is intended to approximate the true one. The first way is to indicate forthrightly the greatest possible error. Thus you may write:

The length of $\overline{AB}$ is $\left(3 \pm \frac{1}{4}\right)$ inches.

Or, if you prefer, you may write

$$m(\overline{AB}) = \left(3 \pm \frac{1}{4}\right) \text{ in inches.}$$

This is understood to mean that the true value of $m(\overline{AB})$ in inches lies between $\left(3 - \frac{1}{4}\right)$ and $\left(3 + \frac{1}{4}\right)$. Thus the greatest possible error is $\frac{1}{4}$ inch and the precision is $\frac{1}{2}$ inch. The same information could be expressed by $m(AB) \in \left[3 - \frac{1}{4}, 3 + \frac{1}{4}\right]$.

Similarly, if we write

$$m(\overline{PQ}) = (2.73 \pm .02) \text{ in meters,}$$

this means that the length of $\overline{PQ}$ is between 2.71 and 2.75 meters. The greatest possible error is .02 meter and the precision .04 meter. This way of indicating results is very common in scientific work and in many ways is the most satisfactory way of recording results. Certainly it is the most explicit.

The other common convention in recording results is as follows. If you wish to convey the idea that a measurement is, for example, to the nearest half inch you record the result in half-inches. In the case of segment $\overline{AB}$ above you would write:

$$m(\overline{AB}) \approx \frac{6}{2} \text{ in inches,}$$

or simply

the length of $\overline{AB}$ is approximately $\frac{6}{2}$ inches.

This would be interpreted to mean that $m(\overline{AB})$ is closer to $\frac{6}{2}$ than to $\frac{5}{2}$ or $\frac{7}{2}$. Thus $2\frac{3}{4} \leq m(\overline{AB}) \leq 3\frac{1}{4}$ so the precision is $\frac{1}{2}$ inch and the greatest possible error $\frac{1}{4}$ inch. If, on the other hand, one writes $m(\overline{AB}) \approx 3$ in inches this would indicate a measurement to the nearest inch so the precision would be 1 inch and the greatest possible error $\frac{1}{2}$ inch. Again, if you see the statement $m(\overline{AB}) \approx 3.0$ in inches you would understand this to mean measurement to the nearest tenth of an inch. In this case the precision would be .1 inch and the greatest possible error .05 inch. You should become familiar with both these ways of recording measurements. Not all texts use the $\approx$ sign for "approximately equal to" but we shall do so as a reminder of the approximate nature of the statements.

So far we have discussed the actual error which may occur in a given measurement, i.e., the greatest possible error. In many cases, however, it is not the error itself which is important but the error in comparison to the size of the measurement made. If you measure the length of your pencil with a greatest possible error of 1 inch, this is not at all remarkable. If you measure the length of your room with a greatest possible error of 1 inch you have done well, for to measure such a distance with an error of no more than 1 inch requires care and attention. If you claim to have measured the distance from a certain point in New York to a certain point in Washington with a greatest possible error of 1 inch probably no one will believe you because it would be so incredibly difficult. The contrast in these cases, each of which would have the same greatest possible error, leads us to introduce the idea of the *accuracy* of a measurement.

Suppose that a length has been measured as (250 ± 5) feet. The approximate measurement is 250 feet with a greatest possible error of 5 feet. The **relative error** is defined to be the ratio $\frac{5}{250}$ or .02. In general the relative error in a measurement is the ratio of the greatest possible error to the magnitude of the measurement made. Sometimes the relative error is expressed as a percent and is called the **percent of error.** In the example above this is 2%. The smaller the relative error (or percent of error) the greater is the **accuracy** of the measurement. Thus the *precision* of a measurement is concerned with the actual greatest possible error while the *accuracy* is concerned with the relative error. As an example, consider the following measurements of segments:

$$m(\overline{AB}) \approx 25.2 \text{ in feet.} \qquad m(\overline{CD}) \approx 625 \text{ in feet.}$$

g.p.e. = .05 in feet.   g.p.e. = .5 in feet.

$$\text{Rel. error} = \frac{.05}{25.2} \approx .002. \qquad \text{Rel. error} = \frac{.5}{625} = .0008.$$

Notice that here we have used the second convention in recording results. The measurement of $\overline{AB}$ is more *precise* since its greatest possible error, .05, is less than .5, the greatest possible error for $\overline{CD}$. On the other hand, the measurement of $\overline{CD}$ is much more accurate since .0008 < .002.

The notation used in the illustration above has flexibility in recording what we wish to say. The statement $m(\overline{AB}) \approx 25.2$ in feet was read as meaning measurement to the nearest tenth of a foot. If we wished to state that this figure was correct to the nearest hundredth of a foot we could have written $m(\overline{AB}) \approx 25.20$. Similarly, the statement $m(\overline{AB}) \approx 25.200$ in feet would mean we are claiming the measure is correct to the nearest thousandth of a foot. However, there occur situations where the notation becomes ambiguous. If you have been on a vacation trip you may tell a friend you drove about 2400 miles. It is highly unlikely that you mean this is correct to the nearest mile or even the nearest ten miles. Most likely you mean that this is correct to the nearest hundred miles. How do you convey this gem of information in a way that will not be ambiguous? You clearly cannot just omit the terminal zeros from the recorded result of 2400 miles or the figure is no longer correct at all. We could, of course, resort to the explicit notation showing the greatest possible error and write (2400 ± 50) miles. There is, however, another procedure which is quite common and which is worth noting. It is what is called **scientific notation** and will be described below.

Any number can be written as the product (or quotient) of a number between 1 and 10 by a certain power of 10. Thus $275 = (2.75) \cdot 10^2$, $1684 = (1.684) \cdot 10^3$, $.017 = (1.7) \cdot \frac{1}{10^2}$. We can write as many or as few terminal zeros as we wish on the first number. This device can be used to indicate the precision intended in a measurement. To write that a distance is 2400 miles to the nearest hundred miles we would write it as $(2.4) \cdot 10^3$ miles. The reader is expected to look at the first figure to see what digits are to be taken seriously. (These are sometimes called the **significant digits.**) We would then realize that the recorded distance was indeed 2400 miles but that the two zeros are mere placeholders. If, on the other hand, we wish to state that the distance is 2400 miles *to the nearest* 10 *miles*, this would be written as $(2.40) \cdot 10^3$ miles.

We shall not seek to make a major production of the scientific notation. As the name implies it is in common use in recording scientific data. In a kind of hybrid form we see this constantly; for example, a newspaper may note that a project has cost the government 2.5 billion dollars rather than $2,500,000,000.

Problem Set 8.8

A. 1. Determine the approximate measure of $\overline{XY}$ below using each of the segments $\overline{AB}, \overline{CD}, \overline{EF}$, and $\overline{GH}$ as unit segments.

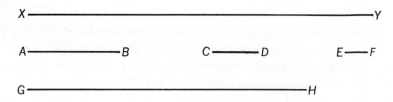

2. Using $\overline{AB}$ pictured below as a unit, find the approximate measures of the other four line segments.

A————————B

3. It is known that a length of 1 inch is approximately 2.54 centimeters.
  a. If a segment has a length of 5.2 inches, what is its length in centimeters to the nearest tenth of a centimeter?
  b. If a segment has a length of 5.2 centimeters, what is its length in inches to the nearest tenth of an inch?
  c. Find to the nearest tenth the number of inches in a segment 1 meter long. (1 meter is the same as 100 centimeters.)

B. 1. Three measurements are indicated below. In each case find the greatest possible error, the precision, and the relative error. Which of the three measurements is the most precise? Which is most accurate?
  a. $m(\overline{AB}) = (110 \pm 2)$ in feet.
  b. $m(\overline{CD}) = (1250 \pm 10)$ in feet.
  c. $m(\overline{EF}) = (1250 \pm 10)$ in inches.

2. Carry out the instructions of problem **B1** for the following three measurements.
   a. $m(\overline{HI}) \approx 12.5$ in feet.
   b. $m(\overline{JK}) \approx 5.16$ in yards.
   c. $m(\overline{LM}) \approx 41.42$ in miles.

3. Carry out the instructions of problem **B1** for the following three measurements.
   a. $m(\overline{PQ}) \approx 12.5$ in feet.
   b. $m(\overline{RS}) \approx 1.25$ in yards.
   c. $m(\overline{TU}) \approx 125$ in miles.

4. The first measurement in problem **B2** could also have been written as $(12.5 \pm .05)$ feet. Express all the other measurements in problem **B2** and problem **B3** in this form.

C. 1. The distance traveled by light in 1 second is approximately 186,000 miles. It is understood that this is to the nearest thousand miles.
   a. Express this in scientific notation.
   b. What is the greatest possible error?
   c. What is the relative error?

2. a. The following measurements are expressed in scientific notation. Express them in the usual form. $(9.3) \cdot 10^7$ miles $(2.70) \cdot 10^4$ feet

   $(3.14) \cdot 10^0$ inches $(4.23) \cdot \dfrac{1}{10^3}$ centimeters

   b. Express each of the following measurements in scientific notation.
   472,000 miles   2575 feet   .00315 meter

3. Find the greatest possible error and the relative error for each of the measurements in problem **C2a.**

D. 1. A distance is measured approximately as 12.5 feet. The relative error is .02.
   a. Find the greatest possible error and the precision.
   b. Express the answer in the form $(12.5 \pm \quad)$ feet. (Notice that it is *not* assumed here that the given measurement is correct to the nearest tenth of a foot.)

2. A segment is measured approximately as 25.3 inches with a greatest possible error of .02 inch.
   a. The true length must be between _____ and _____ inches.
   b. Find the relative error.

8.9 Lengths of Polygons

In the foregoing discussions we have considered finding the lengths of line segments or of objects which are reasonable representations of line segments. We commonly refer to the lengths of curves other than segments or physical objects representing them. What do we mean by this? In a certain naïve sense this is not hard to answer.

If we wish to consider the lengths of curves, such as those below, we may take

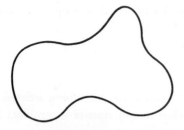 

a string or a piece of fine wire and place it carefully on the curves. If we straighten the string or wire out to a representation of a segment and measure this segment, this suggests what we mean by the length of the curves. You may find it interesting to carry out the suggested process on the two curves above.

You will recognize at once that the physical process mentioned, though highly suggestive, is no satisfactory definition of the length of a curve. A general definition for the length of a curve is a more sophisticated matter than we wish to try to discuss. There is, however, one familiar situation in which the intuitive idea mentioned above leads to a clear-cut meaning for lengths. This is the case of the polygon.

For definiteness, consider the triangle ABC. If, following our intuitive idea,

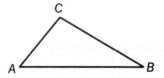

we think of a piece of wire bent into the shape of $\triangle ABC$ and then straightened out, we find that the part of the wire covering $\overline{AB}$ now covers segment $\overline{A'B'}$ of some straight line k. Similarly, the part of the wire covering $\overline{BC}$ now covers $\overline{B'C'}$ and the part covering $\overline{CA}$ covers $\overline{C'A''}$. By the length of $\triangle ABC$ we mean the length of segment $\overline{A'A''}$.

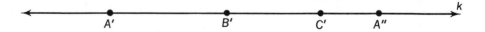

Can the process above be described without the use of the crude device of the bent wire? As you have undoubtedly realized, the answer is "yes." According to our understanding of the physical meaning of congruence it is clear that we have really intended the following three statements to hold: $\overline{AB} \cong \overline{A'B'}$, $\overline{BC} \cong \overline{B'C'}$, $\overline{CA} \cong \overline{C'A''}$. Thus, using the idea of congruence the process may be described as follows: On some convenient line k lay off in succession congruent copies of the sides of $\triangle ABC$. The length of the resulting segment $\overline{A'A''}$ is called the **length** or **perimeter** of $\triangle ABC$. Thus, the determination of the *perimeter* of a triangle (or indeed of any polygon) is reduced to that of finding the length of a certain segment, a procedure we have already discussed.

However, it quickly occurs to us that some of the procedure indicated here can be avoided. If p denotes the measure (in terms of some convenient unit) of the perimeter of $\triangle ABC$, then according to the definition of perimeter $p = m(\overline{A'A''})$. By two applications of Theorem 8.9 we find

$$p = m(\overline{A'A''}) = m(\overline{A'B'}) + m(\overline{B'A''}) = m(\overline{A'B'}) + m(\overline{B'C'}) + m(\overline{C'A''}).$$

We know that $m(\overline{A'B'}) = m(\overline{AB})$. (Why?) Similarly, $m(\overline{B'C'}) = m(\overline{BC})$ and $m(\overline{C'A''}) = m(\overline{CA})$. Thus, by substitution

$$p = m(\overline{AB}) + m(\overline{BC}) + m(\overline{CA}).$$

Since the argument extends at once to polygons with any number of sides, this establishes the following theorem.

Theorem 8.10 *The measure of the perimeter of a polygon is the sum of the measures of the sides of the polygon.*

Although the result of Theorem 8.10 seems trivial, it deserves some respect as the first step in a process which we shall see often. According to its definition, in order to find the perimeter of a polygon one would construct a certain segment ($\overline{A'A''}$ in our example) and then measure it. According to Theorem 8.10 one can instead find the measures of some *other* segments (here the sides of the polygon) and apply the arithmetic process of addition to these measures. Thus, instead of the perimeter being obtained by a direct measurement it is *computed* from certain other measures. It is this process of computing measures by applying arithmetic processes to other measures which will be used so much in the next chapter where we shall measure areas and volumes.

As soon as we start using arithmetic processes, however, added questions about approximations rear their ugly heads. By Theorem 8.10 the measure p of the perimeter of $\triangle ABC$ equals $m(\overline{AB}) + m(\overline{BC}) + m(\overline{CA})$. If, as always happens in practice, we have only approximate values for the measures of the sides, the addition process yields only an approximate value for p. Let us consider an example.

Suppose that, in terms of some convenient unit, $m(\overline{AB}) \approx 12.2$, $m(\overline{BC}) \approx 5.1$, $m(\overline{CA}) \approx 7.8$. Suppose, moreover, that each measurement is to the nearest tenth of a unit. By adding the three given approximations we find that $p \approx 25.1$. How good is this calculated approximation? According to the meaning of greatest possible error we know that

$$12.2 - .05 \leq m(\overline{AB}) \leq 12.2 + .05.$$
$$5.1 - .05 \leq m(\overline{BC}) \leq 5.1 + .05.$$
$$7.8 - .05 \leq m(\overline{CA}) \leq 7.8 + .05.$$

By adding these inequalities (why is this legitimate?) we find

$$25.1 - .15 \leq m(\overline{AB}) + m(\overline{BC}) + m(\overline{CA}) \leq 25.2 + .15,$$

or, equivalently, since $p = m(\overline{AB}) + m(\overline{BC}) + m(\overline{CA})$

$$25.1 - .15 \leq p \leq 25.1 + .15.$$

The greatest possible error in p is .15. An examination of the calculation above shows that the greatest possible error for p was actually obtained by adding the greatest possible errors for each of the three sides. That this statement holds in general for any triangle (indeed for any polygon) is given as an exercise in the problem set. Thus you will prove the following theorem.

Theorem 8.11 *If an approximation to the measure p of the perimeter of a polygon is found by adding approximate measures of the sides, the greatest possible error in p is the sum of the greatest possible errors of the different sides.*

Thus, by Theorem 8.11, when a perimeter p is computed by addition, the result is less *precise* than any of the separate measurements for the sides. It might also be of interest to see how the *accuracy* of the value for p is related to the accuracies of the measurements of the sides. Using the numerical example above we find

$$\text{Rel. error for } \overline{AB} = \frac{.05}{12.2} \approx .0041.$$

$$\text{Rel. error for } \overline{BC} = \frac{.05}{5.1} \approx .0098.$$

$$\text{Rel. error for } \overline{CA} = \frac{.05}{7.8} \approx .0064.$$

$$\text{Rel. error for } p = \frac{.15}{25.1} \approx .0060.$$

The smallest relative error for the three sides is .0041 and the largest is .0098. In this particular example the relative error for p, namely, .0060, lies between these two values. This is actually the general situation. If an approximate value is found for p by adding approximate values for the measures of the sides, the relative error for p is always between the largest and smallest relative errors for the sides. A proof of this is suggested in the problem exercises.

This completes our discussion of length for polygons, or for any set of points which is a union of a finite number of segments.

Problem Set 8.9

A. 1. Use a wire or string to find approximate lengths for the following curves.

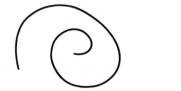 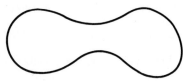

2. Find the measure p in inches of the perimeter of the polygon below by each of the two following methods.

    a. Lay off congruent copies of the sides on some line and make a single measurement of the resulting segment.

    b. Measure each of the sides and add the results. (In both cases measure to the nearest quarter-inch.)

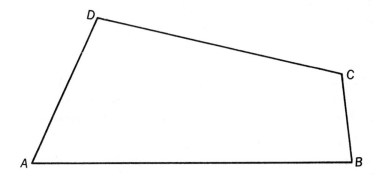

3. Carry out the procedure of problem A2b measuring the sides to the nearest half-inch. What is the greatest possible error in the calculated result in this problem? In problem A2b?

B. 1. The measures of the sides of $\triangle ABC$, in feet, are found to be

$$m(\overline{AB}) = 4.2 \pm .03.$$
$$m(\overline{BC}) = 5.8 \pm .07.$$
$$m(\overline{CA}) = 7.1 \pm .02.$$

    a. Find the greatest possible error and relative error for each of the sides.

    b. Calculate an approximate value for the measure p of the perimeter and find the greatest possible error and relative error in p.

    c. Compare the relative error in p with the relative errors for the three sides.

2. A regular polygon is one in which the sides are all congruent and the angles all congruent. The perimeter in inches of a regular octagon (8-sided polygon) is to be calculated by measuring one side and multiplying the measure by 8. What is the greatest possible error in the measurement of the side if the computed value of p is to be correct to the nearest tenth of an inch?

C. The measures of the sides of $\triangle ABC$ in some convenient unit are expressed as follows in scientific notation.

$$m(\overline{AB}) \approx (1.23) \cdot 10^3, \quad m(\overline{BC}) \approx (8.7) \cdot 10^2, \quad m(\overline{CA}) \approx (5.3) \cdot 10^2.$$

1. Find an approximate value for the measure p of the perimeter, and the greatest possible error for p.

2. Find the relative error in p.

D. 1. In $\triangle ABC$ let $m(\overline{AB}) \approx c$ with a greatest possible error of e_1, $m(\overline{BC}) \approx a$ with greatest possible error e_2, and $m(\overline{CA}) \approx b$ with greatest error e_3.

a. Complete the inequalities below.

$$\underline{\qquad} \leq m(\overline{AB}) \leq \underline{\qquad}$$
$$\underline{\qquad} \leq m(\overline{BC}) \leq \underline{\qquad}$$
$$\underline{\qquad} \leq m(\overline{CA}) \leq \underline{\qquad}$$

b. By addition obtain an inequality of the form

$$\underline{\qquad} \leq p \leq \underline{\qquad}$$

c. According to step **b** what is the greatest possible error in p? Observe that this proves Theorem 8.11 for the case of a triangle.

2. What changes must be made in problem **D1** to make it a proof of the general case of Theorem 8.11?

E. 1. Approximate measures for the sides of $\triangle ABC$ are determined as follows:

$$m(\overline{AB}) \approx 6.2 \text{ with a } \textit{relative} \text{ error of .01.}$$
$$m(\overline{BC}) \approx 10.4 \text{ with a } \textit{relative} \text{ error of .02.}$$
$$m(\overline{CA}) \approx 9.5 \text{ with a } \textit{relative} \text{ error of .03.}$$

a. Find the greatest possible error for each of these measures.

b. If p is computed from these measures find the greatest possible error and the relative error. How does the relative error for p compare with the relative errors for the sides?

2. Outlined below is a proof that, for a triangle, if an approximate value of p is found by adding approximate measures of the sides, then the relative error for p lies between the largest and smallest relative errors for the sides. Note that the steps are the same as those done numerically in problem **E1** above. The proof for any polygon is essentially the same but more messy to write. Complete the proof by supplying supporting statements.

$$\text{Let } m(\overline{AB}) \approx c \text{ with relative error } r_1.$$
$$m(\overline{BC}) \approx a \text{ with relative error } r_2.$$
$$m(\overline{CA}) \approx b \text{ with relative error } r_3.$$

To be specific, suppose r_1 is the smallest relative error, and r_3 the largest, so that $r_1 \leqq r_2 \leqq r_3$. We hope to show the relative error for p is between r_1 and r_3.

(a) Greatest possible error in $m(\overline{AB})$ is cr_1.   (Why?)

(b) $c - cr_1 \leqq m(\overline{AB}) \leqq c + cr_1$.   (Why?)

Similarly

$$a - ar_2 \leqq m(\overline{BC}) \leqq a + ar_2,$$
$$b - br_3 \leqq m(\overline{CA}) \leqq b + br_3.$$

(c) $(a + b + c) - (cr_1 + ar_2 + br_3) \leqq p \leqq (a + b + c) + (cr_1 + ar_2 + br_3)$.   (Why?)

From (c) the approximate value of p is $a + b + c$ and the greatest possible error in p is $cr_1 + ar_2 + br_3$. Thus the relative error in p is $\dfrac{cr_1 + ar_2 + br_3}{a + b + c}$.

(d) But $(a + b + c) r_1 \leqq cr_1 + ar_2 + br_3 \leqq (a + b + c) r_3$.   (Why?)

(e) $r_1 \leqq \dfrac{cr_1 + ar_2 + br_3}{a + b + c} \leqq r_3$.   (Why?)

By (e) the relative error in p is between r_1 and r_3 as we were trying to prove.

8.10 Measuring Circles

As was noted earlier, the general question of length for curves is beyond the scope of this text.

One curve, however, other than the polygons, is of such common occurrence that we must consider its length even if the discussion is somewhat intuitive. This is the circle. A circle is formally defined as the set of all points in a plane at a distance of r units from a point O (of the plane) called the **center** of the circle.

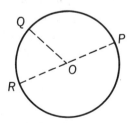

If P is any point of the circle and O its center, the segment $\overline{OP}$ is called a **radius.** Since the measure of each radius is r, any two radii are congruent. (What theorem shows this?) Thus, $\overline{OP} \cong \overline{OQ}$. A segment like $\overline{PR}$, whose endpoints are on the circle and which contains the center O, is called a **diameter.** All diameters are congruent (why?), and hence have the same measure d. Indeed $d = 2r$. (Why?)

As you may have guessed, the usual way to try to define length for a circle is to approximate the circle by polygons. One might consider such a polygon as in diagram (a). This particular polygon has six sides and looks like a reasonable approximation to the circle. Hence we might reason that the length of the polygon should be a reasonable approximation to what we would like to call the **length** (or **circumference**) of the circle. In diagram (b) the same circle is shown with an approximating polygon of twelve sides. This seems to fit the circle

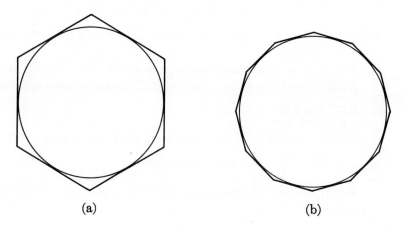

(a)   (b)

even better, so we might imagine that its perimeter would be a still better approximation to what we would like to call the circumference of the circle.

Without attempting to go through all the details, let it be said that this approach by using polygons of more and more sides is a successful one. It can be shown that there is a real number c which we may call the measure of the circumference of the circle. Moreover, c is approximated more and more closely by the measures p of polygons as the number of sides becomes larger and larger.

Now that we have agreed that a circle has a length, how do we find it? In the later chapter on similarity this can be treated more satisfactorily. For the moment let us be wholly naïve and intuitive. Consider the three circles opposite. In each case measure the diameter with a ruler. Take a piece of string or fine wire and use this to find as good approximations as you can to the measure of the circumference. Try to measure to the nearest quarter-inch. Verify the approximate correctness of the entries in the table below and complete the blanks.

	Measure of diameter	Measure of circumference	Ratio of circumference to diameter
Circle 1	$\frac{4}{4}$	$\frac{12}{4}$	3
Circle 2	$\frac{7}{4}$	$\frac{22}{4}$	
Circle 3			

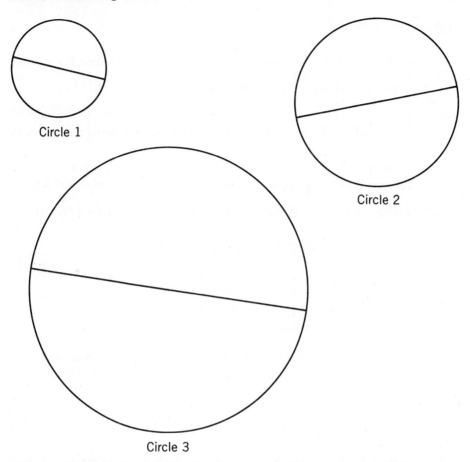

Circle 1

Circle 2

Circle 3

What conjecture seems suggested by the data in the third column? Test this conjecture by carrying out similar measurements on three other circular objects.

Does this data make it seem plausible that the ratio of the measures of the circumference to the diameter of a circle is always the same? This is in fact a correct theorem and we shall assume its validity. It means that for any circle the ratio $\frac{c}{d}$ is some fixed number. It has become traditional to represent this number by the Greek letter π, so we write $\frac{c}{d} = \pi$ or $c = \pi d$. Since $d = 2r$ this relationship may also be expressed by the equation $c = 2\pi r$.

According to our experimental calculations it appears that π is slightly more than 3. This is correct. This number π is interesting in that it can be proved to be another example of a member of the system of real numbers which is *not* rational. It can, of course, be approximated by rational numbers to any desired degree of precision. Thus to two decimal places $\pi \approx 3.14$ and to five decimal places $\pi \approx 3.14159$. Perhaps the most commonly used approximation is the one to four decimal places, $\pi \approx 3.1416$. You may be interested to know that the value of π has been computed to 100,000 decimal places. Such precision has no bearing on any practical measurement problem.

Problem Set 8.10

A. The rational number $\dfrac{22}{7}$ is sometimes used as an approximation for π. Show that this approximation is actually too large.

B. 1. If, for a circle, $r = 4.1$ in feet find the measure c in feet of the circumference. [HINT: Use $\pi \approx 3.14$ and express the result to the nearest tenth of a foot.]

2. If, for a circle, $c = 4.1$ in feet, find the measure r of a radius. [HINT: Use $\pi \approx 3.14$ and express the result to the nearest hundredth of a foot.]

C. A running track is a quarter-mile long. It is in the shape shown, with straight

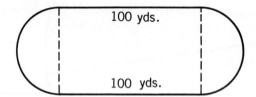

sides 100 yards long and semicircular ends. Find to the nearest tenth of a yard the length of a radius of the circular ends. [HINT: A mile is 1760 yards.]

8.11 A Few Odds and Ends

Keeping track of the greatest possible error in a calculation with approximate data quickly becomes laborious. This will be even more so as we start using other operations than addition and subtraction in the next chapter. It is for this reason that you have very likely, somewhere in your academic career, been taught some such rule as the following:

"Rule of Thumb": In a computation involving addition or subtraction of approximate data, round off the answer to the smallest number of decimal places in any of the figures.

This rule is not a sacrosanct dictum from on high. In fact it is not necessarily correct, but is admittedly easy to apply. To see the point of it consider an example. Suppose that, for a triangle ABC, the approximate measures of the sides are as follows:

$$m(\overline{AB}) \approx 31.6, \; m(\overline{BC}) \approx 25.47, \; m(\overline{CA}) \approx 10.7.$$

This yields at once $p \approx 67.77$. According to the rule of thumb, since two of the figures were given to only one decimal place, we would record the answer to the nearest tenth of a unit and write $p \approx 67.8$.

A person reading the result $p \approx 67.8$ will normally understand this to mean a greatest possible error of .05. We know, of course, that this is not necessarily correct. By Theorem 8.11 the correct greatest possible error is .105. Still, among a set of approximate figures it is highly probable that some are too large and some too small so that the errors may tend to balance each other. Thus, while the error *may* be as large as .105 there is a reasonable chance that it is as small as .05. Hence, although $p \approx 67.8$ is not *necessarily* correct to the nearest tenth, it has a reasonable possibility of being so. It is thus not unreasonable as a listed answer.

On the other hand, if we write $p \approx 67.77$ this would suggest to the reader a greatest possible error of .005. This is almost certainly wrong. Thus the effect of the rule of thumb is to prevent us from being ridiculous by claiming a highly unrealistic precision. If, as is often the case, we are willing to settle for a reasonable probability of correctness, we may find the application of this rule of thumb a great simplification over accurately calculating the greatest possible error at each stage.

In this chapter it has been repeatedly emphasized that any segment may be used as a unit of length. Clearly, however, it becomes useful as a means of communication when a group of people adopt the same units or at least units with known relationships.

Historically, many semistandard units were used. Many of these were associated with parts of the body. In England they were commonly associated specifically with the King's body. Thus, for example, the cubit was distance from the elbow to the tip of the fingers and the foot was the length of a man's foot. Because these vary greatly from person to person, even when the persons are Kings, this was unsatisfactory, and ultimately these terms were standardized to indicate mutually accepted lengths.

Today, in our technological era, it is essential that standard units for linear measure be carefully defined. When the meter was originally adopted it was intended to be one ten-millionth of the distance from the North Pole to the Equator. In point of operational fact it was the distance between two marks on a platinum bar kept under controlled physical conditions to insure minimal change. More recently the meter was redefined to be 1,650,763.73 times the wavelength of orange light emitted by krypton-86. This has the virtue that it can be reconstructed at will in a suitably equipped laboratory. Other standard units of linear measure, such as inch, foot, mile, kilometer, etc., are defined in terms of the meter.

Periodically we hear rumblings concerning the desirability of making the transfer from our common system of inch, foot, mile, etc., to the metric system. The metric system is operationally much simpler, being nicely related to the number ten on which we base our usual system of numeration. It is indeed in many ways a consummation devoutly to be wished, but likewise presents horrendous problems, particularly in the revamping of much technological equipment, to say nothing of revamping our familiar ways of thinking.

8.12 Axioms and Theorems in Chapter 8

Axiom MS1 If $\overline{AB}$ and $\overline{PQ}$ are any segments, there exists on $\overrightarrow{AB}$ a sequence of $n + 1$ points $P_0 = A, P_1, P_2, \ldots, P_n$ such that $\overline{PQ} \cong \overline{P_0P_1} \cong \overline{P_1P_2} \cong \cdots \cong \overline{P_{n-1}P_n}$ where each two consecutive segments on $\overrightarrow{AB}$ have only an endpoint in common and such that $\overline{AB} \subset \overline{P_0P_n} = \bigcup_{i=1}^{i=n} \overline{P_{i-1}P_i}$.

Axiom MS2 If $\overline{AB}$ is any segment and q any positive integer, there exist $q + 1$ points $P_0 = A, P_1, P_2, \ldots, P_q = B$ of $\overline{AB}$ such that $\overline{P_0P_1} \cong \overline{P_1P_2} \cong \cdots \cong \overline{P_{q-1}P_q}$ and such that each two consecutive segments have only an endpoint in common.

Axiom MS3 Let $\overline{PQ}$ be a segment and Z, U points of a line k such that $\overline{ZU} \cong \overline{PQ}$. There is a unique one-to-one correspondence of the points of k with the real numbers having the following properties:

(a) Z has coordinate 0 and U has coordinate 1.

(b) If P_a, P_b, P_c are points of k having coordinates a, b, and c, respectively, then $P_a \in \overline{P_bP_c}$ if and only if $b \leq a \leq c$ or $c \leq a \leq b$.

(c) If P_a, P_b, P_c, P_d are points of k with coordinates a, b, c, and d, respectively, then $\overline{P_aP_b} \cong \overline{P_cP_d}$ if and only if $|a - b| = |c - d|$.

Theorem 8.1 If $B \in \overline{AC}$ and if $\overline{AB}$ and $\overline{BC}$ are segments having measures, then $\overline{AC}$ has a measure and $m(\overline{AC}) = m(\overline{AB}) + m(\overline{BC})$.

Theorem 8.2 If $B \in \overline{AC}$ and if $\overline{AC}$ and $\overline{AB}$ are segments having measures, then $\overline{BC}$ has a measure and $m(\overline{BC}) = m(\overline{AC}) - m(\overline{AB})$.

Theorem 8.3 If $\overline{AB}$ has a measure and if $\overline{AB} \cong \overline{CD}$, then $\overline{CD}$ has a measure and $m(\overline{AB}) = m(\overline{CD})$.

Theorem 8.4 If $\overline{AB}$ and $\overline{CD}$ are segments having measures and if $m(\overline{AB}) = m(\overline{CD})$, then $\overline{AB} \cong \overline{CD}$.

Theorem 8.5 If A and B are points having coordinates a and b, respectively, then $\overline{AB}$ has a measure and $m(\overline{AB}) = |a - b|$.

Theorem 8.6

(a) The real numbers form a field.

(b) The real numbers contain the rationals as a subfield.

(c) The real numbers have an order relation $>$ having the same properties as for the rationals.

(d) For every sequence of closed intervals $[a_1, b_1] \supset [a_2, b_2] \supset [a_3, b_3] \supset \cdots$ there is at least one real number belonging to all the intervals.

(e) For every real number B with $B \geq 0$ there is a unique real number x with $x \geq 0$ such that $x^2 = B$. This number x is denoted by $\sqrt{B}$.

Theorem 8.7 $\overline{AB} \cong \overline{CD}$ if and only if $m(\overline{AB}) = m(\overline{CD})$.

Theorem 8.8 If P_a and P_b are points whose coordinates are a and b, respectively, on a number line k, then $m(\overline{P_aP_b}) = |a - b|$.

Theorem **8.9** If $B \in \overline{AC}$, then $m(\overline{AC}) = m(\overline{AB}) + m(\overline{BC})$.

Theorem **8.10** The measure of the perimeter of a polygon equals the sum of the measures of its sides.

Theorem **8.11** If an approximation to the measure p of the perimeter of a polygon is found by adding approximate measures for its sides, the greatest possible error in p is the sum of the greatest possible errors in the sides.

8.13 Terminal Tasks for Chapter 8

1. To demonstrate experimentally the intuitive meaning of linear measurement as a number of congruent copies of an arbitrary unit necessary for covering a given line segment.
2. To differentiate between the measure of a line segment and its length by identifying the measure of the segment as a number, and the length of the segment as the measure and the unit used to find the measure.
3. To recognize and demonstrate experimentally that the measure of a line segment will vary with the unit selected.
4. To make a number line by associating certain points on the line with coordinates which are rational numbers.
5. To determine the measure of a segment on the number line when the coordinates of the endpoints of the segment are given.
6. To recognize and illustrate that there are points on the number line which are not associated with rational coordinates.
7. To demonstrate geometrically the relation between a rational number and its decimal expansion by setting up the successively decreasing decimal intervals bounding the rational number and associating the endpoints of these intervals with points on a number line.
8. To justify the consideration of the system of real numbers which will provide coordinates to establish a one-to-one correspondence with the points on a line and thus make possible finding the measure of all line segments.
9. To be able to state the ordered field properties for the system of real numbers.
10. To demonstrate experimentally why the technique we use for measuring a line segment results, of necessity, in an approximation to the measure.
11. To write a measure of a line segment, in mathematical symbols, so that the approximate nature of the measure and the greatest possible error are evident.
12. To calculate the greatest possible error and the relative error of a given measurement.
13. To illustrate the difference between the significance of comparing the precision and comparing the accuracy of the measurements of any set of line segments.

14. To demonstrate the effect on the greatest possible error and the relative error when approximate linear measures are added.

15. To perform the necessary calculations to find the perimeter of a polygon and the circumference of a circle, employing the "rule of thumb" in stating the answer.

REVIEW EXERCISES

A. 1. Consider the segments of a number line whose endpoints have coordinates as shown below. Find all cases of congruent segments.

(a) $^-2$ and 5

(b) $\dfrac{7}{2}$ and $\dfrac{5}{3}$

(c) $\dfrac{^-1}{6}$ and $^-2$

(d) $\dfrac{^-3}{2}$ and $\dfrac{11}{2}$

(e) 6 and 3

2. Points C and D of a number line have coordinates $^-4$ and 1, respectively, and R has coordinate 3. Find coordinates for all possible positions of S on the line if $\overline{RS} \cong \overline{CD}$.

B. 1. a. Find the repeating decimal for $\dfrac{12}{37}$.

b. Find the rational number represented by the repeating decimal $.1\overline{63}$.

2. What pattern do you seem to observe in the following infinite decimal: $.10110011100011110000. . . ?$

If the decimal continues according to this pattern, is the real number it represents rational or irrational?

3. Consider the following infinite decimals representing real numbers A, B between 0 and 1:

$$A = .a_1\, a_2\, a_3. . . , \qquad B = .b_1\, b_2\, b_3. . . .$$

State in words how to tell from the decimals which is the larger number.

4. If B is a positive real number, prove that $\sqrt{\dfrac{1}{B}} = \dfrac{1}{\sqrt{B}}$. [HINT: This states that $\sqrt{B}$ and $\sqrt{\dfrac{1}{B}}$ are multiplicative inverses. What does this mean? Note problem **D3** of Problem Set 8.6.]

C. 1. The measures of the sides of $\triangle ABC$ in inches are

$$m(\overline{AB}) = (8 \pm .2), \quad m(\overline{BC}) = (10 \pm .4), \quad m(\overline{AC}) = (12 \pm .5).$$

a. What is the approximate measure p of the perimeter in inches?

    b. What is the greatest possible error of p in inches?

    c. What is the relative error of the perimeter?

2. Which of the following measurements is most precise? Which is most accurate?

    (a) $m(\overline{AB}) \approx 12.5$ in feet.

    (b) $m(\overline{CD}) \approx 6.5$ in inches.

    (c) $m(\overline{EF}) \approx 12.5$ in miles.

3. A flower garden is square. One side is measured as **7** feet to the nearest foot. What is the smallest amount of fence which must be purchased if one is to be *sure* that he has enough to go around the flower garden?

D. 1. If $P \in \overline{AB}$ and if $m(\overline{AB})$ is rational which of the following cases can occur: (a) $m(\overline{AP})$ and $m(\overline{PB})$ are both rational; (b) $m(\overline{AP})$ and $m(\overline{PB})$ are both irrational; (c) $m(\overline{AP})$ is rational and $m(\overline{PB})$ irrational. Explain any cases you claim impossible.

2. A famous theorem in geometry (to be proved in the next chapter) states that for a right triangle the square of the measure of the hypotenuse equals the sum of the squares of the measures of the perpendicular sides. If the two perpendicular sides each have measure 1, what is the measure of the hypotenuse? What problem would arise if we have only rational numbers as measures?

E. On each side of a square, 20 feet on a side, is constructed a semicircle as shown. What is the total length of the circular arcs?

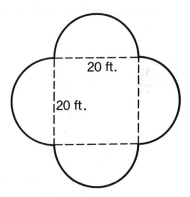

F. 1. Two of your pupils measure the chalk rail in your classroom in handspans. One finds it to be 33 handspans and the other 41 handspans. When they cannot agree they appeal to you. What did you find in this chapter relevant to this question?

2. One of your pupils measures segments $\overline{AB}$, $\overline{BC}$ and $\overline{AC}$ where $B \in \overline{AC}$. He finds that, in inches, $m(\overline{AB}) \approx 4$ and $m(\overline{BC}) \approx 6$, both to the nearest inch. He is surprised to find that $m(\overline{AC}) \approx 11$ to the nearest inch. What did you find in this chapter to help explain this phenomenon?

3. One of your pupils claims that if you take two points right next to each other there will not be room for another point between them. What did you find in this chapter that would help in answering this question?

9 Angle, Area, and Volume

9.1 Measuring Angles

Having examined with considerable detail the topic of linear measure, we can now develop the comparable ideas for measuring angle, area, and volume in much more compact fashion. However, we shall wish always to keep clearly in mind the intuitive motivation for the assumptions to be made.

Let $\angle ABC$ and $\angle XYZ$ be two angles as shown. Let $\overrightarrow{BM_1}$ be the ray on the C

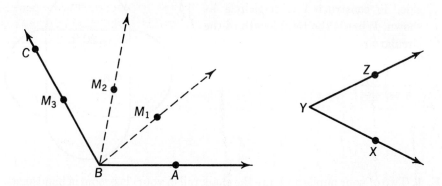

side of $\overleftrightarrow{AB}$ such that $\angle ABM_1 \cong \angle XYZ$. If $\angle XYZ$ is smaller than $\angle ABC$ (note the discussion in Section 5.7), then $\overrightarrow{BM_1}$ will be interior to $\angle ABC$ as shown. In this case we can find $\overrightarrow{BM_2}$ on the C side of $\overleftrightarrow{BM_1}$ such that $\angle M_1BM_2 \cong \angle XYZ$. Continuing this process we find $\overrightarrow{BM_3}$ such that $\angle M_2BM_3 \cong \angle XYZ$. In the illustration, $\overrightarrow{BM_3} = \overrightarrow{BC}$. That is, it takes exactly three congruent copies of $\angle XYZ$ and its interior to cover $\angle ABC$ and its interior. We describe this by saying that the measure of $\angle ABC$, using $\angle XYZ$ as a unit, is 3, or symbolically $m(\angle ABC) = 3$. Notice that this is completely analogous to the situation with segments in which the measure was defined as the number of congruent copies of the unit segment necessary for covering.

As in the case of segments this has the disadvantage that only a limited class of angles are measurable, since in general, as shown in this sketch, none of the

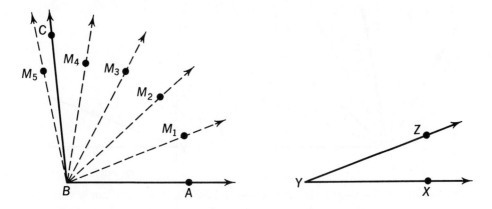

rays $\overrightarrow{BM_i}$ will coincide with $\overrightarrow{BC}$. We can only describe $\angle ABC$ as being between 4 and 5 units but we have not assigned a numerical measure to it.

However, for angles which do have measures with respect to some given unit angle, there are several easy consequences which we will state and illustrate but whose formal proofs will be omitted.

(1) If $\angle ABC$ is measurable and if $\angle ABC \cong \angle PQR$, then $\angle PQR$ is measurable and $m(\angle ABC) = m(\angle PQR)$.

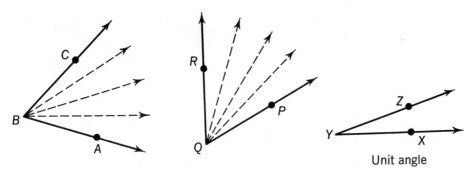

Unit angle

The drawing shows the case when both measures are 4. The same diagram can be considered as illustrating the following converse statement.

(2) If $m(\angle ABC) = m(\angle PQR)$, then $\angle ABC \cong \angle PQR$.

(The formal proof of statement (2) could be given by making continued application's of Theorem 5.22.) Statements (1) and (2) together say that, as far as measurable angles are concerned, the statements $\angle ABC \cong \angle PQR$ and $m(\angle ABC) = m(\angle PQR)$ are equivalent to each other.

(3) If C is interior to $\angle AOB$ and if any two of the angles $\angle AOB$, $\angle AOC$, $\angle COB$ are measurable, then the third is measurable and

$$m(\angle AOB) = m(\angle AOC) + m(\angle COB).$$

The drawing illustrates the case when $m(\angle AOC) = 4$, $m(\angle COB) = 2$, $m(\angle AOB) = 6$.

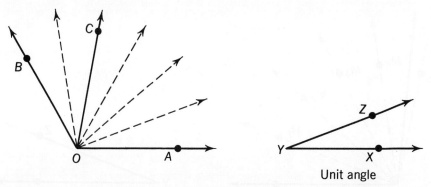

Unit angle

So far in our discussion the unit angle $\angle XYZ$ has been any angle whatever. Suppose, however, that we choose a unit angle such that some integral number n of nonoverlapping congruent copies of the unit angle and its interior just cover a half plane and its bounding line. The next drawing shows the case $n = 8$. The word *nonoverlapping* used here means that the interiors have no point in common.

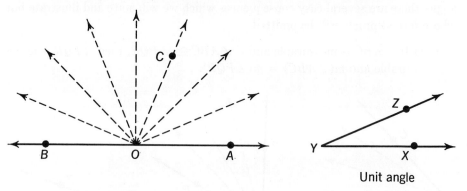

Unit angle

As you are undoubtedly aware, the unit most commonly used in elementary work is the one for which $n = 180$. It is called the **degree.**

(4) If n nonoverlapping congruent copies of the unit angle and its interior cover a half plane and its bounding line, and if $\angle AOC$ is measurable, then its supplement $\angle COB$ is also measurable and

$$m(\angle AOC) + m(\angle COB) = n.$$

For if, as shown just above, it takes three copies of the unit angle and its interior to cover $\angle AOC$ and its interior, then the other five copies will just cover the supplementary angle $\angle COB$ and its interior.

The above diagram with the rays obtained by successively laying off congruent copies of the unit angle reminds us of the corresponding process with segments which led us to invent the number line. With this hint, let us try to associate numbers with these rays as coordinates. The result would be as follows:

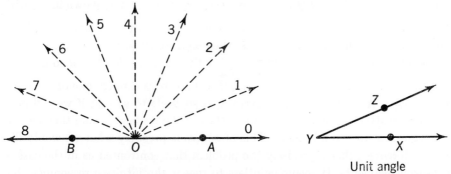

Unit angle

A slight variant of the above figure is obtained by drawing a semicircle with center O. Each ray through O in the given half plane is determined as soon as we know the point where it meets the semicircle. Thus the numbers above can be associated with these points as indicated below. We have in effect a circular scale with coordinates assigned to certain points on the circle.

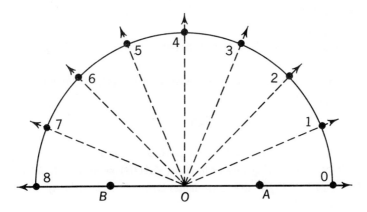

As you are undoubtedly aware, we have essentially been engaged here in inventing the familiar instrument known as the **protractor** except that the scale here is based on a unit angle different from the familiar degree. If we make a model of the essential features of the diagram above, we have an instrument as shown in (a) adapted to the measurement of angles. For example, to use the

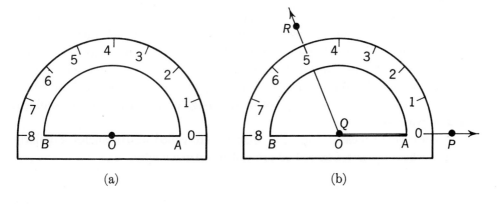

(a)   (b)

protractor to measure $\angle PQR$ it is only necessary to place it as shown in (b) with O at vertex Q and A on $\overrightarrow{QP}$. If, as shown here, the ray $\overrightarrow{QR}$ then passes through the point of the scale having coordinate 5, then $m(\angle PQR) = 5$.

The instrument reminds us again forcibly that most angles do not so far have measures since usually the second ray $\overrightarrow{QR}$ will not pass through one of the numbered points. At the same time, however, it suggests to us that if we did have coordinates attached to all the points of the circular scale we would then be able to assign measures to all angles. This of course is precisely what we would like to do. Moreover, this is precisely the problem that confronted us in the case of measuring segments. It seems pointless to repeat the intuitive reasonings that led us to formulate an axiom that in the real number system appropriate measures would be available. We will therefore formulate at once an axiom for angle measurement which will say essentially that it is possible to assign real measures to all angles and that this can be done in such a way that the geometric properties embodied in statements (1) through (4) will still be true. Specifically, we adopt the following:

Axiom MA *To every angle $\angle AOB$ there can be assigned a real number $m(\angle AOB)$ called its degree measure in such a way that*

(a) *The set of real numbers which are measures of angles is the set of numbers between 0 and 180; i.e.,*

$$\{x \mid 0 < x < 180, x \text{ a real number}\}.$$

(b) *If C is interior to $\angle AOB$, then $m(\angle AOB) = m(\angle AOC) + m(\angle COB)$.*
(c) *$\angle AOB \cong \angle A'O'B'$ if and only if $m(\angle AOB) = m(\angle A'O'B')$.*
(d) *$\angle ABC$ and $\angle PQR$ are supplementary if and only if $m(\angle ABC) + m(\angle PQR) = 180$.*

Part (c) of this axiom embraces the content of the earlier statements (1) and (2). Part (b) affirms statement (3) and part (d) contains statement (4) except that it is for the case $n = 180$. This is what restricts us to the familiar unit of the degree. Finally, part (a) assures us that all real numbers between 0 and 180 are actually measures of angles.

The axiom actually assures us that there is a one-to-one correspondence between the real numbers $0 \leq x \leq 180$ and the points of the protractor scale. The protractor for the degree scale would appear as shown by figure (c). Note that there are different styles of protractors. Frequently the center point O is on the lower edge. It appears clear at once that the right angles are those whose measures are 90. The formal proof of this is given as an exercise in problem **D2** on page 349.

Angles whose measures are less than 90 are called **acute** angles. Similarly angles whose measures exceed 90 are called **obtuse** angles.

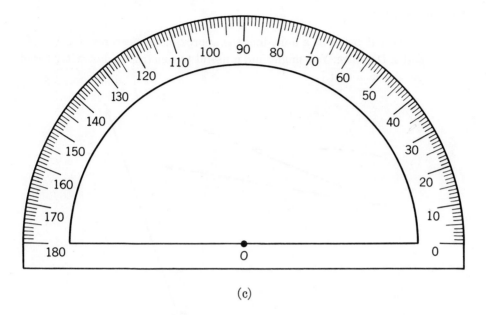

(c)

All the discussion of the last chapter concerning approximate measurement is equally appropriate here. While Axiom MA assures us of the existence of an exact measure for an angle, we have no means of determining the measure exactly. In practice we read the measure to the nearest unit, or half-unit, or whatever division on the scale we can read. As in the case of linear measurement, we use the symbol $\approx$ for "approximately equal to." If we are using a protractor based on $\angle XYZ$ as a unit, the situation in the drawing below would be described

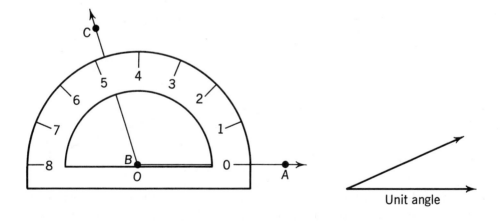

Unit angle

by $m(\angle ABC) \approx 5$. As for linear measure, we may speak of the greatest possible error and relative error in the measurement of angles.

Problem Set 9.1

    A. 1. Using $\angle A$ below as a unit, find the approximate measures of $\angle B$, $\angle C$, and $\angle D$. [HINT: You might find it useful to construct a protractor based on $\angle A$ as a unit.]

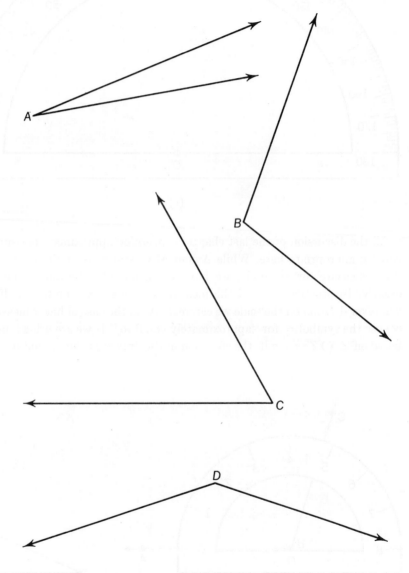

    2. a. Using an ordinary degree protractor find to the nearest degree the measure of each of the angles of $\triangle ABC$, $\triangle FGH$, and $\triangle PQR$ shown at the top of the next page.

      b. Find the sum of the approximate degree measures of each of the triangles. What is the greatest possible error and the relative error for each of these computed sums?

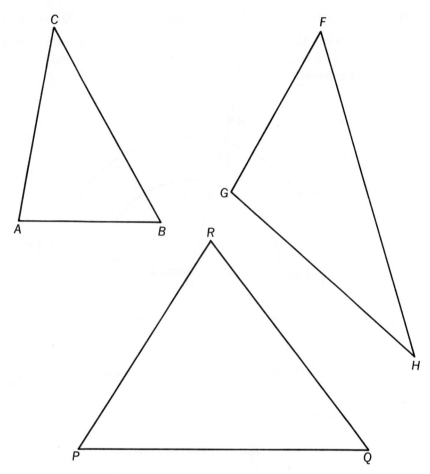

c. On the basis of your results in **b** what seems a reasonable conjecture concerning the sum of the degree measures of the angles of a triangle? Does your work here prove this conjecture? Why?

3. $\triangle ABC$ shown below is intended to be isosceles. Verify this by showing that two sides have approximately equal measures. According to Theorem 5.16, this should mean that a certain pair of angles are congruent. Verify this by showing that two angles have approximately equal measures.

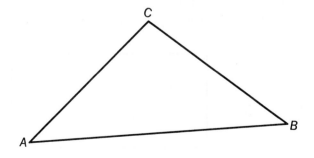

B. 1. A protractor based on the degree unit is placed on $\angle PQR$ as shown with $\overrightarrow{QP}$ passing through the point with coordinate 12 and $\overrightarrow{QR}$ through the point with coordinate 105. What is $m(\angle PQR)$? On what is your conclusion based?

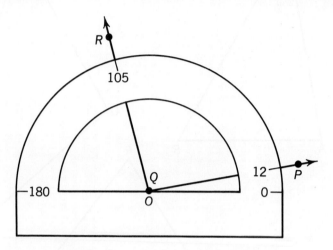

2. If in problem **B1**, $\overrightarrow{QP}$ passes through the point with coordinate p and $\overrightarrow{QR}$ through the point with coordinate r, find $m(\angle PQR)$. Justify your conclusion.

C. 1. Measure the sides and the angles of the figure.

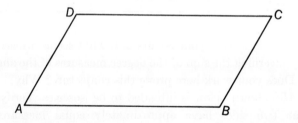

    a. Based on the measurements, what congruences do you seem to observe?

    b. What relation seems to hold between $\angle A$ and $\angle D$?

2. Measure the sides and angles of the following figure. On the basis of these results what congruences do you seem to observe?

D. 1. If C is interior to $\angle AOB$ prove that $m(\angle AOC) < m(\angle AOB)$.

2. Using Axiom MA and the definition of right angle, prove that $\angle ABC$ is a right angle if and only if its degree measure is 90.

3. Let B, C be on the same side of $\overleftrightarrow{OA}$. If $m(\angle AOC) < m(\angle AOB)$, prove that C is interior to $\angle AOB$. [HINT: Consider the three possible positions of C, i.e., C on $\overrightarrow{OB}$, C outside $\angle AOB$, and C inside $\angle AOB$, and show that the first two cases cannot occur. Note that if C is outside $\angle AOB$, then B is inside $\angle AOC$.]

E. Find the measures of the angles of the following quadrilateral to the nearest degree. Find the sum of these four measures. What is the greatest possible error in this computed sum?

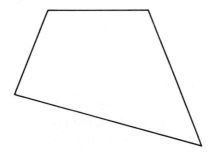

9.2 More about Parallels

Let k_1 and k_2 be lines in a plane met by a transversal k. The eight angles

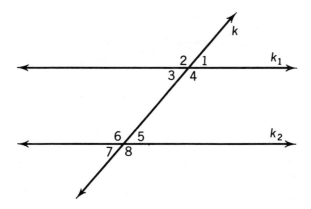

formed have been identified in the above drawing by small numerals written in their interiors. According to Theorem 5.20, if two alternate interior angles are congruent (e.g., $\angle 3 \cong \angle 5$), then $k_1 \parallel k_2$; that is, $k_1 \cap k_2 = \emptyset$. Because of Axiom MA(c) this can be rephrased to say that if $m(\angle 3) = m(\angle 5)$, then

$k_1 \| k_2$. Since $m(\angle 3) + m(\angle 4) = 180$ (why?), the condition $m(\angle 3) = m(\angle 5)$ is equivalent to $m(\angle 4) + m(\angle 5) = 180$. Does the statement $m(\angle 1) = m(\angle 5)$ also imply $k_1 \| k_2$? (Why?)

It was noted in Chapter 5 that, according to Theorem 5.20, if A is a point not on a line k there is a line k' containing A parallel to k, for if A and k are given as in the sketch below it is only necessary to draw k' so that two alternate interior

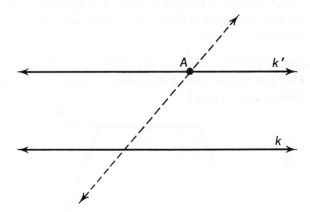

angles have equal measures, i.e., are congruent.

A question *not* answered in Chapter 5, however, is whether the line k' described here is the *only* line through A parallel to k. Let us examine this question intuitively for a moment. Although the definition of parallels makes no mention of distance or congruence, you almost certainly imagine parallel lines having the property that they are a constant distance apart, for example, two edges of this page. Now if parallel lines are to have this property, there certainly could not be two different parallels to k through A. For if, in the drawing below, $\overline{QS}$ and $\overline{RS}$ have the same length as $\overline{AT}$, then $Q = R$ and the two lines $\overleftrightarrow{AR}$ and $\overleftrightarrow{AQ}$ are the

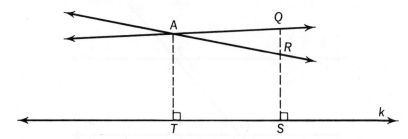

same. This intuitive reasoning leads us to the adoption of a new axiom.

Axiom P *If point A does not lie on line k, there is at most one line k' containing A and parallel to k.*

This new Axiom P together with Theorem 5.20 shows there is always *exactly one* line through A parallel to k.

It is quite likely at this point that you are thinking that it really should not be necessary to adopt Axiom P as an axiom. Can it not instead be proved as a theorem from the axioms already adopted? It certainly seems plausible that this should be so. After all, it was proved (using Theorem 5.20) that there always is a parallel through A. Surely it should not be much harder to show that there is only one! If this seems correct to you, then at least you are in good company, namely, that of all the mathematicians who considered the question for over 2000 years. From the time of Euclid, about 300 B.C., until after A.D. 1800 there was a whole series of attempts to prove the parallel postulate, i.e., our Axiom P or its equivalent. This long range mystery was finally settled in the early nineteenth century with the discovery that there was a perfectly good deductive system (called a non-Euclidean geometry) in which Axiom P was false but all the other axioms true. Hence Axiom P could *not* be proved from the other axioms.

At all events, we shall adopt Axiom P and proceed to obtain some of its consequences.

Theorem 9.1 *If parallel lines k_1 and k_2 are met by a transversal k_3, both pairs of alternate interior angles have equal measures.*

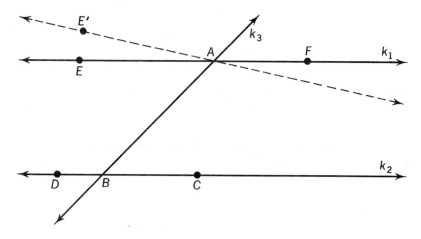

Proof. Using the notation in the diagram, we hope to show that $\angle CBA \cong \angle EAB$ and $\angle FAB \cong \angle DBA$.

We shall resort to a contradiction argument. Suppose that $m(\angle CBA) \neq m(\angle EAB)$. Then $\angle CBA$ is *not* congruent to $\angle EAB$. (Why?) Hence there is a ray $\overrightarrow{AE'}$ different from $\overrightarrow{AE}$ such that $\angle CBA \cong \angle E'AB$. (Why?) This would imply that $\overleftrightarrow{E'A} \parallel k_2$. (Why?) But we are given that $k_1 \parallel k_2$, so this would mean two different lines through A parallel to k_2. This contradicts Axiom P and so is impossible. Thus we are forced to conclude that $m(\angle CBA) = m(\angle EAB)$.

A similar argument could be used to show $m(\angle FAB) = m(\angle DBA)$. Easier yet, by Axiom MA(d), $m(\angle FAB) + m(\angle EAB) = 180 = m(\angle DBA) + m(\angle CBA)$, and since we already know that $m(\angle EAB) = m(\angle CBA)$, it follows that $m(\angle FAB) = m(\angle DBA)$.

In problem **A2** of Problem Set 9.1 you formulated the conjecture (probably already familiar to you) that the sum of the degree measures of the angles of a triangle is 180. With the adoption of Axiom P this is a result which can be proved in our deductive system.

Theorem 9.2 *The sum of the degree measures of the angles of a triangle is* 180.

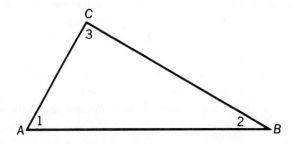

Analysis. Let us try to devise some suitable strategy for attacking this problem. In the notation of the above drawing we notice that we wish to show that

$$m(\angle 1) + m(\angle 2) + m(\angle 3) = 180.$$

This means that we hope to show that $\angle 1$ is supplementary to an angle whose measure is $m(\angle 2) + m(\angle 3)$. How can we produce such an angle? Clearly one way is to draw a congruent copy of $\angle 2$ beside $\angle 3$. How can this be arranged? By Theorem 9.1 this can be done by drawing the line $\overleftrightarrow{CD}$ parallel to $\overleftrightarrow{AB}$ as shown below. Then $m(\angle 2) = m(\angle 4)$ and incidentally $m(\angle 1) = m(\angle 5)$. (Why?) We

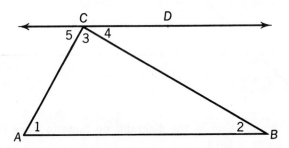

have thus created an angle, namely, $\angle ACD$, such that

$$m(\angle ACD) = m(\angle 3) + m(\angle 4) = m(\angle 3) + m(\angle 2). \quad \text{(Why?)}$$

Recall that we hope to show that $\angle 1$ is supplementary to $\angle ACD$, so we naturally look for angles which are supplements of $\angle ACD$. By definition $\angle 5$ is a supplement of $\angle ACD$, so we know that

$$m(\angle 5) + m(\angle ACD) = 180. \quad \text{(Why?)}$$

Since we already noted that $m(\angle 1) = m(\angle 5)$, this yields the desired result. You should now be able to organize these observations and write a formal proof of the theorem.

Problem Set 9.2

Problems **A1** through **A7** refer to the following plane figure.

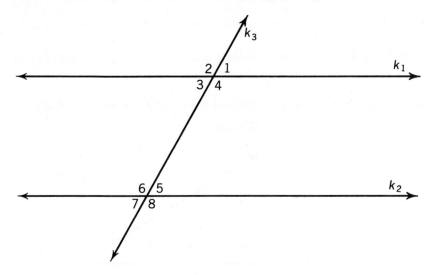

A. 1. If $m(\angle 1) = m(\angle 5)$ prove that $k_1 \parallel k_2$.

[NOTE: Such angles are often called corresponding angles.]

2. a. If $\angle 3 \cong \angle 5$ prove that $\angle 4 \cong \angle 6$.

b. If $\angle 3 \cong \angle 5$ prove that the eight angles labeled above consist of two sets of four congruent angles each.

3. Prove that $k_1 \parallel k_2$ if and only if $m(\angle 1) = m(\angle 7)$.

4. If $m(\angle 3) > m(\angle 5)$ prove that $m(\angle 4) + m(\angle 5) < 180$.

5. If $m(\angle 4) + m(\angle 5) = 180$ prove that $m(\angle 3) + m(\angle 6) = 180$.

6. Which of the following statements imply that $k_1 \parallel k_2$?

    (a) $m(\angle 1) = m(\angle 3)$.   (f) $m(\angle 3) + m(\angle 6) = 180$.

    (b) $m(\angle 1) = m(\angle 5)$.   (g) $m(\angle 1) + m(\angle 8) = 180$.

    (c) $m(\angle 1) = m(\angle 7)$.   (h) $m(\angle 1) + m(\angle 7) = 180$.

    (d) $m(\angle 1) = m(\angle 2)$.   (i) $m(\angle 1) + m(\angle 6) = 180$.

    (e) $m(\angle 1) = m(\angle 8)$.   (j) $m(\angle 2) + m(\angle 8) = 180$.

7. If $k_1 \parallel k_2$ and if $m(\angle 1) = 40$ find the measures of the other seven angles.

B. 1. $\angle 4$ is called an exterior angle of $\triangle ABC$ at B. Prove that $m(\angle 4) = m(\angle 1) + m(\angle 3)$. That is, prove that the measure of an exterior angle

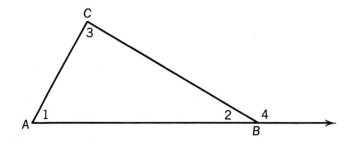

at one vertex equals the sum of the measures of the angles at the other two vertices.

2. Prove that any triangle can have at most one right angle.

C. 1. If k_1, k_2, k_3 are three distinct lines in a plane such that $k_1 \perp k_3$ and $k_2 \perp k_3$ prove that $k_1 \parallel k_2$.

2. If k_1, k_2, k_3 are three distinct lines in a plane such that $k_1 \parallel k_2$ and $k_3 \perp k_1$ prove that $k_3 \perp k_2$.

D. 1. If in the diagram $\overleftrightarrow{AB} \parallel \overleftrightarrow{DE}$ and if $m(\angle DCE) = 88$ and $m(\angle BAC) = 30$

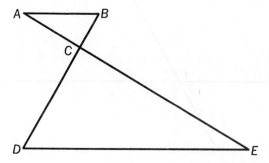

in degrees, find degree measures of all other angles. Do not forget $\angle BCE$ and $\angle ACD$.

2. One of the angles of an isosceles triangle has a degree measure of 20. Find the possible degree measures of the other two angles. [There are two different sets of answers.]

9.3 Special Quadrilaterals

In Chapter 5 we defined a polygon as a simple closed curve which is a union of line segments. In particular a quadrilateral is a polygon which is a union of four

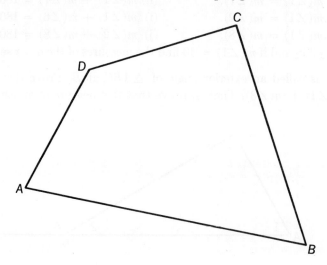

segments, like $ABCD$ in the sketch. The four segments, here $\overline{AB}, \overline{BC}, \overline{CD}$, and $\overline{DA}$, are called the **sides** of the quadrilateral and the points A, B, C, and D its vertices. Two sides which have an empty intersection are called **opposite sides,** while two sides whose intersection is a vertex are **adjacent sides.** Thus, for example, $\overline{AB}$ and $\overline{CD}$ are opposite sides since $\overline{AB} \cap \overline{CD} = \varnothing$, while $\overline{AB}$ and $\overline{AD}$ are adjacent sides since $\overline{AB} \cap \overline{AD} = \{A\}$. Two vertices of the quadrilateral such that the segment joining them is not a side of the quadrilateral are called **opposite vertices.** Thus A and C are a pair of opposite vertices. Similarly B and D are opposite vertices. The line segment joining two opposite vertices is a **diagonal** of the quadrilateral. The angles $\angle BAD$, $\angle CBA$, $\angle DCB$, $\angle ADC$ are the **angles** of the quadrilateral. As in the case of a triangle the angles are determined by the quadrilateral but are not subsets of it. Angles whose vertices are opposite vertices of the quadrilateral are called **opposite angles.** Angles whose vertices are on the same side of the quadrilateral are **adjacent.**

Among the **quadrilaterals** there are a number of special types which are undoubtedly familiar to you. To avoid any possible confusion on meaning of terms, we shall formally define them and obtain some of their important (and intuitively familiar) properties.

> DEFINITION 1: A **parallelogram** is a quadrilateral in which both pairs of opposite sides are parallel.

> DEFINITION 2: A **rectangle** is a parallelogram such that one of its angles is a right angle.

> DEFINITION 3: A **rhombus** is a parallelogram for which some two adjacent sides are congruent.

> DEFINITION 4: A **square** is a rectangle which is also a rhombus; i.e., it has a right angle and a pair of congruent adjacent sides.

At first sight you may be highly dubious about some of these definitions. For example, you certainly envision a rectangle as having four right angles, but the definition seems to call for only one. The point is that if there is one right angle we can *prove* the other three angles must also be right angles. This proof is given as an exercise. Similarly it can be proved that a rhombus (and hence a square) actually must have all four sides congruent.

It is to be noted that rectangles, rhombuses, and squares are all special kinds of parallelograms, which in turn are special kinds of quadrilaterals. If we let Q represent the set of all quadrilaterals, P the set of parallelograms, R the set of rectangles, H the set of rhombuses and S the set of squares, the relationships among these sets can be represented pictorially, as in the sketch at the top of page 356. That is, every rectangle is also a parallelogram and a quadrilateral; every rhombus is a parallelogram and a quadrilateral; every square is a rectangle, a rhombus, a parallelogram, and a quadrilateral. Indeed $S = R \cap H$.

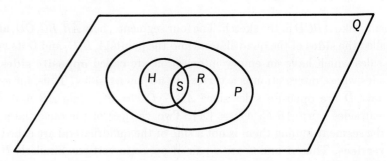

Because of the relationship above, if a theorem is proved for all parallelograms it automatically applies to rectangles, rhombuses and squares. Similarly theorems concerning rectangles hold for squares. Let us proceed to deduce some of the properties of these special quadrilaterals. Other properties are suggested in the exercises.

Theorem 9.3 *Two adjacent angles of a parallelogram are supplementary; i.e., the sum of their degree measures is* 180.

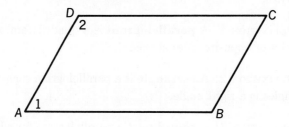

Analysis. We hope to show that if $ABCD$ is a parallelogram, then $m(\angle 1) + m(\angle 2) = 180$. What ideas can we bring to bear on the proof? We actually hope to show that $\angle 1$ and $\angle 2$ are supplementary angles, so possibly it may help to consider angles supplementary to one of the given ones. One possible procedure would be to extend segment $\overline{DC}$ as shown below producing an angle $\angle 3$ supplementary to $\angle 2$. Thus we know that $m(\angle 2) + m(\angle 3) = 180$. (Why?) In order to complete the proof it would only be necessary to show that $m(\angle 1) = m(\angle 3)$.

Do we have any way of knowing this? Yes. Since $\overleftrightarrow{AB} \parallel \overleftrightarrow{CD}$ the equality of these measures follows from Theorem 9.1.

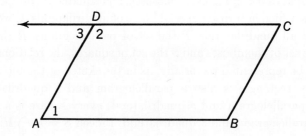

If carefully read, the discussion above constitutes a proof. You should verify this by writing out a formal step-by-step proof.

Theorem 9.4 *Two opposite angles of a parallelogram are congruent.*

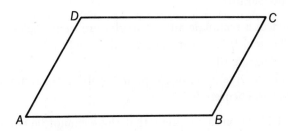

Analysis. We hope to show that $\angle A \cong \angle C$. This is equivalent to showing that $m(\angle A) = m(\angle C)$. Do we know anything about the measures of angles in a parallelogram? The only information on this seems to be the result of Theorem 9.3 about adjacent angles. Will this help? We could use it to conclude that $m(\angle A) + m(\angle D) = 180$ and also that $m(\angle D) + m(\angle C) = 180$. From this it is easy to conclude that $m(\angle A) = m(\angle C)$. It is left for you to write out the details of the proof.

Theorem 9.5 *Opposite sides of a parallelogram are congruent.*

The proof of the theorem is left as an exercise.

Theorem 9.6 *The four sides of a rhombus are all congruent.*

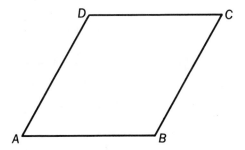

Analysis. We hope to show that all four sides of $ABCD$ in the above figure are congruent, i.e., that the four measures are equal. What do we know, if anything, about the sides of a rhombus? By its definition we know a rhombus has a pair of congruent adjacent sides so we may assume $m(\overline{AB}) = m(\overline{AD})$. Do we know anything about the other sides? Since a rhombus is a special kind of parallelogram any theorem about parallelograms applies to the rhombus. Hence Theorem 9.5 can be applied. Using these hints, write a proof for Theorem 9.6.

Problem Set 9.3

A. 1. What is the intersection set of two opposite angles of a quadrilateral?
  2. What are the possible intersection sets of two adjacent angles of a quad-
    rilateral? In particular, what is the intersection set of two adjacent angles
    of a parallelogram?

B. 1. Prove that in a rectangle all four angles are right angles.
  2. Prove Theorem 9.5. [HINT: Draw a diagonal and prove the resulting
    triangles congruent.]
  3. Give an alternative proof of Theorem 9.4 using the same procedure just
    suggested for Theorem 9.5.

C. 1. If point A is not on line k prove that there cannot be two different lines
    through A perpendicular to k. [HINT: Use a contradiction proof.]
  2. Let k_1 and k_2 be parallel lines and let P, Q be two points on k_1. If $\overline{PS}$ and
    $\overline{QT}$ are perpendicular to k_2 prove that $m(\overline{PS}) = m(\overline{QT})$. [Notice this
    shows that, for two parallel lines, the segments from the points of one
    line perpendicular to the other line all have the same length.]

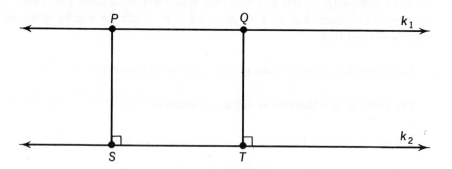

D. 1. The diagonals of parallelogram $ABCD$ meet in a point Q. Show that Q is

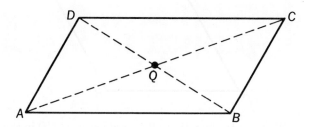

the midpoint of both diagonals, i.e., $\overline{AQ} \cong \overline{QC}$, $\overline{BQ} \cong \overline{QD}$. [HINT: Con-
    sider triangles $\triangle ABQ$ and $\triangle CDQ$.]
  2. Prove the diagonals of a rhombus are perpendicular. [HINT: Theorem 9.6
    and problem **D1** should be useful here.]

9.4 Measuring Plane Regions

Having dealt with measuring segments and angles we turn next to the measurement of plane regions. In Chapter 5 a region in a plane was defined as the union of a simple closed curve and its interior. We wish to assign to a region a number which will be, in some sense, a measure of how "large" the region is. The pattern for the intuitive meaning of measuring a region should be fairly clear on the basis of our past experience. We shall select some unit point set and if the region in question is exactly covered by k nonoverlapping congruent copies of the unit, then the measure of the region with respect to the unit is k. We then say that the *area* of this region is k units. For example, if the square foot is used as a unit we may speak of a region as having an *area* of 15 square feet. In this case the measure is the number 15 and the unit is the square foot. To describe an area it is necessary to indicate both the number (i.e., the measure) and the unit being used just as in the indication of the length of a segment. Just as the unit for measuring segments is a segment and the unit for measuring angles is an angle, so the unit for measuring regions is a region.

As an illustration, if the triangular region bounded by $\triangle ABC$ is adopted as a unit, then the area of the region bounded by $PQRST$ is seen at once to be 15 units.

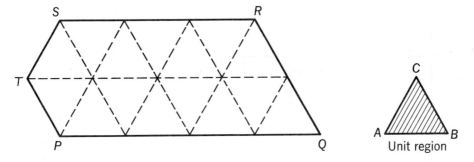

Unit region

Similarly the area of the region bounded by the polygon below in terms of the rectangular region $ABCD$ is 13 units.

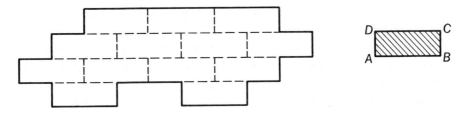

A thoughtful examination of these two illustrations calls several important matters to our attention. First consider the unit region. We are clearly confronted with an immense variety of different-shaped regions as possible unit regions. The intuitive process of measurement envisions that we fit together congruent copies of the unit region to cover parts of the plane without overlapping but without leaving any holes. That is, we should be able to "tile" the plane as we tile a floor, using tiles which are congruent copies of the unit region. This puts some restrictions on our probable choice of unit. For example, a circular region is not adapted for such a use. But even with the restriction the choice is wide. We saw above a triangular region and a rectangular region used. Actually *any* triangular region and *any* rectangular region may be used in tiling the plane. Indeed any parallelogram could be used and (though this is less obvious) any region bounded by a quadrilateral and some hexagonal regions can be used. You may find it interesting to design different tiling patterns for these different-shaped unit regions.

In practice it is customary to choose a square region for the unit region. More specifically, it is customary to choose a square region whose side is one linear unit long. The usefulness of this choice of unit will be made clear shortly. Thus corresponding to each unit of length there is a corresponding unit of area. The unit of area which is a square region one inch on a side is called a **square inch.** Similarly we may speak of the square foot, square yard, square mile, square meter, and square centimeter as units of area.

The second observation is that regions seem less well adapted to the measurement process than either segments or angles. Consider, for example, the following illustration in which an attempt has been made to measure the rectangular

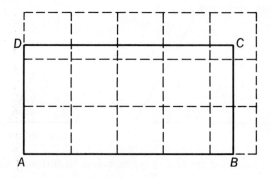

Unit region

region *ABCD* in terms of a unit square region. The region bounded by *ABCD* is not measurable in the sense of being exactly covered by an integral number of copies of the unit region. There are eight copies of the unit which are contained in the region and seven others which are partly inside and partly outside. Thus all we can say is that it has an area between 8 units and 15 units, which is rather a large margin of error. Similarly, the region bounded by curve *C* in the next drawing in terms of the triangular unit region has an area between 14 and 40 units. This is in rather sharp contrast to the situation with segments and angles where we could in general expect to read the measure to the nearest unit. Indeed it means that we should not expect for regions any instrument comparable to the ruler for segments or protractor for angles where an approximate measure can be

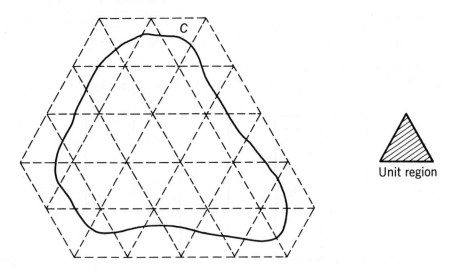

Unit region

read as the coordinate of a point on a linear or circular scale. This lack of an effective instrument for measuring regions means that in practice we rarely measure area directly. Instead, as we shall see, much of our work will be devoted to learning how to *compute* area measures of certain kinds of regions from linear measures that we have already discussed.

The naïve definition of measure for regions that has so far been given applies only to a limited class of regions. As in the cases of segment and angle we wish to adopt axioms extending the area concept to all regions. As a motivation for this let us first note properties which hold for measurable regions, i.e., those to which we have already assigned measures in the intuitive way. We will agree that our unit of area will be the square region one linear unit on each side. Thus we shall now refer to the unit of area as a square unit.

(1) If two measurable regions are bounded by congruent curves, their measures are equal.

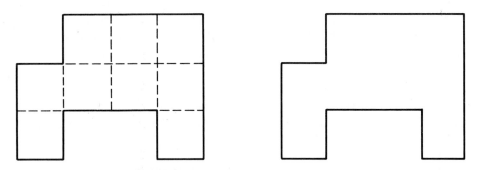

It is intuitively clear that if the bounding curves are congruent, then the regions themselves must be congruent. Hence if one region is covered by 9 copies of the unit region, as shown above, the congruent region will be covered by their 9 images under the congruence—which are also copies of the unit region.

(2) If two measurable regions $\mathcal{R}_1$ and $\mathcal{R}_2$ are nonoverlapping (i.e., have no interior points in common), then $m(\mathcal{R}_1 \cup \mathcal{R}_2) = m(\mathcal{R}_1) + m(\mathcal{R}_2)$.

This simply means that if, as indicated below, it takes 8 copies of the unit region to cover $\mathcal{R}_1$ and 6 to cover $\mathcal{R}_2$, then $\mathcal{R}_1 \cup \mathcal{R}_2$ is covered by $8 + 6$ copies.

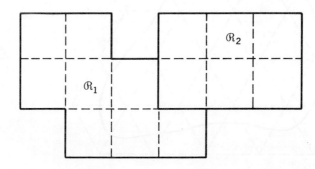

(3) If the measures of length for two adjacent sides of a rectangular region are integers a and b the measure A of its area in square units is given by

$$A = a \cdot b.$$

The accompanying diagram shows the case where the two linear measures are

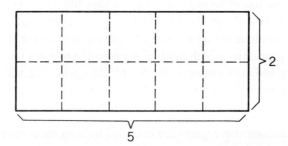

5 and 2. Statement (3) is immediately clear since the information given means that the rectangular region is exactly covered by unit square regions arranged in b rows of a regions each. This, by the very definition of multiplication, implies that the total number A of unit square regions necessary for covering is equal to $a \cdot b$.

Notice, however, one critically important difference from the cases of segment and angle. It is *not* true that two regions having equal measures are always congruent. The two regions shown here each have an area of 4 square units but they

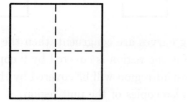

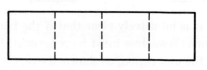

are clearly not congruent. Thus two segments or two angles are congruent *if and only if* their measures are equal. For regions, congruent regions have equal areas by statement (1), but the equality of areas is *not* enough to imply congruence.

As in the case of segments, we may seek to extend the set of regions that can be measured by using fractional parts of the unit region and thereby accepting rational numbers other than integers as measures for regions. Consider, for example, the region bounded by an isosceles right triangle whose congruent sides are each three units long. The attempt to cover this region by copies of the unit

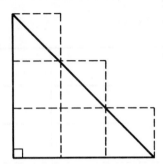

square region yields the situation shown above. There are three copies of the unit square region in the given triangular region and three more which are partly inside and partly outside. Each of these latter unit regions is divided by its diagonal into two congruent triangular parts, each of which may then be reasonably referred to as a half of a square unit. Since it takes three of these half-units to finish covering the given triangular region it is natural to say that the area is $\left(3 + \dfrac{3}{2}\right)$ square units or $\dfrac{9}{2}$ square units.

It may be of interest to see how this introduction of fractional parts of units affects statement (3) above concerning areas of rectangular regions. To be specific, consider a rectangular region $ABCD$ for which the sides have lengths of $\dfrac{5}{2}$ units and $\dfrac{7}{3}$ units, respectively. Since we are allowing the use of fractional parts, let us first consider the unit square region decomposed as shown below into six

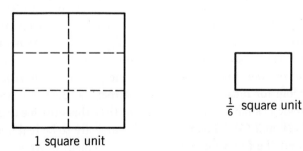

1 square unit $\frac{1}{6}$ square unit

congruent rectangular regions whose sides are $\frac{1}{2}$ unit and $\frac{1}{3}$ unit long, respectively.

Since these six congruent regions cover the unit square region we naturally say each has an area of $\frac{1}{6}$ square unit. Consider now the given rectangular region $ABCD$ as shown below. If $m(\overline{AB}) = \frac{5}{2}$, then $\overline{AB}$ is just covered by 5 copies of a segment whose length is $\frac{1}{2}$ unit. Similarly $\overline{AD}$ is covered by 7 copies of a segment

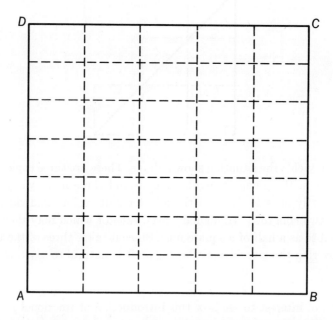

whose linear measure is $\frac{1}{3}$. Thus the dashed lines above show region $ABCD$ covered by 7 rows of 5 congruent rectangular regions. That is, there are $5 \cdot 7$ such regions. Each of these is congruent to what we called $\frac{1}{6}$ square unit. That is, the measure A of area for region $ABCD$ is given by $A = 5 \cdot 7 \cdot \frac{1}{6} = \frac{5 \cdot 7}{2 \cdot 3} = \left(\frac{5}{2}\right) \cdot \left(\frac{7}{3}\right)$.

Notice that this somewhat laborious analysis has merely led back, for the case of rational measures, to the result of statement (3). That is, statement (3) still applies when the linear measures of the sides are rational.

The intuitive considerations above suggest the properties we wish to require in adopting an axiom for measurement of plane regions. Basically we want to require that *all* regions shall have measures and that this area measure shall have properties (1), (2), and (3). The measures of course are to be real numbers. Thus we formally adopt the following axiom on Measurement of Area:

Axiom MAR *To every plane region $\mathcal{R}$ is assigned a real number $m(\mathcal{R})$ called the measure of its area. This measure satisfies the following conditions:*

(a) *If two regions are bounded by congruent curves, their measures are equal.*

(b) *If regions $\mathcal{R}_1$ and $\mathcal{R}_2$ do not overlap, i.e., have no common interior points, then*
$$m(\mathcal{R}_1 \cup \mathcal{R}_2) = m(\mathcal{R}_1) + m(\mathcal{R}_2).$$

(c) *If the linear measures of the sides of a rectangular region are a and b, then its area measure A is given by $A = a \cdot b$.*

At first sight it may seem that Axiom MAR is incomplete in that it fails to mention that the unit of area is the unit square region. Actually this is concealed in part (c) since if $a = b = 1$ it follows by (c) that $A = 1$. That is, the unit square region has been assigned a measure of 1 and hence may be taken as the unit region.

Having motivated and now adopted Axiom MAR, it is important next to learn how to determine areas, at least for some of the simpler regions. It was observed earlier that we seem to have no instrument really appropriate for measuring areas directly. Thus we shall in general look for methods of *computing* area measures from lengths which we can more readily measure. Part (c) of Axiom MAR, stating that $A = a \cdot b$, is the first example of such a computational procedure. It says that the area measure in square units of a rectangular region may be obtained as the product of the linear measures of two adjacent sides.

Can we evolve corresponding computational procedures for finding area measures for other simple regions? Consider first the case of a triangular region. If the line k is drawn through R perpendicular to $\overleftrightarrow{PQ}$ and if $k \cap \overleftrightarrow{PQ} = \{S\}$, then segment $\overline{RS}$ is called the altitude of $\triangle PQR$ from R or the altitude perpendicular to $\overleftrightarrow{PQ}$. Every triangle, therefore, has three altitudes, one perpendicular to the line containing each side. The illustration shows the case when S is between P and Q. Let us try to formulate a conjecture as to the area measure of such a region by using a frankly experimental approach such as might be appropriate with elementary school pupils. You may find it amusing actually to cut models out of paper.

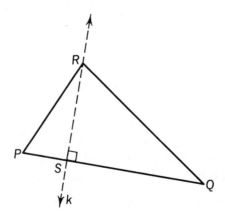

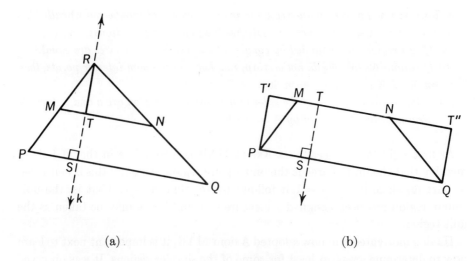

(a)   (b)

If M and N are the midpoints of $\overline{PR}$ and $\overline{QR}$ as shown in diagram (a), draw $\overleftrightarrow{MN}$ and let $\overleftrightarrow{MN} \cap k = \{T\}$. What would you conjecture as to the relation between $\overleftrightarrow{MN}$ and $\overleftrightarrow{PQ}$? Does $\overline{RT}$ seem to be perpendicular to $\overline{MN}$? What would you guess to be the relative lengths of $\overline{RT}$ and $\overline{RS}$? Imagine now that region PQR is cut into three parts by cutting along $\overline{MN}$ and $\overline{RT}$, and suppose the three pieces are reassembled as shown in diagram (b), where $\triangle PMT'$ is the new position of $\triangle RMT$ and $\triangle QNT''$ the new position of $\triangle RNT$. What kind of region seems to be shown in diagram (b)? If, as appears plausible, it is a rectangular region, then we know how to find its area measure. Since the area of $PQT''T'$ in diagram (b) must be the same as for region PQR of diagram (a) (why?), this should yield a good conjecture as to the area measure A of the triangular region.

According to Axiom MAR the area for diagram (b) should be the product of the linear measures of $\overline{PQ}$ and $\overline{PT'}$. For convenience let b and h denote respectively the measures of side $\overline{PQ}$ and of the altitude $\overline{RS}$ perpendicular to $\overleftrightarrow{PQ}$ in $\triangle PQR$. If we are correct in our guess that $\overline{RT}$ is half as long as $\overline{RS}$, it means that $m(\overline{RT}) = \dfrac{h}{2}$. Moreover $\overline{PT'}$ must have the same length as $\overline{RT}$. (Why?) Thus the conjecture for the area A of $\triangle PQR$ becomes

$$A = m(\overline{PQ}) \cdot m(\overline{PT'}) = m(\overline{PQ}) \cdot m(\overline{RT}) = \frac{1}{2} b \cdot h.$$

It would be possible to prove the correctness of this conjecture by establishing the validity of all the guesses on which we have based it. It is easier, however, to approach the actual proof by looking first at the special case of a right triangular region, as in diagram (c). Let $m(\overline{PQ}) = b$ and $m(\overline{QR}) = a$. Since $\overline{QR} \perp \overline{PQ}$ the side $\overline{QR}$ is also the altitude from R. The conjecture above thus reduces to $A = \dfrac{1}{2} a \cdot b$. Since we recognize $a \cdot b$ as the area measure of a rectangle with sides

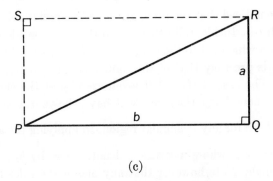

(c)

having measures a and b, let us produce such a rectangle by drawing the dashed segments indicated as parallel to $\overleftrightarrow{PQ}$ and $\overleftrightarrow{QR}$. The formal proof is now easy. We observe that $\triangle PQR \cong \triangle RSP$ (why?), so by Axiom MAR(a) these two regions have the same area measure A. It then follows at once from Axiom MAR(b) and (c) that $A + A = a \cdot b$ or $A = \dfrac{1}{2} a \cdot b$ as we conjectured.

Let us now consider the general case of a triangular region PQR. If the altitude is drawn from R, three possible cases occur, as shown in the sketches below, according to whether point S is interior to $\overline{PQ}$, an endpoint of $\overline{PQ}$ or exterior to $\overline{PQ}$.

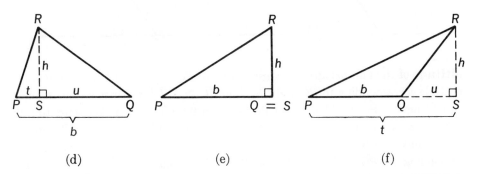

(d)   (e)   (f)

To make the symbolism less forbidding let us adopt the notation $m(\overline{PQ}) = b$, $m(\overline{RS}) = h$, $m(\overline{PS}) = t$, $m(\overline{SQ}) = u$. For the situation shown in sketch (d), S is between P and Q so that $b = t + u$. (What theorem justifies this?) If A is the area measure of $\triangle PQR$, then A is the sum of the measures of $\triangle PSR$ and $\triangle QSR$. (Why?) Since these are right triangles we have already discovered how to find their area measures and we conclude

$$A = \frac{1}{2} t \cdot h + \frac{1}{2} u \cdot h = \frac{1}{2} h \cdot (t + u) = \frac{1}{2} b \cdot h,$$

which is precisely the conjecture we are seeking to prove. In the simplification use has been made of the distributive property of multiplication over addition and of the fact that $b = t + u$.

You will have noticed that the proof given so far applies only to the case illustrated in sketch (d). Incidentally this is also the case considered in our experimental discussion which led to the conjecture. What about the other two cases? The case of (e) is precisely that of the right triangular region and has already been discussed. The case of (f) is left as an exercise at the end of this section. When you have completed this, you will have shown the correctness of the formula $A = \dfrac{1}{2} b \cdot h$ for any triangular region. In applying the area formula, the side used (i.e., the one whose measure is denoted here by b) is often called the **base** of the triangle. Note, however, that any one of the sides may be taken as base, so we really have three different ways of applying the area formula for any triangular region.

The case of a region bounded by a parallelogram now falls out simply. Let $PQRS$ be a parallelogram. Let $\overline{TU}$ be any segment perpendicular to the parallel lines $\overleftrightarrow{PQ}$ and $\overleftrightarrow{RS}$ on the sides $\overline{PQ}$, $\overline{RS}$ of the parallelogram. Then $\overline{TU}$ is called an

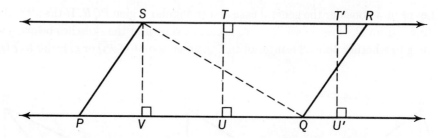

altitude of the parallelogram corresponding to $\overline{PQ}$ and $\overline{RS}$. If $\overline{T'U'}$ is any other altitude corresponding to $\overline{PQ}$ and $\overline{RS}$, then $\overline{TU} \cong \overline{T'U'}$, so these segments have equal lengths. (See problem **C2** of Problem Set 9.3.) Thus it makes sense to talk of the measure h of any altitude corresponding to a side $\overline{PQ}$ of a parallelogram.

For convenience let $m(\overline{PQ}) = b$ and let h be the measure of any altitude corresponding to $\overline{PQ}$. In particular $m(\overline{SV}) = h$. If diagonal $\overline{SQ}$ is drawn, then $\triangle PQS \cong \triangle RSQ$. Thus, using Axiom MAR(a) and (b), the area measure A of $PQRS$ must be twice the area measure of $\triangle PQS$. Using the previous results on triangles this means that $A = 2\left(\dfrac{1}{2} b \cdot h\right)$ or

$$A = b \cdot h.$$

That is, the area measure of any parallelogram is equal to the product of the linear measure of any side and the measure of a corresponding altitude.

It is to be noted that, once having deduced a means of computing area measures for triangular regions, it is possible, at least in theory, to compute the area of any polygonal region, since such a region can always be dissected into triangular ones. For example, the area measure A of the region bounded by polygon $PQRSTU$ on page 369 is the sum of the measures of triangular regions as shown.

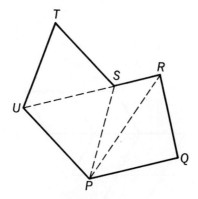

$$A = m(\triangle PQR) + m(\triangle PRS) + m(\triangle PSU) + m(\triangle UST).$$

It is also worth noting that there are many ways of decomposing a polygonal region into triangular ones. A different decomposition of the same region is shown at the right. In this case a point O has been used as a vertex for some of the triangular regions even though it was not a vertex of the original polygon.

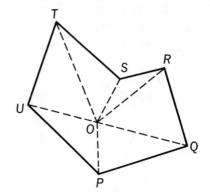

For convenience in reference let us collect the computational results above and state them as a theorem.

Theorem 9.7

(a) *The area measure A of a rectangular region is given by*

$$A = a \cdot b$$

where a and b are the linear measures of two adjacent sides.

(b) *The area measure A of a triangular region is given by*

$$A = \frac{1}{2} b \cdot h$$

where b is the measure of any side and h the measure of the corresponding altitude.

(c) *The area measure A of a region bounded by a parallelogram is given by*

$$A = b \cdot h$$

where b is the measure of any side and h that of a corresponding altitude.

Problem Set 9.4

A. 1. What is the area of the indicated region if the region bounded by rhombus *PQRS* is taken as the unit region?

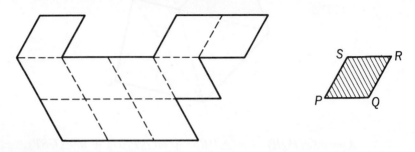

2. The quadrilateral *PQRS* has right angles at *Q* and *S* with the sides having lengths as shown. What is the area in square inches of the region bound by the quadrilateral?

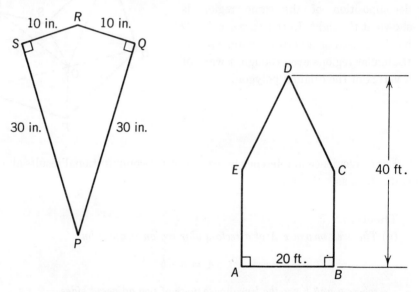

3. The region *ABCDE* above is the union of the region bounded by a square and that bounded by an isosceles triangle. If the measurements are as given, find the area in square feet.

4. a. Determine the number of square inches in a square foot, the number of square feet in a square yard, and the number of square yards in a square mile.

   b. If a region has an area of 160 square feet, find its measure in square yards and in square inches.

5. A segment 1 inch long has a length of approximately 2.54 centimeters.

   a. What is the length in centimeters of a segment 1 foot long?

      b. What is the length in inches of a segment 1 meter long? [1 meter is the same as 100 centimeters.]

B. 1. If a square has a side with measure s, show that its area measure A is given by $A = s^2$.

  2. Show that the area measure A of the triangular region PQR in the diagram below is given by

$$A = \frac{1}{2} b \cdot h.$$

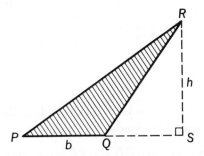

[This is the case of the triangle area formula not discussed in the text.]

3. $\overline{CD}$ and $\overline{EB}$ are altitudes of $\triangle ABC$. In terms of some convenient unit $m(\overline{AB}) = 15$, $m(\overline{CD}) = 18$ and $m(\overline{AC}) = 20$.

  a. Find the area of $\triangle ABC$ in square units.

  b. Find the length of $\overline{EB}$.

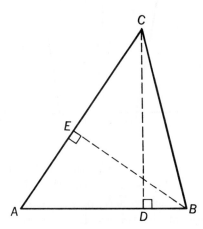

4. In the formula $A = b \cdot h$ for the area measure of a region bounded by a parallelogram, b can be the measure of any side and h that of a corresponding altitude. This seems to give four different ways of computing A. Actually there are only two. Explain why.

C. 1. In the polygonal region shown the segments from O perpendicular to the five sides are all congruent and hence have equal measures h. Prove that the area measure A of the region is given by

$$A = \frac{1}{2}p \cdot h$$

where p is the measure of the perimeter.

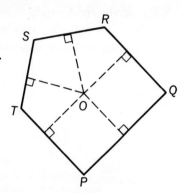

2. Does the proof in problem **C1** depend on the fact that the polygon has just five sides? Can you write a formula for the general case?

D. 1. It is given that $\overline{AB} \parallel \overline{CD}$ and $\overline{EF}$ is perpendicular to both. If, as shown, $m(\overline{AB}) = 9$, $m(\overline{CD}) = 5$, and $m(\overline{EF}) = 10$ in inches find the area of the region in square inches.

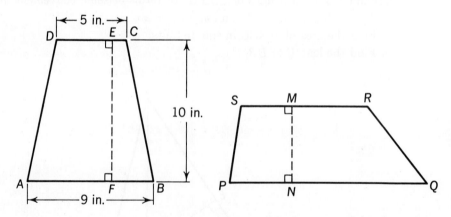

2. A quadrilateral like $PQRS$ in which one pair of opposite sides is parallel, but no assumption is made about the other pair, is called a **trapezoid.** Any segment, such as $\overline{MN}$, perpendicular to the parallel sides is called an **altitude** of the trapezoid. (Note all altitudes are congruent.) If $m(\overline{PQ}) = b_1$, $m(\overline{RS}) = b_2$ and $m(\overline{MN}) = h$ prove that the area measure A of the region is given by

$$A = \frac{1}{2}h \cdot (b_1 + b_2).$$

E. A way of tiling the plane with regions bounded by isosceles right triangles

is shown below. Consider the shaded tile PQR. How many tiles are required
to form the square region on side $\overline{PR}$? How many tiles are required to form
the square region on side $\overline{PQ}$? How many tiles are required to form the
square region on side $\overline{QR}$? What relationship exists between the areas of
these three square regions? [This is a special case of the Pythagorean
Theorem to be discussed in the next section.]

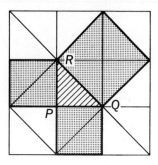

F. 1. Consider the regions bounded by the square and rectangle below. Find
the area and perimeter of each region. How do you account for the fact
that the areas are equal but the perimeters differ?

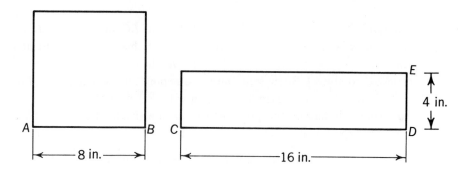

2. A man plans to make a flower bed in the shape of a rectangular region.
He has 20 feet of fence to go around it. He decides to choose one of the
following shapes: 9 by 1 foot; 8 by 2 feet; 7 by 3 feet; 6 by 4 feet; 5 by 5
feet. Find the area in square feet of the resulting flower bed in each case.
What choice gives the bed of greatest area?

G. 1. a. If $ABCD$ and $A'B'C'D'$ are rectangular regions such that $m(\overline{A'B'}) = m(\overline{AB})$ and $m(\overline{B'C'}) = 2 \cdot m(\overline{BC})$, how do their areas compare?
  b. If $ABCD$ and $A'B'C'D'$ are rectangular regions such that $m(\overline{A'B'}) = 2 \cdot m(\overline{AB})$ and $m(\overline{B'C'}) = 2 \cdot m(\overline{BC})$, how do their areas compare?
2. A side of $\triangle A'B'C'$ is three times that of a side of $\triangle ABC$ but the cor-
responding altitude of $\triangle A'B'C'$ is only half as long as that of $\triangle ABC$.
What is the ratio of their areas?

H. 1. In the parallelogram $ABCD$ let $m(\overline{AB}) = b$ and $m(\overline{DE}) = h$. Make a model of the region and cut it along $\overline{DE}$. Show experimentally how to reassemble the pieces to form a rectangular region whose sides have measures b and h. This experiment might have been used to motivate the conjecture that the area measure of a parallelogram is $A = b \cdot h$.

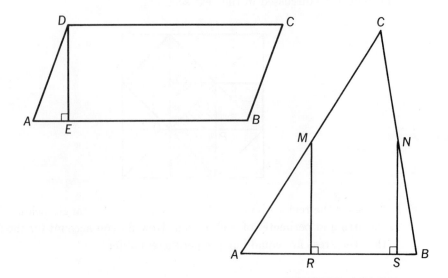

2. In $\triangle ABC$, M and N are midpoints of $\overline{AC}$ and $\overline{BC}$ and $\overline{MR}$ and $\overline{NS}$ are perpendicular to $\overline{AB}$. Make a paper model of this figure and cut along $\overline{MR}$ and $\overline{NS}$. Show experimentally that $\overline{RS}$ has the same length as $\overline{AR}$ and $\overline{SB}$ combined. Show that the three regions can be reassembled into what seems to be a rectangular region with $\overline{RS}$ as one side and with an adjacent side having the same length as an altitude of $\triangle ABC$. This is another experiment which could be used to motivate the conjecture that the area measure of a triangular region is given by $A = \dfrac{1}{2}b \cdot h$.

3. Take a general quadrilateral $ABCD$ with no two sides parallel and no two angles congruent. Make a number of congruent models of the region $ABCD$. Show experimentally how these models can be used to give a paving of the plane.

9.5 Theorem of Pythagoras

Perhaps the best-known single theorem of all geometry can be stated and proved using the ideas of area. It is known as the Theorem of Pythagoras and is concerned with the areas of the square regions on the three sides of a right triangle. You observed a special case of it in problem **E1** of Problem Set 9.4, where you looked at a pattern of triangular tiles. Allegedly it was by examination of such a pattern that the theorem was discovered. As an aid in statement we note that the side of a right triangle opposite the vertex of the right angle is called the **hypotenuse.** It is this theorem to which reference is made in Gilbert and Sullivan's opera "The Pirates of Penzance" when Major General Stanley sings of "many cheerful facts about the square of the hypotenuse."

Theorem 9.8 (Theorem of Pythagoras) *For any right triangle the area measure of the square region on the hypotenuse equals the sum of the area measures of the square regions on the other two sides.*

Proof. Let $\triangle ABC$ be the given right triangle and let the vertex of the right angle be at C. The measures of the sides will be denoted by a, b, c as shown in the drawing below. By Axiom MAR(c) the area measure for a square region of side s units is s^2. Thus the area measures of the three square regions in this theorem are a^2, b^2, c^2 and the claim of the theorem is that $c^2 = a^2 + b^2$.

For reasons that become clear only as a matter of hindsight, let us begin this proof by considering a square region for which each side has measure $(a + b)$.

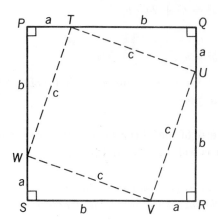
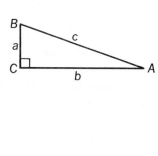

If the dashed lines are drawn we have four triangles, each of which is congruent to $\triangle ABC$. (Why?) Thus,

$$m(\overline{TU}) = m(\overline{UV}) = m(\overline{VW}) = m(\overline{WT}) = c. \quad \text{(Why?)}$$

We wish to show now that $TUVW$ is a square. Consider the three angles formed at V, i.e., $\angle SVW$, $\angle WVU$, and $\angle UVR$. It is clear at once [actually by Axiom MA(b) and (d)] that

$$m(\angle SVW) + m(\angle WVU) + m(\angle UVR) = 180.$$

By the triangle congruences, $\angle SVW \cong \angle A$ and $\angle UVR \cong \angle B$ so that $m(\angle SVW) = m(\angle A)$ and $m(\angle UVR) = m(\angle B)$. By substitution,

$$m(\angle A) + m(\angle B) + m(\angle WVU) = 180.$$

But

$$m(\angle A) + m(\angle B) + m(\angle C) = 180. \quad \text{(Why?)}$$

From these two statements it is seen at once that

$$m(\angle WVU) = m(\angle C) = 90,$$

since $\angle C$ was a right angle. Thus $\angle WVU$ is a right angle. Similarly the angles of $TUVW$ at all four vertices are right angles and the figure $TUVW$ is a square.

The rest of the proof is easy. According to Axiom MAR(b) the area measure of square region $PQRS$ must be the sum of the area measures of square region $TUVW$ and the four right triangular regions $\triangle SVW$, $\triangle RUV$, $\triangle QTU$, $\triangle PWT$. That is, the area measure of $PQRS$ must equal $c^2 + 4\left(\frac{1}{2} a \cdot b\right)$. (Why?)

We already know the area measure of $PQRS$ is $(a + b)^2$. Thus we conclude that

$$(a + b)^2 = c^2 + 4\left(\frac{1}{2} a \cdot b\right).$$

Algebraic simplification shows that

$$a^2 + 2a \cdot b + b^2 = c^2 + 2a \cdot b,$$

from which it follows that

$$a^2 + b^2 = c^2.$$

Since a^2, b^2, c^2 are the area measures of the square regions on the sides of $\triangle ABC$ this is precisely what we were seeking to prove.

It is quite easy to show that the converse of the Theorem of Pythagoras is also true and since this is frequently used it is well to state and prove it.

Theorem 9.9 *If the area measure of the square region on one side of a triangle equals the sum of the area measures of the square regions on the other two sides, the triangle is a right triangle.*

Analysis. We are given that for $\triangle ABC$ $a^2 + b^2 = c^2$ and hope to show that $\angle C$ is a right angle. What strategy can we devise that might assist us? Since we

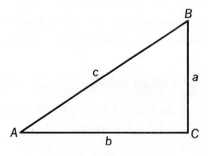
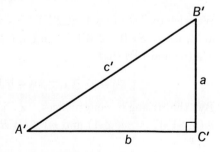

have just proved a theorem about right triangles, perhaps it would be helpful to draw a right triangle and compare it with the given $\triangle ABC$. Thus consider $\triangle A'B'C'$, which has a right angle at C' and with the two perpendicular sides having measures a and b, respectively. For convenience let $m(\overline{A'B'}) = c'$ as shown.

In the diagrams $\triangle ABC$ and $\triangle A'B'C'$ look so much alike that it occurs to us that if we could show $\triangle ABC \cong \triangle A'B'C'$ we would be able to conclude that $m(\angle C) = m(\angle C') = 90$, which is all we want. How could this congruence be established? Since we know nothing about any angle of $\triangle ABC$ the **sas** and **asa** congruence theorems don't look very promising. What about the **sss** theorem (Theorem 5.12)? We already know $\overline{AC} \cong \overline{A'C'}$ and $\overline{BC} \cong \overline{B'C'}$ since their measures are equal. Can we show that $\overline{AB} \cong \overline{A'B'}$ or, equivalently, that $c = c'$? What, if anything, do we know about c and c'? Actually we know that

$$c^2 = a^2 + b^2 = c'^2.$$

What are the reasons for these two equalities? Hence $c = c'$. With this analysis you should now be able to write out the proof.

It is a readily verified arithmetic fact that $3^2 + 4^2 = 5^2$. By the theorem just proved this means that a triangle whose sides have measures 3, 4, 5 (in any unit) must be a right triangle with the vertex of the right angle opposite the side of measure 5. This fact was evidently known in early times to both the Babylonians and the Egyptians and it has been suggested that the Egyptians may have used this fact in laying out right angles. While there is no agreement that this method was actually used, in problem **A3** on page 379 you are asked to explain how it could be done.

The next two theorems are easy consequences of the Theorem of Pythagoras and we shall prove them in this way. You may be interested to know, however, that they can be proved without the Theorem of Pythagoras. Indeed they can be proved without using any of the consequences of Axiom P.

Theorem 9.10 *The hypotenuse of a right triangle is longer than either of the other two sides.*

The proof of this is assigned as an exercise in the following set of problems.

Theorem 9.11 *The measure of any side of a triangle is less than the sum of the measures of the other two sides.*

Proof. If $\triangle ABC$ is any triangle and if the sides have measures a, b, and c, the theorem claims the truth of the following three statements.

$$a + b > c.$$
$$a + c > b.$$
$$b + c > a.$$

We may suppose that the notation is chosen so that $a \leq b \leq c$, i.e., so that a is the measure of the shortest side and c the measure of the longest side. In this case the statements $a + c > b$ and $b + c > a$ are automatically true. (Why?) We then only need show $a + b > c$ where c is the measure of the longest side. Let $\overline{CS}$ be the altitude perpendicular to the longest side. Then one of the following cases occurs just as in the proof of the area formula.

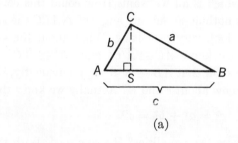

(a)

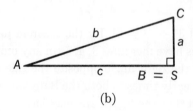

(b)

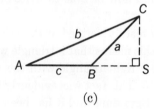

(c)

For diagram (b) it would follow by Theorem 9.10 that $b > c$ and for (c) it would similarly follow that $b > m(\overline{AS}) > c$. Since $b > c$ is false, the last two cases cannot occur and we need only consider the case of part (a). In this case $b > m(\overline{AS})$ and $a > m(\overline{SB})$. (Why?) Thus $a + b > m(\overline{AS}) + m(\overline{SB})$ and since $m(\overline{AS}) + m(\overline{SB}) = c$ (why?), it follows that $a + b > c$. This completes the proof.

Consider the particular case of an isosceles right triangle for which the two congruent sides each have measure 1. Then the measure c of the hypotenuse is

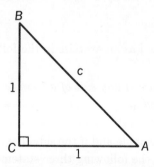

such that $c^2 = 1^2 + 1^2 = 2$. That is, $c = \sqrt{2}$. This you will recall is an example of a real number which is not a rational number. Indeed, it is primarily the use of the Theorem of Pythagoras which injects the nonrational numbers into our considerations, since many of the square roots of rational numbers do prove to be irrational.

Of course, any irrational number can be approximated to any desired number of decimal places by rational numbers. Thus to three decimal places $\sqrt{2} \approx 1.414$ and $\sqrt{3} \approx 1.732$. It would of course be possible to digress here to consider the technique of computing square roots. We choose not to take time for this, however, and instead refer you for approximate values of square roots to a square-root table which is readily available.

Problem Set 9.5

A. 1. The measures of the sides of six triangles are given below. Which of these triangles are right triangles? What theorem are you using in drawing the conclusion?

(a) 6, 8, 10.   (d) 6, 9, 11.
(b) 5, 7, 8.   (e) 7, 24, 25.
(c) 5, 12, 13.   (f) 3, 5, 7.

2. There are two noncongruent right triangles whose sides have integral measures and for which the hypotenuse has measure 25. Find the measures of the other sides for each case.

3. You are given a 12-foot piece of rope with knots tied at 1-foot intervals. Show how this could be used to find the perpendicular to a given line k at a point P.

B. 1. Prove Theorem 9.10.

2. Prove that

$$m(\overline{AB}) + m(\overline{BC}) + m(\overline{CD}) + m(\overline{DE}) \geqq m(\overline{AE}).$$

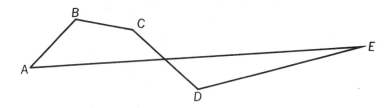

When would the equality sign hold? Does this sort of argument extend to show that segment $\overline{AE}$ is shorter than any other polygonal path from A to E?

C. 1. Show by squaring that $\sqrt{2}$ lies between 1.414 and 1.415.

2. a. If $\triangle ABC$ is an equilateral triangle with each side having measure 2, show that its area measure in square units is $\sqrt{3}$.

b. If the measure of each side of $\triangle ABC$ is s, show that its area measure is $\dfrac{\sqrt{3}\, s^2}{4}$.

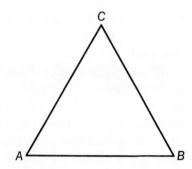

D. For right triangle $\triangle ABC$ form the square with side $a + b$ as shown. The shaded region clearly has measure $a^2 + b^2$. Make a paper model of the shaded region. If V is the point such that $m(\overline{UV}) = a$ cut the model along segments $\overline{PV}$ and $\overline{SV}$. Verify the Theorem of Pythagoras experimentally by showing that the three pieces can be reassembled into a square region whose side has measure c.

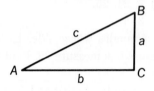

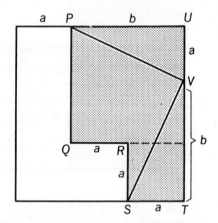

E. If the perpendicular bisector k of $\overline{AC}$ meets $\overline{AB}$ in a point P, prove that $m(\overline{AB}) > m(\overline{BC})$.

[HINT: Draw $\overline{PC}$. Theorem 9.11 may prove useful.]

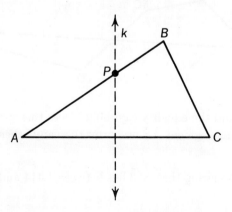

9.6 Circular Regions

Since circles occur so commonly in our experience, it seems desirable to consider the question of area for circular regions even though the treatment is rather intuitive.

Let O be the center of a circle and P a point on the circle. Consider the line k

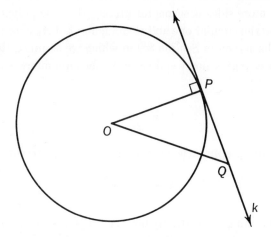

perpendicular to radius $\overline{OP}$ at P. If Q is any point of k other than P, then $\triangle OPQ$ is a right triangle and by Theorem 9.10 $m(\overline{OQ}) > r$ where $r = m(\overline{OP})$. That is, every point of k other than P is outside the circle so k meets the circle only at P. Such a line is called a **tangent** to the circle.

Let us now consider a polygon circumscribed about a circle; i.e., the circle is interior to the polygon and each side of the polygon is tangent to the circle. The segments from the center O perpendicular to these sides are radii and hence all

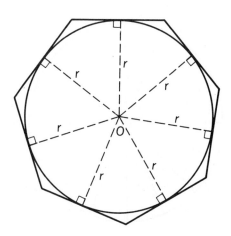

have the same measure r. According to the results of problems **C1** and **C2** of Problem Set 9.4 this means that the area measure A_p of the polygonal region is given by

$$A_p = \frac{1}{2}\, p \cdot r$$

where p is the perimeter measure of the polygon.

Since the circular region is contained in the polygonal region it appears that its area measure A should be less than A_p. On the other hand, if we imagine polygons of more and more sides it seems intuitively that the polygonal region gets closer and closer to the circular one and we imagine that A_p gets closer and closer to A. Recall the discussion in Section 8.9 in which we assumed that as the number of sides increases p gets closer and closer to the circumference c. Since, in the formula

$$A_p = \frac{1}{2}\, p \cdot r,$$

A_p approaches A and p approaches c it seems reasonable to conclude

$$A = \frac{1}{2}\, c \cdot r.$$

Although the reasoning has certainly not been rigorous, the result is indeed correct. Since by Chapter 8 we know that $c = 2\pi r$, the formula above can be written as

$$A = \frac{1}{2}\, (2\pi r) \cdot r = \pi r^2.$$

This is the formula for the area measure of a circular region, a result with which you are very probably familiar.

The following physical experiment, while not proving anything, may help to reinforce the result just obtained. Take a circular disk and cut it apart into some

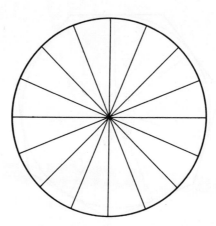

even number, say sixteen, congruent sectors as shown. These pieces can then be reassembled as illustrated below into a region which might perhaps be described as bounded by a disappointed parallelogram and which has the same area measure as the circular region. The top and bottom of this region are each a sequence of circular arcs having a total length of half the circumference of the circle. Since

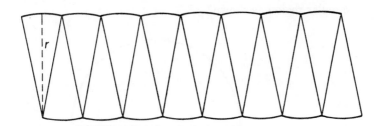

each sector has radius of measure r, the region appears to have a height of about r units. Thus, based on what we know about parallelograms, it seems reasonable that $\frac{1}{2} c \cdot r$ should be a fair approximation to the area measure. The approximation seems increasingly good if we cut the circular region into more and more sectors. This makes geometrically plausible the equation $A = \frac{1}{2} c \cdot r$, which was stated above for the area measure of a circular region. You might find it of interest actually to carry out this experimentation to see how plausibly the figure approximates a parallelogram. In fact when the number of sectors is large it is very close to being a rectangle.

As you will have noted, in this book we have regularly used the dot, $\cdot$, as a symbol of multiplication just as we have used the $+$ sign as a symbol of addition. Thus the product of numbers a and b has been regularly expressed as $a \cdot b$. From your previous work in algebra you are undoubtedly familiar with the convention of omitting the dot and expressing the product of a and b by writing simply ab. This is particularly convenient when doing manipulative work with algebraic expressions since it simplifies the writing. In the remainder of the book we shall frequently make use of this convention. Thus the area formula for a triangular region may be written as $A = \frac{1}{2} bh$.

Problem Set 9.6

A. 1. Find the (approximate) area of a circular region whose radii have a length of 3.2 inches. (Use $\pi \approx 3.14$ and express the answer to the nearest square inch.)

2. The circumference of a circle is 12 feet. Find the approximate area of the circular region.

B. 1. Let circle C_1 have radius with measure r_1 and let circle C_2 have radius with measure r_2.

    a. If $r_2 = 2r_1$, what is the relationship of the area measures A_2 and A_1?

    b. If $r_2 = 3r_1$, what is the relationship of the area measures A_2 and A_1?

    c. If $r_2/r_1 = k$, what is the relationship of the area measures A_2 and A_1?

2. a. If a circle has a radius of measure r, what is the area measure of a semi-circular region as shown?

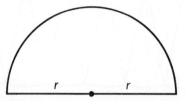

    b. What is the area measure of the region inside the circle bounded by two radii forming an angle of 1°? [HINT: How many congruent copies of such a region are needed to cover the semicircular region in part **a**?]

    c. What is the area measure of the shaded sector AOB if $m(AOB) = \theta$ in degrees?

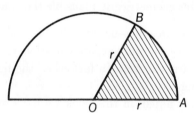

3. The circle shown has radii of length 2 inches. If radii $\overline{OA}$ and $\overline{OB}$ are perpendicular, find the area of the shaded region.

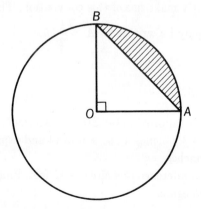

9.7 Approximation for Areas

All the remarks made in Chapter 8 emphasizing that, in practice, measurement is an approximate process are equally appropriate for areas or indeed for any kind of measurement. As before, we may speak of greatest possible error, relative error, etc. An added factor comes into play here, however. As we have noted, in the case of area we practically never use an instrument to measure area directly. Instead we measure certain lengths and use them to *compute* the area measures. We then are forced to ask what effect errors in measuring the required lengths have on the computed area measures. To clarify this situation let us consider a specific example.

Suppose for a rectangular region the lengths of two adjacent sides have been measured as 2.3 inches and 4.5 inches. Further it is understood that in each case the measurement is to the nearest tenth of an inch. We get an approximate value to the area measure A in square inches as $A \approx (2.3) \cdot (4.5) = 10.35$, but how good an approximation is this value of 10.35 square inches? Since, for each length, the greatest possible error was .05 inch, if a and b represent the correct measures of length we know that

$$2.25 \leq a \leq 2.35.$$
$$4.45 \leq b \leq 4.55.$$

Thus the largest possible answer for A (since $A = ab$) is $(2.35) \cdot (4.55)$ while the smallest possible answer is $(2.25) \cdot (4.45)$. That is,

$$(2.25) \cdot (4.45) \leq A \leq (2.35) \cdot (4.55).$$

By calculation this reduces to $10.0125 \leq A \leq 10.6925$. Thus the true value for A might exceed the computed value of 10.35 by as much as $10.6925 - 10.35 = .3425$, or might be less than the computed value by $10.35 - 10.0125 = .3375$. The possible error is very slightly more in one direction than in the other so the *greatest* possible error is .3425. If we use the explicit way of recording results we could therefore say that the area is $(10.35 \pm .3425)$ square inches. Since there is really no virtue in expressing the greatest possible error to four decimal places, we would usually write this as $(10.35 \pm .34)$ square inches. In other words, even though the greatest possible error in each measure was .05, the greatest possible error in the computed product is .34.

For the same problem the relative error in A would be:

$$\text{Rel. error in } A = \frac{.34}{10.35} \approx .033.$$

It might be interesting to compare this relative error with those for the separate measurements of length:

$$\text{Rel. error in } a = \frac{.05}{2.3} \approx .022.$$

$$\text{Rel. error in } b = \frac{.05}{4.5} \approx .011.$$

Thus not only do we get a greatest possible error for A which seems large in comparison with the errors in the separate measurements, but even the relative error is larger. Indeed, for this particular problem the relative error in the area seems to be the sum of the relative errors in the two length measurements.

Since all our area formulas involve us with multiplication, it may be well to consider in general the effect on a product of an error in the factors. Suppose in general that $P = r \cdot s$. Let r_1 be an approximate value of r with a greatest possible error e. Similarly let s_1 be an approximate value of s with greatest possible error e'. Then, just as for the numerical case above,

$$r_1 - e \; \leqq \; r \; \leqq \; r_1 + e.$$
$$s_1 - e' \; \leqq \; s \; \leqq \; s_1 + e'.$$

It follows at once that

$$(s_1 - e') \, (r_1 - e) \; \leqq \; rs \; \leqq \; (s_1 + e') \, (r_1 + e).$$

Since $P = rs$, this means that

$$r_1 s_1 - es_1 - e'r_1 + ee' \; \leqq \; P \; \leqq \; r_1 s_1 + es_1 + e'r_1 + ee'.$$

The greatest amount by which P can exceed the computed value $r_1 s_1$ is therefore $(r_1 s_1 + es_1 + e'r_1 + ee') - r_1 s_1 = es_1 + e'r_1 + ee'$, while the largest possible amount below $r_1 s_1$ is $r_1 s_1 - (r_1 s_1 - es_1 - e'r_1 + ee') = es_1 + e'r_1 - ee'$. The larger of these, namely $es_1 + e'r_1 + ee'$, is therefore the greatest possible error in P. Since the errors e and e' are generally small in comparison with r_1 and s_1, the last term ee' is generally so small we can afford to ignore it. (In the numerical example above this was the .0025 which we ignored.) Thus we obtain

$$\text{Greatest possible error in } P \approx es_1 + e'r_1.$$

If we wish to do so, this could be used as a formula for greatest possible error in a product.

Let us also find the relative error in P. Using the result above

$$\text{Rel. error in } P \approx \frac{es_1 + e'r_1}{r_1 s_1}.$$

A slight bit of calculation shows that

$$\frac{es_1 + e'r_1}{r_1 s_1} = \frac{es_1}{r_1 s_1} + \frac{e'r_1}{r_1 s_1} = \frac{e}{r_1} + \frac{e'}{s_1}.$$

But $\dfrac{e}{r_1}$ is the relative error in r and $\dfrac{e'}{s_1}$ is the relative error in s. That is, we conclude

$$\text{Rel. error in } rs \approx \text{rel. error in } r + \text{rel. error in } s.$$

Thus it appears that the observation made about relative errors in the numerical example was not accidental but illustrates the general situation. Note the consistent use above of the multiplication convention mentioned in the last paragraph of Section 9.6.

The primary moral of the discussion above is not that it is necessary in every calculation to calculate religiously the errors and relative errors, though this can be done when necessary. The point is to recognize that a computed result may not be nearly as precise (or accurate) as the calculation makes it look. Thus in the original problem of calculating area measure for a rectangle that measured 2.3 inches by 4.5 inches, a perfectly correct calculation showed that $A \approx 10.35$ in square inches. On the face of it this looks as if we could expect this result to be correct to the nearest hundredth of a square inch, whereas in point of fact it was found to be correct only to about the nearest .7 square inch. It would have been less deceptive as to the actual facts if we had rounded off our answer to read $A \approx 10.4$ or even $A \approx 10$.

In accord with the findings of the last paragraph it is customary, even if we do not go through the agony of fully computing the errors, to try to list our answers so that they bear some reasonable resemblance to reality, i.e., so that someone reading our results will not be too badly deceived as to the precision intended. To this end you will often see the following very rough rule of thumb applied.

> *Rule of Thumb.* In calculating a product (or quotient) of approximate factors, round off the answer to the smallest number of significant digits in any factor. (You will recall from Section 8.8 that significant digits are those intended to be taken seriously.)

As noted, this is not intended to be exact or sacrosanct, but it avoids the possibility of making excessively wild and meaningless assertions as to precision. For example, suppose that we seek the area measure in square feet of a triangle having one side measuring 12.8 feet and the corresponding altitude 25.1 feet. According to the results of Section 9.4 (Theorem 9.7)

$$A = \frac{1}{2} bh \approx \frac{1}{2} (12.8)(25.1) = 160.64.$$

If we apply the rule of thumb, since each factor was good to three significant figures we would record the answer as

$$A \approx 161 \text{ in square feet.}$$

This suggests to the reader a precision of the nearest square foot, i.e., a greatest possible error of .5 square foot. You may find it interesting to check how near this is to the true facts. Notice that the numerical factor $\frac{1}{2}$ is exact so it is correct to any number of significant figures.

Problem Set 9.7

A. 1. The last problem in the text relates to a triangle for which one side measures 12.8 feet and the corresponding altitude 25.1 feet, with the usual understanding as to the greatest possible error. Compute the greatest possible error in A and compare with the error indicated by using the rule of thumb.

   2. A parallelogram has a side measuring $(8.7 \pm .01)$ centimeters and a corresponding altitude measuring $(12.1 \pm .03)$ centimeters.

     a. Calculate the approximate area in square centimeters.

     b. Find the greatest possible error in the area.

     c. Find the relative error in the area and in each of the sides and verify the results of the text for these relative errors.

   3. A square region has a side measuring 21 feet (to the nearest foot). Find the greatest possible error in the area and record the area in the form (_____ $\pm$ _____) square feet. Compare the result with recording the answer according to the rule of thumb.

B. 1. It is necessary to determine the area of a square region with a relative error of .06 or less. With what accuracy must a side be measured to assure this?

   2. The sides of a rectangle were measured as 25 feet with a relative error of .01 and 36 feet with a relative error of .02. Find the greatest possible error in the computed area.

C. 1. The radius of a circle is measured as 11.4 inches. Find the approximate values of the circumference and the area, recording results according to the rule of thumb. [Note: Take an approximate value for π to the same number of significant figures as the measure for r.]

   2. The circumference of a circle is 8.00 feet. Find the length of the radius in feet and the area in square feet, expressing results according to the rule of thumb. [Take an approximate value of π to as many significant figures as the rest of the data.]

D. Let $Q = \dfrac{a}{b}$. If $a = 50 \pm .2$ and $b = 20 \pm .3$, find the greatest possible error in the computed value of Q. [Watch out for this. There is a catch.] Find also the relative error in Q and compare with the relative errors in a and b.

E. 1. Measure the three sides and three altitudes of $\triangle ABC$ as carefully as

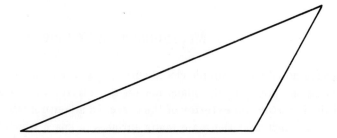

possible. Then use three different sets of these measures to determine the approximate area of the triangular region. Note that the three approximate results will not, in general, be identical but should be reasonably close.

2. Measure as carefully as possible both sets of sides and both altitudes of the parallelogram $ABCD$. Then use these results to make two calculations of the approximate area of the region.

3. Decompose the polygonal region $ABCDE$ *in two ways* into triangular regions. By making suitable measurements compute an approximate area for the region using each of the decompositions.

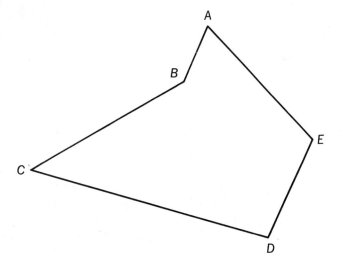

9.8 Measurement of Volume

We have noted that a simple closed curve lying in a plane has the property of separating the points of the plane not on the curve into two sets which were called the **interior** and **exterior** of the curve. In an entirely similar way we are aware of the fact that there are many surfaces in space which have this same property of separating space into two sets, an interior and an exterior. For example, we may speak of a point as being interior to a spherical ball or say that an object is interior to a box. In accord with our previous treatment of such separation properties on a wholly intuitive basis, we shall not attempt to make any formal statement of just what surfaces have this property or even just what is meant by a surface. Instead we shall examine and identify a few of the more common cases. The union of any such surface and its interior we call a **solid region.**

Prism

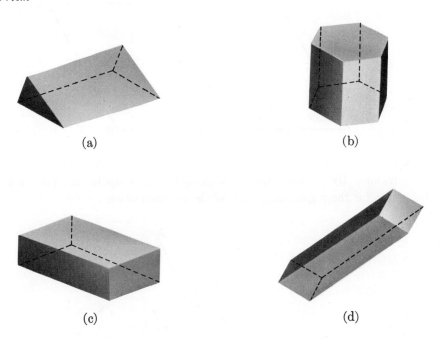

(a)   (b)

(c)   (d)

A prism is a surface which is a union of polygonal regions. It has two faces, generally called **bases,** which are congruent polygonal regions in parallel planes. The other faces are bounded by parallelograms. In (a) of the set of illustrations above, the bases are triangular regions and in (b) the bases are hexagonal regions. Diagrams (c) and (d) have the interesting property that they can be viewed as prisms in three ways. That is, in these cases any pair of parallel faces may be considered to be the bases. If in particular the faces other than the bases are all rectangular regions the prism is called a **right prism.** It was intended that all the diagrams except (d) should represent right prisms.

You may find it interesting to identify examples of different kinds of prisms. By far the most common is the case when all faces are rectangles, i.e., the case of the ordinary chalkbox, or room. This particular kind of prism also carries the mouth-filling name of **rectangular parallelepiped.** A common special case of this is the *cube* where all faces are square regions. The surface of an ordinary child's block is an example of a cube. The block itself would be a good example of a solid region, i.e., the union of the surface (here the cube) and its interior.

Pyramid

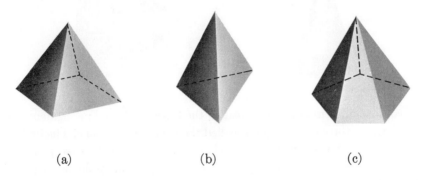

(a)   (b)   (c)

The pyramid likewise is a union of polygonal regions. Its base may be any polygonal region, and the other faces are triangular regions which have a common vertex at a point not in the plane of the base. This point is called the **vertex** of the pyramid. The diagrams above show pyramids with bases which are a square region, a triangular region and a pentagonal region, respectively. Diagram (b) is particularly interesting in that all four faces are triangular regions. Thus it may be viewed as a pyramid in four ways. This type of pyramid is also sometimes called a **tetrahedron.** The classic examples of the pyramid of course are the surfaces of the ancient pyramids of Egypt. These are all pyramids having square regions as bases.

Right Circular Cylinder

This surface contains two congruent circular regions (often called its **bases**) lying in parallel planes and such that the line joining the centers is perpendicular to both base planes. The remainder of the surface (sometimes called the **curved**

surface) is the union of all segments joining points of the two circles and parallel to the segment joining the centers of the bases. The most common examples would be the usual tin cans found in a grocery store. An ordinary piece of pipe is a representation of a right circular cylinder with the bases missing, and the surface of a piece of straight copper wire (if cut off square) would also be a right circular cylinder. Note in this last case that the wire itself would represent the solid region bounded by the cylinder.

Right Circular Cone

This consists of a circular region (called the **base**) and the line segments joining the points of the circle to a point called the **vertex** of the cone. The line joining the vertex to the center of the base is perpendicular to the base plane. The simplest representations would be an ice cream cone or a megaphone (or perhaps a dunce cap).

Sphere

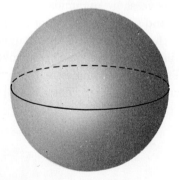

This most familiar of all surfaces consists of all the points of space at a given distance from a point called the **center**. Familiar models include a basketball and the surface of a baseball.

There is of course an infinite variety of other surfaces, some of them quite familiar, like the doughnut shape (called a **torus**). We shall confine our attention, however, to the small group just noted.

For each of the surfaces described we can consider the solid region which it bounds, i.e., the union of the surface and its interior. We then confront once more the wish to measure such a solid region, i.e., to attach to it a number which will describe in some sense how "large" a region it is. By now the idea should be familiar. We shall adopt some convenient solid unit region and ask how many congruent copies of this unit region are needed to cover the solid region to be measured. The measurement of a solid region in this way we call the **volume** of the solid region just as the measurement of a plane region was called its area. Thus if we use a child's block as a unit of volume we might find the volume of a box by finding how many such blocks it takes to fill the box.

Having discussed the case of plane regions, it will not be too shattering a surprise to you if we elect to take as a unit solid region one that is bounded by a cube, each edge of which is one linear unit in length. Thus each face of the unit cube will be a unit of area. The cubic solid region each edge of which is one inch long we call, for obvious reasons, a **cubic inch.** Similarly we may speak of a *cubic foot*, a *cubic centimeter*, etc.

It seems clear at once that in the case of volumes we confront again the situation that occurred for areas. It seems unlikely that there is a nice instrument like the ruler or protractor for measuring volume directly, and resorting to the process of stacking in unit blocks as suggested above is far too cumbersome, even in the cases when it could be done. Thus it seems clear that what we should seek to discover are means of *computing* volumes in terms of things that can be more readily measured. It is this which we shall now discuss.

In this development we are electing to be quite intuitive and heuristic. We shall seek to make the results at least moderately plausible but will make no attempt at formal deduction or statement of axioms. This is being done partly on the theory that you have seen a good deal of deduction in the work with areas, and partly because the inherent complications would require more time than we choose to devote to the topic.

For simplicity of language we shall from now on frequently use phrases such as "volume of a prism" in place of the more correct phrase "volume of the solid region bounded by a prism." You should bear in mind, however, that volume for us always refers to a solid region, not merely its bounding surface.

Volume of a Prism

An altitude of a prism is any segment perpendicular to both base planes. Such segments are in fact the shortest segments from one plane to the other. Since any two such segments are congruent and hence have the same length, it makes sense to speak of *the* measure h of altitude for a prism.

Consider now a right prism whose bases each have area measure B and whose altitude has linear measure h. On page 394 we illustrate this for the case of a rectangular prism, i.e., a rectangular parallelepiped. By definition, B is the number of unit square regions necessary to cover the base. If, on each of the B unit squares covering the base, we place a unit cube, there results a slab one unit thick

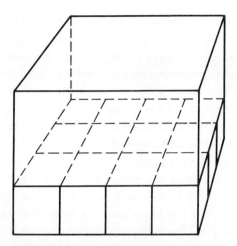

filling the bottom of the prism. This slab consists of B of the unit blocks. Since h is the measure of the height, it will take h such slabs to fill the solid region bounded by the prism. The total number of unit cubes necessary is thus Bh and if V denotes the measure of volume for the region we are led to the formula

$$V = Bh$$

for the volume measure of a right prism. While the diagram shows a rectangular parallelepiped you will notice the reasoning made no specific use of that fact, but applies to any right prism.

You may, with some justice, protest that the argument given supposes that the base is covered exactly with an integral number of unit square regions and that the number h of layers is an integer. Actually this is not necessary. For instance, if, in covering the base, it is necessary to use a half-unit square region, then we clearly use half a unit block to stand on it. Thus in any case the number of blocks in one layer is B whether B is an integer or not. Similar reasoning applies to the case when h is not an integer. Thus it appears at least plausible that the formula $V = Bh$ applies to any right prism.

For the particular case of the solid bounded by a rectangular parallelepiped, let l and w be the measures of the sides of the rectangular base. Then the area measure B of the base is given by $B = lw$. We then obtain the familiar formula

$$V = lwh$$

for the volume measure of a rectangular parallelepiped, i.e., a box.

Parenthetically it may be noted that this formula provides one of the most effective means of helping elementary pupils "see" the truth of the associative property of multiplication. For example, on page 395 one may determine the number of blocks by noting that each horizontal layer contains $4 \cdot 3$ blocks and there are 2 layers so the number of blocks is $(4 \cdot 3) \cdot 2$. On the other hand, the figure can likewise be viewed as consisting of 4 vertical slabs, each of which contains $3 \cdot 2$ blocks. Thus the total number of blocks is $4 \cdot (3 \cdot 2)$. We conclude

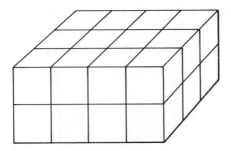

that $(4 \cdot 3) \cdot 2 = 4 \cdot (3 \cdot 2)$, which is an illustration of the associative property of multiplication.

As a matter of fact, the formula $V = Bh$ applies to *any* prism, not just the right prisms. This may perhaps be made plausible by the following physical experiment. Consider a deck of playing cards. When piled up in the usual way [diagram (a) below], they provide a good representation of a solid region which is a rectangular right prism. By pushing the deck sideways it easily assumes a shape which appears to be approximately a prism but no longer a right prism [diagram (b)]. Yet in the two positions the bases (i.e., the cards) are congruent and the height of the deck is the same in both positions. Moreover, the amount of card-

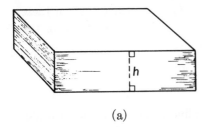
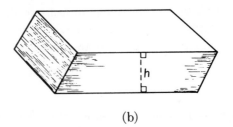

(a)   (b)

board in the deck has clearly not been changed by pushing the cards sideways. Thus it seems reasonable that the volume measure in the second position is still given by $V = Bh$.

Volume of a Pyramid

The segment from the vertex of a pyramid perpendicular to the base plane is called the **altitude** of the pyramid. An experiment similar to the card pushing above makes it plausible that two pyramids, as shown, with congruent bases and altitudes of equal length have equal volumes. But what is the volume?

In the following illustration we see a pyramid inside a prism such that they have a common base and altitude; i.e., the vertex of the pyramid is in the upper base of the prism. It is clear to us at once that the volume of the pyramid is less

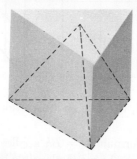

than that of the prism, but how much less? Is it half as large or what? We could use an experimental approach to try to get a hunch. Thus suppose we make models of the prism and pyramid and experiment to see how many times we can fill the pyramid model with salt (or sand, or some other convenient substance) and empty it into the prism. You may find it amusing actually to carry out this experiment with the models indicated in problem **A1** of the next problem set. If so, you should find that it seems to take three fillings of the pyramid to fill the prism. Since the volume measure of the prism is Bh, this means that on these experimental grounds we might conjecture that the volume measure V of the solid region bounded by the pyramid is given by

$$V = \frac{1}{3} Bh$$

where B is the area measure of the base and h the linear measure of the altitude. It happens that this hunch is indeed correct. A second, slightly more sophisticated, experiment leading to the same conjecture is described in Appendix A.

Volume of a Right Circular Cylinder

Several times in our discussions of circles we have found it convenient to think

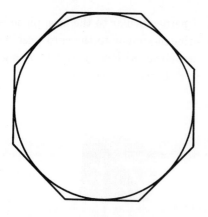

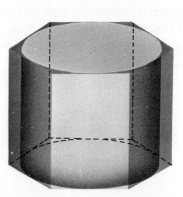

of a circular region as being contained in a polygonal region formed from tangents. As shown by the two preceding drawings, we may use this idea to imagine a cylinder having the circular region for a base as contained in the right prism having the polygonal region for a base. We clearly expect the volume measure V for the cylinder to be less than the volume measure V_p for the prism. We know that $V_p = B_p h$ where B_p is the area measure of the polygonal region. We conjectured earlier that as the number of sides increases the measure B_p approaches the area measure B of the circular region. At the same time it looks highly plausible that the volume measure V_p approaches V, the volume measure of the cylinder. It thus seems a highly plausible conjecture that

$$V = Bh.$$

This statement is indeed a correct one. If r is the measure of a radius of the circle, we know that the area measure B is given by $B = \pi r^2$. Thus the formula above may be rewritten as

$$V = \pi r^2 h$$

where V is the volume measure of the solid region bounded by the cylinder, r is the measure of a radius and h is the measure of an altitude.

Volume of a Right Circular Cone

The argument used for cylinders can also be used for cones. We can think of the cone as contained in a pyramid. The volume measure V_p of the pyramid is $V_p = \dfrac{1}{3} B_p h$ where B_p is the area measure of the polygonal region. As before, it

appears that if we consider polygons of more and more sides V_p will approach the volume measure V of the cone and B_p will approach the area measure B of the circular base. Thus we are led to make the conjecture that

$$V = \frac{1}{3} Bh.$$

This is in fact a correct conjecture. If r is the measure of a radius of the circular base, then, as above, $B = \pi r^2$. By substitution we find that the volume measure V of the solid region bounded by a right circular cone is given by

$$V = \frac{1}{3}\pi r^2 h$$

where r is the measure of a radius and h the measure of the altitude.

Volume of a Sphere

Frankly, this is a much more difficult solid region about which to motivate a conjecture. To avoid too long a digression we shall content ourselves with a very weak-kneed hint.

Consider the solid region $\Re$ bounded by a plane through the center of a sphere and one of the two hemispheres into which this cuts the sphere. If the measure

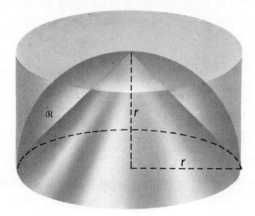

of the radius is r, we see at once that the solid region $\Re$ is interior to a cylinder with radius of measure r and altitude of measure r. The volume measure of this cylindrical region is therefore (by the work above) $\pi r^2 r = \pi r^3$. On the other hand, $\Re$ contains the cone whose radius and altitude each have measure r as shown in the accompanying drawing. The volume of this conical region is $\frac{1}{3}\pi r^2 r = \frac{1}{3}\pi r^3$. Thus the volume measure of $\Re$ should be somewhere between $\frac{1}{3}\pi r^3$ and πr^3. As a guess at an approximate volume for $\Re$ we might take the average of these two results, getting $\frac{2}{3}\pi r^3$. Incredibly enough, this wild shot in the dark not only gives an approximation to the volume measure of $\Re$, but turns out to be *exactly correct*! Since $\Re$ was half of the spherical region, we thus find that the volume measure V of the solid region bounded by a sphere whose radius has measure r is

$$V = \frac{4}{3}\pi r^3.$$

As remarked earlier, this is a very weak basis for a conjecture, but a more ade-
quate one or an honest proof would take longer than we choose to devote to it.
A better discussion may be found for example in the School Mathematics Study
Group text *Geometry*.*

For convenience in reference it is desirable to collect the results obtained above.
Thus we state the following theorem even though we have at best hinted at how
to prove it. Note that we have chosen to omit the dots as multiplication signs in
the formulas.

Theorem 9.12 *The volume measure V of the solid region bounded by each of the
following surfaces is given by the indicated formula.*

(a) *Prism*: $V = Bh$ *where B is the area measure of the base and h the measure
   of an altitude.*

(b) *Pyramid*: $V = \dfrac{1}{3}Bh$ *where B is the area measure of the base and h the measure
   of the altitude.*

(c) *Right Circular Cylinder*: $V = \pi r^2 h$ *where r and h are the measures of radius
   and altitude, respectively.*

(d) *Right Circular Cone*: $V = \dfrac{1}{3}\pi r^2 h$ *where r and h are the measures of radius
   and altitude, respectively.*

(e) *Sphere*: $V = \dfrac{4}{3}\pi r^3$ *where r is the measure of a radius.*

When we considered plane regions, we observed that there were two measures
that were sometimes of interest to us. One of these was the *length* of the bounding curve (called the *perimeter* in the case of a polygon) and the other was the
area of the region. Unfortunately students sometimes confuse these very different
ideas.

In exactly the same way, when a solid region is considered, there are often two
measures of interest to us. One is the *area* of the bounding surface and the other
the *volume* of the solid region. So far in this section we have talked only about the
volume of the solid region. What about the area of the surface? Although this is
an extension of our idea of area, which applied to plane regions only, it is not
difficult, at least in some simple cases, to decide what we would mean.

One could make a purely experimental approach to this question of surface
area by finding how much paint it takes to cover the given surface and then seeing
how large an area of the plane could be covered by the same amount of paint. If,
for example, this were tried on a sphere whose radius has measure r one would
find he had just about enough paint to cover four circular regions in the plane,
each having radius of measure r. On this basis one might conjecture that the area
measure S for this sphere is given by

$$S = 4\pi r^2.$$

* School Mathematics Study Group, *Geometry* (New Haven: Yale University Press, 1961),
pp. 546–562.

This happens to be a correct conjecture though we shall make no attempt at a proof.

You will recall that the general question of the length of a curve involved complications which we chose not to discuss but that in the special case of polygons we could give a meaningful treatment. Similarly, the general question of area for a surface is far too difficult for an honest treatment in a book at this level, but the polyhedrons, i.e., the surfaces formed from polygonal regions can be legitimately discussed.

Consider, for example, the rectangular prism (i.e., ordinary box) whose edges

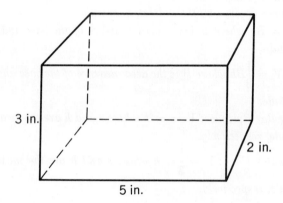

3 in.

2 in.

5 in.

have lengths 5 inches, 3 inches, and 2 inches. This surface consists of six rectangular faces. Two of them have areas of $3 \cdot 5$ square inches, two have areas of $2 \cdot 3$ square inches, and two have areas of $2 \cdot 5$ square inches. By the area measure of this surface we shall mean the sum of the area measures of the six faces. That is, the area of this surface is

$$[2 \cdot (3 \cdot 5) + 2 \cdot (2 \cdot 3) + 2 \cdot (2 \cdot 5)]$$ square inches or 62 square inches.

In general if a surface is a union of plane regions (like the prism or pyramid) its area measure is simply the sum of the area measures of the different regions.

The intuitive idea involved is quite simple. When you are finding the area of a surface you are answering the question "How much material will it take to make a model of this surface?" When you find the volume you are answering the question "How much will this model hold when I get it made?"

If you look at problem **A2** of Problem Set 9.8 you will notice that some curved surfaces, such as the cylinder and cone, can be rolled out into plane regions. It would be reasonable to define their surface areas as the sum of these plane areas. You may find it interesting to discover the surface area formulas for these surfaces, but we shall not seek to investigate it further here. For the cylinder the correct result is

$$S = 2\pi r^2 + 2\pi rh,$$

where r is the measure of a radius and h the measure of an altitude.

It probably is unnecessary to observe that all the remarks about approximation in measurement made earlier apply with equal force to the concepts of volume and surface area discussed in this section. Without trying to make a major issue of it, it is worth recalling that in a computation of products the relative error in the product is very nearly the sum of the relative errors of the factors. Thus consider a rectangular parallelepiped whose edges have lengths of 2.1 inches, 4.6 inches, and 3.2 inches and suppose these are correct to the nearest tenth of an inch. Then the approximate volume measure V in cubic inches is given by $V \approx (2.1)(4.6)(3.2) = 30.912$. The three relative errors in the sides are $\frac{.05}{2.1} \approx .024$, $\frac{.05}{4.6} \approx .011$, and $\frac{.05}{3.2} \approx .016$. Thus the relative error in the computed value of V is approximately $(.024 + .011 + .016) = .051$. The greatest possible error in V is thus approximately $(.051)(30.912) \approx 1.58$, where we have chosen to round off to two decimal places. If the rule of thumb of Section 9.7 were applied mechanically (without computing the greatest possible error) the volume would have been recorded as 31 cubic inches. This suggests to the reader a greatest possible error of .5 cubic inch. We see by our calculation that this is a little optimistic since the correct greatest possible error is three times this size. It is, however, more realistic than writing 30.912 cubic inches, which would suggest a greatest possible error of .0005 cubic inch.

In the problems below, except where stated otherwise, you may assume figures are exact but remember that in practice this is never actually the case.

Problem Set 9.8

A. 1. a. Make models of a right prism and a pyramid using the dimensions on the indicated patterns (or some multiple of the indicated dimensions). Fold on the indicated lines. The joints may be fastened with transparent tape. If you wish to do **b**, leave a base loose in each model. Make $\overline{AB} \cong \overline{BC}$. Properly done, these models will represent a pyramid and a prism having congruent bases and altitudes.

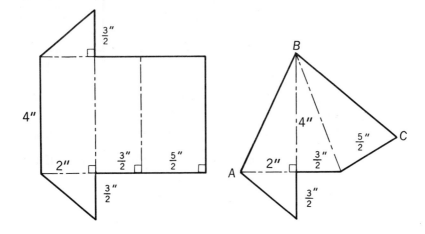

b. Using the models of **a** find experimentally how many times the pyramid model can be filled with salt (or some other convenient substance) and emptied into the prism model. This should yield an experimental confirmation of the volume formula for the pyramid.

2. Using patterns similar to those here and on the next page, make models of the various surfaces. Fold on the indicated lines. Joints may be fastened with transparent tape.

a. Cube. The separate regions are squares.

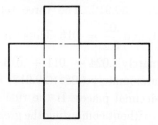

b. Rectangular parallelepiped (rectangular right prism). Two of the figures are squares and the other four congruent rectangles.

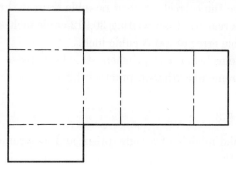

c. Triangular pyramid (tetrahedron). The figures are here equilateral triangles.

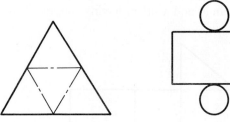

d. Cylinder. Be sure the length of the rectangle is the same as the circumference of the circle.

e. Cone. If the angle at V is a 90° angle, the radius of the small circle should have a measure $\frac{1}{4}$ that of the large circle. If there is a 120° angle at V, the fraction should be $\frac{1}{3}$.

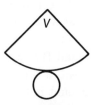

B. 1. If the sides of a rectangular parallelepiped have measures l, w, h, show
that the area measure S of the surface is given by

$$S = 2(lw + wh + lh).$$

2. The base of a right prism is a triangular region bounded by a right
triangle. The perpendicular sides of this triangle have lengths of 6 inches
and 8 inches. The height of the prism is 20 inches.
a. Find in cubic inches the volume of the solid region bounded by the
prism.
b. Find in square inches the surface area of the prism.

C. 1. A man notices a large sandbox in a park. He observes that it is 10 feet
long, 10 feet wide and 2 feet deep. The park superintendent tells him it
cost $4.00 to get enough sand to fill it. The man decides to build a
smaller sandbox in his backyard. He makes it 5 feet long, 5 feet wide
and 1 foot deep. How much will it cost for enough sand to fill it?
2. Two rectangular parallelepipeds are being compared. It is found that the
edges of one are exactly twice as long as the edges of the other.
a. How do the volumes compare?
b. How do the surface areas compare?

D. 1. A man finds he gets a half-glass of orange juice from an orange 2 inches
in diameter. How much can he expect from an (equally juicy) orange
3 inches in diameter? What about an orange 4 inches in diameter?
[Ignore the thickness of the rind.]
2. Consider a hemisphere and cone as shown. Each has a radius of measure
r. The conical container has an altitude of measure $2r$. How do the
volumes of these two containers compare?

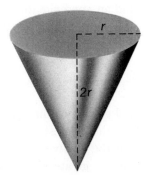

3. Two soft-drink stands sell their drinks in conical cups, but the cups are of different shapes. Stand A uses cups that are 2 inches across the top and 6 inches deep while stand B uses cups 4 inches across the top and 3 inches deep. (Thus stand B's cups are twice as wide but only half as deep.) Both charge 10 cents a cup. Is one a better deal than the other or do you get the same amount in both cases?

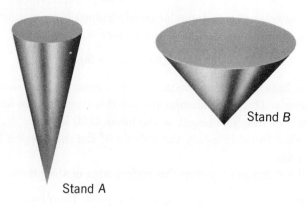

Stand *B*

Stand *A*

E. 1. A cubical region has a volume of 125 cubic feet.
   a. How long is an edge of the cube?
   b. What is the area of the cube?
2. A solid region is bounded by a pyramid. The area of the base is 2 square feet. The height is 12 inches. What is the volume?
3. What is the volume in cubic inches of a solid region bounded by a cube whose edges are 1 foot long? What is the volume in cubic feet of a solid region bounded by a cube whose edges are 1 yard long?
4. The volume of a pyramid is 12 cubic feet and the height is 4 feet. What is the area of the base?
5. What would be the answer to question **E4** if the figure were a prism instead of a pyramid?

F. 1. A box has the shape of a rectangular parallelepiped. Its edges are measured as 10 inches, 12 inches, and 15 inches. It is understood that these are correct to the nearest inch.
   a. Find an approximate value for the volume.
   b. Find (approximately) the relative error and greatest possible error in the volume.
2. The radius of a cylinder was measured as 6 inches with a relative error of .02 and the altitude was measured as 25 inches with a relative error of .01.
   a. Find an approximate value for the volume.
   b. Find the greatest possible error in radius and in height.
   c. Find the relative error in the volume.
   d. Find the greatest possible error in the volume.

3. The edges of two cubes are measured. In both cases the edge was found to be between 6 and 7 inches long. Show that the volume of the region bounded by one cube could be more than 50% larger than that for the other.

4. In the cubes of problem **F3**, could the area of one cube exceed that of the other by 50%? If not, could one exceed the other by $33\frac{1}{3}\%$?

9.9 Measurement in Retrospect

Having now considered measurements of segments, angles, regions and solid regions, it may be useful to survey our experience with the measurement process in general. We observe that in every case we have made a choice of some unit with respect to which the measurement was done. There was wide latitude in this choice of unit. Moreover the unit in each case had the nature of the object to be measured. Thus the unit for measuring segments was a segment, the unit for angle measure was an angle, etc. A unit having been selected, the measurement process itself, described in its simplest terms, consisted in counting how many copies of the unit were needed to cover the object in question. To put it another way, we asked into how many copies of the unit the given figure could be decomposed. In asking this question it is of course necessary to specify what is meant by saying that one figure is a *copy* of another. This was where the concept of congruence played a critical role, since we defined copy to mean **congruent** copy. Thus, in our approach to measuring these geometric figures, the idea of congruence is essentially the key to measurement.

In refining the measurement idea we found it essential to envision the subdivision of our unit into fractional parts and consequent use of fractional measures. Indeed, it ultimately became necessary to envision the use of all real numbers as measures. Thus the objects to which we apply the measurement process are conceived to have the property of being susceptible of any amount of subdivision. In the four cases which we developed there is thus a strong common thread which we can consider the essential idea of the measurement process.

You have undoubtedly been reflecting, however, that we measure many things besides geometric figures. We measure weight, time, speed, electric current, and many other things and it is certainly relevant to ask how much of the common thread above applies to these other measurements. First, it is still true that in every case some unit is chosen with respect to which measurement is to be made. Moreover, in a sense the unit has the nature of the thing being measured; e.g., in measuring weight we select a unit of weight, in measuring time the unit is some interval of time.

The measurement process then means counting how many copies of the unit are needed to match (in some sense) the figure being measured. Here there is a divergence from the geometric discussion above. A copy of the unit certainly cannot in general be defined in terms of the geometric idea of congruence. If one is measuring weight nobody cares whether the copies of the unit weight have the same size and shape. What they must have is the same weight; i.e., they must balance if they are placed in opposite pans of a balance. Thus for weight, the concept of congruence is replaced by the concept of "balancing." A copy of the unit weight is anything which will balance with it. Weighing an unknown object means counting the number of copies of the unit weight necessary to balance the unknown object.

Measurement in general therefore involves both a choice of unit and some concept of equivalence. A copy of the unit is anything which is equivalent to the unit, and measurement of an object means finding how many copies of the unit are needed to produce something equivalent to the unknown object. For the case of the geometric measurement the equivalence concept is congruence, for weight it is the concept of balancing, etc. Thus measurement always involves the idea of some sort of equivalence and a possibility of comparison.

In general the idea of subdivision, of the use of fractional and ultimately real measures, applies to all the different kinds of measurement.

Beyond these general philosophical remarks we shall make no attempt in the text to consider other specific measurement processes. Each necessarily involves its own particular technique, but it should be fairly clear on the basis of this discussion how the different cases relate to each other. In every case we shall find a unit and a basis of comparison.

9.10 Axioms and Theorems in Chapter 9

Axiom **MA** To every angle, $\angle AOB$, can be assigned a real number $m(\angle AOB)$ called its degree measure in such a way that

(a) The set of real numbers which are measures of angles is the set of real numbers between 0 and 180, i.e.,

$$\{x \mid 0 < x < 180, x \text{ a real number}\}.$$

(b) If C is interior to $\angle AOB$, then $m(\angle AOB) = m(\angle AOC) + m(\angle COB)$.

(c) $\angle AOB \cong \angle A'O'B'$ if and only if $m(\angle AOB) = m(\angle A'O'B')$.

(d) $\angle ABC$ and $\angle PQR$ are supplementary if and only if $m(\angle ABC) + m(\angle PQR) = 180$.

Axiom **P** If point A does not lie on line k, there is at most one line k' containing A and parallel to k.

Axiom **MAR** To every plane region $\mathcal{R}$ is assigned a real number $m(\mathcal{R})$ called the measure of its area. The measure satisfies the following conditions:

(a) If two regions are bounded by congruent curves, their measures are equal.

(b) If regions $\mathcal{R}_1$ and $\mathcal{R}_2$ do not overlap, i.e., have no common interior points, then $m(\mathcal{R}_1 \cup \mathcal{R}_2) = m(\mathcal{R}_1) + m(\mathcal{R}_2)$.

(c) If the linear measures of the sides of a rectangular region are a and b, then its area measure A is given by $A = ab$.

Theorem 9.1 If parallel lines k_1 and k_2 are met by a transversal k_3, both pairs of alternate interior angles have equal measures.

Theorem 9.2 The sum of the degree measures of the angles of a triangle is 180.

Theorem 9.3 Two adjacent angles of a parallelogram are supplementary, i.e., the sum of the degree measures is 180.

Theorem 9.4 Two opposite angles of a parallelogram are congruent.

Theorem 9.5 Opposite sides of a parallelogram are congruent.

Theorem 9.6 The four sides of a rhombus are all congruent.

Theorem 9.7

(a) The area measure A of a rectangular region is given by

$$A = ab,$$

where a and b are the linear measures of adjacent sides.

(b) The area measure A of a triangular region is given by

$$A = \frac{1}{2}bh,$$

where b is the measure of any side and h the measure of the corresponding altitude.

(c) The area measure A of a region bounded by a parallelogram is given by

$$A = bh,$$

where b is the measure of any side and h the measure of a corresponding altitude.

Theorem 9.8 For any right triangle the area measure of the square region on the hypotenuse equals the sum of the area measures of the square regions on the other two sides.

Theorem 9.9 If the area measure of the square region on one side of a triangle equals the sum of the area measures of the square regions on the other two sides, the triangle is a right triangle.

Theorem 9.10 The hypotenuse of a right triangle is longer than either of the other two sides.

Theorem 9.11 The measure of any side of a triangle is less than the sum of the measures of the other two sides.

Theorem 9.12 The volume measure V of the solid region bounded by each of the following surfaces is given by the indicated formula.

(a) Prism: $V = Bh$, where B is the area measure of the base and h the measure of an altitude.

(b) Pyramid: $V = \frac{1}{3}Bh$, where B is the area measure of the base and h the measure of the altitude.

(c) Right Circular Cylinder: $V = \pi r^2 h$, where r and h are the measures of a radius and an altitude, respectively.

(d) Right Circular Cone: $V = \frac{1}{3}\pi r^2 h$, where r and h are the measures of a radius and the altitude, respectively.

(e) Sphere: $V = \frac{4}{3}\pi r^3$, where r is the measure of a radius.

9.11 Terminal Tasks for Chapter 9

1. To determine approximately the measure of an angle with respect to a given unit angle.
2. To use the protractor to determine approximately the degree measure of an angle.
3. To determine approximately the area measure of a plane region (a) with respect to any given unit region, (b) with respect to a standard square region as the unit.
4. To use the appropriate formula to calculate the area measure of a plane region bounded by a rectangle, parallelogram, triangle, square or circle.
5. To use the appropriate formula to calculate the volume measure of a solid region bounded by a prism, pyramid, cone, cylinder, or sphere.
6. To demonstrate experimentally (using geometric models) and algebraically (using appropriate formulas) that regions of equal area measure need not be congruent.
7. To use the additive property of area (volume) measure to determine the area (volume) of a region by decomposition into familiar regions.
8. To show, by using the formula or making a drawing, how variations in the linear measures of each region studied in the text affect the area or volume of the region.
9. To demonstrate that plane regions of equal area may have different perimeters.
10. To identify alternate interior angles and corresponding angles formed when a transversal intersects two lines in a plane.
11. To apply the congruence relationship between a pair of alternate interior angles or between a pair of corresponding angles in exercises where two lines are given parallel.
12. To use the angle sum theorem for angles of a triangle in numerical exercises.
13. To state the Pythagorean Theorem in mathematical symbols and apply it in numerical exercises.
14. To determine greatest possible error and relative error in a computed product with approximate data.
15. To use the rule of thumb in expressing results of a product calculation with approximate data.

16. To apply the properties of quadrilaterals, studied in the text, in writing simple deductive proofs.

REVIEW EXERCISES

A. 1. Find the approximate measure of $\angle PQR$ with respect to $\angle ABC$ as a unit.

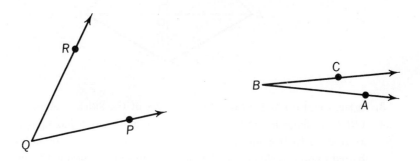

2. Using the region bounded by isosceles right triangle $\triangle ABC$ as unit find the approximate area measure of $FAST$ and $HOPE$. Do these area measures seem to be equal? Are the regions congruent?

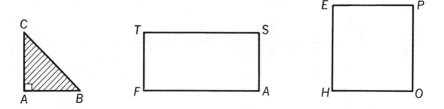

B. 1. The diagram shows a hemisphere with radii each 3 feet long surmounted by a cone 3 feet high. Find the volume in cubic feet of the solid region thus formed.

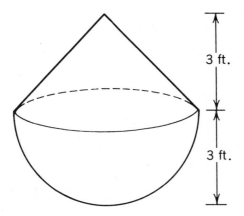

2. In the diagram below $\overline{AC} \perp \overline{BD}$ at O. Moreover, $m(\overline{OA}) = m(\overline{OC}) = 12$, $m(\overline{OD}) = 9$, $m(\overline{OB}) = 5$. Find the area measure in square units of the region bounded by $ABCD$.

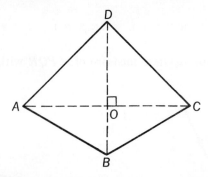

3. In the diagram of **B2** find the measures of the sides of $ABCD$.

4. $ABCD$ in diagram (a) is a square each side of which has measure a. The arc from B to D is an arc of a circle with center A. Find the area of the shaded region. Indicate all the facts you used in deducing this conclusion.

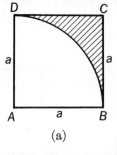

(a)

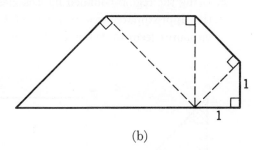

(b)

5. Diagram (b) shows a region which is a union of four regions bounded by isosceles right triangles. The measures of the perpendicular sides of the smallest triangle are 1 as shown. Find the area measure of the region.

C. 1. Find angle measures for the angles of an equilateral triangle. What facts were used in drawing the conclusion?

2. $\triangle ABC$ is an equilateral triangle and D is the midpoint of $\overline{AB}$. Find degree measures for the angles of $\triangle ACD$. What facts were used in drawing this conclusion?

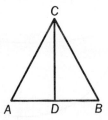

3. An isosceles triangle has an angle with degree measure 40. Find the possible degree measures of the other angles.

D. Two straight roads intersect at O. A man standing at A, 60 yards from O, finds his perpendicular distance from road $\overleftrightarrow{OB}$ is 40 yards. A man standing at B finds his perpendicular distance from road $\overleftrightarrow{OA}$ is 50 yards. How far is B from O?

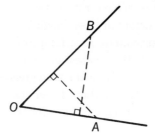

E. 1. A toy manufacturer makes blocks whose surfaces are cubes and paints them. His blocks have edges 2 inches long. He finds the material for 1000 of these blocks costs $50 and the paint for them costs $8. As an experiment he decides to make 1000 larger blocks with edges 4 inches long. How much should he expect to spend for material and how much for paint?

2. For two triangular regions a base of the first is double that of the second but the corresponding altitude of the second is three times that of the first. How do their area measures compare?

F. Two lines k_1 and k_2 in a plane are met by a transversal k, forming eight angles as shown. Write a condition connecting $\angle 1$ with each of the angles $\angle 5$, $\angle 6$, $\angle 7$, $\angle 8$ which will be a necessary and sufficient condition that $k_1 \parallel k_2$.

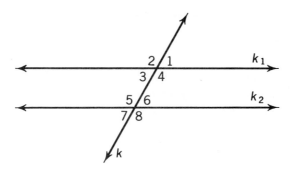

G. 1. Twenty-four tiles 2 inches on a side are arranged to form a rectangular region. What can be said of the areas of the regions that can be formed? What are the perimeters of the different regions that can be formed?

2. On the basis of the experimental data in problem **G1** can you make a conjecture as to what rectangular region of a given area has the least perimeter?

H. 1. The base and corresponding altitude of a triangular region are measured as 12.2 inches and 15.1 inches. If these measurements are to the nearest tenth of an inch find

a. An approximate value for the area.

b. The greatest possible error in the computed area.

c. The relative errors in base, height, and area.

2. Express the approximate area for problem **H1** using the rule of thumb for rounding off. Is the greatest possible error suggested by this recorded answer greater or less than the true greatest possible error?

3. What differences would there be in the answers to problem **H1** if the given numbers had been measures for the adjacent sides of a rectangular region?

4. It is desired to determine the area measure of a circular region with a relative error less than .04. If the radius is measured as $(5 \pm .08)$ inches will this be close enough?

I. 1. Prove that the difference of the measures of two sides of a triangle is less than the third side.

2. If the four angles of a parallelogram are all congruent prove that the parallelogram is a rectangle.

3. Points P,Q are the midpoints of sides $\overline{AB}, \overline{CD}$ of a parallelogram. Prove that $\overleftrightarrow{PQ} \parallel \overleftrightarrow{AD}$.

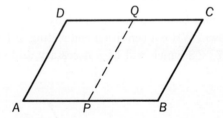

J. 1. Two of your pupils object that the two regions shown should not have the same area because they are clearly not congruent. What did you find in this chapter relevant to this question?

2. Two more of your pupils agree with those in problem **J1** that something is wrong when they find the perimeters of the regions are different. What did you find in this chapter to help in discussing this?

3. There is a table in your classroom which is just twice as long and twice as wide as your pupils' desks. You are discussing area and the pupils find that their desks can be covered by six sheets of paper of a certain size. They cannot understand why 12 such sheets will not cover the table. What did you find in this chapter relevant to this problem?

4. One of your pupils reports that "My father said that when he went to school he learned that a straight line is the shortest distance between two points." What do you find in this chapter which is related to this remark?

5. Your pupils are making models of triangles by fastening paper strips together. One of them tries to use strips whose lengths are 10 inches, 4 inches, and 5 inches and is disturbed because it won't work. What in this chapter is relevant to this difficulty?

6. Your pupils bring you a large marble and some small ones made of the same material. The large one has apparently twice the diameter of the small ones. The pupils are puzzled because two of the small ones won't balance the large one in the balance scale. What did you find in this chapter that relates to their question?

7. One of your pupils has a flying airplane model powered by a rubber band. He likes it so well he builds another one with each dimension just doubled and powers it with two rubber bands. He is disappointed to find it won't fly at all. What do you find in this chapter to help explain this phenomenon?

10 Coordinates and Similarity

10.1 Introduction

In the development of geometry as it has been done in this text, great stress has been laid on the concept of congruence. Intuitively this has referred to two sets of points which "had the same size and shape." A second important relationship which may exist between two point sets is that of *similarity*. A formal definition of the word will be forthcoming in due time but the intuitive idea is that point sets are similar if they "have the same shape" though not necessarily the same size. Thus, occasionally we may see a little girl who looks so much like her mother that we remark "She is the image of her mother." Perhaps a better illustration would be the relation between a picture and an enlargement of it. Certainly in our experience the enlargement "looks like" the picture and the different parts of the enlargement appear to "have the same shape" as the corresponding parts of the original picture but are clearly of different size.

One of the important applications of the idea of similarity is in what might be called indirect measurement. For example, we may wish to determine the height of a building or the width of a river or, in general, any measure of an object to which it is inconvenient or impossible to apply the methods of direct measurement. As we shall see, the idea of similarity provides a useful tool in such situations.

The main purpose of this chapter is to explore this important concept of similarity. It would be possible to approach this in a way quite like our discussion of congruence in Chapter 5. However, there are some advantages to be obtained if we make application of the ideas of describing points by coordinates. Since this is an important idea in its own right, and since the discussion affords an interesting application of algebraic methods to geometric problems, we elect to use this approach. To this end let us consider next the question of attaching coordinates to points in a plane.

10.2 Coordinates in a Plane

In Chapter 8 we explored with some care the idea of the number line, i.e., the idea of associating with points, numbers which could then be used to identify the points. Numbers thus used in identifying points were called **coordinates.** These previous ideas can be used in a very simple way, perhaps already familiar to you, to provide a system for identifying points in a plane by means of coordinates.

Consider two perpendicular lines in the given plane as shown in the following drawing, and let each of them be made into a number line as in Chapter 8.

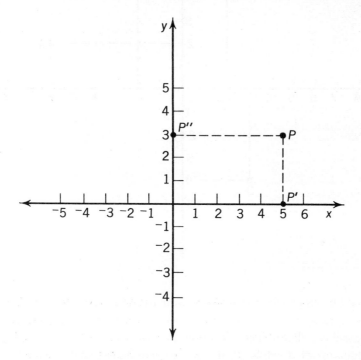

We agree that the point of intersection of the lines (often called the **origin**) shall be the zero point for each of the two scales and that the same unit segment shall be used in forming the two scales. To distinguish the two lines we call one of them the x-axis and the other the y-axis. In the diagram the x-axis is the horizontal one. This is the conventional arrangement though there is nothing sacrosanct about it. We could equally well speak of the "first axis" and the "second axis" instead of x-axis and y-axis. The designation is not important, but it will be vital that we clearly distinguish between them. Let P, as shown, denote any point of the plane and draw perpendiculars from P to the two axes meeting them in P' and P'', respectively. The coordinate of P' on the x-axis is 5 and the coordinate of P'' on the y-axis is 3. Thus with the point P we can associate the pair of numbers (5, 3). These numbers are called the **coordinates** of P. In this way every point of the plane is associated with a unique pair of numbers. Conversely, every pair of numbers is associated with a unique point. For example, (6, 2), (‾2, 4), (0, ‾2), and (‾3, ‾4) are coordinates for A, B, C, and D, respectively, as shown.

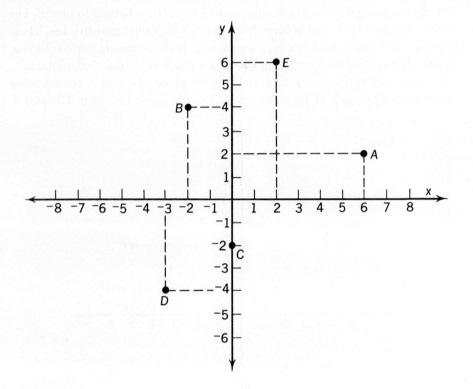

It should be emphasized that the coordinates of a point are an *ordered* pair of numbers. That is, the *first* coordinate determines a point on the *first* axis and the *second* coordinate determines a point on the *second* axis. Thus, as noted, (6, 2) are the coordinates of A while (2, 6) are the coordinates of the entirely different point E.

Any way of identifying points by coordinates (i.e., numbers) is called a **coordinate system.** The particular system described here is called a **Cartesian coordinate system** in honor of the French mathematician and philosopher Descartes, who is usually credited with the basic idea of associating points or other objects with coordinates. There is a touch of irony in this designation since there seems to be no evidence that Descartes ever made use of coordinate axes. Yet, recognition for a fundamental and fruitful idea is certainly due him.

There are various modifications of this system which are in occasional use. For example, the axes are not always taken perpendicular and sometimes the unit segments on the two axes are not required to be congruent. However, the system described above is the only one we shall employ in this text.

An important by-product of identifying points by coordinates is that many geometric properties can now be obtained by arithmetic operations with the coordinates. As an illustration, let us consider the problem of finding the distance between two points. Let P_1 have coordinates $(^-2, 1)$ and let P_2 have coordinates $(4, 3)$. What is the measure of segment $\overline{P_1P_2}$ (in terms of the unit segment used on the axes)?

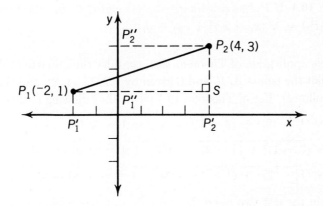

Let the perpendiculars from P_1 and P_2 to the axes be drawn as shown in the diagram, and let S be the intersection of the horizontal line through P_1 and the vertical line through P_2. Then $\triangle P_1SP_2$ is a right triangle and we can use the Theorem of Pythagoras (Theorem 9.8) to find the length of $\overline{P_1P_2}$ if we know the lengths of $\overline{P_1S}$ and $\overline{SP_2}$. $\overline{P_1S}$ has the same length as $\overline{P_1'P_2'}$ (why?), which is seen to be six units, and $\overline{SP_2}$ has the same length as $\overline{P_1''P_2''}$, namely, two units. Thus the measure d of $\overline{P_1P_2}$ satisfies the relation

$$d^2 = 6^2 + 2^2$$

or $d = \sqrt{6^2 + 2^2} = \sqrt{36 + 4} = \sqrt{40}$. You will recall from your work in algebra that if A and B are positive numbers, then $\sqrt{A \cdot B} = \sqrt{A} \cdot \sqrt{B}$. Compare problem **D3** of Problem Set 8.6. Thus we can write $\sqrt{40} = \sqrt{4 \cdot 10} = \sqrt{4}\,\sqrt{10} = 2\sqrt{10}$ so we find $d = 2\sqrt{10}$. If we wish, we can use a square root table to determine an approximate decimal value for d. For most of our work in this chapter, however, this will not be essential.

The procedure above can be done in any given numerical case but gets a little laborious. It occurs to us to ask whether we can do this once and for all in the "general case" and obtain a formula which can be applied mechanically instead of painfully drawing diagrams each time. Thus, suppose that P_1 has coordinates (x_1, y_1) and P_2 has coordinates (x_2, y_2). Using the same diagram as before, this means that, as points on the x-axis, P_1' and P_2' have coordinates x_1 and x_2, respectively. According to Theorem 8.9 this means that $m(\overline{P_1'P_2'}) = |\, x_2 - x_1\,|$. Since $\overline{P_1S} \cong \overline{P_1'P_2'}$ it follows that $m(\overline{P_1S}) = |\, x_2 - x_1\,|$. Similarly, $m(\overline{SP_2}) = m(\overline{P_1''P_2''}) = |\, y_2 - y_1\,|$. Then by the Theorem of Pythagoras the measure d

of $\overline{P_1P_2}$ is such that

$$d^2 = |x_2 - x_1|^2 + |y_2 - y_1|^2 = (x_2 - x_1)^2 + (y_2 - y_1)^2.$$

The last step above uses the fact that $|x_2 - x_1|^2 = (x_2 - x_1)^2$ and $|y_2 - y_1|^2 = (y_2 - y_1)^2$. Why is this true? The measure d of $\overline{P_1P_2}$ is then obtained by taking the positive square root. This result is embodied in the following theorem:

Theorem 10.1 If P_1 has *coordinates* (x_1, y_1) *and if* P_2 *has coordinates* (x_2, y_2), *then* $m(\overline{P_1P_2}) = \sqrt{(x_2 - x_1)^2 + (y_2 - y_1)^2}$.

As a simple application of Theorem 10.1, consider the problem of determining whether or not the points A, B, and C given by $(-2, 1)$, $(1, 2)$, and $(7, 4)$, respectively, are collinear. Use of Theorem 10.1 yields the following results:

$$m(\overline{AB}) = \sqrt{(1 - {}^-2)^2 + (2 - 1)^2} = \sqrt{9 + 1} = \sqrt{10}.$$

$$m(\overline{BC}) = \sqrt{(7 - 1)^2 + (4 - 2)^2} = \sqrt{36 + 4} = \sqrt{40} = \sqrt{4 \cdot 10} = 2\sqrt{10}.$$

$$m(\overline{AC}) = \sqrt{(7 - {}^-2)^2 + (4 - 1)^2} = \sqrt{81 + 9} = \sqrt{90} = \sqrt{9 \cdot 10} = 3\sqrt{10}.$$

Notice that in the last two cases the simplification has made use of the relation $\sqrt{A \cdot B} = \sqrt{A} \cdot \sqrt{B}$. It follows at once from the results that

$$m(\overline{AC}) = m(\overline{AB}) + m(\overline{BC}).$$

But this tells us at once that points A, B, C are collinear, for if they formed a triangle then we would have $m(\overline{AC}) < m(\overline{AB}) + m(\overline{BC})$. (Why?) Thus, since the measure of one segment is the sum of the measures of the other two, the points must be collinear. Indeed, $B \in \overline{AC}$.

The problems below afford examples of other ways in which the distance formula can be used to yield geometric information.

We have seen that a point of the plane can always be described by a pair of coordinates, say $(3, 1)$. We shall commonly refer to this by phrases like "the point represented by $(3, 1)$" or "the point whose coordinates are $(3, 1)$." If a phrase occurs such as "the point $(3, 1)$" it will be merely a shorthand for one of the more nearly correct phrases above. We intend to distinguish between a point and the coordinates which identify it.

Problem Set 10.2

A. 1. a. Give the coordinates of the origin.

   b. Give the coordinates of the four points which lie on the axes and are three units from the origin.

   c. A circle with center at the origin has radius 5. Find the coordinates of the points where this circle is met by a line parallel to the y-axis and containing the point given by $(3, 1)$.

2. Consider these triples of points and answer the questions that follow.
   (1)   (⁻3, 2) (1, 0) (3, ⁻1)
   (2)   (⁻3, 2) (1, 0) (4, 6)
   (3)   (⁻3, 2) (1, 0) (⁻1, ⁻4)
   (4)   (1, 2) (5, 1) (4, ⁻2)
   (5)   (5, 7) (⁻1, ⁻5) (2, 1)
   (6)   (2, 0) (5, 1) (1, ⁻3)

   a. Which of these triples represent collinear points?
   b. Which of these triples represent the vertices of right triangles?
   c. Which of these triples represent the vertices of isosceles triangles?

3. Show that the points represented by the following coordinates are the vertices of a rectangle (make a sketch).

$$(\text{⁻}3, 2) \qquad (2, 2) \qquad (1, 4) \qquad (\text{⁻}2, 0)$$

B. 1. Let the vertices of $\triangle ABC$ have coordinates as follows: A $(0, 1)$, B $(5, 1)$, C $(2, 4)$. Let points A', B', and C' be obtained by doubling the coordinates of A, B, and C, respectively. Thus A', B', and C' have coordinates A' $(0, 2)$, B' $(10, 2)$, and C' $(4, 8)$. Make a sketch showing the six points and draw segments $\overline{AB}$, $\overline{BC}$, $\overline{CA}$, $\overline{A'B'}$, $\overline{B'C'}$, $\overline{C'A'}$.

   a. Find how the lengths of $\overline{AB}$ and $\overline{A'B'}$ compare. Similarly for the pair $\overline{BC}$, $\overline{B'C'}$, and for the pair $\overline{AC}$, $\overline{A'C'}$. Do corresponding segments seem to be parallel?

   b. Measure the angles of $\triangle ABC$ and $\triangle A'B'C'$. How do they seem to compare?

   c. Show that each of the following triples of points is a collinear set: OAA', OBB', and OCC', where O is the origin.

2. Let A, B, C have coordinates as follows: A $(\text{⁻}2, 3)$, B $(2, 1)$, $C(4, 0)$. Let the coordinates of A', B', and C' be obtained by multiplying the coordinates of A, B, and C, respectively, by 3.

   a. Find the coordinates of A', B', and C'.
   b. Show that A, B, and C are collinear.
   c. Compare the lengths of $\overline{AB}$, $\overline{BC}$, and $\overline{CA}$ with the lengths of $\overline{A'B'}$, $\overline{B'C'}$, and $\overline{C'A'}$.
   d. Show that A', B', and C' are collinear.

C. 1. Make a sketch by drawing the segments joining the following points in order:

   (1, 0), (1, 1), (0, 2), (0, 5), (1, 6), (3, 6), (4, 5), (4, 4), (3, 4), (4, 3), (3, 3), (3, 2), (2, 2), (3, 2), (3, 1), (2, 1), (2, 0).

2. Obtain a new set of points by doubling the coordinates of all the points in **C1**. Make the corresponding drawing for this new set of points.

3. How do the drawings for **C1** and **C2** seem to compare? Do the segments in **C2** seem to be parallel to the corresponding segments in **C1**?

D. Consider the line k, which makes a 45° angle with both the x and y axes. If (x, y) represents any point of the line, what relationship is there between x and y? [HINT: Let P with coordinates (x, y) be any point of k and draw the perpendicular lines from P to the two axes. What sort of figure do you seem to obtain?]

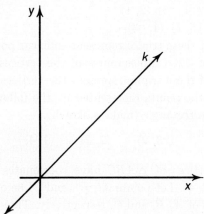

10.3 Homothetic Transformations

In problems **B** and **C** of Problem Set 10.2 we were considering the effect produced on certain sets of points by multiplying all their coordinates by some positive number. We imagined that a set of points, say A, B, and C, was transformed into a new set of points A', B', and C' by this operation. This type of transformation is so useful that we shall examine it briefly. It is called a **homothetic transformation** or sometimes a **dilatation.** We state the formal definition.

> DEFINITION: If k is a fixed positive number and if any point P with coordinates (x, y) is transformed into the point P' with coordinates (kx, ky), this operation is called a **homothetic transformation** (or **dilatation**). More precisely, it is the homothetic transformation with constant k for the given coordinate system.

Notice that, under a homothetic transformation, *every* point (p, q) of the plane is matched with a unique point (kp, kq). Moreover, *every* point of the plane is the image of exactly one point. For example, (r, s) is the image of $\left(\dfrac{r}{k}, \dfrac{s}{k}\right)$. Thus a homothetic transformation provides a one-to-one correspondence of the points of the plane with the points of the plane. While we shall frequently center our attention on what a homothetic transformation does to a particular set of points, we must keep in mind that it actually produces an image for every point. We shall sometimes make use of this fact.

When a point set S' is obtained from a point set S by a homothetic transformation we say that S' is homothetic to S or is a homothetic image of S. If S' is homothetic to S this means that multiplying the coordinates of points of S by some constant $k > 0$ gives the points of S'. It is clear at once that multiplying the coordinates of the points of S' by the positive constant $\dfrac{1}{k}$ will give us back the points of S. That is, there is also a homothetic transformation taking S' to S. Thus the relation of being homothetic is actually a symmetric one and we shall frequently speak of two sets as *homothetic to each other*.

Problems **B** and **C** above illustrate cases when $k = 2$ or $k = 3$. Thus in problem **B2** the point set $\{A', B', C'\}$ is homothetic to the point set $\{A, B, C\}$. Note that in this case both triples of points are collinear.

It will be important for us to discover what effect a homothetic transformation has on certain point sets. This information is contained in the following theorem. We shall, of course, want to prove the different parts of this theorem. However, you will observe that most of the results you could already have guessed from your experience with problems **B1** and **B2** above.

Theorem 10.2

(a) *If a homothetic transformation takes P into P' and if O is the origin, then O, P, P' are collinear points.*

(b) *In a homothetic transformation with $k \neq 1$ the origin is the only fixed point, i.e., the only point carried into itself.*

(c) *If P_1, P_2 are any points and if P_1', P_2' are their images under a homothetic transformation with constant k, then $m(\overline{P_1'P_2'}) = k \cdot m(\overline{P_1P_2})$.*

(d) *A homothetic transformation takes collinear points into collinear points.*

(e) *A homothetic transformation takes any line through the origin O into itself. A homothetic transformation with $k \neq 1$ takes a line m not through the origin into a parallel line m'.*

(f) *If A, B, C are noncollinear points and if A', B', C' are their images under a homothetic transformation, then $\angle ABC \cong \angle A'B'C'$ (i.e., angles always go into congruent angles).*

Before going on to examine the formal proofs it may be of interest to look back at problems **B1** and **B2** of Problem Set 10.2 to see how many of these statements in the theorem were illustrated or conjectured. Statement (a) of the theorem was illustrated in problem **B1c**. Statement (c) of the theorem comes into play in problems **B1a** and **B2c**. An example of statement (d) of the theorem occurs in problem **B2d**. And finally, statement (f) of the theorem is conjectured (though not proved) in problem **B1b**. Thus only statements (b) and (e) of the theorem say anything geometrically new, and even (e) might have been guessed from problems **B1a** and **C3**. As we shall see, in several cases the proofs will be simply duplications of the work above in the numerical examples. We proceed now to the proof.

Proofs

(a) If P has coordinates (x, y), then P' has coordinates (kx, ky) and of course O has coordinates $(0, 0)$. To test for collinearity we find the measures of the three segments as in Section 10.2.

$$m(\overline{OP}) = \sqrt{(x - 0)^2 + (y - 0)^2} = \sqrt{x^2 + y^2}.$$

$$m(\overline{OP'}) = \sqrt{(kx - 0)^2 + (ky - 0)^2} = \sqrt{k^2(x^2 + y^2)} = k \cdot \sqrt{x^2 + y^2}.$$

$$m(\overline{PP'}) = \sqrt{(kx - x)^2 + (ky - y)^2} = \sqrt{(k - 1)^2 (x^2 + y^2)}$$
$$= |k - 1| \cdot \sqrt{x^2 + y^2}.$$

Note that in both the last two equations use has been made of the relation $\sqrt{A \cdot B} = \sqrt{A} \cdot \sqrt{B}$. Observe also that in the second equation we could write $\sqrt{k^2} = k$ since k was known to be positive but in the third equation it was necessary to write $\sqrt{(k - 1)^2} = |k - 1|$ since we did not know whether $k - 1$ was positive or negative. There are thus two cases to consider. Suppose first $k \geq 1$. Then $|k - 1| = k - 1$ and we find at once $m(\overline{PP'}) = (k - 1) \cdot \sqrt{x^2 + y^2} = k \cdot \sqrt{x^2 + y^2} - \sqrt{x^2 + y^2} = m(\overline{OP'}) - m(\overline{OP})$. This is equivalent to

$$m(\overline{OP'}) = m(\overline{OP}) + m(\overline{PP'}).$$

From this we conclude, as in Section 10.2, that O, P, and P' are collinear and indeed that $P \in \overline{OP'}$.

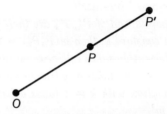

The second case is when $k < 1$. In this situation $|k - 1| = 1 - k$ so that $m(\overline{PP'}) = \sqrt{x^2 + y^2} - k \cdot \sqrt{x^2 + y^2} = m(\overline{OP}) - m(\overline{OP'})$ or, equivalently, $m(\overline{OP}) = m(\overline{OP'}) + m(\overline{PP'})$. Again the points are collinear (why?), but in this case $P' \in \overline{OP}$.

This completes the proof of statement (a). It shows that for $k > 1$ the transformation is a stretching, pulling P away from O while for $k < 1$ it is a contraction pulling P in toward O (both of which seem intuitively plausible). Notice that when $k = 1$ every point is fixed.

(b) This statement merely concerns the question of whether a point (x, y) could be the same as its image point (kx, ky). This occurs when $x = kx$, $y = ky$ or, equivalently, when $x \cdot (k - 1) = 0$, $y \cdot (k - 1) = 0$. If $k \neq 1$ this only happens if $x = y = 0$, i.e., for the origin. This is precisely statement (b). As remarked above, if $k = 1$, then *all* points are fixed; i.e., the transformation doesn't really move anything at all.

(c) Let P_1 and P_2 have coordinates (x_1, y_1) and (x_2, y_2), respectively. Then P_1'

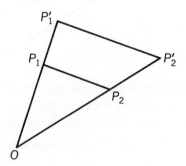

and P_2' will have coordinates (kx_1, ky_1) and (kx_2, ky_2). Application of the distance formula then gives

$$m(\overline{P_1P_2}) = \sqrt{(x_2 - x_1)^2 + (y_2 - y_1)^2}.$$

$$m(\overline{P_1'P_2'}) = \sqrt{(kx_2 - kx_1)^2 + (ky_2 - ky_1)^2}$$
$$= \sqrt{k^2\left[(x_2 - x_1)^2 + (y_2 - y_1)^2\right]}$$
$$= k \cdot \sqrt{(x_2 - x_1)^2 + (y_2 - y_1)^2}.$$

From this we see at once $m(\overline{P_1'P_2'}) = k \cdot m(\overline{P_1P_2})$ as claimed in statement (c).

(d) Let A, B, and C be collinear points with $B \in \overline{AC}$ and let A', B', and C' be their images under a homothetic transformation. Since $B \in \overline{AC}$, we know that

$$m(\overline{AB}) + m(\overline{BC}) = m(\overline{AC}). \quad \text{(Why?)}$$

Multiplication by k, the constant for the homothetic transformation, yields

$$k \cdot m(\overline{AB}) + k \cdot m(\overline{BC}) = k \cdot m(\overline{AC}).$$

Since, by statement (c), $m(\overline{A'B'}) = k \cdot m(\overline{AB})$, $m(\overline{B'C'}) = k \cdot m(\overline{BC})$ and $m(\overline{A'C'}) = k \cdot m(\overline{AC})$ it follows at once that

$$m(\overline{A'B'}) + m(\overline{B'C'}) = m(\overline{A'C'}).$$

From this we conclude that A', B', and C' are collinear (why?), and indeed that $B' \in \overline{A'C'}$.

(e) According to statement (d), collinear points go into collinear points. In particular, the set of points on a line m of the plane go into the points on some line m'. If m passes through O we find by (a) that any point on m goes into another point of m. That is, in this case the line m goes into itself. This is the first part of statement (e). Consider then the case when m does not pass through O, and consider a homothetic transformation with $k \neq 1$.

If m' is the image of m, then either m' is parallel to m or they have a point Q

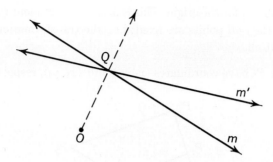

in common. Let us try to prove that m' is parallel to m by using a contradiction argument. That is, we assume there is an intersection point Q and hope to show that this assumption leads to a contradiction. Notice that $Q \neq O$ for $Q \in m$ but $O \notin m$. Where will we find the image Q' of Q? According to (a) Q' must be on $\overrightarrow{OQ}$. Moreover, since $Q \in m$ it must follow that $Q' \in m'$. (Why?) That is, $Q' \in \overrightarrow{OQ} \cap m'$. The only intersection of $\overrightarrow{OQ}$ and m' is Q. Thus $Q' = Q$ so Q is a fixed point. Since $k \neq 1$ this contradicts statement (b), which says that only the origin is fixed. Hence there cannot be a point of intersection Q of m and m'. Thus m and m' can have no common point and are therefore parallel, as we were seeking to show.

(f) Strictly speaking, there are several cases to consider here. However, the geometric ideas are essentially the same in the different cases. We shall therefore content ourselves with looking at one situation, leaving you to examine other cases for yourself.

Suppose that $B \neq O$ and that A and C are on the same side of $\overleftrightarrow{OB}$ as shown in the diagram. Then A' and C' are on the same side as A and C. The diagram shows a case where $k > 1$, though this is not any essential part of the discussion.

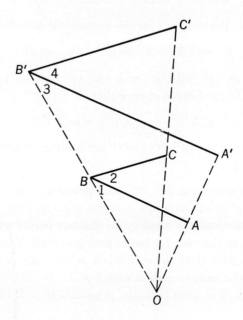

According to statement (e), we know that $\overleftrightarrow{AB} \parallel \overleftrightarrow{A'B'}$ and $\overleftrightarrow{BC} \parallel \overleftrightarrow{B'C'}$. It follows that $\angle OBA \cong \angle OB'A'$ and $\angle OBC \cong \angle OB'C'$. (Why?) If we identify angles by small numerals written in their interiors as shown, this means that

$$m(\angle 1) = m(\angle 3)$$

and

$$m(\angle 1) + m(\angle 2) = m(\angle 3) + m(\angle 4).$$

(What theorems are being used in making these assertions?) By subtraction it follows that $m(\angle 2) = m(\angle 4)$. That is, $m(\angle ABC) = m(\angle A'B'C')$ or $\angle ABC \cong \angle A'B'C'$ as was to be proved.

The results of Theorem 10.2 make it possible for us to visualize a homothetic transformation without specifically referring to coordinates. By statement (a) each point P is carried into point P' on ray $\overrightarrow{OP}$ such that $m(\overline{OP'}) = k \cdot m(\overline{OP})$. Thus we can think of the transformation simply as a stretching (if $k > 1$) away from the origin O. A good intuitive picture of the situation is to think of a point set drawn on a thin rubber sheet. The homothetic set is the one obtained by stretching this sheet uniformly in all directions away from some fixed point O.

As an example, consider the quadrilateral $ABCD$ shown below and suppose we wish to draw the homothetic figure with respect to origin O and with $k = 2$. To find the image point A' of A it is necessary merely to draw the ray $\overrightarrow{OA}$ (shown as a dashed line) and locate A' on this ray so that $m(\overline{OA'}) = 2 \cdot m(\overline{OA})$. Similar remarks apply to finding the images B', C', and D' of the vertices B, C, and D.

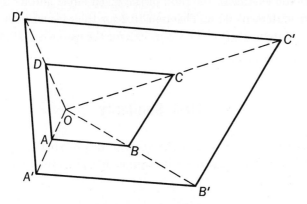

Since, by statement (d) of Theorem 10.2, collinear points go into collinear points, the segment $\overline{AB}$ goes into segment $\overline{A'B'}$. Similarly $\overline{B'C'}$, $\overline{C'D'}$, and $\overline{D'A'}$ are the images of $\overline{BC}$, $\overline{CD}$, and $\overline{DA}$, respectively. Thus the image of a quadrilateral $ABCD$ is quadrilateral $A'B'C'D'$.

The same type of reasoning shows that a homothetic image of any polygon is again a polygon. Moreover, corresponding sides of the two polygons are either parallel or on the same line (why?), and the angles at corresponding vertices are congruent (why?).

Problem Set 10.3

A. 1. Draw a triangle ABC and choose any convenient point O as origin. Draw the three homothetic images of $\triangle ABC$ using the values $k = \frac{1}{2}$, $k = 2$, and $k = 3$.

 2. In the drawings of problem **A1**, measure the angles of $\triangle ABC$ and those of its homothetic image for $k = 3$. Do your results appear to confirm statement (f) of Theorem 10.2? Measure also the sides of $\triangle ABC$ and the homothetic image for $k = 3$. Do these experimental results seem to confirm statement (c) of Theorem 10.2?

 3. Draw a quadrilateral $ABCD$. Using the same value $k = 2$ in each case, draw three homothetic images, one for an origin O_1 interior to $ABCD$, one for an origin O_2 on a side of $ABCD$, and one for an origin O_3 exterior to $ABCD$. What relationship do you seem to observe among these three images?

B. 1. Prove that any homothetic image of a circle is a circle. [HINT: If C is the

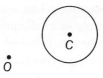

center of the given circle, show that all of the images of points of this circle have the same distance from C', the image of C.] What can be said about the lengths of the radii of the given circle and its image?

 2. Prove statement (f) of Theorem 10.2 for the case when $B = O$.

 3. Prove statement (f) of Theorem 10.2 for the case when $B \neq O$ but A and C are on opposite sides of $\overleftrightarrow{OB}$.

10.4 Similarity

We now turn to a discussion of the general idea of similarity. The intuitive meaning of this word was described in Section 10.1, but the time has now come for a formal definition.

> DEFINITION: Two point sets S and S' are **similar** if there are
> (a) a one-to-one correspondence of the points of S and S' and
> (b) a fixed positive number k such that if $P_1, P_2 \in S$ and P_1', P_2' are their images in S', then $m(\overline{P_1'P_2'}) = k \cdot m(\overline{P_1P_2})$.
> The notation $S \sim S'$ is used to express the fact that S is similar to S'.

As you have probably realized, two homothetic figures are always similar. For surely there is a one-to-one correspondence between the points of a set S and those of a homothetic image S′, and statement (c) of Theorem 10.2 assures us that for such sets $m(\overline{P_1'P_2'}) = k \cdot m(\overline{P_1P_2})$. It is quite possible, however, that two sets might be similar without being homothetic. For example, the two squares $ABCD$ and $A'B'C'D'$ in the diagram are readily shown to be similar but are clearly not homothetic since corresponding sides are not parallel.

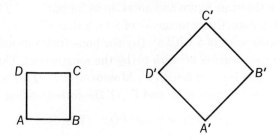

Interestingly, however, we can obtain all the needed facts about similar figures by combining the ideas of homothetic figures from Section 10.3 and the ideas of congruence from Chapter 5. The next theorem shows how these different ideas are related.

Theorem 10.3

(a) *If* S ∼ S′, *then there is a homothetic image* S″ *of* S *such that* S″ ≅ S′.

(b) *If there is a homothetic image* S″ *of* S *such that* S″ ≅ S′, *then* S ∼ S′.

Proof

(a) Since S ∼ S′, we know there is a one-to-one correspondence of the points of S with those of S′. Moreover, if $P, Q \in$ S and P', Q' are the corresponding points of S′, then $m(\overline{P'Q'}) = k \cdot m(\overline{PQ})$.

Let S″ be a homothetic image of S *using the same constant k as for the given similarity*. The homothetic transformation gives a one-to-one correspondence of the points of S and S″. Moreover, if $P'', Q'' \in$ S″ are the points corresponding to $P, Q \in$ S, then $m(\overline{P''Q''}) = k \cdot m(\overline{PQ})$. The one-to-one correspondence of S″ with

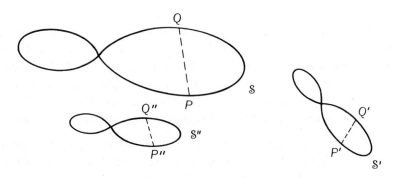

$\mathcal{S}$ (from the homothetic transformation) and the one-to-one correspondence of $\mathcal{S}$ with $\mathcal{S}'$ (by the given similarity) produce at once a one-to-one correspondence of $\mathcal{S}''$ with $\mathcal{S}'$. We have already noted that $m(\overline{P''Q''}) = k \cdot m(\overline{PQ}) = m(\overline{P'Q'})$ so that $\overline{P''Q''} \cong \overline{P'Q'}$. Thus the one-to-one correspondence between $\mathcal{S}'$ and $\mathcal{S}''$ preserves congruence of segments and is therefore a congruence (by the definition of congruent sets in Chapter 5). That is, $\mathcal{S}' \cong \mathcal{S}''$ as was to be proved.

(b) [We can use the same figure and notation as for part (a).] This time we are *given* that there is a homothetic image $\mathcal{S}''$ of $\mathcal{S}$ such that $\mathcal{S}'' \cong \mathcal{S}'$. Then there is a one-to-one correspondence of $\mathcal{S}$ with $\mathcal{S}''$ (by the homothetic transformation) and a one-to-one correspondence of $\mathcal{S}''$ with $\mathcal{S}'$ (by the congruence). This gives at once a one-to-one correspondence of $\mathcal{S}$ with $\mathcal{S}'$. Moreover, if P, Q are any points of $\mathcal{S}$, P'', Q'' the corresponding ones of $\mathcal{S}''$ and P', Q' the corresponding ones of $\mathcal{S}'$, then

$$m(\overline{P''Q''}) = k \cdot m(\overline{PQ}) \quad \text{(Why?)}$$

and

$$\overline{P'Q'} \cong \overline{P''Q''} \quad \text{(Why?)}$$

so that $m(\overline{P'Q'}) = m(\overline{P''Q''})$. From these two equations it follows that $m(\overline{P'Q'}) = k \cdot m(\overline{PQ})$ so by definition the correspondence is a similarity, i.e., $\mathcal{S} \sim \mathcal{S}'$. This completes the proof.

The essence of this theorem is that a test of whether a set $\mathcal{S}$ is similar to a set $\mathcal{S}'$ is to see whether we can blow up (or reduce) $\mathcal{S}$ (by a homothetic transformation) into a set $\mathcal{S}''$ which is actually congruent to $\mathcal{S}'$. This idea quickly yields useful results on similar figures in the following theorem.

Theorem 10.4 *Let $\mathcal{S}$ and $\mathcal{S}'$ be sets such that $\mathcal{S} \sim \mathcal{S}'$. Let $A, B,$ and C be points of $\mathcal{S}$ and let $A', B',$ and C' be their images in $\mathcal{S}'$.*
(a) *If $A, B,$ and C are collinear with $B \in \overline{AC}$, then $A', B',$ and C' are collinear with $B' \in \overline{A'C'}$.*
(b) *If A, B, C are not collinear, then $A', B',$ and C' are not collinear and $\angle ABC \cong \angle A'B'C'$.*

Proof
(a) Let $\mathcal{S}''$ be a homothetic image of $\mathcal{S}$ such that $\mathcal{S}'' \cong \mathcal{S}'$ (as is guaranteed by Theorem 10.3) and let $A'', B'',$ and C'' be the images in $\mathcal{S}''$ of $A, B,$ and C. Since $A, B,$ and C are collinear we know by Theorem 10.2(d) that $A'', B'',$ and C'' are collinear. Since $\mathcal{S}'' \cong \mathcal{S}'$ it follows by Axiom CS7 (Chapter 5) that $A', B',$ and C' are collinear. Indeed, if (as shown) $B \in \overline{AC}$, then the argument shows $B' \in \overline{A'C'}$. Note that there is no assumption that segments $\overline{AB}, \overline{BC},$ etc., be subsets of $\mathcal{S}$.

(b) Since, according to problem **A2** below, similarity is a symmetric relationship (i.e., if $\mathcal{S} \sim \mathcal{S}'$, then $\mathcal{S}' \sim \mathcal{S}$) statement (a) really says that if either of the two triples A, B, C and A', B', C' is a set of collinear points, then the other must be.

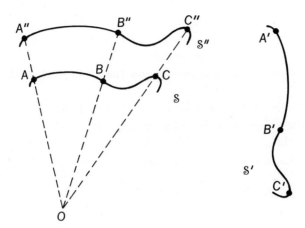

Hence if either set is noncollinear the other must also be noncollinear as is claimed in statement (b). Using the same notation as above (except that A, B, and C are noncollinear this time) we find that $\angle ABC \cong \angle A''B''C''$ by Theorem 10.2(f), while $\angle A''B''C'' \cong \angle A'B'C'$ by Theorem 5.11 since $S'' \cong S'$. Thus $\angle ABC \cong \angle A'B'C'$. This completes the proof.

In simple terms Theorem 10.4 says that for similar figures collinear points always correspond to collinear points and corresponding angles are always congruent. In particular, since segments correspond to segments, any figure similar to a polygon is a polygon (with the same number of sides). Moreover, angles at corresponding vertices are congruent.

The definition of similarity, like that of congruence considered earlier, is intuitively appealing but awkward to use directly. Thus to show that two sets S and S' are similar by using the definition alone it is necessary to set up a one-to-one correspondence between the sets and then to consider *all possible pairs* of points in S and their corresponding images in S'. Since most of the sets we deal with have infinitely many points, this program can be onerous—to put it mildly. What we badly need are some simple criteria that will let us draw conclusions about similarity, at least for certain figures, without excessive labor. This we proceed to consider for the case of the triangle. You will recall that the triangle was also the focal point of discussion for congruence in Chapter 5.

If $\triangle ABC$ is any triangle, then, as has been noted above, any figure similar to $\triangle ABC$ is likewise a triangle. Moreover, if A', B', and C' are the points corre-

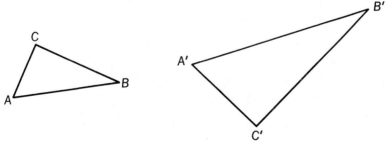

sponding to A, B, and C, respectively, then the new triangle is precisely $\triangle A'B'C'$. When we use the notation $\triangle ABC \sim \triangle A'B'C'$ to indicate this similarity we agree to mean not only that the triangles are similar but that $A \leftrightarrow A'$, $B \leftrightarrow B'$, and $C \leftrightarrow C'$. This is the same convention that was used in the notation for congruence.

For any triangle, six measurable quantities immediately suggest themselves—namely, the three sides and the three angles. We would like to investigate the relationship of these measures to the idea of similarity. The first result is almost painfully obvious but is stated for convenience in reference.

Theorem 10.5 *If $\triangle ABC \sim \triangle A'B'C'$, then*
(a) $\angle A \cong \angle A'$, $\angle B \cong \angle B'$, $\angle C \cong \angle C'$ *and*
(b) $\dfrac{m(\overline{A'B'})}{m(\overline{AB})} = \dfrac{m(\overline{B'C'})}{m(\overline{BC})} = \dfrac{m(\overline{C'A'})}{m(\overline{CA})}.$

Proof. Since $A \leftrightarrow A'$, $B \leftrightarrow B'$, $C \leftrightarrow C'$ in the similarity, statement (a) follows from Theorem 10.4(b) while statement (b) follows from the definition of similarity since $m(\overline{A'B'}) = k \cdot m(\overline{AB})$, $m(\overline{B'C'}) = k \cdot m(\overline{BC})$ and $m(\overline{C'A'}) = k \cdot m(\overline{CA})$.

The real interest here is in trying to reverse the argument. Are there combinations of some of the statements indicated in (a) and (b) above which allow us to conclude that the triangles *must* be similar? As you are probably aware, the answer to this question is "yes." Indeed we shall find several different combinations of facts that are enough to imply similarity.

Theorem 10.6 *If two angles of one triangle are congruent to two angles of a second, the triangles are similar.*

Proof. Let the triangles be $\triangle ABC$ and $\triangle A'B'C'$ and let $\angle A \cong \angle A'$ and $\angle B \cong \angle B'$ as given. Let $\dfrac{m(\overline{A'B'})}{m(\overline{AB})} = k$ and consider $\triangle A''B''C''$ a homothetic

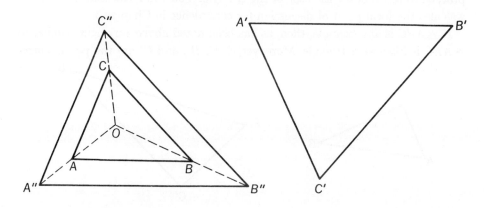

image of $\triangle ABC$ with constant k as shown. Since $\triangle A''B''C''$ is homothetic to $\triangle ABC$ we know that $m(\overline{A''B''}) = k \cdot m(\overline{AB})$ and that $\angle A'' \cong \angle A$ and $\angle B'' \cong \angle B$. (Why?) This means that $\angle A'' \cong \angle A'$, $\angle B'' \cong \angle B'$ and $m(\overline{A''B''}) = m(\overline{A'B'})$ so that $\triangle A''B''C'' \cong \triangle A'B'C'$. (Why?) Since $\triangle ABC$ is homothetic to $\triangle A''B''C''$ which in turn is congruent to $\triangle A'B'C'$, it follows from Theorem 10.3 that $\triangle ABC \sim \triangle A'B'C'$. This completes the proof.

You should observe that if two angles of one triangle are congruent to two angles of a second it is actually true that all three pairs of angles are congruent. Why is this?

Theorem 10.7 *If $\triangle ABC$ and $\triangle A'B'C'$ are such that $\dfrac{m(\overline{A'B'})}{m(\overline{AB})} = \dfrac{m(\overline{B'C'})}{m(\overline{BC})} =$*

$\dfrac{m(\overline{C'A'})}{m(\overline{CA})}$, *then $\triangle ABC \sim \triangle A'B'C'$.*

Proof. We shall try essentially the same trick as in the last theorem. That is, we will try to find a homothetic image of $\triangle ABC$ which will be congruent to $\triangle A'B'C'$.

Let k be the common value of the three given ratios so that $m(\overline{A'B'}) = k \cdot m(\overline{AB})$, $m(\overline{B'C'}) = k \cdot m(\overline{BC})$ and $m(\overline{C'A'}) = k \cdot m(\overline{CA})$. Consider then a $\triangle A''B''C''$ which is a homothetic image of $\triangle ABC$ using this constant k. (Use the same diagram as for Theorem 10.6.) Since $\triangle A''B''C''$ is homothetic to $\triangle ABC$ we find from Theorem 10.2(c) that $m(\overline{A''B''}) = k \cdot m(\overline{AB})$, $m(\overline{B''C''}) = k \cdot m(\overline{BC})$ and $m(\overline{C''A''}) = k \cdot m(\overline{CA})$. This means that $m(\overline{A''B''}) = m(\overline{A'B'})$, $m(\overline{B''C''}) = m(\overline{B'C'})$ and $m(\overline{C''A''}) = m(\overline{C'A'})$ or, equivalently, $\overline{A''B''} \cong \overline{A'B'}$, $\overline{B''C''} \cong \overline{B'C'}$, and $\overline{C''A''} \cong \overline{C'A'}$. It follows that $\triangle A''B''C'' \cong \triangle A'B'C'$. (Why?) Thus $\triangle ABC$ is homothetic to $\triangle A''B''C''$ which in turn is congruent to $\triangle A'B'C'$ so, again, by Theorem 10.3, $\triangle ABC \sim \triangle A'B'C'$ as was to be proved.

There is still a third theorem of this same nature.

Theorem 10.8 *If $\triangle ABC$ and $\triangle A'B'C'$ are such that $\angle A \cong \angle A'$ and $\dfrac{m(\overline{A'B'})}{m(\overline{AB})} = \dfrac{m(\overline{A'C'})}{m(\overline{AC})}$, then $\triangle ABC \sim \triangle A'B'C'$.*

This can be proved using exactly the same procedure as in the last two theorems. This is left to be done as an exercise.

In concluding this section on similarity, it seems well to include a rather familiar result about parallel lines. If we had not chosen to get at similarity by using homothetic transformations, we would probably have tried to prove this result first and then use it to obtain the facts on similar triangles stated in the last three theorems.

The theorem in question concerns the situation arising where three parallel lines k_1, k_2, k_3 in a plane are met by two different transversals k and k'. If k meets k_1, k_2, k_3 in A, B, and C, respectively, there are determined three segments on

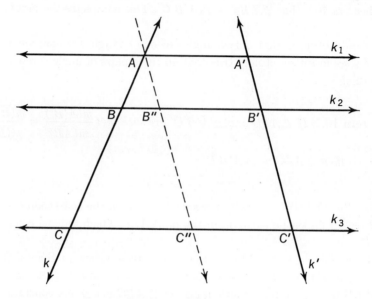

k, namely, $\overline{AB}$, $\overline{AC}$, and $\overline{BC}$. Similarly on k', there are the three corresponding segments $\overline{A'B'}$, $\overline{A'C'}$, and $\overline{B'C'}$. The theorem, which is stated formally below, is concerned with the measures of these segments.

Theorem 10.9 *If three parallel lines are met by two transversals, the ratio of the measures of any two of the segments cut from one transversal equals the ratio of the measures of the corresponding segments on the other transversal.*

Proof. Since there are *three* pairs of segments on a transversal, the theorem really makes *three* claims. Using the notation of the diagram above we are asked to show that

$$\frac{m(\overline{AB})}{m(\overline{AC})} = \frac{m(\overline{A'B'})}{m(\overline{A'C'})}, \frac{m(\overline{AB})}{m(\overline{BC})} = \frac{m(\overline{A'B'})}{m(\overline{B'C'})}, \frac{m(\overline{AC})}{m(\overline{BC})} = \frac{m(\overline{A'C'})}{m(\overline{B'C'})}.$$

If, by chance, it turns out that $k \parallel k'$, then the three segments on k are actually congruent to the corresponding segments on k'. (Why?) In this case corresponding segments have equal measures and the desired results are trivially true.

Consider then the remaining case when k is not parallel to k'. Draw the line through A parallel to k' and meeting k_2 and k_3 at B'' and C'', respectively. We now make the following observations.

ASSERTIONS	SUPPORTING STATEMENTS
(1) $\angle ABB'' \cong \angle ACC''$ and $\angle AB''B \cong \angle AC''C$.	(1) Why?
(2) $\triangle ABB'' \sim \triangle ACC''$.	(2) Why?
(3) $\dfrac{m(\overline{AB})}{m(\overline{AC})} = \dfrac{m(\overline{AB''})}{m(\overline{AC''})}$.	(3) Why?
(4) $m(\overline{AB''}) = m(\overline{A'B'})$ and $m(\overline{AC''}) = m(\overline{A'C'})$.	(4) Why?
(5) $\dfrac{m(\overline{AB})}{m(\overline{AC})} = \dfrac{m(\overline{A'B'})}{m(\overline{A'C'})}$.	(5) Steps 3 and 4.

This is one of the three results to be established. The other two are left to be done as exercises. When this has been done it will complete the proof of the theorem.

Notice one interesting special case—that in which B is the midpoint of $\overline{AC}$, so that $m(\overline{AB}) = m(\overline{BC})$. The theorem then assures us that B' will also be the midpoint of $\overline{A'C'}$. This special case often appears in geometry books in some such form as the following:

If three parallel lines cut congruent segments from one transversal, they cut congruent segments from every transversal.

This special case is easily proved using only the familiar work on congruence and is given as an exercise below in problem **D3**. The general case requires a little more sophisticated treatment which in one way or another makes essential use of the properties of real numbers. In our treatment this was done with the introduction of coordinates.

It should be clear that our entire discussion of similarity has been for point sets lying in a plane, since the basic tool was the use of coordinates in the plane. It will probably come as no surprise to you, however, to learn that the ideas can be readily extended to the similarity of space figures. We shall not attempt to develop this in detail in this book, however.

Problem Set 10.4

A. 1. Prove that if $S \sim S'$ and $S' \sim S''$, then $S \sim S''$. [This states that the similarity relation is transitive.]

2. Prove that if $S \sim S'$, then $S' \sim S$. [This states that the similarity relation is symmetric. This fact was used in the proof of Theorem 10.4(b).]

3. Prove that for any set S it is true that $S \sim S$. [This shows the similarity relation is reflexive. Problems **A1, A2,** and **A3** together show that similarity is an equivalence relation.]

B. 1. Prove that any point set similar to a square is a square.

2. Prove that any point set similar to a parallelogram is a parallelogram.

3. If $ABCD$ is a rectangle with $m(\overline{AB}) = 2 \cdot m(\overline{AD})$, prove that any point set similar to $ABCD$ is also a rectangle with one side twice as long as the other.

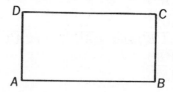

4. If a set δ consists of a circle and its center, show that every set similar to δ is a subset of a circle and its center. [Actually the image *is* a circle and its center but you are not asked to show this.]

5. For triangles, congruent angles imply similarity (Theorem 10.6). Show that this is not true of polygons generally by giving an example of two polygons which are not similar but which have congruent angles.

C. 1. Prove Theorem 10.8.

2. Prove the remaining cases of Theorem 10.9; i.e., prove that in the drawing on page 432,

$$\frac{m(\overline{AB})}{m(\overline{BC})} = \frac{m(\overline{A'B'})}{m(\overline{B'C'})} \quad \text{and} \quad \frac{m(\overline{AC})}{m(\overline{BC})} = \frac{m(\overline{A'C'})}{m(\overline{B'C'})}.$$

D. 1. Suppose it has already been proved (as is true) that two squares whose sides have equal lengths are congruent. Use the method of Theorem 10.7 and the result of problem **B1** to show that any two squares are similar.

2. If $\overset{\leftrightarrow}{DE} \parallel \overset{\leftrightarrow}{AB}$, where $D \in \overline{AC}$ and $E \in \overline{BC}$, as shown in (a) below, prove that

$$\frac{m(\overline{AD})}{m(\overline{DC})} = \frac{m(\overline{BE})}{m(\overline{EC})}.$$

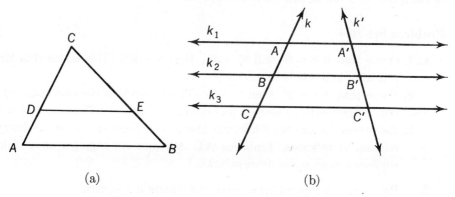

(a)   (b)

3. In diagram (b) above, k_1, k_2, k_3 are parallel and B is the midpoint of $\overline{AC}$.

Without using any of the results proved in this chapter, prove that B' is the midpoint of $\overline{A'C'}$.

10.5 Applications of Similarity

One of the useful applications of similarity is in scale drawings. For instance a floor plan of a house, or a surveyor's sketch of a farm, or even a map of your city, county, or state are all examples of scale drawings. That is, each of these drawings is (at least approximately) *similar* to the object which it represents. We shall examine ways in which such drawings can be used to solve problems. First, however, it will be useful to consider the question of scale.

So far in discussing similarity it has been tacitly assumed that the same unit of measure is applied to the original figure and its image under the similarity. This procedure is frequently awkward in practice. While it is perfectly reasonable to measure the length of a football field in yards, a scale drawing of it of a size that would fit on this page needs to be small enough so that it seems quite inappropriate to measure it in yards. Inches or centimeters would seem much more appropriate units for measuring such a drawing. Let us consider the effect of using different scales in measuring two similar figures.

Let set S be similar to set S'. If A, B are points of S and A', B' the corresponding points of S', we know that there is a positive number k such that $m(\overline{A'B'}) = k \cdot m(\overline{AB})$. Suppose now it proved to be more convenient to use some different unit of measure in S'. Then $\overline{A'B'}$ would have a different measure, say $m'(\overline{A'B'})$, in terms of this new unit. If, for example, $m(\overline{A'B'})$ means the measure of $\overline{A'B'}$ in yards and $m'(\overline{A'B'})$ means the measure in inches, then clearly $m'(\overline{A'B'}) = 36 \cdot m(\overline{A'B'})$. In any case, $m'(\overline{A'B'})$ would be some multiple of $m(\overline{A'B'})$. It then follows that

$$m'(\overline{A'B'}) = 36k \cdot m(\overline{AB}) = k' \cdot m(\overline{AB}),$$

where $k' = 36k$. Thus, even if we use a different unit of measure in S' there is still a positive number, here k', such that if $\overline{AB}$ and $\overline{A'B'}$ are corresponding segments the measure of $\overline{A'B'}$ in one unit is k' times the measure of $\overline{AB}$ in the other unit. This shows that, as far as defining similarity is concerned, it is permissible to use different units in measuring the two sets.

In case different units are used, however, it is important for us to understand what the constant k' indicates. For example, suppose S and S' are similar sets with distances in S measured in yards and those in S' measured in inches. Suppose, furthermore, that, for corresponding points A, $B \in S$ and A', $B' \in S'$,

$$m'(\overline{A'B'}) = 2 \cdot m(\overline{AB}).$$

This means that if A, B are points of S, 1 yard apart [i.e., $m(\overline{AB}) = 1$ in yards], then the corresponding points A', B' of S' are 2 inches apart [i.e., $m'(\overline{A'B'}) = 2$ in inches]. We would describe this by saying that the scale is 2 inches to the yard.

Similarly if A', B' are points of S' which are $4\frac{1}{2}$ inches apart then the corresponding points A, B of S will actually be $2\frac{1}{4}$ yards apart.

This way of designating the scale of a drawing is very common. For example, a blueprint may be marked as being drawn on a scale of $\frac{1}{8}$ inch to the foot or a road map may carry a designation of so many inches to the mile. Thus a certain map of Prince Georges County in Maryland carries the notation "One inch equals approximately $\frac{1}{2}$ of a mile." While we may feel that the word *represents* would be better than *equals* in this sentence, it is clear that we are being told that the scale for this map is about 2 inches to the mile (which is a very large scale as maps go). The same map shows the scale visually, as indicated below.

Scale of Miles

$\frac{1}{2}$ 0 $\frac{1}{2}$ 1

By looking at this we may make reasonable estimates as to the distance between points represented on the map or we could even use this unit to lay off a scale on a strip of cardboard which could then be used directly to make measurements on the map.

The idea of similar figures lends itself well to dealing with many problems in indirect measurement as was mentioned in Section 10.1. For example, it may not be feasible to measure a certain distance directly but it may be quite possible to draw a similar figure to some suitable scale. Then by measuring the drawing it is possible, using the known scale, to find the desired length. An illustration or two will indicate the idea.

> *Example* 1. A rectangular field is 100 yards long and 60 yards wide. Find the length of one of the diagonals.

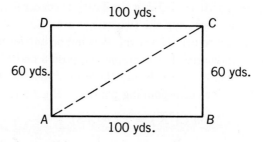

A rough sketch of the field might appear as shown. We are asked to find the length (in yards) of a diagonal $\overline{AC}$ of the field.

Let us approach this problem through the use of scale drawings. To be specific, let us make a scale drawing, as shown below, of the field to a scale of 1 inch to 40 yards. Since we know that any similar image of a rectangle is again a rectangle,

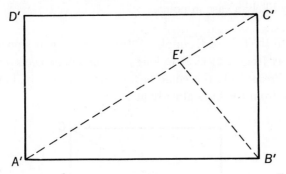

it is easy to draw the figure $A'B'C'D'$. The length of $\overline{A'B'}$ is $\dfrac{5}{2}$ inches and the

length of $\overline{B'C'}$ is $\dfrac{3}{2}$ inches. The (dashed) segment $\overline{A'C'}$ is the segment in the

drawing which corresponds to the desired segment $\overline{AC}$ of the field. Let us actually measure $\overline{A'C'}$ (as carefully as we can) with a ruler. Making this measurement

yields the approximate result $m'(\overline{A'C'}) \approx 2\dfrac{15}{16}$ (in inches). Using the fact that

1 inch represents 40 yards, we find an approximate length of $\left(2\dfrac{15}{16}\right) \cdot (40)$

yards or approximately 118 yards for $\overline{AC}$.

It should be kept in mind that any such process as this depending on the making and measuring of a drawing is necessarily an approximate one, even if we imagine the original data to be exactly correct. Here the intent was to measure

the segment $\overline{A'C'}$ to the nearest $\dfrac{1}{16}$ inch. If this was correctly done we could hope

to have found the length of $\overline{AC}$ to the nearest $\dfrac{40}{16}$ yards $= \dfrac{5}{2}$ yards.

It has probably occurred to you that there is a purely computational method of solving Example 1 which would make no use of scale drawing at all. Let x be the measure of $\overline{AC}$ in yards. Then by the Theorem of Pythagoras it is seen that

$$x^2 = (100)^2 + (60)^2 = 10000 + 3600 = 13{,}600.$$

From this it follows that $x = \sqrt{13600} = \sqrt{400 \cdot 34} = 20\sqrt{34}$. If the measurements of the sides of the field were exact this would mean the exact length of diagonal $\overline{AC}$ would be $20\sqrt{34}$ yards. Resorting to a square root table, we find $\sqrt{34} \approx 5.83$ from which we find the length of $\overline{AC}$ is approximately 117 yards. This checks very well the result obtained from the scale drawing.

The important point here is not that the scale drawing is the best way of attacking a problem. Indeed a computational approach is generally to be preferred when you have the techniques to use it. But the scale drawing does give a very useful means of attacking a wide variety of problems, many of which you may not have the computational skills to deal with in other ways. The next example is very likely a case in point.

Example 2. In the field of Example 1 a tree is growing at a point E two thirds of the way from A to C. How long a string will be needed to stretch from B to E? Presumably this could be done experimentally, but can the result be found from the data already at hand?

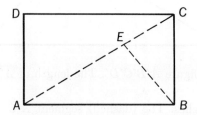

We are asked for the length (in yards) of the segment $\overline{BE}$. Using the same scale drawing as before, the image of E is the point E' two thirds of the way from A' to C'. After locating this point we measure the segment $\overline{B'E'}$ and find its length to be approximately $1\frac{5}{16}$ inches. Using, as before, the known scale of 1 inch to 40 yards, this gives us the desired length of the segment $\overline{BE}$ as approximately $\left(1\frac{5}{16}\right) \cdot (40)$ yards, i.e., approximately 52.5 yards.

It is quite probable that you do not recognize how to make a computational attack on this problem. Such a method does indeed exist and you may be interested to know that by using it the correct result (to the nearest tenth of a yard) is found to be 52.1 yards. The simple approach above, however, involving nothing more than the idea of similarity, has given a good approximation to the desired solution.

A third example relates to a set of points other than a rectangle.

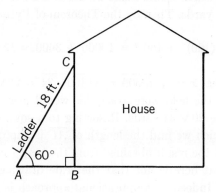

Example 3. A ladder 18 feet long leans against the side of a house. The ladder makes an angle of 60° with the ground. How high up will the ladder touch the house, and how far away from the house is the base of the ladder?

The ladder, the house, and the ground form a right triangle ABC as shown. It is easy to draw a triangle similar to this one to a given scale, say 1 inch to 9 feet. A larger scale like 1 inch to 6 feet or 1 inch to 3 feet would be better but not as well adapted to showing in a text. You may wish to make your own drawing using a larger scale. The scale drawing would look like the diagram below. The hypotenuse $\overline{A'C'}$ is made 2 inches long. By measurement the lengths of $\overline{A'B'}$ and $\overline{B'C'}$ are found to be approximately $1\frac{0}{16}$ and $1\frac{12}{16}$ inches, respectively. Using

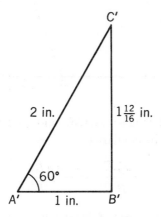

the given scale of 1 inch to 9 feet we obtain the approximate lengths of 9 feet and 16 feet, respectively, for $\overline{AB}$ and $\overline{BC}$. The approximate correctness of the results could be checked using the Theorem of Pythagoras. (Actually the 16 feet is a little high, as the correct result is around 15.6 feet, but 16 is correct to the nearest foot.)

Each of the three examples above has been solved by intentionally drawing a set of points similar to the one in which we are interested. You will observe that in making these drawings we have freely used the facts, noted on page 429, that a figure similar to a polygon is a polygon with the same number of sides and that corresponding angles are congruent. Thus in Examples 1 and 2 the scale drawing was already known to be a rectangle. Sometimes, however, a problem occurs in which we can already recognize similar figures and hence can avoid the trouble of making a drawing. The following is such a problem.

Example 4. On a sunny day a flagpole cast a shadow (on level ground) 24 feet long. At the same time a nearby fencepost 5 feet high cast a shadow 2 feet long. How tall is the flagpole?

The sun is far enough away so that we can think of the rays as being essentially

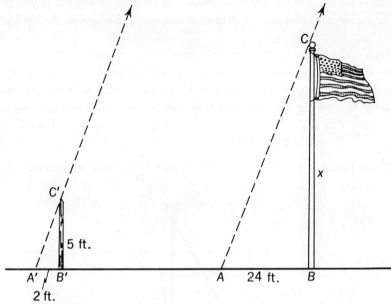

parallel. Then the two triangles $\triangle ABC$ and $\triangle A'B'C'$ are similar. (What theorem shows this?) By the similarity

$$\frac{m(\overline{BC})}{m(\overline{B'C'})} = \frac{m(\overline{AB})}{m(\overline{A'B'})}.$$

Hence if x is the measure (in feet) of $\overline{BC}$ it follows that

$$\frac{x}{5} = \frac{24}{2}$$

or $x = 60$, so the flagpole is 60 feet tall.

Problem Set 10.5

A. 1. Below is a floor plan of a room. The scale is $\frac{1}{8}$ inch to the foot. Find:

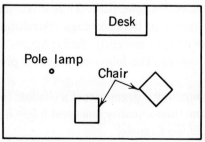

a. The dimensions of the room.

b. The distance from the pole lamp to the nearest corner of the desk.

2. A ship sails 10 miles on a straight course and then turns 35° to the left as shown. It sails 5 miles on this new course. Make a scale drawing of your

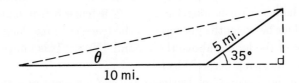

own to find approximately:

a. The distance of the ship from its starting point.

b. The measure of the angle θ.

c. The distance of the ship from the line of the original course.

3. A rectangle $ABCD$ is 30 feet long and 20 feet wide. Use a scale drawing to find approximately the distance from vertex B to the midpoint T of $\overline{EC}$.

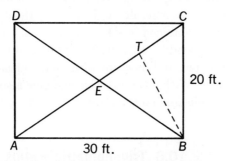

4. A rectangular floor is 10 feet by 24 feet. Find the distance between a pair of opposite corners:

a. By use of a scale drawing.

b. By making a suitable computation.

B. 1. A kite becomes tangled in the top branches of a tree. The boy holding the kite string notices that when he pulls it tight the string makes a 50° angle with the horizontal. If the boy is 40 feet from the base of the tree, and if his hand holding the string is 4 feet from the ground, use a scale drawing to find the height of the tree.

2. $\triangle ABC$ is an equilateral triangle each side of which is 20 feet long. Consider the segment from C to the midpoint M of $\overline{AB}$.

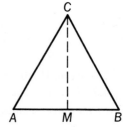

    a. Show that the degree measures of the angles of $\triangle ACM$ are 60, 30, and 90.

    b. Use the Theorem of Pythagoras to find the exact length of $\overline{CM}$.

    c. Use a scale drawing to verify the length of $\overline{CM}$. In comparing with the exact result you may use the fact that $\sqrt{3} \approx 1.732$.

3. A ladder 15 feet long leans across a fence 8 feet high. The section of ladder between the ground and the fence is 10 feet long. How high is the top of the ladder above the ground. [NOTE: It is unnecessary to make a scale drawing here. (Why?)]

4. Use the Theorem of Pythagoras (and a square root table if needed) to find the distance from the foot of the ladder to the foot of the fence in problem **B3** above.

C. 1. Take a road map of your state and observe where the scale of miles is shown. Use this to lay off, on a strip of cardboard, a mileage scale to use for this map. Note that this mileage indicator is nothing but a ruler marked in nonstandard units. Use this to determine the distance between several pairs of cities. If the map has a chart indicating distance between cities, compare your results with those on the chart.

    2. The distances obtained in **C1** are presumably airline distances. Take a fine wire and bend it to fit the indicated road between two cities. Then straighten it out and measure with your mileage indicator to find the road distance. With good luck this will give results in better agreement with those indicated on the chart.

10.6 Trigonometric Ratios

Suppose that S and S' are similar point sets. If A, B, C, $D \in S$ and if A', B', C', D' are the corresponding points of S' the definition of similarity assures us that there is some fixed positive constant k such that $m(\overline{A'B'}) = k \cdot m(\overline{AB})$ and $m(\overline{C'D'}) = k \cdot m(\overline{CD})$. Moreover we observed in the last section that this was true even if we chose to use different units of measure for the two sets. From the two equations above we see at once that

$$\frac{m(\overline{A'B'})}{m(\overline{C'D'})} = \frac{k \cdot m(\overline{AB})}{k \cdot m(\overline{CD})} = \frac{m(\overline{AB})}{m(\overline{CD})}.$$

It turns out that this observation is the clue to some interesting developments in this section and for this reason we dignify it by writing it as a theorem.

Theorem 10.10 *If* $S \sim S'$, *then the ratio of the measures of two segments with endpoints in* S *equals the ratio of the measures of the segments whose endpoints are the corresponding points of* S'.

Of course as we take different pairs of segments in S the ratios will vary but Theorem 10.10 assures us that whatever ratio we get for a pair of segments in S will be the same as for the corresponding segments in S'.

In Section 10.5 you explored (and we hope were impressed by) the possibility of using similar figures (i.e., scale drawings) as a means of determining approximate solutions to problems in length and angle measurement. It is to be expected that you were also impressed with the fact that in practice it is quite a laborious procedure, particularly if the drawing is to be done with enough care to produce reasonably good results. Certainly any devices that would decrease the labor would be gratefully received.

One thought that comes to mind would be the desirability of preserving our drawings in case they could be used again in a later problem. If this were to be done in any useful way we would want to compile a catalog of drawings which might prove useful. The task of compiling a complete collection of drawings of all possible shapes would seem to be out of bounds even in this day of high-speed computers. However, if we limit ourselves to some of the simplest and most common shapes we might make a useful beginning.

Consider, for example, the second drawing made for Example 3 of Section 10.5. It was a right triangle $\triangle A'B'C'$ in which one of the angles was a 60° angle. Any two right triangles having 60° angles are similar. (Why?) Thus the same drawing could be used for *any* problem concerning a right triangle with a 60° angle. If we imagine right triangles drawn for angles with each integral number of degrees from 1° to 89°, this collection of drawings could be very useful.

Further reflection suggests a way of simplifying matters even more. After the triangle $\triangle A'B'C'$ was drawn, what use did we make of it? We measured the sides but from then on we used only these measures. Thus once the sides have been measured it is only necessary to make a record of the numbers. We then have no need to preserve the drawing. In recording results it becomes necessary to identify clearly which numbers go with which segments. To this end, some agreement on terminology is desirable.

In a right triangle $\triangle ABC$ as shown below, let us center attention on one of the acute angles, say $\angle A$. We then observe that the hypotenuse and one of the two perpendicular sides (here $\overline{AB}$) lie on the rays forming $\angle A$. We may therefore refer to $\overline{AB}$ as the *side on the angle*. The other of the two perpendicular sides (here

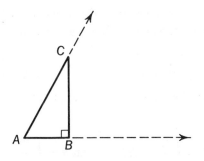

$\overline{BC}$) is, except for its endpoints, interior to $\angle A$ and so may properly be called the *side in the angle*. Another common terminology is to call $\overline{AB}$ the *adjacent side* since it is "next to" the vertex A of the angle and to call $\overline{BC}$ the *opposite side* since it is the side opposite vertex A. We elect to use the former terminology here. The information on the triangle shown on page 439 can therefore be recorded as follows:

Angle	*Hypotenuse*	*Side on angle*	*Side in angle*
60°	2.00	1.00	1.75

The only difference between the results recorded here and those in the earlier example is that we have chosen here to express the results as decimal numerals. We have of course deceived ourselves slightly in that it is reasonably clear that measurements are not good to the nearest hundredth of an inch.

The procedure suggested would make it possible to summarize the data for right triangles in quite compact and usable form. In practice it is customary to take one more step. We are never actually interested in the lengths of the sides of the triangles. Any triangle similar to the ones recorded would do just as well. It is always the *ratios* of the measures of these sides which are of interest to us, so in practice we record only these ratios. Notice that by Theorem 10.10 these ratios would be the same for any two similar triangles so they depend only on the angle measure.

To be specific, if the degree measure of an angle of a right triangle is denoted by θ we define the sine of the angle (sin θ, for short) as the ratio of the measure of the side in the angle to the measure of the hypotenuse. Similarly, the tangent of

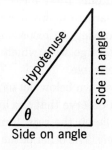

the angle (tan θ, for short) is the ratio of the measure of the side in the angle to the measure of the side on the angle. Thus we can write

$$\sin \theta = \frac{m(\text{side in angle})}{m(\text{hypotenuse})}, \quad \tan \theta = \frac{m(\text{side in angle})}{m(\text{side on angle})}.$$

By use of the data recorded above we find approximate values of sin 60° and tan 60° as

$$\sin 60° \approx \frac{1.75}{2} \approx .87, \quad \tan \theta \approx \frac{1.75}{1} \approx 1.75.$$

For convenience we show here a table of sines and tangents of angles at 1 degree intervals.

Table of Trigonometric Ratios

Angle (degrees)	Sine	Tangent	Angle (degrees)	Sine	Tangent
1	.02	.02	46	.72	1.04
2	.03	.03	47	.73	1.07
3	.05	.05	48	.74	1.11
4	.07	.07	49	.75	1.15
5	.09	.09	50	.77	1.19
6	.10	.11	51	.78	1.23
7	.12	.12	52	.79	1.28
8	.14	.14	53	.80	1.33
9	.16	.16	54	.81	1.38
10	.17	.18	55	.82	1.43
11	.19	.19	56	.83	1.48
12	.21	.21	57	.84	1.54
13	.22	.23	58	.85	1.60
14	.24	.25	59	.86	1.66
15	.26	.27	60	.87	1.73
16	.28	.29	61	.87	1.80
17	.29	.31	62	.88	1.88
18	.31	.32	63	.89	1.96
19	.33	.34	64	.90	2.05
20	.34	.36	65	.91	2.14
21	.36	.38	66	.91	2.25
22	.37	.40	67	.92	2.36
23	.39	.42	68	.93	2.48
24	.41	.45	69	.93	2.61
25	.42	.47	70	.94	2.75
26	.44	.49	71	.95	2.90
27	.45	.51	72	.95	3.08
28	.47	.53	73	.96	3.27
29	.48	.55	74	.96	3.49
30	.50	.58	75	.97	3.73
31	.52	.60	76	.97	4.01
32	.53	.62	77	.97	4.33
33	.54	.65	78	.98	4.70
34	.56	.67	79	.98	5.14
35	.57	.70	80	.98	5.67
36	.59	.73	81	.99	6.31
37	.60	.75	82	.99	7.12
38	.62	.78	83	.99	8.14
39	.63	.81	84	.99	9.51
40	.64	.84	85	1.00	11.43
41	.66	.87	86	1.00	14.30
42	.67	.90	87	1.00	19.08
43	.68	.93	88	1.00	28.64
44	.69	.97	89	1.00	57.29
45	.71	1.00			

This brief table embodies all the information that we could obtain from the 89 drawings that we imagined earlier. You realize, of course, that the data recorded here are in general not exact. Indeed, the only exact entries are those for sin 30° and tan 45°. The figures given are the closest possible approximations to two decimal places. Much more extensive tables are available giving results to much greater precision and for angles expressed in fractional parts of degrees. It is perhaps worth noting that the actual computation of tables like that on page 445 is not done by the simple process of drawing and measuring. More sophisticated techniques are used which we cannot discuss here. Observe that, according to the table, the value of tan 60° which we obtained by the measuring process is really a little high.

Actually for a right triangle there are six possible ratios for the sides. In a full development of trigonometry (which is what is being touched on lightly here) names would be given to all six of these ratios and tables would be computed for all six ratios. For our purposes here, however, it will be sufficient to use merely the sine and tangent ratios. The possibilities for making use of the data in the tables can be shown by a few examples.

Example 1. A wire from the top of a telephone pole to the ground makes an angle of 55° with the ground. If it reaches the ground 20 feet from the base of the pole, how high is the pole?

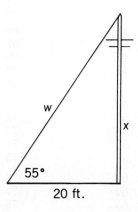

Let x be the measure, in feet, of the height of the pole. The side whose measure we are given and the side whose measure we want to know are, respectively, the side on the angle and the side in the angle. This suggests using the tangent ratio. By definition

$$\tan 55° = \frac{x}{20}.$$

According to the table tan 55° $\approx$ 1.43 so $\frac{x}{20} \approx 1.43$ and $x \approx 28.6$. Thus the height of the pole is about 28.6 feet.

Example 2. In the problem of Example 1, find the length of the wire.

Since we now know the lengths of the two perpendicular sides and want the length of the hypotenuse, one method would be to use the Theorem of Pythagoras. Another way would be to consider the ratio for sin 55° since this involves the hypotenuse. If we do this we discover

$$\sin 55° = \frac{x}{w} \approx \frac{28.6}{w}.$$

Since sin 55° ≈ .82 this yields .82 ≈ $\dfrac{28.6}{w}$ or

$$w \approx \frac{28.6}{.82} \approx 34.9.$$

Thus the length of the wire is approximately 34.9 feet.

Notice that in each case attention is called to the fact that results are only approximate. While we prefer not to go into detail here as to just how much accuracy or precision can be expected, you should use reasonable common sense in indicating results. For example, it is true that to five decimal places $\dfrac{28.6}{.82} \approx$ 34.87805 but no one in his right mind would say the length of the wire is "about 34.87805 feet."

It is worth noting that sometimes the table may be used to find an angle. This is illustrated below.

Example 3. If the end of a house is as shown, find the angle θ which the roof makes with the horizontal.

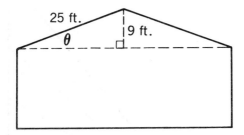

According to the definition of sin θ we find

$$\sin \theta = \frac{9}{25} = .36.$$

By reference to the table it is seen that θ is about 21°. In this problem why was the ratio sin θ used instead of tan θ?

Problem Set 10.6

A. 1. Solve problem **B1** of Problem Set 10.5 by using the table of trigonometric ratios.

2. Solve problem **A2c** of Problem Set 10.5 by using the table of trigonometric ratios.

3. In problem **B3** of Problem Set 10.5 find the approximate degree measure of the angle the ladder makes with the ground.

4. a. Use the results of problem **B2** of Problem Set 10.5 to find exact values of sin 60°, tan 60°, sin 30°, tan 30°.

b. Using the fact that $\sqrt{3} \approx 1.732$, find each of the results of part **a** correct to three decimal places.

B. 1. a. Show that, for every acute angle θ, tan $\theta >$ sin θ.

b. If statement **a** above is true, how do you explain the first five entries in the table?

2. a. Show that, for every acute angle θ, sin $\theta < 1$.

b. If statement **a** is true, how do you explain the last five entries in the table?

C. 1. Use the table to find the approximate degree measure of the angle θ for which tan $\theta = 3$ sin θ.

2. Make a careful drawing like the one shown in which the degree measures of the angles formed are 10, 20, 30, 40, and 50. By measuring the lengths verify the entries in the table for these angles. Keep in mind that the ratios you calculate are approximations and may not be in exact accord with the table entries. To simplify computation make the length of the base an integral number of inches.

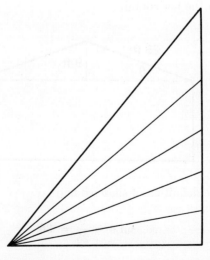

D. 1. A plank 13 feet long has one end on the ground and the other resting on a box $3\frac{1}{2}$ feet high. What is the degree measure of the angle the plank makes with the ground?

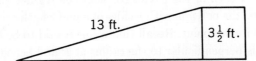

2. A second plank has one end resting on a box 3 feet high and the other end on the ground 12 feet from the box. Does the plank make a larger or smaller angle with the ground than the plank in problem **D1**?

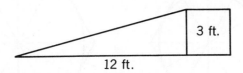

E. 1. An airplane flying at 20,000 feet passes directly over a radio tower as shown in the diagram. At this instant the pilot observes a town. He notices that to look at it he has to look down at an angle of 25° with the horizontal. How far is the radio tower from the town?

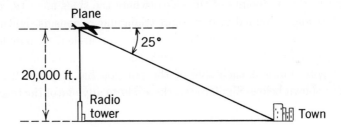

2. The motors in the plane of problem **E1** can be heard for a distance of $8\frac{1}{2}$ miles. Could an observer in town hear the plane at this instant? One mile is 5280 feet. Notice that here it is necessary to consider the straight-line distance from the plane to the observer.

10.7 The Length of a Circle

You will recall that the discussion of the length or circumference of a circle in Chapter 8 did not have an adequate foundation. Without much real evidence we leaped blindly to the assumption that the ratio of the measure of the circumference to that of the radius was the same for all circles. The ideas of similarity developed in this chapter enable us to make this assumption somewhat more palatable so that it does not seem quite such an unjustified leap of faith.

Consider any two circles C and C' and let the measure of the radii be r and r', respectively. For each of the circles consider the regular circumscribed polygon with n sides, i.e., the polygon with n sides of equal length each of which is tangent to the circle at its midpoint. Recall that a line is said to be tangent to a circle at a point P if it is perpendicular to the radius at P and hence (by Chapter 9) does not meet the circle again. The drawing below shows the case for $n = 6$. If lines

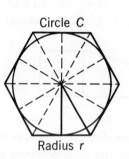

Circle C

Radius r

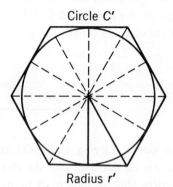

Circle C'

Radius r'

are drawn from the center of each circle to the vertices of the corresponding polygon and to the midpoints of the sides (where the sides meet the circle) the polygonal region is divided into $2n$ right triangular regions as shown.

If we examine one of the triangular regions for circle C we note that one of the two perpendicular sides is a radius while the other is a half of one of the sides of the polygon. Thus, if each side of the polygon has measure $2s$, we have the measures shown below. Similar remarks apply to any one of the triangular regions for C'.

For each of the triangular regions the degree measure of the angle at the center of the circle must be $\dfrac{180}{n}$. (Why?) Hence all such angles are congruent. Thus the triangular regions in the illustration are similar. (Why?) We can conclude by Theorem 10.10 that

$$\frac{s}{r} = \frac{s'}{r'}.$$

If p_n is the measure of the perimeter for the polygon about C and p'_n the corresponding measure for the polygon about C' we know that $p_n = 2ns$ and $p_n' = 2ns'$. (Why?) It then follows easily that

$$\frac{p_n}{r} = \frac{2ns}{r} = 2n\left(\frac{s}{r}\right) = 2n\left(\frac{s'}{r'}\right) = \frac{2ns'}{r'} = \frac{p_n'}{r'}.$$

That is, the ratio of the perimeter of the polygon to the radius is the same for the two circles. We conjectured in Chapter 8 that as n became larger and larger (i.e., as we considered polygons with more and more sides) the perimeter of the polygon would approach the circumference of the circle. Thus we expect that p_n approaches c, the circumference of C, and p_n' approaches c', the circumference of C'.

If $\frac{p_n}{r} = \frac{p_n'}{r'}$ and if p_n and p_n' approach c and c', respectively, it seems clear that we should expect that

$$\frac{c}{r} = \frac{c'}{r'}.$$

This would mean that for any two circles the ratio of circumference to radius is always the same, i.e., must equal some fixed number. If this fixed number is called 2π we are led to the result of Chapter 8 that

$$c = 2\pi r.$$

This argument should make you feel a little better satisfied with the formula for the circumference of a circle. It could be made into an honest proof by taking time to develop adequately the ideas of limits. In this book, however, we will content ourselves with being intuitive at this point.

10.8 The Pantograph

An interesting instrument called the **pantograph** can be used to produce homothetic images of plane figures. Since it is an application of the ideas of this chapter it will be described briefly.

The instrument is formed from four rigid bars representing segments $\overline{OB}$, $\overline{BP'}$, $\overline{AP}$, and $\overline{PC}$. The bars are connected at A, B, C, and P so that $\overline{AP} \cong \overline{BC}$ and

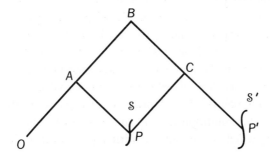

$\overline{AB} \cong \overline{PC}$. This makes figure $APCB$ a parallelogram. (Why?) Moreover, the lengths of the segments are chosen so that

$$\frac{m(\overline{OB})}{m(\overline{OA})} = \frac{m(\overline{BP'})}{m(\overline{AP})}.$$

Let this common ratio be called k. The joints at A, B, C, and P are not rigid but are merely pivots around which the two joined bars are free to rotate. The endpoint O is fixed but all other parts of the instrument are free to move in the plane.

The operation of the instrument is as follows: If the point P is allowed to trace some point set $\mathcal{S}$, then the point P' (where we may imagine a pencil mounted) will trace out the set $\mathcal{S}'$ homothetic to $\mathcal{S}$ with origin O and with k as the proportionality factor.

It is not difficult to show that the instrument will indeed perform as indicated. Note first that $\angle OAP \cong \angle OBP'$. (Why?) Also, we are given that

$$\frac{m(\overline{BO})}{m(\overline{AO})} = \frac{m(\overline{BP'})}{m(\overline{AP})} = k.$$

It follows then by Theorem 10.8 that $\triangle OAP \sim \triangle OBP'$. If this is true it means that $\angle AOP \cong \angle BOP'$ (why?), so that O, P, and P' are collinear. Moreover,

$$\frac{m(\overline{OP'})}{m(\overline{OP})} = \frac{m(\overline{OB})}{m(\overline{OA})} = k. \quad \text{(Why?)}$$

That is, O, P, and P' are collinear and $m(\overline{OP'}) = k \cdot m(\overline{OP})$, which shows that set $\mathcal{S}'$ is homothetic to $\mathcal{S}$ with origin O and ratio k as was claimed above.

10.9 Further Use of Coordinates

We have already seen examples of the usefulness of coordinates in approaching geometric problems. They provide a way of using the ideas and methods of algebra to deal with geometric questions. In pursuing this end it is useful to devise ways of describing important geometric figures such as lines, circles, circular regions, parabolas, etc., by algebraic statements. The systematic study of these questions is one of the principal goals of the branch of mathematics called **analytic geometry.** While such a study goes beyond the scope of this book, it will be instructive to consider a few simple examples.

Consider the line k perpendicular to the x-axis at $(2, 0)$. Can we describe in an algebraic way the points which lie on k? If (x, y) are the coordinates of any point P of k, can any statement be made about these coordinates? It is clear at once that for P to lie on k the first coordinate x must equal 2. Thus the statement $x = 2$ is true for all points of k. Moreover, any point whatever whose first coordinate satisfies this condition is on k. In other words, line k can be described as the set of points which satisfy the condition $x = 2$. Since the condition is an

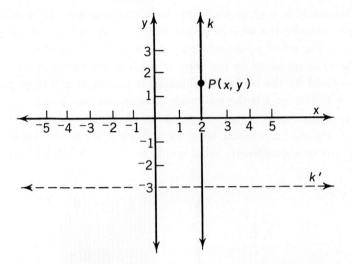

equation we refer to it as *the equation of k*. In a precisely similar way $y = {}^-3$ is the equation of line k' parallel to the x-axis and three units below it. The equation of the x-axis is $y = 0$ and the equation of the y-axis is $x = 0$ as should be clear by the definition of the coordinates.

   Sometimes statements involving inequalities are useful in describing sets. For example, what is the set of points described by the statement $x \geq 2$?

   What does it mean about a point P to say that its coordinates (x, y) satisfy the condition $x \geq 2$? Presumably it means that to reach P from the origin O it will be necessary to move 2 or more units to the right and then some suitable distance vertically. Clearly all such points are either on the line k with equation $x = 2$ or to the right of k. Conversely, for any point P on or to the right of the line k it must be true that $x \geq 2$. Hence the set of points satisfying the condition $x \geq 2$ is the union of the line k noted above and the half plane to the right of k. This set is indicated by the vertical shading in the following illustration.

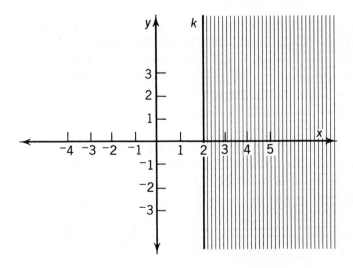

Not infrequently it may require more than one statement to describe a set. For example, identify the set S of points which satisfy both of the statements $x \geq 2$, $y \leq 1$. The set of points satisfying $x \geq 2$ was just identified. It is shown again in the drawing below by the vertical shading. Similarly the set satisfying $y \leq 1$ (indicated by the horizontal shading) is the set of points on and below the line $y = 1$. The set S is the set which satisfies *both* conditions; i.e., it is the intersection of the two sets just described. In the diagram S is represented by the checked region, i.e., shaded both ways. Such a set is sometimes called a **quarter plane** or a **quadrant.** What would be the set S which is described as

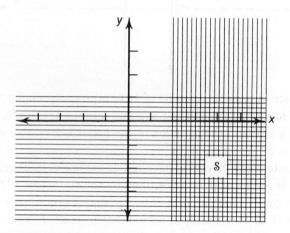

the set satisfying *at least one* of the conditions $x \geq 2$, $y \leq 1$? Note that it is the union of the sets described separately by $x \geq 2$ and by $y \leq 1$.

Notice that, if we use the notation introduced in Chapter 1, the set S above could be described as the set of points whose coordinates satisfy the condition $(x \geq 2) \wedge (y \leq 1)$, while the set S is the set whose coordinates satisfy $(x \geq 2) \vee (y \leq 1)$.

In identifying lines by algebraic statements (in this case equations) we have thus far considered only lines parallel to one of the axes. Let us turn to the consideration of other lines. Although undoubtedly you already know the facts of the case, let us proceed as though it were a brand new problem. Consider first a line k through the origin different from the axes. Diagram (a) on the next page shows the case when the line is rising as we move to the right while in (b) it is falling.

Let P_1, P_2, and P_3 be any points whatever on line k, and draw the perpendiculars to the x-axis meeting it at points Q_1, Q_2, and Q_3 as shown. It then follows that the three triangles $\triangle OQ_1P_1$, $\triangle OQ_2P_2$, and $\triangle OQ_3P_3$ are similar to each other. (Why?) According to Theorem 10.10, this means that

$$\frac{m(\overline{Q_1P_1})}{m(\overline{OQ_1})} = \frac{m(\overline{Q_2P_2})}{m(\overline{OQ_2})} = \frac{m(\overline{Q_3P_3})}{m(\overline{OQ_3})}.$$

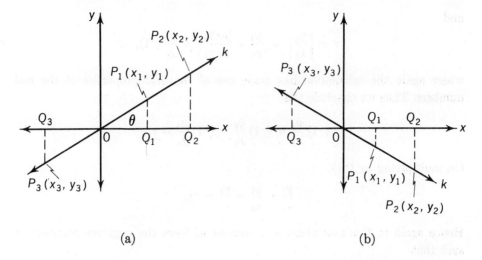

(a)   (b)

From the definition of coordinates $m(\overline{Q_1P_1}) = |\,y_1\,|$, $m(\overline{OQ_1}) = |\,x_1\,|$, and similarly for the other points. The relation above therefore becomes

$$\frac{|\,y_1\,|}{|\,x_1\,|} = \frac{|\,y_2\,|}{|\,x_2\,|} = \frac{|\,y_3\,|}{|\,x_3\,|} = r,$$

where we have let r represent the common value of these three ratios. In (a) if a point, like P_1, lies on the upward ray from O both coordinates are positive so that $|\,x_1\,| = x_1$, $|\,y_1\,| = y_1$. Hence

$$r = \frac{|\,y_1\,|}{|\,x_1\,|} = \frac{y_1}{x_1}.$$

If a point, like P_3, lies on the opposite ray both coordinates are negative so that $|\,x_3\,| = {}^-x_3$ and $|\,y_3\,| = {}^-y_3$. Hence in this case

$$r = \frac{|\,y_3\,|}{|\,x_3\,|} = \frac{{}^-y_3}{{}^-x_3} = \frac{y_3(-1)}{x_3(-1)} = \frac{y_3}{x_3}.$$

Here the last two equalities make use of the properties of additive inverses in the field of real numbers. Hence there is a number m (here the positive number r) such that

$$\frac{y_1}{x_1} = \frac{y_2}{x_2} = \frac{y_3}{x_3} = m.$$

In the case of (b) the situation is similar except that here the coordinates are always of opposite sign. Hence, for example, $|\,x_1\,| = x_1$, $|\,y_1\,| = {}^-y_1$, $|\,x_3\,| = {}^-x_3$, $|\,y_3\,| = y_3$. Thus

$$r = \frac{|\,y_1\,|}{|\,x_1\,|} = \frac{{}^-y_1}{x_1} = \frac{y_1(-1)}{x_1(1)} = \frac{y_1}{x_1}(-1)$$

and

$$r = \frac{|\, y_3 \,|}{|\, x_3 \,|} = \frac{y_3}{{}^{-}x_3} = \frac{y_3(1)}{x_3(-1)} = \frac{y_3}{x_3}(-1),$$

where again the calculation has made use of the field properties of the real numbers. Thus we conclude that

$$(-1)\frac{y_1}{x_1} = (-1)\frac{y_2}{x_2} = (-1)\frac{y_3}{x_3} = r.$$

Or, multiplying by (-1),

$$\frac{y_1}{x_1} = \frac{y_2}{x_2} = \frac{y_3}{x_3} = {}^{-}r.$$

Hence again in this case there is a number m (here the negative number ${}^{-}r$) such that

$$\frac{y_1}{x_1} = \frac{y_2}{x_2} = \frac{y_3}{x_3} = m.$$

In either case for a line k through the origin (other than an axis) we have seen that there is a number m such that all points on k satisfy the equation

$$y = mx.$$

It is easy to verify that, conversely, any point (x, y) whose coordinates satisfy this equation does lie on k. In other words, k may be described as the set of points (x, y) for which $y = mx$. This relation is therefore called **the equation of k.**

The number m in the discussion above is called the **slope** of line k. Diagrams (a) and (b) on page 455 show, respectively, lines of positive and negative slope. Notice that if we set $m = 0$ in the equation $y = mx$, we obtain the equation of the x-axis, so we shall say the x-axis has slope 0. In (a) if θ denotes the angle which is the union of the positive ray on the x-axis and the upward ray of k from O, then it follows immediately from the definition that

$$m = \frac{y_1}{x_1} = \tan \theta.$$

For the case of diagram (b) the angle θ is obtuse and we have not defined trigonometric ratios for obtuse angles. You will not be surprised, however, to learn that in a more extensive discussion of trigonometry it is useful to define $\tan \theta$ for all angles. When this is done the relation $m = \tan \theta$ is actually true for all lines which have slopes.

The only case of lines not yet considered is that of lines not through the origin and not parallel to the y-axis. Suppose k is such a line. Since k is not parallel to the y-axis it must meet the y-axis in some point given by $(0, b)$. The next illustration shows the case when $b > 0$. If P with coordinates (p, q) is any point of k, we are seeking a relationship between the numbers p and q. Let us draw the line

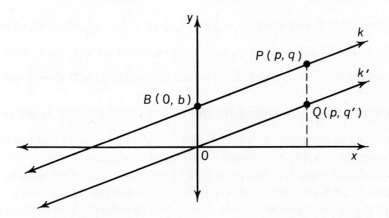

k' through the origin parallel to k. If the vertical line through P meets k' in Q, the figure $OQPB$ is a parallelogram. Thus $m(\overline{QP}) = m(\overline{OB}) = b$. (Why?) Clearly the first coordinates of P and Q are the same, so the coordinates of Q can be given as (p, q'). Moreover since, for the case shown, k is above k' we observe that $m(\overline{QP}) = q - q'$, so we conclude that $q = q' + b$.

We discovered just above that line k' has an equation $y = mx$, and since Q is on k' the coordinates of Q must satisfy the equation so that $q' = mp$. From the statement $q' = mp$ and $q = q' + b$ we find at once that $q = mp + b$. This is a relation connecting the coordinates of any point P on line k. It says that any point (p, q) of k is one of the points satisfying the equation $y = mx + b$.

Conversely, consider any point, say (r, s), which satisfies the equation—i.e., suppose $s = mr + b$. There is a point of k whose first coordinate is r, say (r, t). (Why is there such a point?) Since *any* point of k has been shown to satisfy the equation $y = mx + b$, we see that $t = mr + b$. Thus $t = mr + b = s$ and the point (r, t) is the same point as (r, s). Hence we conclude that (r, s) is on k. That is, k consists of exactly those points which satisfy the equation $y = mx + b$, so we speak of this as the equation of k. An entirely similar argument shows that this result likewise applies to the case when $b < 0$.

The number m associated with line k in the discussion above is the slope of the line k' parallel to k through the origin. It is natural to carry over the language and call the number m the slope of k. If two distinct lines k_1 and k_2 have the same slope m this means they are parallel to the same line k' through the origin and hence are parallel to each other. Conversely, if two lines are parallel they certainly have the same parallel k' through the origin and hence have equal slopes. This result may be stated formally as follows.

Theorem 10.11 *Two distinct lines, not parallel to the y-axis, are parallel if and only if their slopes are equal.*

As an example, consider the sets of points whose coordinates satisfy the equations $x - 2y + 4 = 0$, and $2x - 4y - 9 = 0$, respectively. These two equations are equivalent to the equations $y = \frac{1}{2}x + 2$ and $y = \frac{1}{2}x - \frac{9}{4}$. Since the equations

are both of the form $y = mx + b$, we identify the first set as a line k_1 with slope

$\frac{1}{2}$ and passing through $(0, 2)$ while the second set is a line k_2 with slope $\frac{1}{2}$ and pass-

ing through $\left(0, \frac{-9}{4}\right)$. According to Theorem 10.11 lines k_1 and k_2 are parallel

since the slopes are equal. You may find it interesting to verify this parallelism
by attempting to apply the process you learned in algebra of solving the equations simultaneously, i.e., finding a pair of numbers (x, y) that satisfies both
equations. If such solutions exist, the point (x, y) would be on both lines. If you
attempt the solution you will find it impossible. This shows there is no point on
both lines so the lines are parallel.

   You will observe that we have shown that all lines may be described as sets
of points whose coordinates are the solution sets of equations. It may be well to
state formally the facts about such equations.

Theorem 10.12 *Every line k has an equation of the form*

$$Ax + By + C = 0,$$

with A and B not both 0. Conversely, every such equation is the equation of a line.

   Proof. The proof is really just a reminder of what we have already discovered.
If a line k is parallel to the y-axis, it has an equation $x = r$, which is of the required form with $A = 1$, $B = 0$, $C = -r$. If k is not parallel to the y-axis, it has
an equation $y = mx + b$, which is of the required form with $A = m$, $B = -1$,
$C = b$. Thus every line has an equation of the given form.

   Conversely, consider any equation $Ax + By + C = 0$ with A, B not both 0.

If $B = 0$, then $A \neq 0$ and the equation can be rewritten as $x = \frac{-C}{A}$, which we

know is the equation of a line parallel to the y-axis. If $B \neq 0$, the equation can

be rewritten as $y = \left(\frac{-A}{B}\right)x + \left(\frac{-C}{B}\right)$, which is recognized as the equation of a

line with slope $m = \frac{-A}{B}$ and with $b = \frac{-C}{B}$. This completes the proof.

   You probably recall that in your work in algebra, equations such as $Ax +$
$By + C = 0$ were called linear equations. It is because of Theorem 10.12 that
the geometric word *linear* has come to be attached to a kind of equation. Equations like $Ax + By + C = 0$ are called linear because their graphs are lines.

   In concluding this section on coordinates it may be helpful to consider how to
find the slope of a line through two points and how this may be used to find the
equation of the line. Let (x_1, y_1) and (x_2, y_2) be the coordinates of two distinct

points P_1 and P_2. If $x_1 = x_2$ we see at once that k is parallel to the y-axis so the equation is $x = x_1$. In this case we have given no meaning to the word slope. In any other case we know line k has an equation of the form $y = mx + b$. Since

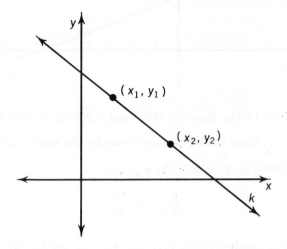

line k passes through both points, both sets of coordinates satisfy the equation. That is, we know that

$$y_1 = mx_1 + b.$$
$$y_2 = mx_2 + b.$$

By subtraction it follows that $y_2 - y_1 = m(x_2 - x_1)$ or

$$m = \frac{y_2 - y_1}{x_2 - x_1}.$$

This formula for the slope m of a line lends itself to a simple geometric interpretation of slope. Imagine that we propose to move from point P_1 to point P_2 of line k by making first a horizontal motion and then a vertical motion. The required horizontal motion is represented by the number $x_2 - x_1$, and the required vertical motion by $y_2 - y_1$. For example, if $x_2 - x_1 = 4$ and $y_2 - y_1 = ^-3$ this means that to get from P_1 to P_2 one can make a horizontal motion 4 units to the right (i.e., in the positive x-direction) and 3 units down (i.e., in the negative y-direction). The slope of a line is then, according to the formula, the ratio of the numbers representing the vertical and horizontal motions for a move from one point of the line to another. You will remember that the idea of associating a number with a motion along a line was discussed in Chapter 8.

Once the slope has been found for line $\overleftrightarrow{P_1P_2}$, its equation can readily be obtained. The method will be illustrated by an example. Find the equation of the line through $(^-2, 3)$ and $(4, 1)$. According to the formula, the slope m is given by $m = \dfrac{1-3}{4-^-2} = \dfrac{^-2}{6} = \dfrac{^-1}{3}$. Now let (x, y) represent any point on the line except

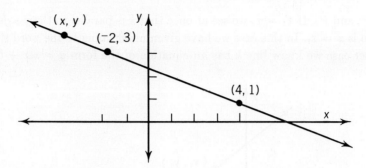

$(^-2, 3)$. The slope of the line, by the same formula, is also given by $m =$ $\dfrac{y - 3}{x - (^-2)} = \dfrac{y - 3}{x + 2}$. Since these two expressions for the slope m are equal we find that the coordinates (x, y) satisfy the equation

$$\frac{y - 3}{x + 2} = \frac{^-1}{3}.$$

Multiplying by the multiplicative inverses of $\dfrac{1}{x + 2}$ and $\dfrac{1}{3}$ yields

$$\frac{y - 3}{x + 2} \cdot \frac{x + 2}{1} \cdot \frac{3}{1} = \frac{^-1}{3} \cdot \frac{x + 2}{1} \cdot \frac{3}{1}.$$

By the associative and commutative properties of multiplication and the multiplicative identity this becomes

$$(y - 3) \cdot \frac{(x + 2)}{(x + 2)} \cdot 3 = (^-1) \cdot (x + 2) \cdot \frac{3}{3},$$

or

$$3(y - 3) = ^-1(x + 2).$$

Since $y - 3 = y + {}^-3$, use of the distributive property of addition yields

$$3y + {}^-9 = {}^-x + {}^-2.$$

Adding the additive inverses of ^-x and $^-2$ then yields

$$(x + 2) + (3y + {}^-9) = (x + 2) + (^-x + {}^-2) = (x + {}^-x) + (2 + {}^-2) = 0.$$

Use of the commutative and associative properties of addition reduces this to

$$x + 3y + {}^-7 = 0,$$

or, equivalently,

$$x + 3y - 7 = 0.$$

This is the equation of the desired line. You may be interested to check that both $(4, 1)$ and $(^-2, 3)$ do satisfy this equation so this equation does represent the desired line.

The above discussion has been written out in detail to illustrate how the various structural properties of the real number system are actually involved in justifying our familiar algebraic manipulations. In practice one commonly resorts to various short cuts, but it is actually the properties noted above which make these procedures legitimate.

Problem Set 10.9

A. 1. Show on a sketch the set of points satisfying all three of the following statements: $x \geq {}^-1$, $x \leq 1$, $y \geq 0$.
   2. Show on a sketch the set of points satisfying the following statement: $(y \geq 1) \wedge (x = 3)$. What kind of a point set is this?
   3. Show on a sketch the set of points satisfying all three of the following statements: $x \geq {}^-1$, $x \leq 3$, $y = 4$. What kind of point set is this?

B. 1. Write inequalities which describe the infinite strip indicated below.

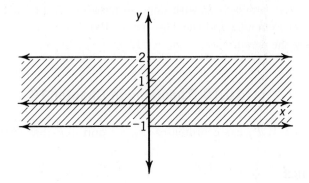

   2. Write inequalities to describe the rectangular region whose vertices are $(1, {}^-1)$, $(5, {}^-1)$, $(5, 2)$, $(1, 2)$.
   3. Make sketches showing the sets of points whose coordinates (x, y) satisfy each of the following conditions: (a) $y \geq \frac{1}{2} x$; (b) $y \leq 3x$; (c) *both* conditions in (a) and (b).

C. 1. Find equations of the lines joining the following pairs of points
   a. $({}^-1, 2)$, $(2, 4)$.   **c.** $(3, 1)$, $(3, {}^-4)$.
   b. $(0, 4)$, $(6, 1)$.   **d.** $(5, {}^-2)$, $(8, {}^-2)$.
   2. What are the slopes of each of the following lines? Are there any cases of parallelism?

$$2x - y + 8 = 0 \qquad 2x + y - 6 = 0 \qquad 4x - 2y + 5 = 0$$

   Make a sketch showing all three lines on the same set of axes.
   3. Describe the set of points satisfying both the following statements

$$y \geq 2x + 5 \qquad y \leq 2x - 1$$

D. A line k_1 through the origin has slope m_1, and so passes through the point

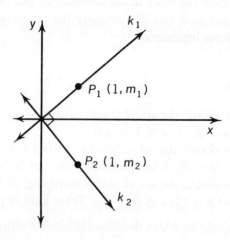

$P_1 (1, m_1)$. Similarly k_2 with slope m_2 passes through $P_2 (1, m_2)$. If $k_1 \perp k_2$, use Theorem 10.1 and the Theorem of Pythagoras to show that the slopes satisfy the condition $m_1 \cdot m_2 = {}^-1$.

10.10 Theorems in Chapter 10

Theorem 10.1 If P_1 has coordinates (x_1, y_1) and if P_2 has coordinates (x_2, y_2), then $m(\overline{P_1P_2}) = \sqrt{(x_2 - x_1)^2 + (y_2 - y_1)^2}$.

Theorem 10.2

(a) If a homothetic transformation takes P into P' and if O is the origin, then O, P, and P' are collinear.

(b) In a homothetic transformation with $k \neq 1$ the origin is the only fixed point, i.e., the only point carried into itself.

(c) If P_1, P_2 are any points and P_1', P_2' are their images under a homothetic transformation with constant k, then $m(\overline{P_1'P_2'}) = k \cdot m(\overline{P_1P_2})$.

(d) A homothetic transformation takes collinear points into collinear points.

(e) A homothetic transformation takes any line through the origin into itself. A homothetic transformation with $k \neq 1$ takes a line m not through the origin into a parallel line m'.

(f) If A, B, and C are noncollinear points and if A', B', and C' are their images under a homothetic transformation, then $\angle ABC \cong \angle A'B'C'$.

Theorem 10.3

(a) If $\mathcal{S} \sim \mathcal{S}'$, then there is a homothetic image $\mathcal{S}''$ of $\mathcal{S}$ such that $\mathcal{S}'' \cong \mathcal{S}'$.

(b) If there is a homothetic image $\mathcal{S}''$ of $\mathcal{S}$ such that $\mathcal{S}'' \cong \mathcal{S}'$, then $\mathcal{S} \sim \mathcal{S}'$.

Theorem 10.4 Let $\mathcal{S}$ and $\mathcal{S}'$ be point sets such that $\mathcal{S} \sim \mathcal{S}'$. Let A, B, and C be points of $\mathcal{S}$ and let A', B', and C' be their images in $\mathcal{S}'$.

(a) If A, B, and C are collinear with $B \in \overline{AC}$, then A', B', and C' are collinear with $B' \in \overline{A'C'}$.

(b) If A, B, and C are not collinear, then A', B', and C' are not collinear and $\angle ABC \cong \angle A'B'C'$.

Theorem 10.5 If $\triangle ABC \sim \triangle A'B'C'$, then

(a) $\angle A \cong \angle A'$, $\angle B \cong \angle B'$, $\angle C \cong \angle C'$ and

(b) $\dfrac{m(\overline{A'B'})}{m(\overline{AB})} = \dfrac{m(\overline{B'C'})}{m(\overline{BC})} = \dfrac{m(\overline{C'A'})}{m(\overline{CA})}.$

Theorem 10.6 If two angles of one triangle are congruent to two angles of a second, the triangles are similar.

Theorem 10.7 If $\triangle ABC$ and $\triangle A'B'C'$ are such that $\dfrac{m(\overline{A'B'})}{m(\overline{AB})} = \dfrac{m(\overline{B'C'})}{m(\overline{BC})} = \dfrac{m(\overline{C'A'})}{m(\overline{CA})}$, then $\triangle ABC \sim \triangle A'B'C'$.

Theorem 10.8 If $\triangle ABC$ and $\triangle A'B'C'$ are such that $\angle A \cong \angle A'$ and $\dfrac{m(\overline{A'B'})}{m(\overline{AB})} = \dfrac{m(\overline{A'C'})}{m(\overline{AC})}$, then $\triangle ABC \sim \triangle A'B'C'$.

Theorem 10.9 If three parallel lines are met by two transversals, the ratio of the measures of any two segments cut from one transversal equals the ratio of the measures of the corresponding segments on the other transversal.

Theorem 10.10 If $s \sim s'$, then the ratio of the measures of two segments with endpoints in s equals the ratio of the measures of the segments whose endpoints are the corresponding points of s'.

Theorem 10.11 Two distinct lines, not parallel to the y-axis, are parallel if and only if their slopes are equal.

Theorem 10.12 Every line has an equation of the form $Ax + By + C = 0$, with A, B not both 0. Conversely any such equation is the equation of a line.

10.11 Terminal Tasks for Chapter 10

1. To identify the symbols in the distance formula and associate the variables in the formula with coordinates of points in the Cartesian plane.
2. To apply the distance formula in the solution of problems which require demonstrating that three points (whose coordinates are given) are collinear, or the vertices of a right triangle or the vertices of an isosceles triangle.
3. To select from a set of drawings those which represent homothetic images of a given set of points.

4. To estimate, for two sets of points which are the homothetic images of each other, whether the homothetic constant $k \gtreqless 1$.

5. To draw the homothetic image of a polygonal set of points for a given origin and a given constant, $k > 0$.

6. To indicate awareness of the properties of similar triangles by listing the relationships among the three pairs of angles and among the three pairs of sides of two similar triangles.

7. To select and use the appropriate properties of similar triangles in solving suitably composed applied problems.

8. To recognize a situation in which a problem may be solved by making a scale drawing.

9. To make a scale drawing.

10. To define the sine and tangent trigonometric functions for an acute angle of a right triangle.

11. To select and use the appropriate trigonometric function to solve problems in which the mathematical representation of the situation is a right triangle.

12. To apply the properties of similarity of general point sets in writing deductive proofs of simple theorems.

13. To describe a simple point set by an equality or an inequality written in mathematical symbols associated with the Cartesian plane.

14. To identify a simple point set described by an equality or inequality, written in mathematical symbols associated with the Cartesian plane.

15. To identify parallel lines by examining the equations which describe them.

16. To write the equation of a line on two given points whose coordinates are provided.

17. To define the slope of a line geometrically in the Cartesian plane and algebraically by a formula.

REVIEW EXERCISES

A. Consider the set of points whose coordinates are as follows:

$$A \ (0, 2), \quad B \ (7, 3), \quad C \ (1, 0), \quad D \ (2, -2).$$

1. Find a set of three of these points which are collinear.

2. Find a set of three of these points which are the vertices of an isosceles triangle.

3. Find a set of three of these points which are the vertices of a right triangle.

4. Find two triples of these points which are the vertices of congruent triangles.

B. 1. Draw a triangle ABC and choose a convenient point O. Draw the figure homothetic to $\triangle ABC$ with origin O and constant $k = 3$.

2. In the diagram you have drawn for problem **B1,** draw the altitude $\overline{AD}$ of $\triangle ABC$ and the corresponding altitude of the homothetic triangle. What do you seem to observe about the lengths of these two altitudes? What do you seem to observe about the points D and D' which are the feet of these altitudes?

C. 1. A vertical flagpole casts a shadow 30 feet long on level ground. A nearby tree at the same time casts a shadow 54 feet long. If the flagpole is known to be 40 feet high, how much taller is the tree than the flagpole?

2. In problem **C1,** find the distance from the top of the flagpole to the tip of its shadow and the corresponding distance for the tree.

3. A ship starts at point A and sails 10 miles due east. It then turns 40° to the left and sails another 10 miles. It then makes a 30° left turn and sails another 10 miles. Use a scale drawing to find its distance and direction from the starting point.

4. A man whose eye is 6 feet above the ground stands 30 feet from the base of a flagpole. To see the top of the pole he must look up at an angle of 65° with the horizontal. Use a scale drawing to find the height of the pole.

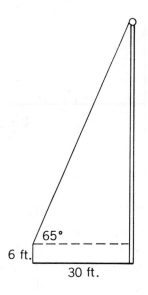

5. Do problem **C4** by using the table of trigonometric ratios.

6. A ladder 36 feet long leans against a house. If it touches the house 24 feet above the ground find the angle the ladder makes with the ground. (Assume the ground is level.)

D. 1. Let S, S', S'' be three sets of points in the plane. If $S \cong S'$ and $S' \sim S''$, show that $S \sim S''$.

2. Let $\triangle ABC \sim \triangle A'B'C'$ and let k be the constant of proportionality. If M is the midpoint of $\overline{BC}$ and if M' is the midpoint of $\overline{B'C'}$, prove that $m(\overline{A'M'}) = k \cdot m(\overline{AM})$.

3. Let $D \in \overline{BC}$ be such that, in $\triangle ABC$, $\overline{AD} \perp \overline{BC}$; i.e., $\overline{AD}$ is an altitude of the triangle. If $\triangle ABC \sim \triangle A'B'C'$ and if D' is the image of D in the similarity, prove that $\overline{A'D'}$ is an altitude of $\triangle A'B'C'$. If k is the constant of proportionality for this similarity, show that $m(\overline{A'D'}) = k \cdot m(\overline{AD})$.

4. Let $\triangle ABC$ and $\triangle A'B'C'$ be triangles and O a point such that $A \in \overline{OA'}$, $B \in \overline{OB'}$ and $C \in \overline{OC'}$, and the lines $\overline{OA'}$, $\overline{OB'}$, $\overline{OC'}$ are all distinct. If $\overline{AB} \parallel \overline{A'B'}$ and $\overline{BC} \parallel \overline{B'C'}$, prove that $\overline{AC} \parallel \overline{A'C'}$.

E. 1. Make sketches showing the sets of points whose coordinates satisfy each of the following sets of conditions:

    a. $x \geq 1$.

    b. $x \leq 3$.

    c. $x \geq 1$ and $x \leq 3$.

    d. $x \geq 1$, $x \leq 3$, $y \geq 0$, and $y \leq 2$.

2. Write three inequalities such that points whose coordinates satisfy them are the points of set S as shown. The set S does not include its bounding lines.

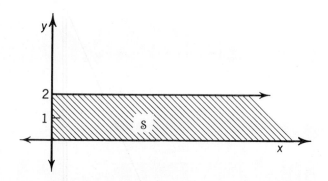

3. Sketch the set of points satisfying the condition $y < x + 1$.

F. 1. Among the following six lines, indicate all the pairs of parallel lines.

    (a) $x - 2y + 4 = 0$.   (d) $2x - 3y - 6 = 0$.

    (b) $2x + 3y - 6 = 0$.   (e) $3x - 6y + 5 = 0$.

    (c) $2x - 4y + 7 = 0$.   (f) $4x + 6y + 9 = 0$.

2. Consider the quadrilateral $ABCD$ whose vertices are given by $A(-4, -1)$, $B(0, 2)$, $C(4, 0)$, $D(0, -3)$. Decide whether the quadrilateral is a parallelogram by finding the slopes of the opposite sides.

3. Find the equations of the four lines containing the sides of the quadrilateral $ABCD$ of problem **F2.**

APPENDIX A   Motivation for the Pyramid Volume Formula

Imagine a stack of cards of varying sizes piled up as shown. They appear to approximate a pyramid. This particular sketch is intended to suggest a square pyramid, though the shape of the base is irrelevant in the discussion. It seems

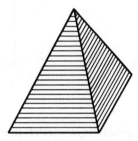

plausible moreover that by taking thinner cards and more of them we can make the approximation to the pyramid as good as we like.

By pushing the stack of cards sideways we can make the stack appear to represent other pyramids, for example, as shown in the second illustration, where the vertex is above the left front corner of the base instead of over the center of the base. This works very well in an actual manipulative experiment. Since the material actually present is the same in both drawings, it is a natural conjecture that the volume measures of the pyramids represented should be equal. We see that the two pyramids in question have congruent bases and altitudes of equal measure so the experiment above suggests the following conjecture.

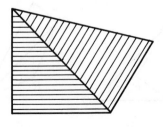

Conjecture *If two pyramids have congruent bases and altitudes of equal measure, the volume measures of the solid regions they bound are equal.*

If we were seriously attempting an axiomatic development of volume measure we might adopt this conjecture as an axiom. More likely yet we would adopt a stronger form of it, often called Cavalieri's Principle, as is done for example in *Geometry* by the School Mathematics Study Group. Since our goals here are more modest, we shall use the Conjecture only for making more plausible the formula for the volume measure of a pyramid.

We consider first a triangular pyramid $PQRP'$ as shown in diagram (1) and let B be the area measure of base $\triangle PQR$ and h the measure of the altitude. Recall that the altitude of a pyramid is the segment from the vertex perpendicular to the base plane.

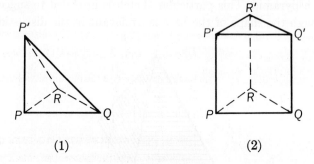

(1)   (2)

We may then consider the prism $PQRP'Q'R'$ in diagram (2) for which points P, Q, R, P' are the same as before. A base of this prism is the triangular region PQR and hence it has area measure B, while the prism and the pyramid have the same altitude measure h. Hence the volume measure of the prism in diagram (2) is given by Bh.

The solid region in diagram (2) may be dissected into three triangular pyramids by two plane cuts, one through points P', R, Q and the other through points Q, P', R'. This dissection is indicated in diagram (a) below with the three separated pieces shown at (b), (c), and (d).

The solid in (b) is again merely the given triangular pyramid of (1) in the pre-

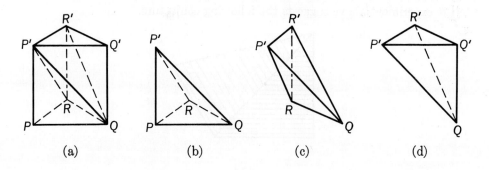

(a)   (b)   (c)   (d)

vious illustration. Now let us compare the three solids in (b), (c), and (d). If we consider PQR and $P'Q'R'$ as bases for diagrams (b) and (d), respectively, then these pyramids have congruent bases since the two bases of a prism are always congruent. Moreover, the altitudes of these pyramids have equal measures since an altitude measure of either pyramid is merely the perpendicular distance between the parallel planes containing $\triangle PQR$ and $\triangle P'Q'R'$. Hence, if we are to depend on the conjecture made above we conclude that the solid regions indicated in (b) and (d) have the same volume measure V.

Let us now compare the solid regions in (b) and (c). As has been noted earlier, for a triangular pyramid (or tetrahedron) any one of the four faces may be considered as base. For this comparison let the plane regions bounded by $\triangle PP'R$ and $\triangle R'RP'$ be chosen as the bases for (b) and (c). Notice that the vertex corresponding to these bases is, in both cases, the same point Q. Upon referring to (a) it is seen that $\triangle PP'R$ and $\triangle R'RP'$ are congruent since they occur by drawing the diagonal $\overline{P'R}$ in the parallelogram $PRR'P'$. Hence the pyramids in (b) and (c) have congruent bases and indeed these bases lie in the same plane, i.e., $PRR'P'$. Since in both cases point Q is the vertex opposite these bases it follows that the altitudes are the same segment and hence have equal measures. Hence the pyramids in (b) and (c) have congruent bases and altitudes of equal measure and, by the conjecture, should have equal volume measures V.

The three pyramids in (b), (c), (d) therefore seem to have the same volume measure V. Referring to (a) it then follows that the volume measure of the prism should be $V + V + V$ or $3V$. Since it has already been observed that this volume measure is Bh, we conclude that $3V = Bh$ or

$$V = \frac{1}{3} Bh.$$

This is precisely the formula for the volume of a pyramid which we were seeking to make plausible. Notice that we here assume volume measures are additive just as was done for area measures.

You will have noticed that the discussion as given seems to apply only to the case of a triangular pyramid, but it is easy to extend it to cover any pyramid. Consider, for example, the pyramid shown below with vertex O and whose base

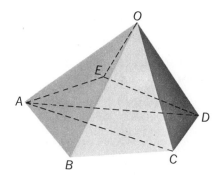

is a region bounded by a pentagon. The solid region bounded by $OABCDE$ can be dissected into regions bounded by triangular pyramids by passing planes through OAC and OAD, thus producing triangular pyramids $OABC, OACD, OADE$. Since each of these pyramids has O for the vertex opposite their bases, they all have the same altitude, which is also the altitude of the original pyramid. Let the measure of this common altitude be h. If B is the area measure of the base $ABCDE$ of the given pyramid, then

$$B = B_1 + B_2 + B_3,$$

where B_1, B_2, B_3 are the area measures of $\triangle ABC$, $\triangle ACD$, and $\triangle ADE$, respectively. Since the volume measure V of $OABCDE$ is the sum of the volume measures of the three triangular pyramids, we obtain, using the result above for the triangular pyramids,

$$V = \frac{1}{3}B_1 h + \frac{1}{3}B_2 h + \frac{1}{3}B_3 h = \frac{1}{3}h(B_1 + B_2 + B_3) = \frac{1}{3}Bh.$$

The simplification has used the distributive property of multiplication over addition. This shows that the formula $V = \frac{1}{3}Bh$ applies to the given pentagonal pyramid. The extension to any type of pyramid should now be clear.

Models to illustrate the dissection of a triangular prism into triangular pyramids of equal volume as indicated in the discussion are readily constructed. The patterns below may be used. Use either the dimensions indicated or any dimensions proportional to them. The vertices in these patterns have been lettered to correspond to the notation in the drawing on page 468. In each case fold along the dashed lines keeping the letters on the outside of the surface. Edges may be sealed with tape.

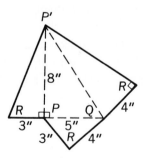

Note the two segments marked $\overline{P'R}$ are congruent. The length is about 9.4 inches. The two right angles at P simplify the drawing.

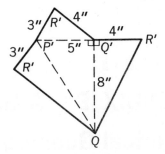

Note the two segments marked $\overline{QR'}$ are congruent. Their lengths are about 9 inches. The two right angles at Q' simplify the drawing.

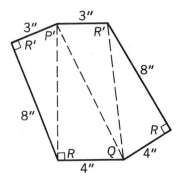

Note the three right angles marked. Segments $\overline{RP'}$, $\overline{QP'}$, and $\overline{QR'}$ are as in the other two figures.

APPENDIX B   A Glimpse
of Spherical Geometry

The surface of the earth is approximately spherical in shape. Hence our ordinary travels take place on a surface which is roughly spherical. It thus seems desirable to give a brief introduction to the geometry on a sphere. The approach will be largely intuitive, depending heavily on observations from our everyday experiences, but the insights may be revealing.

If O is the center of a sphere and W any point of the sphere, then segment $\overline{OW}$ is called a **radius.** All radii of a sphere are congruent and hence have the same measure r. Similarly, a segment whose endpoints are on a sphere and which contains the center O is called a **diameter.** Thus $\overline{OP}$, $\overline{OQ}$, and $\overline{OR}$ are radii and $\overline{PR}$ is a diameter. The measure of any diameter must be $2r$ so all diameters of a given sphere are congruent.

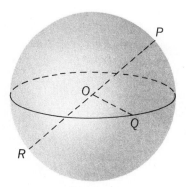

The surfaces of many familiar objects like oranges. Ping-pong balls, and basketballs are approximately spherical in shape and we shall use our experience with such objects to motivate conjectures about the sphere. Note that a football is not spherical in shape.

Let us first consider the question of the intersection set of a sphere and a plane. If we imagine an orange held above a table, it seems clear that the sphere represented by the orange and the plane represented by the table top have no common points. Thus in this case the intersection set is $\varnothing$, the empty set. Similarly, if the orange is placed on the table it seems to barely touch the table top. This leads us to imagine that the intersection set consists of a single point. To consider the possibilities other than these two somewhat trivial cases, let us imagine the orange sliced with a knife. Indeed let us imagine a series of parallel slices as indicated below. Anyone who has tried this experiment should find it plausible

that the intersection sets of each of the plane cuts with the surface of the orange is a circle. Moreover, the circles for different cuts seem to have different radii and the largest radius seems to be obtained from the cutting plane which contains the center of the sphere.

While these conclusions are here merely conjectures based on purely experimental evidence, it would be possible to establish them as theorems by suitably expanding our axiom system. Hence, for convenience we shall state them as a theorem. Notice clearly, however, that the theorem has not been proved.

Theorem B.1 *The intersection set of a sphere and a plane is a circle, a point, or the empty set. The circles with greatest possible radius for a given sphere are obtained from planes through the center of the sphere. In this case the center of the circle is the center of the sphere and every radius of the circle is a radius of the sphere.*

Because of Theorem B.1 the intersection set of a sphere and a plane through the center of the sphere is called a **great circle** of this sphere. Any other circle of intersection is called a **small circle** of the sphere. An excellent illustration of these ideas may be obtained from an ordinary globe representing the earth's surface. Examination of such a globe reveals a set of circles, as shown on the next page, containing the North and South poles N and S. These are commonly called the **meridian circles.** The cutting plane for any such circle must contain the diameter $\overline{NS}$ and hence the center O. Thus the meridian circles are all great circles. Then there is on the globe another set of circles running around the poles as shown. These are the circles of latitude. The only one of the circles of latitude which is a great circle is the Equator. The others are examples of small circles.

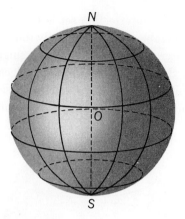

When two points A and B lie on a circle, there are clearly two paths on the circle from A to B. These are often called the *arcs* of the circle determined by A and B. In the accompanying sketch one of the arcs contains Q while the other

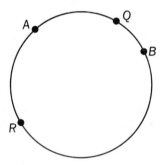

contains R. If A and B are endpoints of a diameter the two arcs are called **semi-circles.** On the globe the arcs of the meridian circles determined by N and S are semicircles. These arcs of the meridian circles are frequently called simply the **meridians.**

An interesting question naturally presents itself with respect to a sphere. If one wishes to move from one point to another on a sphere but wishes to travel the shortest possible distance, what path should be followed? That is, what curves on the sphere play the role of lines in the plane in providing paths of minimum length? We can, of course, attempt to gain some insight experimentally by taking a model of a sphere and a piece of thread and examining the position the thread assumes when held so that it passes through two points of the sphere but is pulled as tight as possible. Let us imagine this experiment applied to the familiar case of a globe to see if it suggests a conjecture.

Suppose points A and B in the next illustration are points of the same meridian of the globe. If the thread-stretching experiment is carried out for points A and B, it will appear that the stretched thread seems to follow the meridian. Since we have identified the meridian circles as great circles, this effect suggests that a

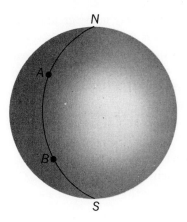

path of minimum length should be an arc of a great circle. The conjecture is in fact correct and we shall state it as a theorem.

Theorem B.2 *If A and B are points of a sphere, there is always on the sphere a path of minimum length joining A and B. Such a path is always an arc of a great circle.*

A proof of this theorem is beyond the scope of this book. Indeed you should recognize that the very question it tries to answer is really quite a sophisticated one. It presumably requires us not only to understand the meaning of length along a great circle but also to understand the meaning of length for other curves on the sphere and to have means of comparing lengths for all the different curves on the sphere joining A and B.

Since the great circles play such an important role on the sphere, it would be well to examine them a little more closely. Suppose that we consider the question of finding a great circle containing two given points A and B. Such a great circle must be the intersection set of the sphere and a plane containing the points A and B and also the center O of the sphere. Two different situations arise. If A and B are endpoints of a diameter as in diagram (a), then every plane containing A and B contains the diameter $\overline{AB}$ and hence the center O. Since there are infinitely

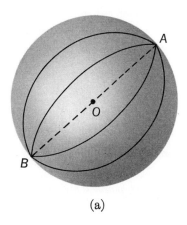

(a)

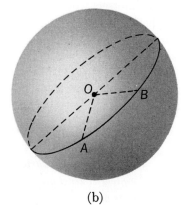

(b)

many such planes, there are infinitely many great circles containing the endpoints of a diameter. Thus if A and B are endpoints of a diameter there are infinitely many "shortest paths" on the sphere from A to B, each of which is half a great circle. This is illustrated on the globe by the meridians, each of which is a "shortest path" between the North and South poles.

The second situation, when A and B are not endpoints of a diameter, is shown in diagram (b). This time points O, A, B do not lie on a line. Thus there is exactly one plane containing $O, A,$ and B (why?), and hence exactly one great circle containing A and B. Of course there are two arcs from A to B on this great circle, one of them greater than a semicircle and the other less. Clearly only the shorter one can be a path of minimum length. Thus in this case there is a unique shortest path.

Let us consider now the situation that arises if we have two different great circles C_1 and C_2 on a sphere. Each of these great circles is obtained from a cutting plane containing the center O of the sphere. The two planes π_1 and π_2 thus must have a line k through O as their intersection set. Since any line through O meets the sphere in two points A and B which are endpoints of a diameter, it follows

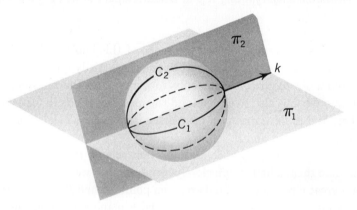

that both great circles contain the points A and B. Hence any two different great circles must intersect in points which are endpoints of a diameter.

A more naïve argument leading to the same conclusion that great circles always intersect would be the following. Circles C_1 and C_2 each cut the sphere into two hemispheres. Since a hemisphere cut by C_2 cannot very well be wholly contained in a hemisphere cut by C_1 it follows that the cutting circles must cross each other.

It may be well to collect the observations about great circles into a theorem.

Theorem B.3

(a) *There is a great circle containing any two points A and B of a sphere. If $\overline{AB}$ is a diameter there are infinitely many such great circles and if $\overline{AB}$ is not a diameter there is exactly one.*

(b) *Any two distinct great circles of a sphere intersect in two points which are endpoints of a diameter.*

The results of this theorem permit us to notice some interesting contrasts
between the sphere and the plane. We have observed that the great circles on the
sphere play the role of lines in the plane in that they provide the paths of shortest
length. In the plane, however, there is always a unique line containing two points
(Theorem 4.2), while by Theorem B.3 there is sometimes an infinite number of
great circles containing two points. Similarly, in the plane two lines may be
parallel (i.e., have an empty intersection), while by Theorem B.3 every two great
circles intersect. Thus there can be no such thing on the sphere as "parallel"
great circles. Some other interesting likenesses and contrasts between the geometries of the sphere and the plane come to light in the discussion of angle and area
below.

In Chapter 9 we gave some consideration to the area of a sphere and were led
to the formula

$$S = 4\pi r^2,$$

where r is the measure of a radius and S the measure of area for the sphere. Here
we shall be interested in considering areas of certain subsets of the sphere. If
$\mathfrak{R}$ is a subset of a sphere for which it is meaningful to talk about area, we may
denote the area measure by $m(\mathfrak{R})$. As for the case of area in the plane, we shall
assume two properties for area of sets on a sphere.

(1) If $\mathfrak{R}_1 \cong \mathfrak{R}_2$, then $m(\mathfrak{R}_1) = m(\mathfrak{R}_2)$ [See diagram (a).]
(2) If $\mathfrak{R}_1 \cap \mathfrak{R}_2$ consists of a finite number of curves (or points), then
$m(\mathfrak{R}_1 \cup \mathfrak{R}_2) = m(\mathfrak{R}_1) + m(\mathfrak{R}_2)$. [See diagram (b).]

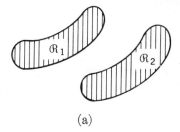   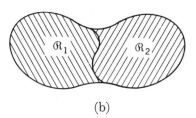

(a)   (b)

As a simple illustration of these properties consider a sphere divided into two
hemispheres $\mathfrak{IC}_1$ and $\mathfrak{IC}_2$ by a great circle C. Since the two hemispheres are con-

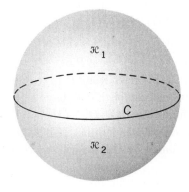

gruent, property (1) says that $m(\mathcal{K}_1) = m(\mathcal{K}_2)$, i.e., their area measures are equal. Since $\mathcal{K}_1 \cap \mathcal{K}_2 = C$, it follows from property (2) and the area formula for a sphere that

$$m(\mathcal{K}_1) + m(\mathcal{K}_2) = m(\mathcal{K}_1 \cup \mathcal{K}_2) = 4\pi r^2.$$

That is, $m(\mathcal{K}_1) = 2\pi r^2$. This merely says that half a sphere has half the area of the whole sphere—surely not a shattering surprise! Notice that we have chosen to use the word *hemisphere* to include the points of the cutting circle C.

Let us identify some of the sets on a sphere which we may wish to discuss. Consider two semicircles of distinct great circles on a sphere having a common endpoint P. The other ends of the great circle arcs are at Q, the other end of the diameter containing P. If A and B as shown are points of these arcs, they may be identified as arcs $\widehat{PAQ}$ and $\widehat{PBQ}$. The union of these two arcs might be called

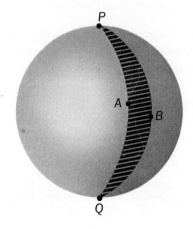

a spherical angle (just as a union of two rays in a plane was called an angle). By this definition a spherical angle has two vertices which are diametrically opposite points. In the drawing above they are P and Q. The set shown by the shading in the drawing is called the **interior** of the spherical angle and the union of a spherical angle and its interior is called, because of its shape, a **lune.**

If C is a great circle on a sphere and T is a point of the sphere not on C, the hemisphere determined by C which contains T may be described as the T side of C. This terminology allows us to give a formal definition of lune. If C_1 is the great circle containing $\widehat{PAQ}$ and C_2 the great circle containing $\widehat{PBQ}$, the lune determined by spherical angle $\widehat{PAQ} \cup \widehat{PBQ}$ is the intersection of the hemisphere on the B side of C_1 and the hemisphere on the A side of C_2. When there is no confusion we will denote $\widehat{PAQ} \cup \widehat{PBQ}$ simply as $\angle P$ or $\angle Q$.

Imagine now 360 great semicircles from P to Q dividing the sphere into 360 congruent lunes. Consecutive lunes of this set have a great semicircle in common. Otherwise two of these lunes have $\{P, Q\}$ as their intersection set. Any one of these lunes may be considered a unit lune. If it takes exactly α of these unit lunes to cover the lune bounded by $\angle P$ we will say that the measure of $\angle P$ is α, i.e., $m(\angle P) = \alpha$. As usual the idea of angle measure can be extended from integers to rationals to reals so we may imagine any spherical angle to have a unique real number as a measure.

Since by definition the union of 360 unit lunes is the entire sphere, it follows from properties (1) and (2) that each unit lune has an area measure of $\dfrac{4\pi r^2}{360}$ or

$\dfrac{\pi r^2}{90}$. If spherical $\angle P$ has a measure of α, then the lune determined by $\angle P$ is the

union of α nonoverlapping unit lunes so its area measure must be $\dfrac{\pi r^2 \alpha}{90}$. This may

be stated as a theorem:

Theorem B.4 *If a spherical angle has measure α, the area measure of the lune bounded by this angle is $\dfrac{\pi r^2 \alpha}{90}$.*

You will notice that the argument given tacitly supposes α is an integer. The theorem is true in any case but, in general, would require a more sophisticated treatment.

Let S be a set on a sphere. If $P \in S$ consider the point P' opposite to P, i.e., the point P' such that $\overline{PP'}$ is a diameter. Let S' be the set of opposite points. Then clearly there is a one-to-one correspondence between the points of S and

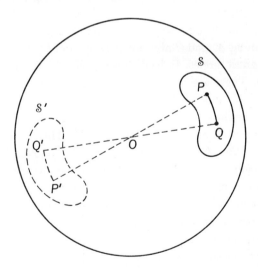

those of S'. If $P, Q \in S$ and if P', Q' are their images in S' we notice that $\overline{OP} \cong \overline{OP'}$, $\overline{OQ} \cong \overline{OQ'}$ (why?) and $\angle POQ \cong \angle P'OQ'$. (Why?) This means $\triangle OPQ \cong \triangle OP'Q'$ (by **sas**) so that $\overline{PQ} \cong \overline{P'Q'}$. Thus the one-to-one correspondence preserves congruence of segments so by definition $S \cong S'$. That is, every set on a sphere is congruent to its opposite set.

Let $A, B,$ and C be three points of a sphere which do not belong to the same great circle. In this case no two of the points can be endpoints of the same diameter. (Why?) Thus by Theorem B.3 there are unique great-circle arcs of shortest length joining each pair of the points. The union of these three shortest arcs is

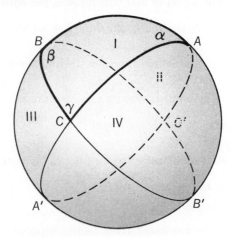

called a **spherical triangle.** From each of the vertices there are two great circle arcs so we may speak of the angle measure for the angle formed for each vertex. Let the measures for angles having vertices A, B, and C be α, β, γ, respectively. For a spherical triangle the interior may be defined essentially as for a plane triangle and the union of a spherical triangle and its interior is a spherical triangular region.

Let A', B', and C' be the points opposite to A, B, and C, respectively. Then the great circle containing A, and B also contains A' and B'. Similar remarks apply to the other two great circles. Indeed these circles divide the sphere into eight triangular regions. These are bounded by triangles ABC, ABC', $AB'C$, $AB'C'$, $A'BC$, $A'BC'$, $A'B'C$, and $A'B'C'$. For each of these triangles there is another whose vertices are the three opposite points. Thus the following pairs of triangular regions are opposite each other: ABC and $A'B'C'$; ABC' and $A'B'C$; $AB'C$ and $A'BC'$; $AB'C'$ and $A'BC$. According to our discussion above, this means that the eight triangular regions on the sphere are congruent in pairs. By property (1) these opposite regions must have equal area measures.

Let us introduce notations for the four possible area measures as follows:

   I is the area measure for ABC and $A'B'C'$.
   II is the area measure for ABC' and $A'B'C$.
   III is the area measure for $A'BC$ and $AB'C'$.
   IV is the area measure for $AB'C$ and $A'BC'$.

The union of region ABC and region ABC' is the lune for the angle at C. Since the angle measure for this angle is γ this means that

$$\text{I} + \text{II} = \frac{\pi r^2 \gamma}{90}.$$

Notice that this conclusion uses Theorem B.4 and property (2). In a precisely similar way we find that

$$\text{I} + \text{III} = \frac{\pi r^2 \alpha}{90},$$

$$\text{I} + \text{IV} = \frac{\pi r^2 \beta}{90}.$$

Addition of these three equations yields the conclusion that

$$3 \cdot \text{I} + \text{II} + \text{III} + \text{IV} = \frac{\pi r^2}{90} (\alpha + \beta + \gamma). \tag{1}$$

Since the sphere is the union of the eight triangular regions, the area measure of the sphere must equal the sum of the area measures of the eight regions. Thus

$$2 \cdot \text{I} + 2 \cdot \text{II} + 2 \cdot \text{III} + 2 \cdot \text{IV} = 4 \pi r^2$$

or, equivalently,

$$\text{I} + \text{II} + \text{III} + \text{IV} = 2 \pi r^2. \tag{2}$$

If equation (2) is subtracted from equation (1) we find

$$2 \cdot \text{I} = \frac{\pi r^2}{90} (\alpha + \beta + \gamma) - 2 \pi r^2 = \frac{\pi r^2}{90} (\alpha + \beta + \gamma) - \frac{180 \pi r^2}{90}.$$

Making use of the distributive property in the system of real numbers, we can rewrite this as

$$2 \cdot \text{I} = \frac{\pi r^2}{90} (\alpha + \beta + \gamma - 180).$$

Finally, division by 2 yields the result

$$\text{I} = \frac{\pi r^2}{180} (\alpha + \beta + \gamma - 180).$$

Thus we have obtained a formula for the area measure of a spherical triangle. We state this result as a theorem.

Theorem B.5 *If the angles of a spherical triangle have measures* α, β, γ, *the area measure* I *of the triangular region is given by* $\text{I} = \dfrac{\pi r^2}{180} (\alpha + \beta + \gamma - 180)$.

You may find it helpful in following the reasoning above to make drawings on the surface of a ball or other spherical object.

Theorem B.5 has an interesting and rather unexpected by-product. Since the area measure, I, of a triangular region must be positive, it follows that the number $\alpha + \beta + \gamma - 180$ in the parentheses must be positive. That is, $\alpha + \beta + \gamma - 180 > 0$ or, equivalently, $\alpha + \beta + \gamma > 180$. Since α, β, and γ are the angle measures for any spherical triangle, this conclusion may be stated as follows:

Theorem B.6 *The sum of the angle measures for any spherical triangle exceeds* 180.

It is of interest to consider again here the comparison between geometry on the sphere and in the plane. Having mentioned spherical triangles, we might ask whether the familiar theorems on plane triangles are still valid for spherical triangles. It is indeed true that many of the results about plane triangles hold also for spherical ones. For example, if two sides and the angle containing them for one spherical triangle are congruent to (i.e., have the same measures as) the corresponding parts of a second, then the two spherical triangles are indeed congruent. Similarly the **asa** and **sss** congruence theorems hold also for spherical triangles, though we shall not attempt to prove these statements.

Our discussion of spherical triangles shows, however, that there are also some sharp contrasts. In particular, Theorem B.6 shows that the sum of the angle measures for a spherical triangle always *exceeds* 180, which is very different from the familiar situation in the plane where the sum of the angle measures *equals* 180. Moreover, according to Theorem B.5 the greater the area measure, I, of a triangle, the larger the number $\alpha + \beta + \gamma - 180$ must be. Thus for two triangles with different areas the sum of the angle measures must be different. Because not all spherical triangles have the same angle sum, knowing the measures of two angles does not allow us to determine the measure of the third angle.

Perhaps an even more surprising consequence of Theorem B.5 is that on the sphere there can be no such thing as similar triangles, if by similar triangles we mean triangles of different size but whose angles have equal measures. This follows at once from the formula

$$I = \frac{\pi r^2}{180} (\alpha + \beta + \gamma - 180).$$

For if two triangles each have angles with measures α, β, and γ, the formula guarantees that their area measures are the same, so that the triangles cannot, in this sense, be of different size. Upon reflection you may find it very difficult to imagine two spherical triangles on the same or congruent spheres with angles of equal measures (and hence with equal area) which are not just alike, i.e., congruent. If you do have this difficulty it may interest you to know that there is a good reason for it. The fact is that if two spherical triangles have angles with equal measures the triangles must be congruent. Thus instead of finding similar triangles we have a new congruence theorem.

Theorem B.7 *If two triangles on a sphere have corresponding angles with equal measures, the triangles are congruent.*

You will realize that we have not proved this theorem, though our investigations have led to conjecture that it might be true.

APPENDIX C   Maps

The fact that the earth's surface is approximately spherical makes the problem of maps of a sphere a particularly important one. One of the simplest and, in many ways, most satisfactory ways of making a map of the earth is to make the map on a sphere. The map is then essentially just a small scale replica of the earth. Any two spheres are similar in the sense that we used the term in Chapter 10, so if we idealize the earth as a perfect sphere (i.e., ignore its irregularities) the representation of the earth on a small sphere is genuinely a figure similar to the earth's surface. Thus a distance on the small sphere is merely some fixed multiple of the actual corresponding distance on the surface of the earth. This is the type of map which is represented by the ordinary globes which are such common features of most classrooms and many homes. For example, consider a globe which has a diameter of 16 inches. Since the diameter of the earth is approximately 8000 miles, this globe is a scale model of the earth in which a 1-inch distance on the globe corresponds to a 500-mile distance on the surface of the earth.

Globes, however, are not always practical for our needs. If we wish a large detailed map of a certain country or state it might require a globe of unhandy proportions. For instance, if we want a map where 1 inch on the map corresponds to 20 miles on the earth's surface, the globe would need to have 25 times the diameter of the one above. This would mean a diameter of 400 inches or something over 33 feet, surely an awkward size to have in the classroom. Of course we may argue that in such a case we are not interested in looking at the whole sphere at once. It would be quite possible to break up the surface of the sphere into sections of some reasonable size and examine only the section in which we are interested. This is certainly a possible approach. However, even these sections of a sphere leave something to be desired. For example, they don't lie flat and are awkward to store. There would be much to be said for a map that would be flat. Such maps could be printed on ordinary paper, they could be bound in books, they could be conveniently used on a flat desk, etc. This is what we ordinarily mean when we talk about a map, i.e., it is a representation of some part of the (spherical) surface of the earth on a flat sheet of paper.

When one draws a flat map of a part of a sphere, what he is really doing is setting up a one-to-one correspondence between the points of the given region on the sphere and the points of some suitable region in a plane. The process of setting up such a one-to-one correspondence is called a **mapping** of the spherical region on a plane. Thus as the word is used here the process of mapping means drawing of a map.

The apparently innocuous request for a flat map of a spherical surface produces surprising problems. The basic difficulty may be sensed by the following simple experiment. Take a hollow rubber ball and cut a section out of it. (The ball will never be the same again!) Then take this section and try to flatten it out on the top of a desk. A little experimentation will make it plausible that a part of a sphere wasn't intended for this. In order to make a piece of it lie flat some parts of it have to be stretched and others compressed. You may even find the piece of ball splitting at the edges. In other words, to make a piece of a sphere fit on a plane it has to be distorted. This is the experimental evidence (though naturally not a proof) of the following fact:

There is no mapping of a region of a sphere to a region of the plane which preserves all distances.

This means it is not possible to find a mapping of a part S of a sphere to a part $\mathfrak{I}$ of a plane such that the distance of d (along the great-circle arc) from A to B

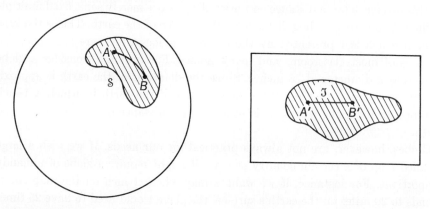

equals the distance $m(\overline{A'B'})$ between the image points for every pair of points A and B. In fact the situation is worse than this. There is not even a mapping for which there is a scale factor k, i.e., for which $d = k \cdot m(\overline{A'B'})$. If there were such a mapping we could always find a homothetic image of $\mathfrak{I}$ (as discussed in Chapter 10) for which distances are actually preserved. This unpleasant fact may be stated as follows.

Theorem C.1 *There is no mapping of a region of a sphere to a region of a plane for which the spherical distances are a constant multiple of the corresponding plane distances.*

Stated negatively, this says that every possible plane map of a part of the earth will be distorted. It will not really look the way the earth does and in one way or another will be deceptive. This is disturbing since we clearly dislike the idea of a map which is distorted and may deceive us. We would like a "good" map. However, this is one of the facts of life which we have to live with. If we want a "good" map it must be curved. If we insist on a flat map we must accept some distortion. The only choice we have is the kind of distortion we are willing to accept. Thus there are many different kinds of maps, each with some assets and each with some deficiencies.

As an example, consider one of the more common types of maps—the Mercator map or projection. On this map the meridians on the sphere are represented by vertical lines and the circles of latitude by horizontal lines. This is indicated crudely in the illustration below. Here the meridian containing A and P is

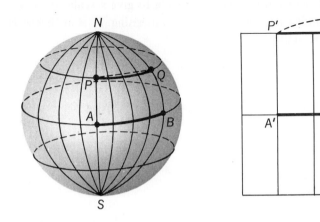

mapped into line $\overleftrightarrow{A'P'}$. Similarly meridian BQ is mapped into line $\overleftrightarrow{B'Q'}$. The arc AB of the equator maps into segment $\overline{A'B'}$ and arc PQ of another circle of latitude as shown maps into segment $\overline{P'Q'}$. Now on the map segments $\overline{A'B'}$ and $\overline{P'Q'}$ have the same length. It is clear that on the sphere, however, arcs AB and PQ are *not* the same length. Arc AB is an arc of a great circle, while PQ is the corresponding arc of a small circle and is clearly shorter. Since, under the mapping, two different lengths on the sphere appear equal on the map it is clear that the mapping has produced a distortion.

The fact that this particular kind of map clearly is somewhat deceptive may also be seen in another way. In the diagram points P and Q lie on a small circle. We know, however, that the shortest path from P to Q is an arc of a great circle. This great circle arc is indicated by the dashed path from P to Q. The image on the map of this great circle arc would be some path from P' to Q' as shown by the dashes. Looking at the map it appears that $\overline{P'Q'}$ would represent the shortest path, but as we know this is wrong since the shortest path is actually represented by the dashed path.

You may find it an interesting experiment to stretch a string between two points on a globe and then mark on a map a number of the points through which the string passes. The path on the map through these points represents the shortest route on the globe, though in general it will not look like the shortest route on the map.

It is not the purpose here to give a detailed description of different kinds of maps, though this is an interesting study. It is rather to help you realize that any flat map of a spherical surface must be treated with some caution, and that the reason we do not make a really "good" map is that there aren't any. Perhaps we should mention the scale of miles which is printed on many maps. This indicates that a certain distance on the map corresponds to a certain distance on the earth—for example, that 1 inch on the map stands for 10 miles on the earth. You may object that we have just finished saying that such a scale is impossible for a flat map of a section of a sphere. This is in fact correct. However, for a map covering a fairly restricted region it may be possible to give a scale which will yield results which are sufficiently accurate to have meaning. It is in this sense that these scales are to be understood.

APPENDIX D
A Geometric Fantasy

In the consideration of geometry in this book we have consciously attempted to devise a deductive system which could appropriately be used to describe the space of our physical experience. Thus, when axioms were selected they were deliberately motivated by the results of our physical experiences. No pretense has been made of giving a complete development of geometry from axioms. Rather we have looked at small blocks of deductive work interspersed with sections that were quite frankly intuitive. It has been suggested, however, that these holes *could* be filled, and that the entire discussion could be considered as part of a single large deductive system. This system is commonly called Euclidean geometry, although Euclid would not recognize many of the axioms which we have chosen to adopt.

In order to obtain a better perspective on the relation between the deductive system we have invented and the physical space it was intended to describe, let us indulge in a little fantasy.

Imagine a colony of tiny ants living on the surface of a huge sphere. Moreover, let these be essentially two-dimensional ants. That is, they have no conception of any motion or position other than on the surface of the sphere which is their home. Thus to talk of going inside the sphere or looking at it from the outside would have no significance to them. However, there is need in the colony for some sort of a theory to correlate and describe their experiences in their spatial environment. Thus one of the more intellectual members of the colony undertakes to develop a geometry for them. Consider the steps that he takes in making this development.

First he observes that he has an intuitive idea of location and decides that he will use the word *point* for this. He recognizes that the word point has not been actually defined but that location is the geometric idea he will have in mind when he speaks of a point. He then goes out to do some experimentation. He observes that when he and a friend, standing at different points, pull a string as tight as possible between them, the string seems to assume a definite position. The ant geometer decides that he will say that the set of points on which the string lies when pulled as tightly as possible will be called a **segment.** Thus if the ant stands at A and his friend at F, segment FA is the set of points indicated in the

drawing. Moreover, the ant observes that if his friend stands at F while he backs away, holding the string tight, there seems to be only one way in which he can go if he wants the stretched string still to lie on A. This leads him to conceive of

the idea that a segment may be extended indefinitely in either direction and he decides to call the set of all points obtained by extending a segment FA the *line* FA. As a result of his experience with the string he then adopts the following axiom.

Axiom 1 *There is a unique line on two distinct points.*

He also introduces the term *ray* as the set of points obtained when a segment is extended in only one direction. This enables him to define an angle as a union of two rays not on the same line but having the same endpoint.

The experience of the ant in noting that different segments may be exactly covered by the same piece of string leads him to define congruent segments and then congruent angles and triangles. These considerations lead him to measurement of segments and angles based on the idea of congruence. In particular, he introduces the concept of a right angle to describe the situation shown below,

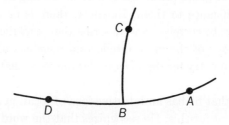

where angle ABC is congruent to angle CBD. The ant now makes observations on another geometric figure. He considers a line k and a point P not on k. He considers first the line PQ on P perpendicular to k. He then examines the different

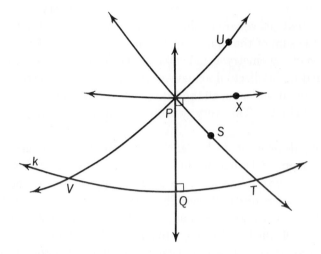

lines containing P. For example, he looks at a line like PS where angle SPQ is much smaller than a right angle. It seems clear to him that this line meets k in a point T on the S side of PQ. On the other hand, for line PU where angle UPQ is much greater than a right angle it seems clear to him that line PU meets k in a point V on the opposite side of PQ. He then considers the lines on P whose rays are interior to angle SPU. He imagines himself standing at P. When he faces in the direction of S he finds there is an intersection with k, namely T, which is in front of him. By the time he has turned to the direction of U there is still an intersection with k, namely V, but now it is behind him. He reasons that there must be some direction where the intersection jumps from in front of him to behind him. Since by his Axiom 1 no line can meet k twice, there should be some position where a line through P fails to meet k. He calls two lines which do not meet parallel and reasons that there then must be at least one line parallel to k containing P. As a matter of fact, he finds he can prove this on the basis of his Axiom 1 (together with the other axioms which he has formulated but which we have not specifically noted). In particular, the line PX perpendicular to PQ at P is proved to be such a line.

The ant now ponders the question of whether this is the only line on P which does not meet k. He finds a real problem here. If a line on P is almost but not quite perpendicular to PQ it is clear that if it meets k it will be a long way off. Thus it becomes more and more difficult to verify experimentally the closer the line is to PX. However, it seems plausible to him that all other lines through P do ultimately meet k, and so he adopts an axiom.

Axiom 2 *If a point P is not on a line k there is exactly one line containing P and parallel to k.*

Having adopted this axiom, he now finds he can obtain a number of interesting results. He finds, for example, that the sum of the measures of the angles of a triangle in a suitable unit is always 180, he develops a theory of similar figures, and he proves that the square of the measure of the hypotenuse for a right triangle equals the sum of the squares of the measures of the other two sides.

The creation of a geometry as indicated above is recognized by the ants as one of the outstanding intellectual achievements in the history of the colony. It is taught as a required subject in all the ant schools and is made a basis for a rapidly developing technology. This very success, however, ultimately precipitates a crisis.

As the colony develops its technical skills it embarks on a program of exploration. Among the projects is one in which exploring parties are sent out in different directions. They are to follow a line as long as supplies permit and then return to the colony to report observations. The first party started out in the direction described by the colony as north and with the most meticulous care followed this line. It then returned to the colony to report. The second party started out in the direction designated as east in the colony and likewise followed this line with the greatest care. They were horrified and astonished when, after a long trip, they crossed the trail of the previous party. It was unbelievable. According to all their calculations they should be getting steadily further away from the trail followed by their colleagues in the other party, yet here it was. The report of this party, upon its return, was a scientific bombshell. The scientists of the colony examined the instruments and reports of the two expeditions but found nothing amiss. Newspaper rumors that the scientific reports were fabrications and that neither party had taken a trip at all proved to be unfounded.

To try for a confirmation or a refutation of the facts reported, two new expeditions were sent, one starting west and the other northeast. These two expeditions started simultaneously. Again using the utmost care, the two groups followed the indicated lines and this time the two parties actually met each other. Moreover, the point of meeting was, as nearly as could be determined, exactly where the trails of the other two parties crossed and the distance traveled by all four parties appeared to be the same. Furthermore, the west party discovered that it was precisely following the former trail of the east party. To verify this, instead of retracing their steps they pushed on and ultimately returned to the colony from the east, though they had started west and followed a line.

It was now proved beyond a shadow of doubt that the predictions based on the classical ant geometry were not in accord with the observed physical facts.

The colony was in a furor. The ant congress appointed an investigating committee which called in the superintendent of schools and all the geometry teachers. There were bitter charges of professional incompetence. There were even dark suspicions of deliberate subversion of the minds of the ant youth by representatives of a nearby colony of red ants. However, it appeared that this colony was also teaching the classical ant geometry to *their* young ants, so nothing came out of this except an argument as to which colony invented the classical geometry in the first place. Nevertheless, the charges of having improperly allowed unsound doctrines to be taught in the schools was sufficient to cause the firing of the superintendent of schools and all the geometry teachers. Let us leave the resulting dilemma in the hands of the ant congress while we assess the problem from our perspective.

In reading the section above you will certainly not have been surprised at the difficulty that arose. After all, our knowledge of spherical geometry is fully in accord with the discoveries of the ant exploring parties, and they are merely discovering what we already knew to be the facts of spherical geometry. Their lines are what we call great circles and they have merely confirmed the fact that two great circles (lines to them) actually meet in two points and that all great circles through one point have a second point in common. We would, of course, identify the second point as the other endpoint of the diameter through the first, but we cannot explain this to the ants as they have no conception of three-dimensional space.

Having noted this, however, it remains to assess the responsibility. Our first inclination is to lay the blame on the now safely dead inventor, or perhaps (like the congressional committee) on his intellectual successors, the professional geometers. You surely must have squirmed uncomfortably when the ant formulated his Axiom 1 which you knew was actually not correct. Similarly, we knew that Axiom 2 was incorrect since, on a sphere, two great circles always intersect, and hence true ant geometry can actually not have such things as parallel lines. Similarly, on the sphere we know the angle sum for a triangle is not constant and there are no similar triangles. Thus we may seek to lay the blame on the inventor ant or his successors.

A more charitable attitude might arise, however, if we ask on what basis the ant could have been expected to avoid these difficulties. After all, Axiom 1 was formulated on the basis of his experimental evidence and it must be admitted that this evidence was very convincing. The examples which have now shown him incorrect by no stretch of the imagination could have been available to him. Thus, he cannot really be charged with any flagrant oversight in formulating his axioms, even though they have been now proved fallacious. However, having excused him for the initial blunder, we may join the congressional ant committee in questioning his professional competence or that of his successors. If the geometry that he invented is as bad as it now appears, surely he or some of his successors should have been able to spot some logical errors in the development. They should not have been guilty of passing off such unsound developments to innocent and immature students who would swallow them with uncritical docility and hence be intellectually subverted.

In evaluating this last charge we are really considering the adequacy of the logical development of the classical ant geometry from the indicated axioms. To this end it might be well to compare classical ant geometry with our familiar

Euclidean plane geometry. It has surely not been lost on you that Axioms 1 and 2, about which we have been arguing, are among the axioms of Euclidean plane geometry. It is true that we have made no attempt to formulate a complete set of ant axioms but the fact is that the other axioms adopted by the ant are those of Euclidean plane geometry. Thus the classical ant geometry is precisely the same as our Euclidean plane geometry. That is, the system of geometry invented by the ant is exactly the system we have been studying in this book. This fact causes us to take a second look at the charges of professional incompetence noted above. Do we really think the ant geometers should have discovered logical fallacies in the classical ant geometry? If so, we must be able to discover the same logical fallacies in our ordinary Euclidean plane geometry, since it consists of the same deductions from the same set of axioms. Because we are unaware of any such logical deficiencies (and frankly doubt that such exist), we must clear the ant geometers of any charges of incompetence.

The discussion above naturally raises the question of what is the status of the classical ant geometry. We appear to have concluded that it is logically above reproach. That is, it is a series of deductions correctly obtained from an adopted set of axioms. It is a very excellent abstract mathematical system as we know. Its flaw in the present situation lies in the fact that it does not perfectly fit the physical situation. It is an example of what is often called a **mathematical model.** That is, it is an abstract mathematical system which has been employed in dealing with a certain physical problem. You already knew (and the ants have now discovered) that the model does not perfectly correspond to the physical situation. On the other hand, it should not be ignored that it was for a long time adequate for the uses of the ant colony. It was the basis of the very technology which ultimately revealed its deficiencies. Though it now appears that the model is not adequate for the ant space taken as a whole, it evidently gives an excellent approximation to the facts when applied to a limited section of the sphere. Thus we may view the classical ant geometry as a model which is very convenient and which gives excellent approximate results for small regions of the sphere, though not for very large regions.

You may feel that it is a very sloppy business to employ a mathematical model which doesn't actually quite fit the physical facts. Surely we should employ a model that completely fits *all* the facts of the given situation. Some reflection on the matter, however, should convince you that we almost never use a perfect mathematical model of a physical situation. In practice we look at the physical facts and abstract from them what seem to be the most essential ideas. That is, we construct for ourselves a mathematical model and solve a problem concerning the model. If we have not been too incompetent in our evaluation of what facts are important we may hope that the solution will have a reasonable relation to the original physical problem, but rarely do we work with a model that perfectly fits all the physical facts.

Consider, for example, the following problem. A vertical flagpole is to be braced by a wire running from a point on the pole 30 feet up to a point on the ground 40 feet from the base. How long a wire is necessary?

The student confronted with this problem will normally draw a diagram such

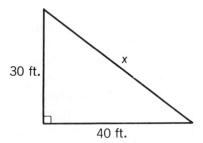

as the one illustrated. He will presumably then use the Theorem of Pythagoras and write

$$x^2 = 30^2 + 40^2$$
$$x^2 = 900 + 1600 = 2500$$
$$x = 50.$$

He concludes that the required wire is 50 feet long. Moreover, any mathematics teacher will mark the solution correct. Does this model really represent all the physical facts, and can the solution be taken at its face value as the absolutely correct answer? Consider the following questions. How is the wire to be attached to the pole? If it is to be wrapped around, the diameter of the pole becomes relevant, yet we idealized the pole as a segment. Even if it is to be fastened in some other way there needs to be some allowance for wire used in the fastening. Moreover, we have idealized the wire into a segment, yet the physicist points out that it is not possible to avoid sag in the wire. In addition, the wire has a certain amount of elasticity (stretch) to it and the amount of sag will depend on the weight of the wire, its elasticity, etc. Thus the solution we gave is actually for a highly idealized problem, i.e., it is a solution to a problem concerning a mathematical model. To construct a model that would take care of the questions raised here would be to complicate the problem beyond all reason (and probably beyond all possibility for solution by us). This is not to discount the usefulness of our solution, but is to say that we must recognize it for what it is—an exact solution to an idealized problem which is close enough to be useful as applied to the physical situation. It is not in any sense an exact solution to the physically stated problem.

To return to our ant colony, the point is that their classical geometry is a mathematical model which is found to give excellent approximations to the physical facts for small portions of the sphere and will continue to be used for this purpose. Of course, the ant scientists will certainly want to busy themselves with creating a new model (i.e., a new geometry) which will correspond better to the new observed data of their space, but this is likely to be a more complicated model, and will be used only where it is necessary for increased accuracy. The classical geometry will probably continue in the schools, though the teachers will be more cautious in referring to axioms as "self-evident facts" or in claiming that the conclusions are in an absolute sense "true" as applied to their sphere.

Indeed, you should realize that what has been suggested above as a probable procedure of the ant colony is exactly what we do all the time. We are aware that we live on a roughly spherical surface. Thus, as far as our moving about on the earth is concerned, we should more properly use the ideas of spherical geometry, yet in point of fact we do not do so. Thus if someone tells us that he started from home and went 30 miles east and 40 miles north, we conclude he is 50 miles from home, since that would be the prediction of Euclidean geometry. Actually this is not exactly correct and you are invited to think of a position on the earth (assumed spherical) where the correct answer is 40 miles. [HINT: Consider a position near the North Pole.]

The parable (or is it an allegory?) of the ants suggests the question of the relation of Euclidean geometry to the space of our physical experience. We have certainly made an effort to devise a deductive system (i.e., geometry) which would be appropriate to apply to physical space. We adopted axioms based on the best insights of our physical experiences. We note, however, that this was also true for the ants. All we can claim for our geometry is that it is a mathematical model which has "worked out" satisfactorily in practice. Whether it is in any sense a "perfect" model for physical space or whether it yields merely a good approximation to physical reality is a debatable question, perhaps even an unanswerable one. Observe the ants discovered their geometry was not a perfect one for their space. Some physical experiences suggest that the Euclidean model may not be the ultimate ideal model for our space and that for some purposes more sophisticated models can be useful.

The above is not to subvert anyone's faith in Euclidean geometry. It is not about to be supplanted by some other system because its usefulness has been too clearly demonstrated. Nevertheless we should recognize it for what it is, namely, a mathematical model, a system of deductions from a stated set of axioms. Its theorems are statements which we know can be deduced from the axioms but we cannot assert that they are "true" in an absolute philosophical sense when applied to our physical space.

As a historical note, you may be interested that there are other geometries (deductive systems) which could also be used very acceptably to relate our experiences in physical space. The first example of such a geometry was discovered independently in the early 1800's by a Russian named Lobachewsky, a Hungarian named Bolyai, and a German named Gauss. It was largely this discovery of other possible geometries that clarified the question discussed here, namely, "What is the relationship between a geometry and physical space?"

Index

LIST OF SYMBOLS

Symbol	Meaning	Page
$=$	is equal to	1
$\neq$	is not equal to	5
$>$	is greater than	2
$<$	is less than	2
$\geqq$	is greater than or equal to	7
$\leqq$	is less than or equal to	215
$\ngtr$	is not greater than	16
$\nless$	is not less than	16
$+$	plus	1
$-$	minus	5
$a \cdot b$	a times b	2
$\div$	division	8
$\dfrac{a}{b}$	fraction	2
^-a	the additive inverse of a	1
i_1	identity element (usually for addition)	76
i_2	identity element for multiplication	87
x^{-1}	the multiplicative inverse of x	87
^+a	positive integer	7
$(\ \ )$	parentheses (symbol of grouping)	5
$[\ \ ]$	brackets (symbol of grouping)	36
$(a - b)$	the equivalence class containing $(a - b)$	213
$\dfrac{a}{b}$	the equivalence class containing $\dfrac{a}{b}$	243
10^{-n}	$\dfrac{1}{10^n}$	261
$S \wedge T$	statement S *and* statement T	6
$S \vee T$	statement S *or* statement T	7
not–S	negation of statement S	8
$P \rightarrow Q$	statement P implies statement Q	10
$P \leftrightarrow Q$	statement P is true if and only if statement Q is true	19
$\forall_n$	for all n	11
$\exists_n$	for some n	14